PHYSIOLOGY OF THE AMPHIBIA

PHYSIOLOGY

OF THE AMPHIBIA

EDITED BY

JOHN A. MOORE

DEPARTMENTS OF ZOOLOGY
BARNARD COLLEGE AND COLUMBIA UNIVERSITY
NEW YORK, NEW YORK

1964

ACADEMIC PRESS New York and London

ACADEMIC PRESS INC.
111 Fifth Avenue, New York, New York 10003

United Kingdom Edition published by
ACADEMIC PRESS INC. (LONDON) LTD.
Berkeley Square House, London W.1

LIBRARY OF CONGRESS CATALOG CARD NUMBER: 64-20320

PRINTED IN THE UNITED STATES OF AMERICA.

CONTRIBUTORS

B. C. ABBOTT, Department of Physiology and Biophysics, University of Illinois, Urbana, Illinois

LUCENA JAEGER BARTH, Department of Zoology, Barnard College, New York, New York

ALLAN J. BRADY, Los Angeles County Heart Association, Cardiovascular Research Laboratory, UCLA Medical Center, Los Angeles, California

GEORGE W. BROWN, JR., Department of Biochemistry and Nutrition, The University of Texas Medical Branch, Galveston, Texas

INGRITH J. DEYRUP, Department of Zoology, Barnard College, New York, New York

WILLIAM ETKIN, Albert Einstein College of Medicine and The City College, New York, New York

G. E. H. FOXON, Department of Biology, Guy's Hospital Medical School, London, England

AUBREY GORBMAN, Department of Zoology, University of Washington, Seattle, Washington

WILLIAM G. REEDER, Department of Zoology, University of Wisconsin, Madison, Wisconsin

S. MERYL ROSE, Department of Anatomy, Tulane University, New Orleans, Louisiana

PREFACE

In many branches of animal biology it is assumed that *the* animal is *the* frog. This is less so today than a generation ago, now that the techniques and equipment for experimentation with homothermic vertebrates have improved. Nevertheless, a variety of species of amphibians still play an enormously important role in physiology—both in research and in the training of students. It is surprising, therefore, that there are no recent and general books covering the physiology of the amphibians. This lack is the reason for our volume.

Considering the importance of the amphibians in biological investigations, we have sought to provide a treatment that will be useful for the advanced student, for specialists in fields other than amphibian physiology (who will wish to relate information about the amphibians to their own studies), and for the physiologist concerned largely or entirely with amphibians.

The domain of physiology is interpreted here somewhat more broadly than is usual. In addition to customary topics such as digestion, respiration, and metabolism, we have other aspects not usually included in physiology. We have chosen to consider the special usefulness that amphibians have served in answering questions about the physiology of development, metamorphosis, and regeneration. The treatment of other topics ordinarily expected in a discussion of physiology, and originally intended to be considered here, will be taken up in a future volume.

One of the more interesting things that impressed the contributors to this volume is the many and large gaps that still remain in our knowledge of amphibian physiology. Far from closing the field with these chapters, therefore, we hope to have shown how really open it still is.

March, 1964   JOHN A. MOORE

vii

CONTENTS

4.   PHYSIOLOGY OF THE AMPHIBIAN HEART

Allan J. Brady

5.   WATER BALANCE AND KIDNEY

Ingrith J. Deyrup

6.   AMPHIBIAN MUSCLE

B. C. Abbott and A. J. Brady

7. ENDOCRINOLOGY OF THE AMPHIBIA

Aubrey Gorbman

8. METAMORPHOSIS

William Etkin

9. THE DEVELOPMENTAL PHYSIOLOGY OF AMPHIBIA

Lucena Jaeger Barth

10. REGENERATION

S. Meryl Rose

THE METABOLISM OF AMPHIBIA

George W. Brown, Jr.

"...all vital action may...be said to be the result of the molecular forces
of the protoplasm which displays it." Thomas Henry Huxley (1868).

I. Introduction

The present chapter is devoted to a discussion of certain aspects of the
metabolism of Amphibia. This is a prelude to the special phases of the
physiology and biochemistry of this class which are treated in subsequent
chapters. All physiological processes ultimately must be explained in terms
of the numerous reactions taking place in various cells, and it is the purpose

here to provide a broad view of the metabolic activities which support these processes.

At the present time there are some ten thousand original papers dealing with material which could be included under the heading of this chapter. These are currently being sifted for a longer presentation (Brown, 1963). In a treatise such as this, selection of material and reference citations was inevitable and difficult, and the subject matter of many noteworthy papers had to be omitted. Unfortunately, it has not been possible to include many structural formulas which would aid the reader in following metabolic sequences. For these and for the more intimate details of metabolic processes, reference should be made to standard biochemical texts such as those of Fruton and Simmonds (1958), Cantarow and Schepartz (1962), White *et al.* (1959), and West and Todd (1961).

A list of the abbreviations used in the present writing is given.*

Thermodynamic considerations. A portion of the material presented deals with energy metabolism. For this reason it was deemed advisable to include wherever possible throughout the chapter data on the free energy change for reactions cited. The free energy (Gibbs' free energy) change for any reaction is given by

* The following are abbreviations used in this chapter:

AMP, adenosine-5'-monophosphate

ADP, adenosine-5'-diphosphate

ATP, adenosine-5'-triphosphate

cal, gram-calories

CoA, coenzyme A

DNA, deoxyribonucleic acid

DOPA, dihydroxyphenylalanine

DPN^+ and DPNH, oxidized and reduced forms of diphosphopyridine nucleotide

E.T.S., electron transport system

FAD and $FAD \cdot 2H$, oxidized and reduced forms of flavin adenine dinucleotide

FMN and $FMN \cdot 2H$, oxidized and reduced forms of flavin adenine mono-nucleotide

Kat-*f*, katalase fähigkeit

kcal, kilogram-calorie

M, molar (moles per liter)

P_i, inorganic orthophosphate

PP_i, inorganic pyrophosphate

Q_{O_2}, microliters O_2 per hr per mg dry weight of tissue

q_{O_2}, microliters O_2 per hr per mg wet weight of tissue

Q_{10}, ratio of (rate of reaction at $t + 10°$)/ (rate of reaction at t)

RNA, ribonucleic acid

R.Q., respiratory quotient (volume of CO_2/volume of O_2)

R.T., room temperature

(s), solid substance

STP, conditions of 0° centigrade and 1 atmosphere pressure

t = degrees centigrade

T = °Kelvin (absolute)

TPN^+ and TPNH, oxidized and reduced forms of triphosphopyridine nucleotide

Tris, tris(hydroxymethyl)amino-methane

μ, 10^{-6} meter

μg, 10^{-6} gram

μliter, 10^{-6} liter

$\sim$, energy-rich bond or approximate sign

$\cong$, approximately equal to

Δ, change in the quantity.

F, free energy

H, heat content (enthalpy)

S, entropy

$$\Delta F = \Delta H - T\Delta S \tag{1}$$

where ΔF = change in free energy
ΔH = change in heat content (enthalpy)
ΔS = change in entropy
T = absolute temperature (°Kelvin)

The convention of Lewis and Randall (1923) is employed whereby if at constant temperature and pressure ΔF is negative, the reaction tends to proceed from left to right as written. When ΔF is positive, the reaction tends to proceed in the reverse direction. If $\Delta F = 0$, the reaction is at equilibrium.

The notation, ΔF^0 ($= \Delta G^0$) represents the standard free energy change.* The notation, $\Delta F^{0\prime}$, represents the free energy change at pH 7 with all reactants and products except H^+ at unit thermodynamic activity. Knowledge of the standard free energy change for a reaction allows calculation of the equilibrium constant from the well known relationship:

$$\Delta F^0_{T_0} \text{ (calories)} = -RT\ln K_{eq} = -4.58T \log_{10} K_{eq} \tag{2}$$

In any system allowed to go from state A to state B at constant temperature and pressure, the maximum work, w', obtainable from the reaction which can be applied to useful purposes is given by

$$w' = F_A - F_B = -\Delta F \tag{3}$$

Thus, if the free energy change, ΔF, is negative, w' is positive and represents the maximum useful work which can be done.

Unless specified otherwise, the free energy change associated with a given reaction is that for the number of moles prefixed to reactants and products of specified ionic charge, in solution, as they appear in the chemical equation. Free energy changes cited should be regarded as best approximations only. The magnitude of free energy changes of most reactions occurring *in vivo* is not known because of meager information on concentrations of reactants and products at the site of the reaction. The application of free energy changes to problems in biochemistry is discussed in some detail by Pardee and Ingraham (1960) and by Klotz (1957).

Much of the thermodynamic data given is provided by values (or calculated therefrom) to be found in the literature (for example, see Lewis and Randall, 1923; Parks and Huffman, 1932; Latimer, 1938; Burton and

---

* The standard free energy change, ΔF^0, is the free energy change at 25° C (298° Kelvin) for a reaction in which reactants and products are in the standard state: solutes, 1 M thermodynamic concentration; gases, 1 atmosphere pressure (perfect gas); liquids, the pure liquid.
The symbol, $\Delta F^{0\prime}$, is used when all reactants and products are in the standard state except for H$^+$ which is at 10^{-7} M, i.e., pH 7. Subscripts are used for temperatures other than 298° K.

Krebs, 1953; Holzer, 1956; Krebs and Kornberg, 1957; Benzinger *et al.*, 1959; Cohen and Brown, 1960).

II. Over-all Energy Metabolism

The mature amphibian egg contains an energy-rich reserve of material in the form of carbohydrate, lipid, and protein—in amounts sufficient to carry the fertilized ovum through the embryonic stages of development. Moreover, it is equipped with the genetic information necessary to effect an orderly progression of transformations throughout this period. Carbohydrate (glycogen) and lipid account for about 8 % and 25 %, respectively, of the dry weight of mature *Rana* spp. eggs; an even greater percentage of the dry weight is accounted for by the yolk (Barth and Barth, 1954). The yolk material consists largely of phosphoprotein, but it contains, in addition, various other compounds, including RNA, phospholipids, acid-soluble organic phosphates such as nucleotides, and inorganic phosphate. All of the vitamins and cofactors required for the various enzymic reactions of embryogenesis are found within the egg. Probably most, if not all, of the various metal ions required for certain enzymic reactions are present as well.

The reserve materials of the egg are largely depleted by the time the larval stage with the onset of feeding is reached, except in those cases where the larval stages take place entirely within the egg such as with the Surinam toad, *Pipa pipa*. While it is not safe as yet to assume that the onset and relative rates of utilization of reserve materials are the same for all species of Amphibia, one can generalize from the observations already made: glycogen is broken down, probably at least to some extent at first anaerobically, then aerobically, followed by oxidation of fat. Inasmuch as embryogenesis involves the formation of new cells and is a growth process in spite of absence of external nutrition, it can be anticipated that the protein is largely spared an oxidative fate and is reorganized into new protein for the newly formed cells.

As pointed out by Barth and Barth (1954), the amount of "active" protoplasm which is directly responsible for the metabolism of the egg is insignificant in comparison with the stores of glycogen, fat, and protein; hence, the early energetic requirements of the egg are very small during the stages of cleavage, blastulation, and early gastrulation. G. ten Cate (1953) has summarized some of the metabolic events occurring during embryogenesis: The enzymes which are first active are hydrolytic (glycolytic) in nature. During the first few days carbohydrate is broken down as shown by a decrease in total carbohydrate with a resultant increase in lactic acid (anaerobic glycolysis). Subsequently, there is a rise in respiratory activity shown by increases in cytochrome oxidase, succinoxidase, and O_2 consumption.

The assumption of aerobic metabolism during embryonic development is accompanied by a decrease in lactic acid. At this point pyruvate presumably is converted to acetylSCoA and is oxidized via the Krebs tricarboxylic acid cycle rather than acting as the hydrogen acceptor for reduced DPNH generated from anaerobic glycolysis in the early stages (see Section IV,C,1).

A. RESERVE MATERIAL AND EMBRYOGENESIS

By the use of simultaneous equations, Løvtrup (1953a) finds with the axolotl, *Ambystoma mexicanum*, that the succession of energy sources during embryonic and larval development is carbohydrate, fat, and protein—the protein utilization not beginning until the carbohydrate is exhausted. Figure 1 shows the *rate* of utilization of these substances in this species as a function of embryonic development. It can be seen that the maximum rate of utilization of carbohydrate takes place during neurulation and that this utilization precedes that of fat and protein. Fat combustion begins as the rate of carbohydrate utilization falls off and reaches a maximum during the larval stages. Protein is not utilized until the larval stages. Of the carbohydrate which was initially present in the egg, some 65% is broken down anaerobically, according to Løvtrup.

In the case of *Ambystoma mexicanum*, Løvtrup (1953a) finds that the phosphoprotein of the yolk is not utilized before the tail-bud stage and is apparently not related to combustion of protein. During late larval stages at the time of maximum oxygen uptake, 41% of the total lipids and 16% of the protein have been utilized.

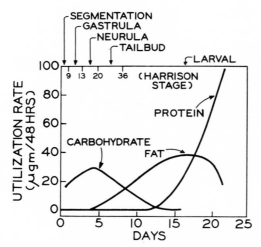

Fig. 1. Rate of utilization of reserve materials in the embryonic and larval development of *Ambystoma mexicanum*. After Løvtrup (1953a).

The reactions through which energy is made available for embryonic work are discussed in a later section (IV). While it is clear that such reactions make available the free energy of these storage or reserve foodstuffs, we still lack information on the efficiency of these processes in terms of the trapping of the theoretical amount of free energy available from them. It is a matter of observation that such energy carries the organism at least to the free-swimming stage, soon after which the larval amphibian becomes dependent upon food available in the environment for further growth, differentiation, and development.

B. OXYGEN CONSUMPTION

1. Consumption of Oxygen during Development

A considerable body of work on Amphibia deals with studies on the primary organizer or neural inductor of the embryo. An important phase of this work has been the analysis of chemical and respiratory changes in various parts of the embryo during development. Such studies were undertaken because it was thought that they would lead to a better understanding of biochemical events associated with the phenomenon of biological induction.

Brachet (1935a), carried out some early studies on the metabolism of frog eggs (*Rana fusca*) during development and showed that the act of fertilization did not result in demonstrable changes in oxygen uptake. Fertilized and unfertilized eggs (during a 1-hour period following fertilization) exhibited O_2 uptakes of 1.15 ± 0.02 μliters per hour per egg. However, respiration of blastulas was higher than that of eggs immediately before or after fertilization. The R.Q. (respiratory quotient) of unfertilized eggs was 0.99, while that of fertilized eggs was 0.66 (range, 0.55–0.73), and this decrease in R.Q. was attributed to an increase in the O_2 consumption by the spermatozoa. In addition, Brachet showed that mitotic events in frog eggs are accompanied by slight cyclic variations in O_2 uptake with at least two peaks corresponding to prophase and anaphase. The dorsal lip of the blastopore (organizer) was thought be the center of intense respiratory activity, more elevated than neighboring regions (Brachet, 1935b).

These early studies and those prior to 1948 are discussed at length in the excellent critique of Boell (1948). Boell has summarized the values of ten reports on the ratio of respiration by the dorsal lip region to that of ventral ectoderm. These data lead to a mean value (and mean deviation) for this ratio of 1.16 ± 0.14. It thus seems that if the respiration of the dorsal lip is higher than ventral ectoderm, it is only slightly so. Variations in experimental results are attributed by Boell to the failure of various workers to use corresponding areas of dorsal lip and ventral ectoderm for comparison.

Considerable differences in O_2 uptake do in fact exist in different areas of the same gastrula as shown by later studies which are summarized by Boell (1948). A gradient in respiratory activity extends from the animal to the vegetal pole with the highest rate of respiration residing in the more anterior part of the presumptive neural plate as shown in Table I. Thus, the relative respiratory rate of dorsal lip tissue depends upon which regions of the gastrula are taken for comparison. If the respiratory rates of the different parts of the gastrula are corrected for "inactive" materials such as lipid and pigment, the rates become approximately identical, as pointed out by Boell. Much of the early work thus seems to have led to a *cul-de-sac* in terms of attributing inductive action to a higher respiratory metabolism in the dorsal lip region than in the presumptive neural plate—or for that matter, in other parts of the gastrula.

Results of measurement of the R.Q. of various gastrular regions are in complete accord mainly because this is a ratio and is independent of mass of tissue. During cleavage stages the over-all R.Q. of amphibian eggs is approximately 0.66 and rises sharply to about 1.0 during gastrulation (Brachet, 1934). In 1948, Mendes (see Boell, 1948) followed the R.Q. of *Rana pipiens* from fertilization of the egg to the prefeeding period. Newly fertilized eggs and embryos in early cleavage stages exhibit an R.Q. of unity, but it then drops to about 0.7 in late blastula, followed by a rise again during gastrulation. Much speculation can be centered around an interpretation of these R.Q. values in terms of type of material undergoing oxidation. It should be pointed out that such interpretations can be highly erroneous inasmuch as glucose, lactic acid, and acetate, for example, yield an R.Q. value of unity upon complete oxidation to CO_2 and water. Also,

TABLE I

RESPIRATION OF VARIOUS REGIONS OF AMPHIBIAN GASTRULA[a]

(Summary of 103 experiments)

Region	Q_{O_2}[b]	Average probable error
Dorsal lip	2.1	0.07
Presumptive neural plate	4.9	0.28
Anterior ectoderm	4.5	0.16
Posterior ventral ectoderm	3.0	0.19
Yolk endoderm	1.3	0.09
Right lateral ectoderm	3.1	0.14
Left lateral ectoderm	3.4	0.31
Chorda mesoderm	1.2	0.09

[a] From Boell (1948).
[b] Microliters O_2 per hr per mg dry weight.

as pointed by Boell (1948) complete oxidation of protein with ammonia instead of urea as the nitrogenous end product can lead to a value near unity. In this connection there is reason to believe that enzymes for the synthesis of urea are absent or are low in activity during embryonic stages (Brown *et al.*, 1959), indicating that the nitrogenous end product is ammonia at this time.

While interpretation of R.Q. values leaves much to be desired in alleging that carbohydrate breakdown is involved in gastrulation, Woerdemann's (1933) observation that glycogen disappears from the dorsal lip tissue during invagination, and later confirmation of this by Heatley (1935) and Heatley and Lindahl (1937) indicate that carbohydrate is in fact utilized.

The increase in O_2 consumption by the developing embryo is gradual, and there seem to be no abrupt changes which can be associated with particular events during gastrulation and differentiation. The increase is logarithmic as is any growth process. Two phases of oxygen uptake have been detected which lead to a break in the uptake curve between 5 and 7 days of development, depending upon species. Adequate explanations for the existence of the two phases do not exist.

Considerable interest has been taken in the respiration of hybrids because of their ability to show normal development up to a certain stage, followed by an arrested development (Moore, 1941). Hybrid eggs of *Rana pipiens* ♀ × *Rana sylvatica* ♂ exhibit a normal oxygen consumption during cleavage and gastrulation. But after the beginning of gastrulation the rate fails to increase, while the R.Q. remains at 0.87 as in normal eggs. The R.Q. of the hybrids is greater than that of normal eggs during their postgastrular stages (Barth, 1946). The growth block is attributed to one involving energy production in the hybrids.

Oxygen consumption of tadpoles of *Xenopus laevis* was measured by Fletcher and Myant (1959) who found considerable differences depending upon whether wet or dry weights were taken. The wet weight of tadpoles increases from the first day of hatching until the onset of metamorphosis. Dry weight remains rather constant until the fifth day after hatching and then begins to increase. The over-all changes lead to a rapid decline in the dry weight:wet weight ratio from about 0.2 at the first day to 0.05 by the tenth day. This ratio then remains rather constant until metamorphosis, at which time the dry weight:wet weight ratio rises to a value of about 0.12. The authors observed a marked increase in the Q_{O_2} from 2.0 to 9.0 during the first 5 days after hatching. The Q_{O_2} fell rapidly to about 3.0 between the tenth and twentieth days and then remained constant until metamorphosis. The value fell to about 1.8 toward the end of tail resorption.

All of the tadpoles studied by Fletcher and Myant (1959) evidenced a distinct and continuous decrease in wet weight and Q_{O_2} upon treatment with solutions of thyroxine or triiodothyronine (4 μg/100 ml, and 2 μg/100 ml, respectively). These findings are similar to those of Etkin (1934) who observed no rise in the Q_{O_2} of *Rana catesbeiana* at metamorphosis. It thus appears that the action of thyroxine in stimulating metamorphosis in Amphibia may involve phenomena distinct from the action of this hormone in mammals, where the basal metabolic rate is increased. Fletcher and Myant point out that many years ago Kendall showed that metamorphosis could be induced by acetyl thyroxine, but that this analogue had no effect on the O_2 consumption by mammals. It is further pointed out that Amphibia usually do not eat during metamorphosis, so that any fall in Q_{O_2} which has been observed may not be directly associated with the effect of thyroxine.

From an evolutionary standpoint, stimulation of metamorphosis by thyroxine and its analogs may have arisen earlier than its metabolic effects such as increasing the O_2 consumption in homoiotherms. The metabolic rate of tadpoles is determined by temperature and stage of development, whether or not the thyroid gland is functioning, according to Fletcher and Myant.

Oxygen can be taken up without yielding useful energy as in the case of amino acid oxidases which pass their hydrogens directly to oxygen to form hydrogen peroxide. Oxygen consumption can be used as a rough measurement of the energy expenditure only if a large proportion of the energy utilized stems from oxidative metabolism via the cytochrome system. If it can be shown that this latter situation obtains, approximately 4.7×10^{-3} calories of heat per μliter of O_2 are produced regardless of whether carbohydrate, fat, or protein is being combusted. A closer value can be obtained if one knows the R.Q. and the amount of nitrogenous end product (ammonia or urea) by application of the principles of indirect calorimetry. During the early developmental stages of Amphibia it would appear that O_2 uptake does not account for the energy expenditure of embryonic work. In the absence of information on the rate of production of lactate, in addition to knowledge of the R.Q. and nitrogenous end product, values for oxygen uptake tell little about the metabolic energy-yielding processes of embryos.

2. Oxygen Requirements in the Adult*

Fromm and Johnson (1955) have summarized values on the respiratory metabolism of Anura which appeared in the literature from 1849 to 1954.

* Probably the first quantitative measurements on the oxygen uptake of frogs were those of Regnault and Reiset (1849). They obtained a value of 44.1 μliters O_2 per gm body weight of frogs (of average body weight, 57.2 gm) at 15°. They also observed a fasting R.Q. of about 0.7. The species was probably *Rana esculenta*. These early workers recognized that oxygen uptake showed seasonal variations: "Il est à prêsumer aussique leur respiration n'est pas la même dans les diverses saison."

In general, maximal oxygen consumption was observed during the spring (spawning season), and minimal consumption during the winter. Values for the R.Q. varied from below 0.7 to higher than 1.4. Values for the R.Q. which are greater than 1.0 are thought to arise from the conversion of carbohydrate to fat. Irregularities in the summarized data are attributed to differences in nutritional status, pre-experiment environmental conditions, activity of the animals, and collection of data at various temperatures. Unfortunately, such summarized data are of little quantitative value, since, as is indicated in Section II,C,2, consumption of O_2 is a function of body weight, and none of the weights corresponding to O_2 consumption data are given. The values summarized elsewhere (Spector, 1956) also suffer in this respect, although it is fairly clear that the oxygen consumption (when measured at 19°–20°) by frogs during the summer may be as high as 6 times that of the winter value.

Fromm and Johnson (1955) sought to eliminate factors which would cause an increase over the resting value and measured the O_2 consumption and CO_2 production of *Rana pipiens* immobilized with *d*-tubocurarine (Abbott Labs.). Frogs were maintained under feeding and temperature conditions such as to simulate natural environments during the various seasons. Their data are summarized in Table II. Oxygen consumption of spring frogs was found to be higher than either summer or autumn and winter frogs; a similar trend occurred in the case of CO_2 production but with only slight differences in summer, fall, and winter frogs. The R.Q. was higher during the fall and winter and was lower during spring and summer. Differences in the R.Q.'s are ascribed to the 4° temperature at which autumn- and winter-simulated frogs were maintained (as opposed to spring- and summer-simulated frogs held at 22°–28°); there is an attending decrease in oxygen consumption as a result of this lower temperature.

TABLE II
RESPIRATORY METABOLISM OF *Rana pipiens*[a]

Simulated season	Oxygen consumption[b]	CO_2 production[b]	Respiratory quotient (R.Q.)	Estimated calories/hr/gm body weight[c]
Spring	39.6	32.5	0.82	0.186
Summer	33.8	27.1	0.80	0.159
Autumn	21.8	25.7	1.20	0.102
Winter	23.9	27.7	1.16	0.112

[a] Adapted from Fromm and Johnson (1955). Respiratory measurements at 22°–25° (gas volumes corrected to S.T.P.). See text for other experimental conditions.

[b] In μliters per hr per gm body weight.

[c] These values are obtained from the assumption that the caloric content of foodstuffs being oxidized is 4.7×10^{-3} calories per μliter of O_2 (carbohydrate, 5.0×10^{-3}; protein, 4.5×10^{-3}; fat, 4.7×10^{-3}).

Values on the O_2 consumption obtained by these workers are generally lower than those reported by others. The observation finds ready explanation in the fact that the curarized animals must have been respiring only cutaneously, for the amount of d-tubocurarine employed would certainly have diminished, if not have stopped, the buccal-pharyngeal movements necessary for respiration via the lungs. This fact is not mentioned by the authors.

Cutaneous respiration by amphibians is quite high and under environmental conditions may be of the same magnitude as the simultaneous pulmonary respiration. During hibernation all of the oxygen uptake may be by the cutaneous route (Bishop, 1950). Under conditions of low temperature, transport of oxygen by the blood need not involve hemoglobin. A specimen of *Xenopus laevis* (partially mature female) was examined by de Graaf (1957) and was found to have no observable cellular elements of the blood except for bodies giving the appearance of spindle cells. No normal mature erythrocytes were present in stained sections of the spleen although other blood elements were present and appeared normal. It would seem that *Xenopus laevis* and *Rana* sp. (Serfaty and Gueutal, 1943), and presumably other amphibians as well, can survive under conditions of low temperature and relatively low bodily activity in the absence of oxyhemoglobin. Oxygen is more soluble in water the lower its temperature, and the plasma alone can deliver sufficient oxygen to the tissues under such circumstances.

Seasonal variations have been observed in oxygen uptakes of salamanders by Vernberg (1952) who measured the O_2 consumption of the red-backed salamander, *Plethodon cinereus*, and of the two-lined salamander, *Eurycea bislineata*, acclimatized at 1° and 10°, at three different periods of the year. Lowest rate of O_2 consumption at 10° was noted during October–November and highest consumption during May–June. For *Plethodon cinereus* weighing 0.85 gm, O_2 uptake in μliters per hour per gram body weight was 30.3 ± 1.2 and 37.4 ± 0.5 for these periods, respectively. The Q_{10} for oxygen uptake for *Plethodon cinereus* and for *Eurycea bislineata* for the periods, October–November, February–March, and May–June were, respectively, 1.17, 3.65; 2.16, 2.60; and 2.63, 3.65. Vernberg has suggested that an inherent seasonal cycle operates for each of these species of salamanders.

Evans (1939) has noted that the rate of oxygen consumption is higher in aquatic than in the more terrestrial species of plethodontid salamanders.

C. ENERGY REQUIREMENTS

1. Regulatory Factors

Three major factors govern the energy requirements of adult amphibians: (1) physical activity; (2) temperature; and (3) synthetic biochemical work.

These three factors are not independent variables. The amount of physical activity (jumping, swimming) in which an amphibian engages depends upon the temperature; the lower the temperature, in general the lower the physical activity. However, sufficient reduction of temperature to induce hibernation may *suppress* physical activity entirely so that the energy requirement is even lower than if it were just a case of *reduction* of activity. Synthetic biochemical work, such as synthesis of fat as a winter reserve, will also depend upon temperature, because the rate of reactions is directly dependent upon temperature. However, synthetic biochemical work such as that employed in production of oöcytes, for example, may be linked with foraging activity which provides the nutrients for such reproductive activity. That such work is not inappreciable is seen in the case of *Rana pipiens* in which there is a 200 to 700% increase in total lipid substances of ovaries during ova production (Boyd, 1938).

The fact that amphibians are poikilothermic endows them with certain advantages over homoiotherms. Though they lack the ability to differ much in temperature from their environment, with a correspondingly lowered rate of chemical reactions at lower temperatures, they require much less food and can go for long periods (in rare cases up to a year) on reserve materials. In addition, as in the case of tadpoles and small frogs, for example, they can be smaller in size than can mammals or birds. The lower limit of size for mammals is about 2.5 gm (Bishop, 1950); homoiotherms smaller than this would have such a large surface: volume ratio that they would be unable to consume enough food to maintain their prescribed body temperature. The long-tailed shrew (*Sorex cinereus*), which weighs about 3.4 gm has a basal O_2 consumption (air temperature, 24°–28°; body temperature, 38°) of 13,700 μliter per hour per gram body weight (Bishop, 1950). On the other hand, a frog of equivalent weight, for example, *Hyla cinerea* or *Hyla versicolor* would have, under approximately basal conditions at 25°, an O_2 consumption of only about 100 μliters per hour per gram body weight. This is $1/137$ that of the shrew of the same weight. The range of metabolic rates for small mammals and birds has been said to be from 18 to 180 times that for Amphibia (Noble, 1931). A small specimen of *Pseudacris nigrita* weighing 200 mg has an O_2 consumption of only 58 μliters per hour or about 1.4 cm³ per 24 hr under approximately basal conditions at 25°. This volume of oxygen corresponds to that which would be required to combust only about 1.4 mg of protein (calculated from values given in Table III).

Enzymes are generally more active *in vitro* at temperatures higher than usually experienced *in vivo* by amphibians in their natural habitat (for example, see rate-temperature plot of ornithine transcarbamylase of *Rana catesbeiana* given by Brown *et al.*, 1959). Hence, as pointed out by Noble (1931), amphibian energy sources are made available at a much slower rate than in the homoiotherms.

TABLE III
CALORIC (HEAT) CONTENT OF FOODSTUFFS

Item	Carbohydrate	Protein	Fat
Kcal per gm	3.7–4.3	4.3	9.4
Liters CO_2 per gm	0.75–0.83	0.78	1.43
Liters O_2 per gm	0.75–0.83	0.97	2.03
Respiratory quotient	1.0	0.80	0.707
Kcal per liter O_2	5.0	4.5	4.7
Kcal per mole O_2	112	101	105
Kcal per gm-atom O	56	51	53
Available free energy[a] (kcal per gm-atom O)	−21	−21	−21

[a] Maximum energy available for useful work through ATP generated by the electron transport system. [Based on the formation of 3 molecules of ATP per atom of oxygen; and $\Delta F^{0\prime}$ of hydrolysis of ATP as −7.0 kcal/mole. See Eq. (9).]

While terrestrial amphibians follow fairly closely the ambient temperature, evaporation of water from the skin of *Rana esculenta* in an environmental temperature of 30° can cool this frog as much as 4.6° (Rubner, 1924), and in the case of *Plethedon glutinosus* at 20° as much as 9.2° (Hall and Root, 1930). Since the amount of moisture in the atmosphere controls the rate of evaporation and hence the cooling effect, humidity affects the metabolic rate of Amphibia.

2. Calculation of Energy Requirements

The principles of direct or indirect calorimetry may be employed for determining the metabolic rate of Amphibia. It is beyond the scope of the present chapter to cover these principles, and reference is made to standard works for their discussion (Krogh, 1916; Lusk, 1928; Peters and Van Slyke, 1932; Brody, 1945; Hawk *et al.*, 1947).

Classic energy metabolism studies deal with the *production of heat* from foodstuffs which are oxidized, as opposed to free energy changes which represent the maximum useful work obtainable. The heat produced from foodstuffs by living organisms in most cases very nearly corresponds to that of $-\Delta H$, the negative change in heat content or enthalpy [see Eq. (1)]. The quantity, $-\Delta H$, is equal to the heat of combustion as realized in a bomb calorimeter.

The free energy changes associated with oxidative reactions provide for useful work in the form of external work, and the internal work of syntheses, secretion, circulation, exchanges of materials, etc. The heat produced by the organism, in contrast to a heat engine, is the end product rather than the motive power of the body processes (Brody, 1945).

Table III lists numerical values useful in calculations dealing with energy metabolism. It should be noted that the quantity of heat associated with a given volume or mole quantity of O_2 consumed is very nearly the same for carbohydrate, protein, and fat. This is the result of the fact that the greater part of the terminal oxidation of all foodstuffs takes place through the electron transport system in which electrons are delivered to oxygen (see Section IV,B). For an average mixed diet, the value of 4.7 kcal per liter of O_2 consumed can serve as an approximate value for the heat production.

If one assumes the free energy of hydrolysis of ATP to be 7.0 kcal per mole (see Benzinger *et al.*, 1959), 21 kcal of free energy for each gram-atom oxygen, or 42 kcal of free energy for each mole of oxygen taken up are made available under standard state conditions at pH 7.

Davison (1955) has clearly shown that the rate of oxygen consumption of seven species of frogs could be divided into three groups, each of which followed Rubner's (1883) surface law that the basal metabolic rate is proportional to $W^{2/3}$, where W = body weight:*

$$O_2 \text{ uptake/hr } = kW^{2/3} \tag{4a}$$

i.e.,

$$O_2 \text{ uptake} \left(\frac{\mu\text{liters}}{\text{hr}} \right) = k \left(\frac{\mu\text{liters}}{\text{hr} \times \text{gm}^{2/3}} \right) W^{2/3} \tag{4b}$$

and

$$O_2 \text{ uptake} \left(\frac{\mu\text{liters}}{\text{hr} \times \text{gm}} \right) = kW^{-1/3} = \frac{k}{\sqrt[3]{W}} \tag{4c}$$

(where W is body weight in grams)

From a double-log plot of rate of oxygen consumption vs. body weight, three different proportionality constants, k, were obtained (but not given) which divided the frogs into the three groups: (1) *Rana catesbeiana, Rana pipiens*, and *Rana clamitans*; (2) *Rana sylvatica*; and (3) *Hyla versicolor, Hyla cinerea*, and *Pseudacris nigrita*. Table IV summarizes some of the observations of Davison, and values have been calculated for k and for the approximate heat production associated with O_2 uptake by the seven species of frogs. Values have also been calculated for the proportionality constant, K, in the expressions:

$$\text{Heat production} \left(\frac{\text{cal}}{\text{hr}} \right) = K \left(\frac{\text{calories}}{\text{hr} \times \text{gm}^{2/3}} \right) W^{2/3} \tag{4d}$$

---

* The exponent, 2/3, corresponds to the ideal situation with respect to the surface law of Sarrus and Rameaux (see Brody, 1945; Kleiber, 1947). I recognize that the exponent of Eq. (4a) may assume other values.

TABLE IV

Metabolic Rates of Some Frogs[a]

(Measured at 25° C)

Species	W (gm.)	$\dfrac{\mu \text{liters } O_2}{\text{hr} \times \text{gm}}$	$\dfrac{\text{Calories}^b}{\text{hr} \times \text{gm}}$	k^c	K^d
Rana catesbeiana	350	43	0.20	304	1.43
Rana pipiens	35	93	0.44	304	1.43
Rana clamitans	35	93	0.44	304	1.43
Rana sylvatica	6.0	108	0.508	196	0.920
Hyla cinerea	4.5	102	0.479	168	0.790
Hyla versicolor	4.5	102	0.479	168	0.790
Pseudacris nigrita	1.0	162	0.761	162	0.761

[a] Adapted from Davison (1955).

[b] Gram-calories.

[c] k has the units $(\mu \text{liters } O_2) \times \text{hr}^{-1} \times \text{gm}^{-2/3}$.

[d] K has the units, $\text{cal} \times \text{hr}^{-1} \times \text{gm}^{-2/3}$; $K = 4.7 \times 10^{-3} k$, for the units employed here.

or

$$\text{Heat production} \left(\frac{\text{calories}}{\text{hr} \times \text{gm}} \right) = K W^{-1/3} = \frac{K}{\sqrt[3]{W}} \tag{5}$$

Several examples are provided to show how these equations can be used in calculations dealing with energy metabolism.

Example 1: The total heat production of a *Rana pipiens* weighing 10 gm and held under approximate basal conditions at 25° is required. From Table IV, $K = 1.43$. Therefore, according to Eq. (4d), heat production $= 1.43(10)^{2/3} = 6.65$ cals per hour.

Example 2: What would be the hourly oxygen consumption of this animal under these conditions?

On a mixed diet, 1.0 μliter O_2 corresponds to 4.7×10^{-3} calories (see footnote, Table III). Hence,

$$O_2 \text{ consumption} = 6.65 \, \frac{\text{cal}}{\text{hr}} \times \frac{1.0 \, \mu\text{liter } O_2}{4.7 \times 10^{-3} \text{ cal}} = 1410 \, \mu\text{liters/hr} = 1.41 \text{ cm}^3/\text{hr}$$

Alternately, the oxygen consumption can be calculated directly from Eq. (4b):

$$O_2 \text{ consumption} = k W^{2/3} = 304 \times 10^{2/3} = 1410 \, \mu\text{liters/hr}$$

Example 3: Does the fat body of a frog provide sufficient energy for metabolic needs during hibernation?

Let us suppose a 27-gm frog of *Rana* sp. to have a fat body equivalent to 5% of the body weight, or 1.35 gm, of which 75% is oxidizable fat. According to Table III this would provide:

$$1.35 \text{ gm fat body} \times \frac{0.75 \text{ gm fat}}{\text{gm fat body}} \times \frac{9.5 \text{ kcal}}{\text{gm fat}} = 9.62 \text{ kcal}$$

With the value of $K = 1.43$ from Table IV and employing Eq. (4d) this frog would have a heat production of

$$1.43 \times (27)^{2/3} = 1.43 \times \frac{27}{\sqrt[3]{27}} = 1.43 \times 9.00 = 12.9 \text{ cal/hr}$$

It is clear that this amount of fat would support the energy requirement of this frog for $9620/12.9 = 746$ hrs or 31 days at a temperature of $25°$. Under conditions of hibernation at $5°$, the energy requirement would be $1/4$ that at $25°$ (assuming a Q_{10} of 2). Thus, this frog should be able to hibernate 4 months before exhausting the lipid reserves of the fat body.

Fromm (1956) has measured by direct calorimetry the monthly heat production of *Rana pipiens*, which were curarized, and found the heat production to be from 0.64 to 0.95 cal per hour per gram body weight at $22°$–$28°$, in general agreement with older observations (Krehl and Soetbeer, 1899; Hill, 1911–1912b). Unfortunately, Fromm again provides no individual weights so that it is not possible to see whether heat production is directly proportional to O_2 consumption. Note that the heat production based upon O_2 uptake in the curarized animals (see Table II) is much less than that observed by direct measurement. The data of Fromm (1956; Table I), lead to the puzzling ratio of about 20 kcal heat produced per liter of O_2 consumed instead of about 4.7 (cf. Table III, this chapter). This is no doubt due to the fact that cutaneous respiration alone leads to hypoxia, with considerable heat production stemming from anaerobic reactions. There of course would then be no simple relationship, if any, between heat production and oxygen consumption under such circumstances, and the value for the ratio indicated above would be much greater than 4.7.

Contrary to Fromm's statement that no relationship exists between heat production and some power of the body weight, the average value for animals in each weight range cited in his Table II (Fromm, 1956), satisfies the observed heat production for all weight ranges for $K = 2.26 \pm 0.06$ in Eq. (5).

It would be desirable to have simultaneous measurements of heat production and O_2 uptake of normally respiring and resting amphibians of known weight to compare the heat production determined by direct and indirect calorimetry. The indirect method may be of more value than otherwise thought for Amphibia. Hill (1911–1912a) by direct calorimetry found that the heat production of frogs (most likely *Rana temporaria*) was 0.56 cal per hour per gram body weight at $21.4°$. Eight frogs totaling 100 cc $\cong$ 100 gm, i.e., frogs averaging 12.5 gm, were employed to establish this value. If one takes the value for K of 1.43 given in Table IV for *Rana* spp. and calculates the heat production from Eq. (5) for a 12.5-gm frog, a value of

0.62 cal per hour per gram body weight is obtained at 25°, in very good agreement with the value found by Hill. It is not clear, however, that the frogs employed by Hill belong in the first group of Table IV.

Calculations on the energy of foraging may be made in the following manner: If a 30-gm frog leaps 50 cm (vertical height) each minute for 12 hr (720 min) it does 30 gm $\times$ 50 cm per leap $\times$ 720 leaps $= 1.08 \times 10^6$ gm–cm of work. This is equivalent to 25.3 calories (1 gm–cal $= 4.27 \times 10^4$ gm–cm). If the efficiency to accomplish this work is 25%, food equivalent to $25.3/0.25 = 100$ cals would be required. This amounts to 23.2 mg of protein (Table III), or to 47 insects weighing 10 mg each and containing usable food equivalent to 5% of their body weight as protein.

III. Vitamins and Pigments

A. PIGMENTS

As early as 1840 (Ascherson, 1840, see F. A. Brown, 1950), it was shown that the movement of pigments in specialized cells of the integument brought about color changes in amphibians. These cells, the chromatophores, are under the control of the hormone, intermedin, secreted by the intermediate lobe of the pituitary. The structure of the chromatophore, methods of action, color patterns, and influences of environment are discussed in detail elsewhere (F. A. Brown, 1950; Noble, 1931).

At least nine substances, including 2-amino-4-hydroxypteridine (AHP = Bufo-chrome 2), riboflavin, FMN, and FAD, can be extracted from the skin of *Bufo vulgaris* (Hama and Obika, 1958). As a general rule, Bufo-chrome 2 is seldom found in Amphibia, but in the case of *Bufo vulgaris*, it appears at the limb-bud stage. The gold pigment of male *Rana temporaria* is known to be a pterin; according to Ziegler-Günder (1956), it is identical with that from the "sepia" mutant of the fruit fly, *Drosophila melanogaster*.

The pituitary principle, intermedin, which is responsible for expansion of the melanophore with resulting pigment dispersion, has recently been subjected to extensive purification and structural analysis. It has been found (see Hofmann, 1962) that intermedin exists in two forms, termed α-MSH and β-MSH (MSH = melanophore-stimulating hormone), both of which are straight-chain polypeptides. The melanophore-stimulating activity of the α-type from pig, beef, horse, monkey, and human pituitaries is now known to contain 13 amino acid residues.

Surprisingly enough, the sequence is identical with the 13 N-terminal residues of the corticotropins except for the acetyl group on serine at the N-terminal end, and for the amide group on valine at the carboxy-terminal

end: acetylserine·tyrosine·serine·methionine·glutamic   acid·histidine·
phenylalanine·arginine·tryptophan·glycine·lysine·proline·valineNH₂. No
species differences have been found with respect to the structure of α-MSH,
but unfortunately, only mammalian species have been examined so far.

In the case of β-MSH, species differences within Mammalia do exist
with respect to the length of the peptide chain and to the number of amino
acid residues (18 or 22 residues). But, as is the case also with α-MSH,
β-MSH contains, regardless of source to date, the heptapeptide sequence:
methionine·glutamic   acid·histidine·phenylalanine·arginine·tryptophan·
glycine. A synthetic heptapeptide of this sequence was recently shown by
Li *et al.* (1961) to possess melanophore-stimulating activity in hypophysectomized *Rana pipiens*. It thus seems likely that this sequence occurs in the
melanophore-stimulating hormone(s) of amphibian pituitaries. It will be of
interest to see how the remainder of an MSH peptide molecule compares
with those now known for several mammals.

Melanin pigments are frequently observed in fairly large amounts in the
liver of amphibians. According to de Robertis (1939), liver contains both a
yellow and a brown pigment. The brown pigment contains ionic iron
whereas the yellow pigment is iron-free. Liver pigments of *Bufo arenarum*
increase in amount during autumn and winter (Southern Hemisphere) and
reach a maximum during October. The quantity of pigment increases during
fasting or under conditions of high temperature. Metabolism of these pigments appears to involve the parenchymal cells of the liver and the reticuloendothelial cells of both liver and spleen.

The visual pigments are discussed below in connection with vitamin A.

B. THE VITAMINS

The vitamin requirements of Amphibia have not been established, but it
is nonetheless clear that most, if not all, of the vitamins that appear as
necessary adjuncts for growth, maintenance, and reproduction in Mammalia
are also necessary in Amphibia. Vitamins serve directly or indirectly as
substrates or cofactors for enzymic reactions.

Vitamin A. Vitamin A is a derivative of a group of related carotenoid
pigments which structurally are unsaturated hydrocarbons. Vitamin A
includes two compounds, vitamin A_1 and vitamin A_2, which differ in the
degree of unsaturation in a substituted 6-carbon ring attached to a polyene
chain containing conjugated double bonds and terminating in a hydroxyl
group (see Section IIIC for structures). Preformed vitamin A is not usually
part of the diet of frogs (for *Rana temporaria* see Morton and Rosen, 1949).
The vitamin is formed from β-carotene and occurs largely in liver. The

hydroxylated carotenes, such as xanthophyll, are absorbed more readily than is carotene. Carotenes are more widely distributed in the various organs of the frog than is vitamin A. Vitamin A_2 was not detected in *Rana temporaria* liver fat (Morton and Rosen, 1949). Seasonal variations in vitamin A, carotenes, and hydroxylated carotenes occur, with an especially large drain on the vitamin A reserve during the reproductive period. The conversion of carotene to vitamin A in frogs and tadpoles probably occurs in the gut.

Vitamins A_1 and A_2 occur in the eyes of *Triturus carnifex* to the extent of 0.030 μg and 0.039 μg per eye, respectively (Collins *et al.*, 1953a). *Ambystoma tigrinum* assimilates vitamin A and stores it in the liver (Collins *et al.*, 1953b). Storage of β-carotene does not occur, and large amounts appear in the feces after feeding this compound. It seems possible to raise these animals in the absence of detectable amounts of exogenous vitamin A without producing signs of avitaminosis A. Either the requirement is small, vitamin A_1 is synthesized, or some other substance replaces this vitamin for visual function in *Ambystoma tigrinum*, according to Collins and co-workers.

Vitamin D. Skin fat and ripe ovaries of *Rana temporaria* contain the vitamin D precursors, 7-dehydrocholesterol and ergosterol (Morton and Rosen, 1949). Larvae of *Rana fusca* treated with vitamin D show a typical calcium salt turbidity in the gelatinous tissue of the tail fin (Štefl, 1937). Calcium is released from the bones of Amphibia after injection with vitamin D (see Schlumberger and Burk, 1953).

Vitamin C (ascorbic acid). Venom of *Bufo vulgaris* contains 20–32 (average, 26.6) mg ascorbic acid/100 ml (Zimmet and Dubois-Ferrière, 1936a, b). The vitamin is widely distributed throughout the body, highest levels being found in the brain, lowest levels in the blood. During metamorphosis of *Bufo vulgaris*, ascorbic acid increases from 6 to 23 mg/100 gm in the whole animal (Bucci, 1951). It is thought that the toad can synthesize sufficient ascorbic acid for its needs. The common Indian toad, *Bufo melanostictus*, synthesizes ascorbic acid in the kidney but not in the liver (Roy and Guha, 1958). This is thought to represent the situation in earlier stages of vertebrate evolution, for this is the case with reptiles and birds of older natural orders. This enzymic ability of the tissues is reversed in recent orders of birds and in those mammals which synthesize ascorbic acid in the liver. Clearly we need information on ascorbic acid synthesis in more species of Amphibia to further explore this evolutionary consideration. [For seasonal variations in ascorbic acid of *Rana temporaria*, see Nespor (1936)].

Thiamine. Eye tissue of *Rana nigromaculata* contains vitamin B_1 (Hara, 1949). Free thiamine shows considerable variation depending upon individual, and seasonal and physiological conditions, but thiamine pyrophosphate (cocarboxylase) remains essentially constant (100 μg/100 gm tissue). Free thiamine may or may not occur in muscle of amphibians, depending upon species, but thiamine pyrophosphate has been found to occur in muscle wherever sought in Amphibia (Koller, 1941). Both substances have been detected in muscle of *Hyla arborea*, *Bufo vulgaris*, and *Triton cristatus* (Koller, 1941). The content of thiamine pyrophosphate in *Bufo bufo* is minimal at egg maturity and at the beginning of embryogenesis (Petrucci, 1955). Concentration is maximal at the late stages of embryogenesis. During maturation of the egg the content is lowered. In concentrations greater than $1:10^8$, thiamine inhibits certain rhythmic variations in the diameter of frog blood vessels (Brecht and Meiners, 1941). Thiamine pyrophosphate functions as a coenzyme for reactions involving oxidative decarboxylation.

Riboflavin. Ammoniacal extracts of the skin of numerous amphibians show a fluorescence pattern indicating the presence of riboflavin (and pterin) (Günder, 1953). Riboflavin occurs in the liver, kidney, eye, and adrenal glands of Amphibia. In *Rana viridis* it occurs in highest concentration in the adrenal glands (72 μg per gram fresh tissue) (Nollet and Raffy, 1940). Values for the liver (5–6.5 μg per gram fresh tissue) are of the same order as those observed in various fishes and marine turtles. Riboflavin has been detected in the eyeball of *Rana nigromaculata* (Yagi, 1950). About 70 % of the riboflavin in the retina is in the form of an ester. Increased melanization of *Ambystoma* may be related to an increased riboflavin content (Fontaine *et al.*, 1941). The vitamin constitutes a part of the structure of FMN and FAD, which function as electron acceptors in certain oxidation reactions.

Pyridoxine, etc. The presence of transamination reactions in Amphibia (Chan, 1960; Yamamoto, 1960) suggests the occurrence of the coenzyme, viz., pyridoxal phosphate. Little is known about the levels of vitamin B_6 in Amphibia.

Nicotinic acid and nicotinamide. DPN, which contains nicotinamide as part of its structure, is known to be present in *Rana pipiens* and in *Bufo vulgaris* from the two-cell stage to the free-swimming tadpole. Maximal values were observed at gastrulation and minimal values at about the beginning of the first movements (Lindahl and Lennerstrand, 1942). Numerous reactions are known in Amphibia which require nicotinamide-containing DPN and TPN.

Thioctic acid. D-α-Thioctic acid content of parts of the eye of *Rana nigromaculata* was found to be (in millimicrograms per milligram dry weight): outer segments of rods, 2.0; whole retinas, 8.6; choroids, 13.6 (Hanawa *et al.*, 1960). Thioctic acid showed no effect *in vivo* on regeneration of rho-

dopsin. The vitamin is known to be concerned with oxidative decarboxylation reactions in plants, animals, and bacteria.

Pantothenic acid. This appears to be a necessary growth factor for Amphibia (for *Bufo vulgaris* see Catolla-Cavalcanti, 1951). The vitamin is
part of the coenzyme A molecule concerned with acylation reactions.

Folic acid and vitamin B_{12}. These are probably required and not synthesized by Amphibia. The folic acid antagonist, aminopterin, exhibits a
local depression on leg growth of tadpoles (Mustakallio and Telkkä, 1954).
Vitamin B_{12} exerts a slight protection against this inhibition. Folic acid
antagonists decrease oviduct growth in estradiol-treated *Rana clamitans*
(Goldsmith *et al.*, 1950). Folic acid is concerned with reactions involving
1-carbon compounds (formate, formaldehyde). The role of vitamin B_{12} in
animal metabolism is not clear; lack of the vitamin produces pernicious
anemia.

Coenzymes Q (Ubiquinones). These compounds, with the general structure,

participate in electron transfer in the electron transport system. The
coenzyme exists in numerous forms which differ only in the length of the
polyisoprenoid side chain. That member which contains a side chain of 10
isoprenoid units is termed coenzyme $Q_{10}(CoQ_{10})$. It has been detected in
heart and leg muscle of *Rana catesbeiana* to the extent of 23 mμmoles and
11 mμmoles per gram wet weight, respectively (Lester and Crane, 1959).

Other vitamins. Information on other vitamins and/or coenzymes such
as vitamin E, vitamin K, and biotin is scanty in the case of Amphibia.

C. THE VISUAL CYCLE

Visual pigments of the eyes of vertebrates are conjugated proteins in
which the aldehyde of vitamin A functions as a prosthetic group. Two
forms of prosthetic groups are known: (1) the aldehyde of vitamin A_1,
termed retinine$_1$, and (2) the aldehyde of vitamin A_2, termed retinine$_2$.
Conjugation of retinine$_1$ with the protein, opsin, yields the visual pigment,
rhodopsin; conjugation of retinine$_2$ with this protein yields the visual pig-

ment, porphyropsin. These relationships are shown below:

Vitamin A_1

R_1CHO = Retinine$_1$

Opsin + Retinine$_1$ = Rhodopsin

Vitamin A_2

R_2CHO = Retinine$_2$

Opsin + Retinine$_2$ = Porphyropsin

Wald (1942, 1945, 1958) has made the interesting observation that tadpoles of *Rana catesbeiana* employ porphyropsin for the visual process, but that during metamorphosis this pigment is replaced by rhodopsin. These observations on the predominance of porphyropsin in retinas of premetamorphic *Rana catesbeiana* tadpoles have been confirmed by Wilt (1959) who has shown that about 80% of the visual pigments are in the form of porphyropsin; after metamorphosis the only pigment present is rhodopsin. Figure 2 illustrates the reactions involved in producing the nerve impulse when light falls upon the retina and in regenerating the photosensitive pigment. Neo-b vitamin A, one of the isomers (11-*cis*) of vitamin A, is oxidized by retinal alcohol dehydrogenase to yield neo-b retinine which combines with opsin to form rhodopsin (or porphyropsin). Light (hν) striking the retina causes an isomerization of the pigment to the all-*trans* configuration yielding metarhodopsin which is converted to opsin and all-*trans* retinine. Retinal alcohol dehydrogenase now reduces this to the all-*trans* vitamin A which can be isomerized in liver to reform the 11-*cis* isomer, neo-b vitamin A. All-*trans* retinine may also undergo isomerization to neo-b retinine in the retina. The only apparent difference in the cycle in the pre- and postmetamorphic tadpoles is in the use of different forms of retinine.

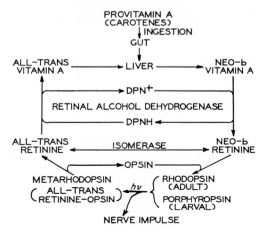

Fig. 2. The visual cycle in Amphibia. (Adapted from various sources.)

Rhodopsin of the retinal rods of frog is reported by Wolken and Schwertz (1956) to have a molecular weight of 60,000 compared with that of only 40,000 for cattle eye rhodopsin. First year larvae of *Rana catesbeiana* contain 9.3×10^{-11} moles of retinine$_2$, or 5.6×10^{13} molecules per retina (Wilt, 1959). During the second year of larval life the visual pigment increases twofold as does the size of the eye.

Wilt (1959) brings together reports that show that the phenomenon of visual pigment transformation is not unique to *Rana catesbeiana*, but that it occurs in several amphibians. The nature of the visual pigment in various organisms may be of evolutionary significance. If a generalization can be made, it would be that porphyropsin is found in fresh-water fish, and in amphibians with a predilection for a watery habitat, and that rhodopsin occurs in terrestrial and marine vertebrates. The completely aquatic toad, *Xenopus laevis*, has for its visual pigment porphyropsin, accompanied by a small amount of rhodopsin (Wald, 1955). In this and other respects (see Section IV,E,4), *Xenopus laevis* may resemble transitional amphibians which were not quite successful in escaping from their embryonic and larval confines. Information as to the visual pigments in the lungfishes might shed considerable light on the evolutionary sequence of the visual pigments.

IV. Intermediary Metabolism

The interconversions of metabolites within the cell are mediated, with but few exceptions, by enzymes. Certain reactions occur spontaneously in the absence of enzymes, such as the decarboxylation of acetoacetate and the reversible dissociation of carbonic acid to carbon dioxide and water.

In the latter case the velocity of the uncatalyzed reaction is insufficient, in mammals at least, to afford good respiratory exchange of bound forms of carbon dioxide of the blood with that of the alveolar air in the lungs. Presumably the same situation obtains in the lungs or gills of Amphibia, and the reaction is found to undergo catalysis by the action of the enzyme carbonic anhydrase.

While enzymes exhibit a certain amount of specificity with respect to reacting substrates, sufficient examples exist in the literature (see Boyer *et al.*, 1959–1963) attesting to the fact that specificity is, in general, relative. Greatest specificity is usually shown toward a given optical form. It is this more or less general specificity of enzymes that prevents a metabolic Tower of Babel and insures that the over-all metabolism remains coherent. In members of a given species we find various metabolic differences brought about by different levels of enzymes, cofactors, and metabolites as a result of subtle genetic differences, diet, or environmental conditions. When such conditions become extreme, as for example when the pancreas no longer secretes sufficient insulin, the resultant metabolism is no longer regarded as normal, but pathological. Unless measures are taken to relieve this pathology and restore an acceptable metabolic state, complications become more likely, leading in the extreme to death. This regulation or maintenance of conditions near a normal or mean value has been termed *homeostasis*. More recently this concept has been called *negative feedback* by analogy with electronic devices, such as the automatic volume control of radio receivers.

In the case of Amphibia, the over-all metabolic state enjoys considerable deviation from the mean value. Marked seasonal adaptive changes in the levels of many metabolites occur in Amphibia. Almost complete dependence upon fat stored in the fat body of hibernating amphibians alters dramatically the metabolic picture one observes in the same animal at other times of the year.

It is impossible to consider all of the reactions of intermediary metabolism at this time. The list of such reactions is prodigious; possibly over 2000 different reactions take place almost simultaneously in a liver cell. Under discussion here will be those general areas upon which so much of the animal economy depends—those involving the major foodstuffs and storage products, the carbohydrates, fats, and proteins, and their oxidation, syntheses, and interconversions.

Excursions into other areas are dependent upon information available in the literature dealing with metabolic or enzymic experiments conducted on amphibians or on their tissues, broken-cell preparations, or isolated enzymes. Information in many areas is nonexistent and for the sake of presenting a unified picture it will be necessary to assume the existence of certain reactions which have not been formally demonstrated to occur in Amphibia but which are known to be present in other vertebrates.

A. MAJOR METABOLIC PATHWAYS

Catabolic reactions involving carbohydrates, amino acids, and lipids for the most part yield the common intermediate, acetylSCoA, which can enter the tricarboxylic acid cycle (acetylSCoA + oxalacetate → citrate) (Krebs, 1954) with subsequent oxidation to CO_2 and water as shown in Fig. 3. Fatty acids derived from neutral fats, phospholipids, and glycolipids can be converted completely to acetylSCoA. In the conversion of glucose to acetylSCoA only two-thirds of the carbon appears in this intermediate because of the loss of 2 carbons as CO_2 in the conversion of 2 molecules of pyruvate to 2 molecules of acetylSCoA. Because of the large negative ΔF associated with this latter reaction, acetylSCoA cannot be reconverted to pyruvate; hence fatty acids do not lead to a net synthesis of carbohydrate. Pyruvate can also enter the tricarboxylic acid cycle in a reaction involving fixation of CO_2. Glycerol derived from fat can be channeled into the area of carbohydrate metabolism.

Amino acids derived from proteins may be thought of as of two types: (1) ketogenic amino acids which yield acetylSCoA or acetoacetate without going through pyruvate, and (2) glycogenic amino acids which yield pyruvate or intermediates of the tricarboxylic acid cycle such as oxalacetate (from aspartate) or α-ketoglutarate (from glutamate) and which subsequently may yield pyruvate and hence glucose. The only completely ketogenic amino acid is leucine, which can be converted to 3 moles of acetylSCoA. Phenylalanine, tyrosine, and isoleucine are both ketogenic and glucogenic while all other amino acids which appear in proteins are glucogenic. Glucogenic amino acids all lead to pyruvate which can be converted to acetylSCoA. In theory, then, all amino acids are potentially ketogenic;

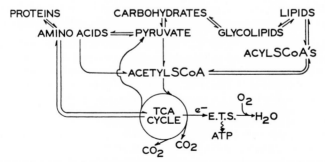

Fig. 3. Interrelationships of major foodstuffs in Amphibia. E. T. S. = electron transport system; TCA cycle = Krebs tricarboxylic acid cycle. (See text for discussion.)

however, the formation of ketone bodies (acetoacetate, β-hydroxybutyrate, acetone) does not generally take place to any [great extent in the intact animal when the supply of pyruvate precursors is ample.

An inspection of Fig. 3 will show that protein and carbohydrate may be interconverted or may be converted irreversibly to fat. These conversions refer to *mass conversions* and not merely to an exchange of carbon; as shown by isotope experiments (see Chaikoff and Brown, 1954), fatty acid carbons can be converted to glucose carbons, but this does not represent a net conversion of mass.

Oxidation of fatty acids via the tricarboxylic acid cycle does not require any net input to the cycle from sources other than acetylSCoA generated from these acids, for their carbon is completely accounted for by the CO_2 produced during operation of the cycle. Fats occupy a different position metabolically than do either proteins or carbohydrates, for once fat is formed (in the case of vertebrates) its fatty acids can be used principally *only* as an energy source. The economy afforded the organism by storage of fat for hibernation is at once evident; it insures that growth processes will be arrested during hibernation, thus conserving energy; it conserves protein, which makes up a good portion of cellular structure; and it provides the organism with a substance of greater caloric content on a weight basis than do the other major foodstuffs (see Table III).

Interconversions and transformations within the area of intermediary metabolism are taking place at all times in what might be termed a *dynamic equilibrium* (Schoenheimer, 1942).* Numerous metabolic interdigitations obtain, and the various subareas interact at many points.

It should be noted that the routes concerned with the synthesis and degradation of protein, carbohydrate, and fat from their respective precursors—amino acids, pyruvate, and acetylSCoA—are not simple reversals of a single pathway as might be anticipated from the reversible arrows shown in Fig. 3. At least at one point the synthetic and degradative routes for each of these major substances diverge.† It is these divergences which

* "Life is, so to speak, a flame, and simultaneously with the growth, building-up, process, there is a continuous oxidation, levelling, or catabolic process as predicted by the second law of thermodynamics. This maintenance cost is, perhaps, in part at least, the price paid for maintaining the thermodynamically unstable and statistically improbable complexly living, growing, evolving configuration, in the face of the opposite tendency of levelling disorganization to increase in entropy, as predicted by the second law of thermodynamics." Brody (1945).

† "If in any system an irreversible process occurs, it is possible, with sufficient ingenuity, to devise a mechanism by which in actuality, or at least by thought, every part of the system may be restored to its original condition at the expense of a degradation in the standard system." Lewis and Randall (1923). ["Irreversible process" as used here is in the thermodynamic sense, meaning the total entropy of all systems is increased.]

allow for a dynamic equilibrium or steady state rather than the establishment of a condition of equilibrium which would be incompatible with the living state. The continuous flux of material along innumerable pathways affords a delicate control over the levels of metabolites and makes possible rapid physiological responses to various metabolic demands which tend to displace the cell from its metabolically poised position.

B. THE TRICARBOXYLIC ACID CYCLE AND ELECTRON TRANSPORT SYSTEM

1. Nature of the Process of Aerobic Oxidation

Under aerobic conditions the combined activity of the tricarboxylic acid cycle and associated electron transport system makes available, in the form of ATP, a portion of the free energy change associated with the oxidation of acetylSCoA to CO_2 and water. Because of the availability of reactions leading to acetylSCoA from carbohydrate, fat, and protein, the cell can derive a large percentage of the free energy made available from oxidation of these substances by means of a single energy-yielding device. The following sequence in highly abbreviated form summarizes the enzymic steps of the tricarboxylic acid cycle: oxalacetate + acetylSCoA → citrate → cis-aconitate → isocitrate → oxalsuccinate → CO_2 + α-ketoglutarate → CO_2 + succinate → fumarate → malate → oxalacetate ⋯ . The summation of the individual reactions constituting this cycle when reduced to its simplest terms is:

$$CH_3COSCoA + 3\ H_2O \rightarrow 2\ CO_2 + HSCoA + 8\ [H] \tag{6}$$

The tricarboxylic acid cycle is not a typical combustion process, for it proceeds isothermally in such a manner as to release four pairs of hydrogen atoms to organic carriers, one pair being given up at each of four reaction steps of the cycle. This is very important, for the cell is not geared to handle the chemical potential of 8 [H] all at once. The pairs of hydrogens are in fact transferred to TPN, Fe-flavin, DPN, and another DPN, yielding the reduced forms of these carriers. The reduced carriers are subsequently reoxidized as they pass their hydrogens to the electron transport system, a system of iron pigments (cytochromes) and ancillary substances (Green, 1959).

Transfer of electrons during the oxidation of a DPNH-linked reaction would appear to be: substrate → DPNH → flavin → cytochrome b → cytochrome c → cytochrome a → cytochrome a_3 (cytochrome oxidase) → O_2 . Geared to their passage down the redox potential gradient of the electron transport system is the formation of the high-energy compound ATP at three alternate steps. The reduced carriers, DPNH and TPNH, each yield 3 molecules of ATP while the flavin (Fe-flavin·2H) yields 2 molecules of ATP. However, one of the reactions of the tricarboxylic acid cycle

(α-ketoglutarate $\rightarrow$ succinate $+$ CO_2) yields an equivalent of 1 molecule of ATP at the substrate level for each acetylSCoA entering the cycle. Thus an average of 3 ATP's are formed for each pair of hydrogens removed from intermediates of the cycle, intermediates whose concentration remains constant because of the entry of 2 carbons as acetylSCoA and the loss of (these) 2 carbons as CO_2.

At the distal end of the electron transport system the 4 pairs of hydrogen atoms are passed on to O_2 by cytochrome oxidase to yield water:

$$8[H] + 2 O_2 = 4 H_2O \tag{7}$$

Addition of Reactions (6) and (7) yields

$$CH_3COSCoA + 2O_2 = 2 CO_2 + H_2O + HSCoA \tag{8}$$

$$\Delta F^{0'}_{298} = -200 \text{ kcal}$$

The oxidation of acetylSCoA as in Reaction (8) has associated with it a free energy decrease of 200 kcals for each mole of acetylSCoA oxidized. This is the theoretical maximum of energy available for useful work to the organism in oxidation of 1 mole of acetylSCoA via the tricarboxylic acid cycle and associated electron transport system. The phosphorylation of ADP associated with passage of hydrogens (electrons) from carriers to oxygen via the electron transport system and the generation of an equivalent of one ATP at the substrate level in the tricarboxylic acid cycle account for the phosphorylation of 12 moles of ADP for each acetylSCoA oxidized.

Phosphorylation of ADP may, for simplicity, be represented by the endergonic reaction,

$$MgADP^{-1} + P_i^{-2} + H^+ = MgATP^{-2} + H_2O \tag{9}$$

$$\Delta F^{0'}_{310} = +7.0 \text{ kcal} \qquad \text{(Benzinger } et\ al.,\ 1959)$$

The formation of 12 moles of ATP represents the trapping of $12 \times 7.00 = 84$ kcal of the 200 kcal [see Reaction (8)] available from the oxidation of 1 mole of acetylSCoA. This represents an over-all efficiency of 42% in the trapping of the free energy theoretically available. The other 58% is lost in the form of heat in the phosphorylative process. Ultimately the 84 kcal will appear completely in the form of heat unless the organism does external work or carries out an excess of synthetic over degradative work such as the storage of energy-rich compounds.

2. Occurrence in Amphibia

It is surprising that studies on the tricarboxylic acid cycle are virtually absent in the case of Amphibia. So much of the animal economy depends upon this synthetic (see Krebs et al., 1951) and energy-yielding device that it pervades nearly every metabolic area. In conjunction with the electron transport system it is responsible for over 90 % of the energy made available under aerobic conditions for (a) synthesis of high-energy compounds (storage products), (b) maintenance of structural elements of the cell, and (c) for the performance of nervous, muscular, and secretory activity.

In some early studies, muscle extract of a frog (probably *Rana* sp.) was used as an enzyme source (Wagner-Jauregg *et al.*, 1934) for the oxidation of malic acid, a tricarboxylic acid cycle intermediate.

Hunter and Hunter (1957) have clearly demonstrated the presence of the tricarboxylic acid cycle in frog skin of *Rana pipiens*. The following enzymes were demonstrated on the basis of oxygen uptake over that of endogenous controls after addition of various cycle intermediates to flasks containing pieces of skin: fumarase (fumarate → malate), malic dehydrogenase (malate → oxalacetate), *isocitric* dehydrogenase (*isocitrate* → oxalsuccinate), succinoxidase (succinate → fumarate). In addition, the participation of cyctochrome *c* in oxygen uptake and the presence of glycerophosphate dehydrogenase (glycerophosphate → glyceraldehyde-3-P) and glutamic dehydrogenase (glutamate → α-ketoglutarate) were also demonstrated. Inhibition studies with cyanide, malonate, and sulfite suggest that this system is essentially that of the tricarboxylic acid cycle of Mammalia.

In a study of the effect of metabolic inhibitors on the ovulatory process in *Rana pipiens*, Rondell and Wright (1958) could best explain their findings in terms of reactions of glycolysis, the tricarboxylic acid cycle, and the cytochrome-cytochrome oxidase system. The pattern of incorporation of $C^{14}O_2$ into various intermediates of eggs and embryos of *Rana pipiens* is again highly suggestive of the occurrence of the cycle (Cohen, 1954). The C^{14} appeared in compounds expected to be labeled by CO_2-fixing reactions, reactions of the cycle, and closely related enzymic reactions involving aspartate, glutamate, malate, succinate, fumarate, and citrate. Incorporation occurred at all stages studied, from the unfertilized egg through the gastrula.

The above studies and information of an indirect nature leave little doubt but that the tricarboxylic acid cycle occurs in Amphibia. It is hoped, however, that formal documentation of its occurrence in various species will be provided soon.

The tricarboxylic acid cycle and its associated electron transport system occur in the mitochondria of cells (as studied largely in Mammalia). G. ten Cate (1959) has made the observation that the citric acid content of embryos of *Rana esculenta* increases sigmoidally between Shumway (1940) stages 10 and 25 and suggests that this is related to an increase in mitochondria which contain tricarboxylic acid cycle enzymes.

It is certain that succinic dehydrogenase,

$$
\begin{array}{c}
\text{COO}^- \\
| \\
\text{HCH} \\
| \\
\text{HCH} \\
| \\
\text{COO}^-
\end{array}
+ \text{Fe-flavin} =
\begin{array}{c}
\text{COO}^- \\
| \\
\text{HC}{=}\text{CH} \\
| \\
{}^-\text{OOC}
\end{array}
+ \text{Fe-flavin} \cdot 2\text{H}
\tag{10}
$$

       Succinate   Fumarate

and the system for the oxidation of the reduced iron-flavin, via the cyto-chrome system, i.e., succinoxidase, occur in Amphibia [myocardium of larval and adult heart of *Ambystoma tigrinum* and *A. punctatum* (=*maculatum*) (Cooper and Copenhaver, 1956); embryos of *Rhacophorus schlegelii* (Ohara and Suyama, 1952); liver mitochondria of developing *Xenopus laevis* (Boell and Weber, 1955)]. It is further known that cytochrome oxidase is present [mitochondria of *Rana pipiens* eggs (Recknagel, 1950); mito-chondria of *Xenopus laevis* tadpole liver (Boell and Weber, 1955); *Bufo bufo* embryos (Petrucci, 1957, 1959)].

There is some controversy concerning the levels of cytochrome oxidase during amphibian development. For example, Petrucci (1957) found little change in its level in *Bufo bufo* up to hatching (with a slight suggestion of a minimum at Shumway stage 18) whereas the studies of Lang and Grant (1961) on *Rana pipiens*, indicate a marked decline up to stage 18 followed by a slow recovery to a plateau at stage 25 as shown in Fig. 4.

The electron transport picture is complicated by the fact that there are

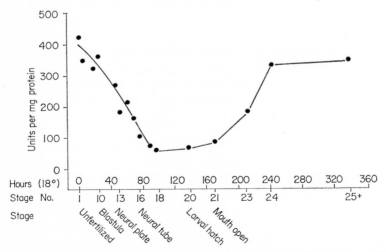

Fig. 4. Cytochrome oxidase during frog embryogenesis. After Lang and Grant (1961).

several cytochrome-*c* reductases that intermediate between hydrogen donors and cytochrome oxidase. Lang and Grant (1961) have found that DPN-, TPN-, and succinate-cytochrome *c* reductases are present at varying levels (in terms of units per milligram protein) during the embryogenesis of *Rana pipiens*, the latter reductase showing little activity until shortly after the mouth opens (stage 21).

C. CARBOHYDRATE METABOLISM

1. Anaerobic and Aerobic Glycolysis

It appears to be established that tissues of Amphibia can break down glycogen or glucose by the classic Embden-Meyerhof-Parnas pathway. Many, if not all, of the enzymes, substrates, cofactors, and products of glycolysis have been measured or observed in eggs or tissues (or their cell-free extracts) of numerous amphibians (see Barth and Barth, 1954; and see below).

Glycolysis proper (see Fig. 5) may be divided for didactic purposes into two parts: (1) phosphorylative reactions which prepare glycogen or hexoses for later phosphate transfer reactions, and (2) transfer of high-energy phosphate from phosphorylated 3-carbon compounds to ADP to yield the energy-rich ATP. The reactions of (1) and (2) constitute the anaerobic

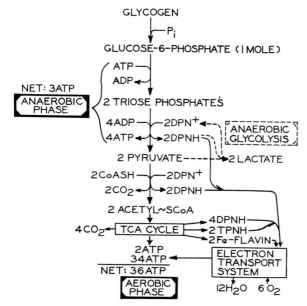

Fig. 5. Generation of energy during anaerobic and aerobic phases of glycolysis.

phase. Pyruvate acts as the electron acceptor for DPNH formed during the oxidation of the triose phosphates, and it yields the end product of anaerobic glycolysis, lactate. ATP, which is generated at the substrate level in anaerobic glycolysis, is the result of an oxidation which yields glyceric acid-1,3-diphosphate and the reduced hydrogen carrier, DPNH. This carrier must eventually give up its hydrogens, or the level of the oxidized form of DPN would decrease, ultimately preventing the oxidative step from taking place and bringing glycolysis to a halt.

It should be noted that anaerobic glycolysis, *perforce*, does not result in any net change in the oxidation level of carbon, for the empirical formula (CH_2O) is the same for both typical carbohydrates and lactic acid. The energy of anaerobic glycolysis stems from cleavage of a carbon-carbon bond and a rearrangement of oxygen and hydrogen atoms about the carbons.

In aerobic glycolysis, pyruvate, instead of being converted to lactate, is oxidatively decarboxylated to acetylSCoA (see Fig. 5). The DPNH formed as a result of this oxidation, and the DPNH, TPNH, and Fe-flavin·2H formed by oxidation of acetylSCoA in reactions of the tricarboxylic acid cycle, are reoxidized via the electron transport system yielding ATP in the process.

Not much energy is made available to the organism under conditions of anaerobic glycolysis compared with that obtained from aerobic glycolysis. Of the 52 kcal of free energy theoretically available under standard conditions from the conversion of 1 mole of glucose (as glycogen) to lactic acid, only about 21 kcal of free energy is trapped in the form of 3 net moles of ATP. However, this is an efficiency of 41%. Only 2 net moles of ATP are formed, or about 14 kcal of free energy are trapped if we start with glucose. This is because of the necessity of phosphorylating glucose with ATP in the glucokinase reaction:

$$\text{Glucose} + \text{ATP} \rightarrow \text{glucose-6-P} + \text{ADP} \tag{11}$$

However, the aerobic phase of glycolysis leads to the production of 36 ATP's. Thus the aerobic phase of glycolysis accounts for 36/39 or 92% of the free energy trapped in the conversion of *glycogen* to CO_2 and water.

The complete oxidation of 1 mole of solid glucose to CO_2 and water, has

$$C_6H_{12}O_6 \ (s) + 6O_2 = 6CO_2 + 6H_2O \tag{12}$$

$$\Delta F_{298}^{0'} = -688 \text{ kcal/mole glucose}$$

associated with it a standard free energy decrease of 688 kcal. The production of 38 moles of ATP coincident with this oxidation represents $38 \times 7.0 = 266$ kcal, or an efficiency of about 39% in the trapping of the free energy theoretically available for doing useful work. As a comparison, this is the theoretical efficiency of a steam engine operating with boiler and exhaust temperatures of 219° and 27° centigrade, respectively.

2. Glycolytic and Related Enzymes Studied in Amphibia

a. *Phosphorylase*. (Glycogen → glucose-1-P) The enzyme is present before fertilization in eggs of *Rana pipiens, Bufo americanus*, and *Ambystoma tigrinum* (Barnes, 1939). The level decreases 50 % upon cleavage, but at gastrulation it is 45 % higher than in the unfertilized egg. It is active during embryonic development of *Bufo vulgaris* (Kurata *et al.*, 1955).

b. *Phosphoglucomutase*. (Glucose-1-P ⇌ glucose-6-P) The enzyme is present during embryonic development of *Bufo vulgaris* (Kurata *et al.*, 1955).

c. *Phosphohexose isomerase*. (Glucose-6-P ⇌ fructose-6-P) The enzyme occurs in embryos of *Bufo vulgaris* (Kurata *et al.*, 1955).

d. *Aldolase*. (Fructose-1,6-diphosphate ⇌ 2 triose phosphates) Kurata *et al.* (1954) have assayed the enzyme in minces of eggs of *Rhacophorus schlegelii*. A peak in activity was noted 10 hr after fertilization.

e. *Triose phosphate dehydrogenase*, i.e., *glyceraldehyde-3-phosphate dehydrogenase*. (Glyceraldehyde-3-P → glyceric acid-1,3-diphosphate) The enzyme occurs in frog egg (J. Brachet and L. Rapkine, 1950, cited in Barth and Barth, 1954).

f. *Hexokinase*. (Hexose → hexose-6-P) See Reaction (11). The enzyme(s) has been shown to occur in extracts of *Rana temporaria* brain (Kerly and Leaback, 1957). The extract exhibited both glucokinase (greater and fructokinase (lesser) activity, and activity was comparable to that of other vertebrate classes tested.

g. *Glucose-6-phosphatase*. (Glucose-6-P → glucose) During both normal and induced metamorphosis of *Rana grylio* the activity of this enzyme in liver increases (Frieden and Mathews, 1958).

h. *Amylase*. (Starch → maltose) The blood of *Bufo arenarum* contains 2,900–17,800 Somogyi amylase units, and the level appears to be unrelated to sex or season (Levin, 1955). It occurs in the plasma but not in the corpuscles. Levin found it also to be present in bile but absent in the urine. The enzyme is demonstrable in 2- to 3-week-old embryos of the giant salamander, *Megalobatrachus japonicus* (Takahashi, 1935).

i. *Glycerophosphatase*. (α-glycerophosphate → glycerol) Takahashi (1935) found the enzyme to be present in 2- to 3-week-old embryos of the giant salamander.

j. *Glucose-6-phosphate dehydrogenase = Zwischenferment*. (Glucose-6-P → δ-gluconolactone-6-P) The enzyme has been purified from frog muscle (Wagner-Jauregg *et al.*, 1935). It is one of the enzymes (along with aldolase above) which is part of an alternate oxidative route for conversion of glucose-6-phosphate to triosephosphate and CO_2 as shown in the over-all reaction:

$$3 \text{ Glucose-6-P} + 6 \text{ TPN}^+ \rightarrow 5 \text{ glyceraldehyde-3-P} + 3 \text{ CO}_2 + 6 \text{ TPNH} \quad (13)$$

It is of interest to note that TPNH can be oxidized by a TPNH-cytochrome-c reductase which is present during all stages of embryonic development of *Rana pipiens* (Lang and Grant, 1961). The oxidative bypass, i.e., the pentose phosphate or Warburg-Dickens shunt (Wood, 1955), has not been investigated in Amphibia. Until its relative importance for the breakdown of carbohydrate and production of energy has been evaluated in Amphibia, conclusions drawn from any quantitative data obtained from glycolytic studies must be held in abeyance.

3. Glycogen and Glycolysis during Development

Frog glycogen is known to be similar to rabbit glycogen with respect to molecular weight, attack by β-amylase, and type of bond at the branching point (Afanasyeva and Stepanenko, 1956). It consists of a backbone of α-1,4 glycosidic residues with α-1,6 linkages at the branching point as shown in Fig. 6. However, molecules of frog glycogen are said to be more compact than those of the rabbit because of the higher degree of branching in the frog glycogen (species not given).

At the onset of embryonic development the carbohydrate content of a single *Rana pipiens* egg (free of jelly) was: total carbohydrate, 104 μg; glycogen, 73.2 μg; free carbohydrate, 1.0 μg; unidentified carbohydrate, 29.8 μg (Gregg, 1948). Glycogen decreases from 73.2 μg per fertilized egg to 31.0 μg at the time of hatching (Shumway stage 20). This decrease compares favorably with the decrease in total carbohydrate and it is concluded that "glycogen is the first energy-rich compound to be utilized by the

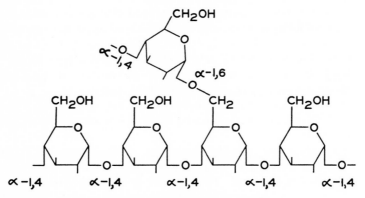

Fig. 6. Portion of glycogen molecule.

developing egg" (Barth and Barth, 1954). Frog eggs can be subjected to anaerobic conditions without harm continuously from fertilization to hatching; it would thus seem that anaerobic glycolysis (of glycogen) can supply the energy requirements for this period.

If all of the glycogen were utilized from the fertilized egg to the hatching stage under anaerobic conditions, with energy being supplied by *anaerobic* glycolysis with an efficiency of 41 %, calculation will show that approximately 9 millical of energy would be available per egg to do embryonic work. If there are no other sources of energy this would be the maximum quantity of energy required for all the work of embryonic development up to hatching. However, there is reason to believe that when anaerobic conditions prevail additional energy may be derived from high-energy labile phosphates contained in the eggs (Barth and Barth, 1954).

An approximate value for the amount of free energy available for the work of embryonic development from the fertilized egg of *Rana pipiens* to its hatching under aerobic conditions may be arrived at on the basis of the loss of glycogen up to hatching. The complete oxidation of glycogen to CO_2 and water may be represented as:

$$C_6H_{10}O_5 \quad + \quad 6O_2 = 6CO_2 + 5H_2O \tag{13a}$$

Glucose residue
of glycogen
(molecular weight = 162)

$$\Delta F^0 \;=\; -700 \text{ kcal mole of residue}$$

$$\Delta H^0 \;=\; -688 \text{ kcal/mole of residue}$$

The loss of 42.2 μg of glycogen up to the time of hatching (Gregg, 1948) represents the utilization of $42.2/162 = 0.260$ μmole of glucose residues. Such oxidation releases $(700 \times 10^{-3} \text{ cal}/\mu\text{mole}) \times 0.260$ μmole $= 182 \times 10^{-3}$ cal of free energy per egg under standard conditions. If the efficiency of trapping this available energy is 39 %, then the amount of free energy concerned directly with embryonic development would be $0.39 \times 182 \times 10^{-3} = 71$ millical per egg.

The "caloric content," i.e. the heat of combustion $(-\Delta H)$, of 42.2 μg of glycogen can be obtained from the value for the caloric equivalent of glycogen, 4.25 kcal per gm (rounded off to 4.3 in Table III):

$$4.25 \text{ (kcal per gm)} \times 42.2 \times 10^{-6} \text{ (gm per egg)} = 179 \times 10^{-6} \text{ kcal per egg}$$

$$= 179 \text{ millical per egg}$$

or from the enthalpy datum associated with Eq. (12a):

$$688 \times 10^{-3} \text{ (cal per } \mu\text{mole)} \times 0.260 \text{ } \mu\text{mole} = 179 \times 10^{-6} \text{ kcal per egg}$$

$$= 179 \text{ millical per egg}$$

Because the energy associated with the entropy term, $T\Delta S$ [see Eq. (1)], is small with respect to ΔH for the oxidation of glycogen according to Eq. (13a), ΔF differs only slightly from ΔH.

For further discussion of glycogen utilization during embryogenesis see Brachet and Needham (1935), Nowiński (1939), Needham *et al.* (1938, 1939), Gregg and Pomerat (1942), Jaeger (1945), Cohen (1954), and the excellent review by Barth and Barth (1954).

Glycogen can be deposited prematurely in the liver of frogs and toads at the beginning of larval life through injections of adrenocorticotropic hormone (ACTH) or cortisone (Beaumont, 1955). Differentiation of the adrenal cortex occurs at the beginning of larval life, and failure to deposit liver glycogen at this time is attributed to the absence of adrenocortical hormones and not to the absence of liver enzymes for glycogen synthesis. In frog tadpoles, glycogen is stored in the liver prior to resorption of the tail, and such glycogen is catabolized during the active resorptive process (Bilewicz, 1938). Thus, reserve material other than tail protein is utilized during metamorphosis. It is known that frog larvae (*Rana catesbeiana*) will metamorphose with as much as 60 % of the length of the tail excised (Paik and Cohen, 1960).

4. Glycogen in Tissues

Glycogen is found in the double visual cells in 5-day old tadpoles of *Rana temporaria* (Saxén, 1955), but its physiological role here is incompletely understood. Glycogen is not found in the single visual cells. Saxén suggests that the glycogen serves as a nutritional reserve for growing tissue. Glycogen normally appears in Anura at larval stage II (stage of Taylor and Kollros, 1946), but it can be delayed until stage VII in the toad, *Discoglossus picta* (Beaumont, 1956). Addition of glucose to the medium containing intact tadpoles brings about its early appearance (stage I). Hypophysectomy or thyroidectomy does not prevent this. Thus, pituitary hormones are not essential for such deposition, and, as Beaumont has shown, explants of stage I liver of *Discoglossus picta*, cultured in a medium containing 1 % glucose, yield histochemically demonstrable glycogen.

On the basis of wet weights, the percentages of glycogen for various tissues of *Rana fusca* in March were reported by Bleibtreu (1910) to be: liver, 8.7; eggs, 1.1; muscle, 1.00; nerve, 0.07; skin (below limit of detection by method then employed).

Glycogen appears in the apical portions of the Sertoli cells and tubular lumens of the testes as well as along surfaces of the spermatocytes (Burgos, 1955). It is found in all parts of the nervous system of *Ambystoma maculatum* with the exception of cell nuclei (Janosky and Wenger, 1956); during proliferation, glycogen accumulates in the cells of the nervous system, and during the process of differentiation it rapidly disappears.

5. Factors Influencing Carbohydrate Levels

There are considerable fluctuations of carbohydrate levels in Amphibia. Athanasiu (1899) pointed out long ago that "die Menge des Froschglykogens ihr Maxima im Herbst und ihr Minima im Sommer hat." These studies dealt with *Rana fusca* and *R. esculenta.* Athanasiu also indicated that liver glycogen does not disappear during the winter, but that a great loss occurs during the spring. A wide seasonal variation in liver glycogen content of *Rana esculenta* and *R. temporaria* was observed by Kato (1910). During November the liver glycogen content was reported to be 14%, but only 1% in June. The ovaries remained rather constant at 2%.

Goldfederova (1926) showed that the glycogen of the liver, muscles, and ovaries of *Rana fusca* and *R. esculenta* were greatest during the winter, which was also true for the quantity of fat. Levels of both carbohydrate and fat fell to minimal levels just before the reproductive period (May for *Rana fusca*, July for *R. esculenta*). While the high level of glycogen found in frog tissue during hibernation has in more than one instance been thought to arise from stored fat, it is difficult to reconcile this with known biochemical pathways.

Muscle of *Rana pipiens* obtained in the spring and kept several weeks at 4° apparently does not break down glycogen when contracting exhaustively under anaerobic conditions in spite of a muscle glycogen level as high as 0.5% (Barger and Johnson, 1941). A suitable explanation as to the source of energy for such contraction cannot be offered for this observation. Glycogenolysis by liver slices has been studied in the case of *Rana temporaria* over a temperature range of 7°–21° by Tindal (1956). Glucose production increased upon addition of adrenaline or noradrenaline (activation of phosphorylase?). Thyroxine or insulin had no effect *in vitro* although glucose production was lowered *in vivo* by administration of insulin 19 hr before treatment.

The mean blood sugar level of *Rana temporaria* caught in the field without exciting the animals was 38 ± 1.4 mg/100 ml from April through October (Smith, 1954). A marked hyperglycemic response to excitement could be elicited during the spawning season in March and continuing through the summer. The response was reduced in September and absent in October. This response parallels the cycle of seasonal thyroid activity, and Smith suggests that thyroxine inhibits the destruction of certain circulating adrenergic compounds. Smith (1950) earlier reported higher blood sugar values (54–62 mg/100 ml) for *Rana temporaria* caught during the spawning season (March), during June and July, and again in November. Hyperglycemia in summer occurs at a time when there is a rapid development of the fat body. When fat is no longer stored in the fat body nor glycogen in the liver, the blood sugar values are lower ($\sim$40 mg/100 mg).

Xenopus laevis develops diabetes (230 mg/100 ml blood sugar) upon removal of the pancreas (Slome, 1936). The toad can be made into a typical Houssay animal if the pituitary is removed prior to extirpation of the pancreas; such an animal shows a blood sugar level of 45–63 mg/100 ml. Hypophysectomy alone leads to normal blood sugar levels and increases the tolerance for glucose. Absence of insulin due to removal of the pancreas is thought to interfere with the phosphorylation of glucose. Failure of the phosphorylative step presumably prevents the entrance of glucose to the cells leading to a depletion of glycogen in the tissues and an increased blood sugar level.

Smith (1953) has reinvestigated the long latent period (1 to 2 days) for the production of hypoglycemic convulsions in *Rana temporaria*. Frogs kept at 17°–20°, when injected with 4 units of insulin via the dorsal lymph sac, registered no change in mean blood sugar level in the first 90 min. After 5 hr the level fell to 3 $\pm$ 0.7 mg/100 ml. Muscle glycogen was nearly halved in the period from 5 to 24 hr after insulin, to 0.32 $\pm$ 0.06 %. Convulsions appeared at a muscle glycogen content of 0.23 $\pm$ 0.05 %. On the contrary, changes in liver glycogen in the first 24 hr were not significant. This is in contrast to mammals, which show a rapid decrease in liver glycogen after insulin injection.

Some frogs seem to be able to tolerate extremely low levels of blood glucose. Twenty-eight per cent of a group of *Rana catesbeiana* bullfrogs observed by Wright (1959) had levels below the limit of detection (average value of all animals, 13.5 mg/100 ml) without signs of hypoglycemic convulsions. There appeared to be no correlation between the blood glucose level and the nutritional state.

Rana catesbeiana bullfrogs are also unusual in that they appear to be refractory to injections of alloxan (Wright, 1959). The dose of alloxan usually used to produce alloxan diabetes in rats does not damage the pancreatic islet tissue of these frogs. However, the animal will die if the pancreas is removed.

Slome (1936) has made the interesting observation that the fasting blood sugar level of *Xenopus laevis* kept on a black background (37.0 $\pm$ 2.7 mg/100 ml) is higher than that of animals kept on a white background (25.4 $\pm$ 1.0 mg/100 ml). But Ohnishi (1951) reports that the blood sugar of white-adapted frogs is higher than that of black-adapted frogs.

The effect that temperature and season (which may or may not be completely dependent upon temperature effects) have upon the metabolic and sexual activities of Amphibia appears to be related to endocrine changes and the possible superposition of these changes upon biological rhythms inherent in the organism, those established in the previous year, or those mediated by as yet unknown factors. In this connection, F. A. Brown *et al.* (1958) have observed that fluctuations in the O_2 consumption of *Triturus viridescens* are correlated with cosmic radiation—a surprising finding, but not necessarily meaning that cosmic radiation causes the changes in O_2 consumption.

Certainly much can be explained in terms of alterations of metabolic pathways as brought about by changes in temperature, for all reactions do not follow the van't Hoff rule of a doubling of reaction rate for a 10° increase in temperature. Many examples exist attesting to the endocrine control of metabolism. Partial explanations for metabolic alterations can be given in terms of changes in levels of the hormones and the resultant of these with reaction rates for metabolic processes, rates which are also modified, differentially, by temperature change. While we know something about endocrines and about metabolic reactions and their time-temperature coordinates, the curve of the intersection of their respective surfaces is not clearly defined. In the case of Amphibia, we are in possession of too few facts to orient this curve in the multidimensional coordinate system of the intact animal.

D. LIPID METABOLISM

In spite of our clear understanding of fat metabolism based on studies carried out largely on mammals, pigeons, and microorganisms, we know little if anything about intermediary lipid metabolism in Amphibia. The reader is directed to the recent numerous reviews devoted to reactions of lipid metabolism (Chaikoff and Brown, 1954; Lynen, 1955; Kennedy, 1957; Stumpf, 1960; Stumpf and Barber, 1960).

Provisionally, we can assume that the reactions occurring in other organisms also may occur in Amphibia, but it is emphasized that these have not been clearly established in this class. While it is not anticipated that there will be observed a fundamentally different scheme of lipid synthesis and degradation in Amphibia from that of Mammalia, for example, some interesting variations may occur. There is some suggestion that the typical reactions of ketogenesis may be modified in the case of hibernating amphibians, which subsist entirely upon reserves of the fat body (Lardy, 1960). The reader is again reminded that at least a part of the discussion in this section is an extrapolation to Amphibia of results obtained largely from studies on warm-blooded animals and on microorganisms.

1. Fatty Acid Oxidation

The oxidation of fatty acids as outlined by Knoop (1904–1905) in his early studies on β-oxidation is summarized by the over-all reaction:

$$CH_3(CH_2)_{14}COOH \rightarrow 8\ C_2 \rightarrow 16\ CO_2 \qquad (14)$$

Palmitic acid   Two-carbon
(for example)   fragments

For rather complete discussions of the history and significance of the C_2 fragment ("active acetate" = acetylSCoA) see Decker (1959) and Chaikoff and Brown (1954).

The over-all process of fatty acid oxidation is now known to be carried out in the following manner, where RCH_2CH_2COOH is a fatty acid:

(a) Formation of a fatty acyl ester of coenzyme A:

$$RCH_2CH_2COOH + ATP + CoASH \overset{Mg^{++}}{=} RCH_2CH_2COSCoA + ADP \qquad (15)$$

(b) Dehydrogenation to yield the α,β-unsaturated derivative:

$$RCH_2CH_2COSCoA + FAD = RCH{=}CHCOSCoA + FAD{\cdot}2H \qquad (16)$$

(c) Hydration to yield the β-hydroxy derivative:

$$RCH{=}CHCOSCoA + H_2O = R\overset{OH}{\underset{|}{C}}HCH_2COSCoA \qquad (17)$$

(d) Further dehydrogenation to the β-keto derivative:

$$R\overset{OH}{\underset{|}{C}}HCH_2COSCoA + DPN^+ = R\overset{O}{\underset{\|}{C}}CH_2COSCoA + DPNH + H^+ \qquad (18)$$

(e) Thiolytic cleavage with CoASH to yield the acylSCoA of two carbons less than the original fatty acid, and acetylSCoA:

$$R\overset{O}{\underset{\|}{C}}CH_2COSCoA + CoASH = RCOSCoA + CH_3COSCoA \qquad (19)$$

The five enzymes which catalyze the above reactions are (a) acyl thiokinase, (b) acyl dehydrogenase, (c) enoyl hydrase, (d) β-hydroxyacyl dehydrogenase, and (e) β-ketoacyl thiolase. There may be at least three different acylthiokinases which act on fatty acids of different chain lengths.

The residual acylSCoA can be carried successively through Reactions (16)–(19), until, for acids of the even-carbon series, the fatty acid is converted completely to acetylSCoA. These can be oxidized via the tricarboxylic acid cycle (see Fig. 3) and yield energy in the form of ATP.

2. Lipid Synthesis

There is evidence to suggest that the synthesis of fatty acids is not strictly the reverse of the steps for the formation of acetylSCoA (Brady,

1960). Up to the present time, evidence is only circumstantial that lipid substances are synthesized by reversal of some of the known degradative pathways.

Our knowledge on synthesis of lipids by Amphibia is confined to a few observations of the incorporation of C^{14}-labeled acetate into lipid material. Conversion of acetate-1-C^{14} to total lipids, fatty acids, and cholesterol by intact frogs has been studied by Anciaux (1952).

The findings are rather typical in that they resemble those obtained in numerous experiments with mammals (see Chaikoff and Brown, 1954). One concludes from these experiments that acetate is first activated to acetylSCoA and is then converted as follows:

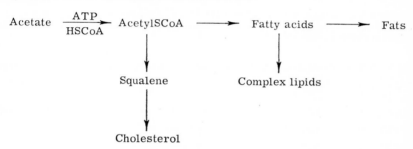

Acetate-1-C^{14} is converted *in vitro* to cholesterol-C^{14} by sheathed and desheathed sciatic nerve of *Rana catesbeiana* as demonstrated by Saunders and Friess (1959). In the absence of information to the contrary, the synthesis of cholesterol by frog nerve is presumed to follow the same pathway as in mammals. These workers also found that choline-1,2-C^{14} was incorporated into cholesterol by a pathway which can be postulated as follows:

$$\text{Cholin} \rightarrow \text{betaine} \rightarrow \text{glycine} \rightarrow \text{serine} \rightarrow$$
$$\text{pyruvate} \rightarrow \text{acetate} \rightarrow \text{squalene} \rightarrow \text{cholesterol} \tag{20}$$

3. Other Considerations

a. Fat Bodies. Amphibian fat bodies are especially rich in lipids as can be verified easily by examination with a hand lens. In the case of the Italian great newt, *Triturus carnifex*, this fat-storage organ contains as much as 55–65 % lipid on a wet weight basis as indicated in Table V (Collins *et al.*, 1953a).

Maximal development of the fat body occurs in the fall. During the winter the amount of lipid gradually decreases as it is used as an energy source. This is followed by a rapid and further depletion of the fat body in the spawning season. According to Athanasiu and Dragoiu (1910), fat not used during the winter may even appear in the urine during the spring.

TABLE V

LIPID CONTENT OF ORGANS OF THE ITALIAN GREAT NEWT *Triturus carnifex*[a]

(Assays on 140 specimens)

Organ	Fresh weight (gm)	Lipid weight (gm)	% Lipid (wet weight)
Liver	34.7	0.802	2.31
Fat body (male)	1.83	1.14	62.3
Fat body (female)	1.38	0.767	55.6
Ovaries	7.10	0.187	2.63
Testes	4.72	0.119	2.52
Spleen	2.44	0.010	0.41
Alimentary tract	79.5	2.59	3.26
Carcass	73.0	0.705	0.97

[a] From Collins *et al.* (1953a).

During the summer there is a rapid rate of fat deposition in the fat body (for *Rana esculenta* see Ackerman, 1949; for *Rana temporaria* and for literature keys see Smith, 1954).

Gonadal activity is related to the physiological state of the fat body (Morton and Rosen, 1949). Removal of one fat body causes the ovary on the same side to be smaller than the contralateral ovary.

The lipid of the fat bodies is largely in the form of triglycerides. In the case of the Formosan toad, *Bufo melanostictus*, the triglyceride content of the total fat-body lipid was found to be 98.3%, consisting of 41% saturated (palmitic and stearic) and 59% unsaturated acids (Tsukamoto and Ohtaki, 1949a). Small quantities of free fatty acids, carotenoids, and unsaponifiable matter which is largely cholesterol are found in the fat body (for *Rana tigrina* and *R. rugulosa* see Tsukamoto and Ohtaki, 1949b). For the fatty acid composition of the fat body in *Bufo arenarum* consult Cattaneo and de Sutton (1951) and Cattaneo *et al.* (1951). Hilditch (1940) concludes that depot fats of Amphibia and fishes contain approximately the same amount of palmitic acid (8–15%) but that this is more than the amount found in rats and birds (6–8%).

b. Liver and Muscle Lipids. Ackerman (1949) has carried out an extensive investigation of seasonal variations in the lipid content of *Rana esculenta*. During the summer, the phospholipid content of female frogs ranged from 1 to 2% and, in general, varied with the content of the liver neutral fat and cholesterol esters. Free cholesterol varied from specimen to specimen, ranging from zero to 1%; neutral fats (1.95–3.76%) and cholesterol esters (0.64–1.33%) were also variable. Decreases in amount of lipid in frogs during the winter are mainly due to loss of neutral fat. A fatty infiltration of the liver occurs prior to ovarian development. The amount of total lipid in the liver of spring frogs is markedly reduced, including a reduction in the amount of neutral fats and cholesterol esters.

The phosphatide content of male frog muscle is reported to be greater in spring and summer and less in winter and fall than that of the muscle of female frogs (Iosifova, 1939), suggesting a greater metabolic swing of such compounds in the male than in the female. Anciaux (1952) concludes that the fatty acids of liver and muscle of the frog have a much shorter half-life, i.e., a greater rate of turnover or renewal, than do those of mammals. Athanasiu and Dragoiu (1910) observed significant amounts of fat in striated frog muscle, especially during the winter.

c. *Acetylation Reactions.* Acetylation reactions, involving both physiological and foreign amines, have been investigated extensively (Decker, 1959). In a treatise on detoxication mechanisms, Williams (1949) points out that the acetylation of sulfonamides occurs in all vertebrates studied with the exception of the dog, turtle, and certain species of frogs.

Those amphibians which are known to conjugate most sulfonamides are the spadefoot toad (*Scaphiopus holbrookii*), the nebulous toad (*Bufo valliceps*), and the tree frog, *Hyla cinerea*. *Rana pipiens* and *Rana catesbeiana* are thought not to conjugate sulfonamides. At least some frogs synthesize hippuric acid (benzoylSCoA + glycine → hippuric acid). Homogenates of *Rana catesbeiana* liver can acetylate *p*-nitroaniline at a slow rate with acetylSCoA (Newbold, 1960).

Acetylation of choline and its hydrolysis is intimately related to the conduction of the nerve impulse (Nachmansohn and Wilson, 1951):

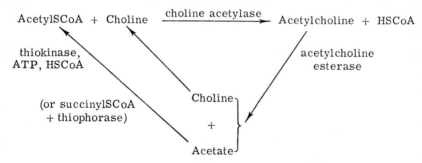

Acetylcholine esterase (choline esterase) is thought to be an essential part of the sodium pump mechanism is muscle (van der Kloot, 1956). It is known that there is an increased permeability of nerve to sodium ions associated with transmission of the nerve impulse.

d. *Lipase during Embryonic and Larval Development.* Lipases (triglyceride → glycerol + 3 fatty acids) are presumed to hydrolyze fats before the fatty acids can undergo β-oxidation. Lipase, as studied in homogenates

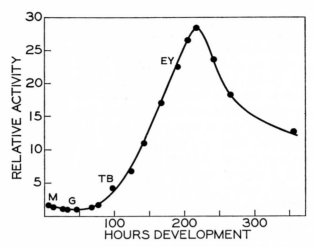

Fig. 7. Lipase activity of *Rana esculenta* during embryonic development. Relative lipase activity versus hours of development. M = morula, G = gastrula, TB = tail bud, EY = end of yolk. Adapted from Urbani and Scollo-Lavizzari (1955).

of embryos and larvae of *Rana esculenta*, shows low activity during the first 75 hr to the tail-bud stage as depicted in Fig. 7 (Urbani and Scollo-Lavizzari, 1955). At this time there is a rapid increase in lipase activity which reaches its maximum at about 220 hr, i.e., 40 hr into the larval stages, at which time the yolk material has been depleted. That this production of lipase is not just incidental is shown by the work of Bialascewicz and Mincóvna (1921) who reported that the total fat during development of *Rana temporaria* decreases during the time that the activity for lipase increases. The decline in activity beyond 220 hr appears to be logarithmic up to 350 hr.

E. AMINO ACID AND PROTEIN METABOLISM

Nitrogen metabolism in Amphibia involves reactions dealing with protein, amino acids, amines, amides, purines, pyrimidines, hormones (e.g., thyroxine), melanins, chromatophore pigments, urea, numerous coenzymes, etc. The intermediary aspects of nitrogen metabolism are concerned in large measure with reactions for the removal of amino groups from amino acids in the form of ammonia (amino acid and amine oxidases, dehydrases, and desulfhydrases), transfers of amino groups between amino acids and α-keto acids (transaminases), and reactions for the incorporation of ammonia into organic compounds (synthetases of one type or another). These latter aspects have been reviewed recently (Cohen and Brown, 1960). Enzymes of some of the more common reactions, with particular reference to Amphibia, appear below.

1. Degradative Reactions

a. *Proteinases and Peptidases.* Proteins subjected to the action of various proteinases and peptidases are hydrolyzed to their constituent amino acids:

$$(\text{Protein})_{n \text{ residues}} + (n - 1)\ H_2O \rightarrow n \text{ amino acid molecules} \qquad (21)$$

$$\Delta F^{0'}_{298} = -4 \text{ kcal (per mole of } H_2O)$$

$$= -4 \text{ kcal (per bond cleaved)}$$

Proteinase activity is present in the cleaving egg (for *Rana esculenta* see Urbani and de Cesaris-Coromaldi, 1954) and progressively decreases in activity until the tail-bud stage followed by an increase until the yolk is consumed (also compare Fig. 1). A fall in enzymic activity in the transition from embryonic to larval life occurs. In tail-bud embryos, activity is higher in the caudal than in the cephalic portion. The proteinase activities of *Bufo vulgaris* embryos and larvae have been studied (Urbani and de Cesaris-Coromaldi, 1955).

b. *Hatching Enzyme.* Embryos contain an enzyme which digests the vitelline membrane. The enzyme may be species-specific (Cambar, 1953). In this connection, a proteolytic enzyme precipitable in 50 % ammonium sulfate concentration and active at pH 7 (optimum) toward hemoglobin, gelatin, and egg mucin, is present in embryos of the toads *Bufo vulgaris* and *Discoglossus pictus* (Minganti and Azzolina, 1955).

c. *Peptidases.* Løvtrup, (1953b) has measured di- and tripeptidase activities of embryonic *Ambystoma mexicanum*:

$$\text{Alanylglycine}^{\pm} + H_2O = \text{alanine}^{\pm} + \text{glycine}^{\pm} \qquad (22)$$

$$\Delta F^{0'} = -4 \text{ kcal}$$

Dipeptidase activity is present in gastrulae of *Rana pipiens* (Barth and Sze, 1953). Dipeptidase of nucleated erythrocytes is higher than that of unnucleated erythrocytes. Relative levels in three species of Amphibia were as follows (Urbani, 1955a):

Triton cristatus > *Rana esculenta* > *Bufo vulgaris*

d. *Phosphoprotein Phosphatase.* Harris (1946) discovered an enzyme occurring in frog eggs of *Rana pipiens* and of *Rana catesbeiana* that cleaves phosphate from phosphoproteins such as casein, hen's egg vitellin, or yolk of frog eggs:

$$\text{Phosphoprotein} + H_2O \rightarrow \text{protein} + P_i \qquad (23)$$

Presumably this enzyme makes available the protein and phosphate from yolk platelets of the frog egg during embryonic development. The enzyme shows little if any activity toward glycerophosphate or phenylphosphate, typical substrates for acid and alkaline phosphatases. The pH range of this enzyme in the case of homogenates of *Rana pipiens* embryos was from 3.0 to 6.8 with a maximum at pH 5.0 (Barth and Jaeger, 1950). This enzyme, as well as ATPase (ATP + H_2O → ADP + P_i), resides in the yolk material but not in the yolk-free fraction. It has been thought that a phosphotransferase makes ATP available by the reaction,

$$\text{P-protein} + \text{ADP} \to \text{ATP} + \text{protein} \tag{24}$$

The existence of such a reaction is open to question unless the linkage of phosphate to the protein is of the high-energy type, which it probably is not since most, if not all, of the phosphate of phosphoproteins is linked to the serine residues (Hill *et al.*, 1959).

Mezger-Freed (1953) has noted changes in phosphoprotein phosphatase activity during embryonic development of *Rana pipiens*. In addition to its occurrence in eggs, phosphoprotein phosphatase occurs in various organs of the rat, mouse, guinea pig, and hamster (Feinstein and Volk, 1949).

e. Amino Acid Oxidases (Specific and Nonspecific). Both D- and L-amino acid oxidases exist, and they catalyze the reaction:

$$\text{Amino acid}^{\pm} + \text{FAD} + H_2O = NH_4^+ + \alpha\text{-keto acid}^- + \text{FAD}\cdot2H \tag{25}$$

$$\text{FAD}\cdot2H + O_2 = H_2O_2 + \text{FAD} \tag{26}$$

$$\text{Net: amino acid}^{\pm} + O_2 + H_2O = NH_4^+ + \alpha\text{-keto acid}^- + H_2O_2 \tag{27}$$

$$\Delta F^{0\prime} = -7 \text{ kcal}$$

D-Amino acid oxidase has been shown to occur in homogenates of liver of *Rana esculenta* and of *Triton cristatus* (Krebs, 1935), and of *Ambystoma tigrinum* (Schooler and Brown, 1960). Homogenates of *Rana esculenta* kidney are about three times as active as the liver preparations (Krebs, 1935).

The rate of production of ammonia from several amino acids by frog kidney breis has been investigated by Balinsky and Baldwin (1962). The micromoles of NH_3 produced per hour per gram wet weight of kidney breis from *Xenopus laevis* and from *Rana temporaria*, respectively, were found to be: (from) L-alanine, 14 and 7.9; glycine, 8.7 and 2.5; L-leucine, 8.0 and 3.6; L-lysine, 1.1 and 2.9; and D-alanine, 70 and 191. The most rapid formation of ammonia appears to be via a D-amino acid oxidase which is more active in *Rana temporaria* than in *Xenopus laevis*.

f. Amino Acid Dehydrases (Example, Serine Dehydrase)

$$\text{Serine}^{\pm} = \text{pyruvate}^- + NH_4^+ \tag{28}$$

$$\Delta F^{0\prime} = -7 \text{ kcal}$$

A reaction similar to the one described takes place in the case of homoserine or threonine, yielding α-ketobutyrate and ammonia. These enzymes are termed dehydrases because the mechanism of the reaction first involves a postulated dehydration.

The deamination of L-serine by kidney breis of *Xenopus laevis* and of *Rana temporaria* has been studied by Balinsky and Baldwin (1962). Presumably these workers measured the activity of a serine dehydrase, although the possibility that ammonia arose from transamination followed by oxidative deamination is not ruled out.

g. Amino Acid Desulfhydrases (Example, Cysteine Desulfhydrase)

$$\text{Cysteine}^{\pm} + H_2O = \text{pyruvate}^- + HS^- + NH_4^+ + H^+ \tag{29}$$

$$\Delta F^{0\prime} = -7 \text{ kcal}$$

The reaction with homocysteine is similar, leading to α-ketobutyrate, sulfide, and ammonium ions. The reviewer could find no reports on the occurrence of this enzyme in Amphibia.

h. Histidase (= Histidine α-Deaminase)

$$\text{Histidine}^{+\pm} = \text{urocanic acid}^{\pm} + NH_4^+ \tag{30}$$

The enzyme occurs in frog liver (species not given) (Edlbacher, 1926, 1943; Edlbacher and Kraus, 1930), and specifically in adult *Rana pipiens* liver. Histidase activity can be induced in pre-gastrula cells of *Rana pipiens* by incubation with histidine (Stearns and Kostellow, 1958).

i. Amidases (Example, Glutaminase)

$$\text{Glutamine}^{\pm} + H_2O = \text{glutamate}^{\pm-} + NH_4^+ \tag{31}$$

$$\Delta F^{0\prime}_{298} = -3.42 \text{ kcal}; \qquad \Delta H^{0\prime}_{298} = -5.16 \text{ kcal}; \qquad T\Delta S^{0\prime}_{298} = -1.73 \text{ kcal}$$

(Benzinger *et al.*, 1959)

Glutaminase no doubt occurs in tissues of Amphibia, but no reports as to its occurrence in them could be found. Steenholt (1944) could not demonstrate asparaginase (asparagine $\rightarrow$ aspartate + ammonia) in liver extracts of *Rana esculenta*, although it is known to occur in liver of fishes. If asparaginase is present in Amphibia, it is probably of lower activity than in Mammalia.

j. Tryptophan Peroxidase. Tryptophan peroxidase catalyzes the reaction:

$$\text{Tryptophan}^{\pm} + O_2 = \text{formylkynurenine}^{\pm} \tag{32}$$

The level of the enzyme in adult *Rana pipiens* liver homogenates was found by Stearns and Kostellow (1958) to be increased fourfold by injection of L-tryptophan. These workers reported that exposure of *Rana pipiens* embryos to $0.01\ M$ L-tryptophan just prior to gastrulation induces the formation of the enzyme, but Spiegel and Frankel (1961) were unable to confirm this observation. This raises anew the question of the role in development of the induction of enzymes by their corresponding substrates.

2. Synthetic Reactions

Reactions involving the uptake of ammonia are very limited in animal tissues of most species. All Amphibia of course synthesize protein from glutamate and other amino acids. Synthetic reactions of considerable importance in studies with Amphibia are given below.

a. *Glutamic Dehydrogenase.* This enzyme catalyzes the reversible reductive amination of α-ketoglutarate and occurs almost universally:

$$
\begin{array}{l}
\text{COO}^- \\
|\\
\text{CO} \\
|\\
\text{HCH} \\
|\\
\text{HCH} \quad + \text{H}^+ + \text{NH}_4{}^+ + \text{DPNH} \\
|\qquad\qquad\qquad\qquad\qquad\text{(TPNH)} \\
\text{COO}^- \\
\alpha\text{-Ketoglutarate}
\end{array}
\quad = \quad
\begin{array}{l}
\text{COO}^- \\
|\\
\text{HCNH}_3{}^+ \\
|\\
\text{HCH} \\
|\\
\text{HCH} \quad + \text{DPN}^+ + \text{H}_2\text{O} \\
|\qquad\qquad\text{(TPN}^+\text{)} \\
\text{COO}^- \\
\text{L-Glutamate}
\end{array}
\tag{33}
$$

$$\Delta F^0 = -17.8 \text{ kcal}$$

$$\Delta F^{0\prime} = -7.9 \text{ kcal}$$

The enzyme has been demonstrated to occur in homogenates of liver of *Rana catesbeiana* (de Groot, 1960) and in tail tissue of *Rana japonica* under precocious thyroid metamorphosis (Yamamoto, 1960) where the enzyme decreased in activity before onset of metamorphosis.

b. *Glutamine Synthetase.* Uptake of ammonia also occurs via the reaction catalyzed by glutamine synthetase:

$$\text{Glutamate}^{\pm} + \text{ATP} + \text{NH}_4{}^+ \overset{\text{Mg}^{++}}{=} \text{glutamine}^{+-} + \text{ADP} + \text{P}_i \tag{34}$$

$\Delta F^{0\prime} = -4.3$ kcal (calculated from the thermodynamic equilibrium constant for all ionic species present at pH 7.0)

No glutamine synthetase activity was demonstrable in adult *Rana catesbeiana* liver under conditions used for assay of the mammalian enzyme. The level of free glutamine in frog liver is only 20% that found in rat liver (Kennan, 1961).

c. *Carbamyl Phosphate Synthetase.* This enzyme catalyzes the synthesis of carbamyl phosphate from CO_2 and ammonia. It is discussed in Section IV,E,4 [see Fig. 11]. Carbamyl phosphate is an intermediate in the synthesis of urea (Jones *et al.*, 1955), and of ureidosuccinate, i.e., carbamyl aspartate, in the synthesis of pyrimidines (Reichard, 1959).

d. Transaminases. Amino acids can undergo transamination with α-ketoglutarate (reversibly) to yield glutamic acid and the corresponding α-keto acids:

$$
\begin{array}{c}
\text{COO}^- \\
| \\
\text{CO} \\
| \\
\text{HCH} \\
| \\
\text{HCH} \\
| \\
\text{COO}^-
\end{array}
\; + \;
\begin{array}{c}
\text{COO}^- \\
| \\
\text{HCNH}_3{}^+ \\
| \\
\text{R}
\end{array}
\underset{\substack{\text{Pyridoxal} \\ \text{phosphate}}}{\rightleftharpoons}
\begin{array}{c}
\text{COO}^- \\
| \\
\text{HCNH}_3{}^+ \\
| \\
\text{HCH} \\
| \\
\text{HCH} \\
| \\
\text{COO}^-
\end{array}
\; + \;
\begin{array}{c}
\text{COO}^- \\
| \\
\text{CO} \\
| \\
\text{R}
\end{array}
\quad (35)
$$

α-Ketoglutarate   L-Amino acid   L-Glutamate α-Keto acid

$$\Delta F^0 \cong 0$$

The coenzyme for the reaction is pyridoxal phosphate. Transaminases are widespread in occurrence, and aspartate-α-ketoglutarate transaminase has been assayed in tissues of Amphibia (Imai, 1959; Yamamoto, 1960; Chan, 1960) (see Table VI). Numerous amino acids will transaminate with α-ketoglutarate in a brain homogenate of *Rana nigromaculata* (Imai, 1959). Because of the general low activity of L-amino acid oxidase in liver (at least in mammals, and probably in Amphibia as well) considerable amino acid nitrogen may undergo Reaction (35) and the reverse of Reaction (33) sequentially to yield ammonia by the over-all reaction,

$$
\begin{array}{c}
\text{RCHCOO}^- \\
| \\
\text{NH}_3{}^+
\end{array}
+ \text{DPN}^+ + \text{H}_2\text{O} = \text{RCOCOO}^- + \text{DPNH} + \text{NH}_4{}^+ + \text{H}^+ \quad (36)
$$
$$\text{(TPN}^+\text{)} \qquad\qquad\qquad\qquad\qquad \text{(TPNH)}$$

The over-all process is known as transdeamination.

e. Protein Synthesis. During the last 5 years several groups of workers (for references, see Allen *et al.*, 1960a) have demonstrated that amino acids

TABLE VI
ASPARTATE-α-KETOGLUTARATE TRANSAMINASE ACTIVITY[a]

Species	Tissue	Micromoles oxalacetate per hr per gm liver wet weight[b]
Rana catesbeiana (premetamorphic)	Liver	113
Rana catesbeiana (froglet)	Liver	340
Rana catesbeiana (adult)	Liver	500
Rana catesbeiana (adult)	Heart	350
Ambystoma tigrinum (adult)	Liver	356
Ambystoma tigrinum (adult)	Heart	178

[a] Unpublished observations of Chan (1960), to whom the writer is indebted for making available these data.

[b] Under optimal conditions at pH 7.8 in Tris buffer, 21°.

are activated prior to incorporation into protein. This activation involves the conversion of an amino acid to a high-energy intermediate:

$$\text{Amino acid} + \text{ATP} + \text{enzyme} \rightarrow \text{aminoacyl} \sim \text{AMP-enzyme} + \text{PP}_i \quad (37)$$

The activated amino group is then transferred to soluble RNA molecules (transfer RNA) of relatively low molecular weight ($<40,000$) containing 70–90 nucleotides (Allen et al., 1960b):

$$\text{Amino acyl} \sim \text{AMP-enzyme} + \text{RNA} \rightarrow \text{amino acid-RNA} + \text{AMP} + \text{enzyme} \quad (38)$$

In some manner not as yet completely defined, condensations of amino acid-RNA molecules in or on ribosomal particles (template RNA) lead to protein:

$$(\text{Amino acid-RNA})_n \rightarrow \text{protein (of } n \text{ residues)} + n\text{RNA} \quad (39)$$

The above sequence of reactions has not been established as occurring in tissues of Amphibia. Until evidence to the contrary is presented, we may presume that a similar set of reactions will describe protein synthesis in this class.

The activating enzymes appear to be specific for given amino acids. What is of considerable interest is the manner by which regulation of specific sequences of amino acids is brought about during embryonic and larval development, or even in the adult for that matter. Whether changes during development occur in transfer RNA or template RNA, which presumably lines up the amino acid-RNA complexes, is not known. But the observation of Finamore and Frieden (1960) that RNA increases during tadpole metamorphosis signifies some underlying fundamental changes in the protein-synthesizing system(s) during this critical period.

3. Amino Acids and Proteins during Development

Embryogenesis is a growth process requiring synthesis of new material in successive developmental stages. As the organism becomes more complex in the course of development and differentiation, new proteins are formed to yield specialized structural entities (membranes, intracellular structures, etc.), and special proteins including enzymes. Much attention has been given to the amino acid pattern during this development in an effort to determine how the cell accomplishes its numerous tasks. Special interest has centered around new types of protein which are synthesized both in embryonic and in larval development. At present we are not in a position to pinpoint the underlying basic changes—we can only view the morphological changes coincident with such alterations and attempt to relate both of these to the economy afforded the organism.

a. Amino Acids. In early blastulae of Triton alpestris seven free amino acids and one peptide can be detected (Chen, 1956). At the beginning of gastrulation these increase in amount with a rapid rise in later embryonic development. It is not surprising that those amino acids which are involved in numerous amino acid transformations, e.g., aspartate, glutamate, and glutamine, are maintained at a high concentration throughout embryonic development. Conspicuously absent or at a low concentration during embryonic development of *Xenopus laevis* are the free amino acids, threonine, phenylalanine, methionine, and histidine (Deuchar, 1956). These four amino acids are not synthesized by mammals or birds. Their low concentration probably reflects the fact that they are conserved by being recycled into new protein. Whole embryos of *Xenopus laevis* are known to contain free aspartate, glutamate, glycine, arginine, valine, glutamine, α-alanine, β-alanine, and leucine (Deuchar, 1955). None of these are essential amino acids, at least for mammals.

In their study of the amino acid pattern in *Triton palmatus* and *T. alpestris*, Chen and Rickenbacher (1954) isolated a peptide containing six known and one unknown amino acids from the former organism at late developmental stages. Changes in the levels of seven free and twelve nonprotein amino acids have been studied in *Rana pipiens* from the unfertilized egg to the completed neurula (Kutsky et al., 1953). An unusually high concentration of glycine was observed, which may be related to the fact that glycine is an intact precursor for purines and hence nucleic acids. Glycine-1-C^{14} is known to be taken up rapidly from the cytoplasm into the nuclei by *Xenopus laevis* (Waddington and Sirlin, 1954) and presumably by other animals as well. In this connection, it is of interest to note that in the sea urchin, *Strongylocentrotus purpuratus*, 85 mole % of the concentration of thirteen amino acids in the unfertilized egg is in the form of free glycine (Kavanau, 1953). It is surprising that Kurata and Mukawa (1955) could detect only the free amino acid glycine by chromatography of *Rhacophorus schlegelii* and of *Bufo vulgaris* before the neurula stage. This may represent a failure to detect free amino acids at concentrations lower than that of glycine, which could be the free amino acid predominating before the neurula stage.

b. Proteins. The above studies point to very active proteolytic and proteogenic processes during the course of development of the amphibian egg. Because these processes are largely balanced one against the other there results very little change in total protein during embryonic development. That new *kinds* of protein are indeed synthesized during such development is illustrated by the increase in activity of various enzymes during embryogenesis (see Urbani, 1955b), by the appearance of antigens (Flickinger and Nace, 1952; Clayton, 1953; Spar, 1953), by changes during segmentation in the solubility and precipitability characteristics of proteins

(Ranzi and Citterio, 1955), and by changes in the electrophoretic pattern of proteins (Denis, 1960). Inasmuch as embryonic development proceeds in the absence of external metabolites in the case of Amphibia, newly synthesized protein with its radically changed properties must come from reserve material which is more or less biochemically amorphous.

In an excellent comparative study, Frieden and co-workers (1957; Herner and Frieden, 1960) have shown the striking changes in level and electrophoretic mobility of blood proteins during anuran metamorphosis. Sera of young *Rana catesbeiana* tadpoles exhibit a very low concentration of protein corresponding in migration to that of albumins and show as well a low total serum protein concentration (1.0 %) and low albumin:globulin ratio (0.11).

After thyroxine-induced metamorphosis, the percentage of albumin was found by the Florida workers to increase as did total serum protein (to 1.7 %) and the albumin:globulin ratio (to 0.25). In the froglet and adult frog the protein profile assumes that commonly seen in the case of normal adult human serum. In the case of *Rana hecksheri* tadpoles, the albumin fraction was completely absent, but in the adult animals serum albumin attained 35 % of the total serum protein. The increase in the albumin fraction (increased albumin:globulin ratio) is suggested as serving the economy of frogs by aiding in conservation of body water through maintenance of oncotic pressure, and hence blood volume, a factor which is more critical for terrestrial than for pond life.

Frieden *et al.* point out that an increase in the albumin:globulin ratio is consistent with the effects of thyroxine. It might be expected that *Xenopus laevis* would not show such striking changes in serum proteins on passage to the adult state because of its completely aquatic habitat. However, the albumin:globulin ratio continues to increase even in the young adult, and the electrophoretic profile resembles that of human serum proteins more than does that of the Ranidae (Herner and Frieden, 1960).

The major blood-forming organ of the adult bullfrog, *Rana catesbeiana*, is the spleen (Jordan and Speidel, 1923a, b). The function may in part be taken over temporarily in the spring by the red marrow of the long bones. Under larval conditions, the kidney is an important site of erythropoiesis. In the tadpole, the intertubular region of the kidney has a dense population of erythrocytes, leucocytes, and transitional forms. McCutcheon (1936) suggests that the difference in "fetal" and adult hemoglobin may be attributed to their different loci of formation (mesonephros in the tadpole, and spleen and bone marrow in the adult).

Tadpole erythrocytes of *Rana catesbeiana* are elliptical discs with major and minor axes of 22.6 and 13.9 μ. Erythrocytes of tadpoles are reported to be somewhat more numerous (3.4 × 10^5/mm^3) than those of the adult

(2.5 × 10⁵/mm³) (McCutcheon, 1936). More recently, Herner and Frieden (1961) reported that there is an increase, rather than a decrease, in the red cell count and hemoglobin concentration during metamorphosis of the Ranidae. The increase was quite marked in the case of *Rana catesbeiana* and *R. hecksheri*, less so in *R. grylio*.

Polycythemia may be induced in *Triturus orientalis* by the intraperitoneal injection of ascorbic acid or by dilute cobaltous chloride solutions. An increase in red cell production by the spleen shows that it is the erythropoietic center of the salamander (Chang *et al.*, 1943). *Amphiuma* erythrocytes are the largest of any animal (greatest diameter, 70 μ) (Nobel, 1931).

Tadpole and adult frog hemoglobin of *Rana catesbeiana* both have a molecular weight of ∼68,000 and exhibit the same heme-heme interaction (Riggs, 1951). There is no significant effect of changes in pH on the oxygen equilibrium of hemoglobin derived from tadpole blood. This is opposed to the large Bohr and reverse Bohr effects (changes in O_2-combining capacity upon change in pH) which are seen with the adult hemoglobin. Tadpole hemoglobin has about seven times the affinity for O_2 at pH 6 of the adult hemoglobin. The hemoglobin saturation curves are shown in Fig. 8.

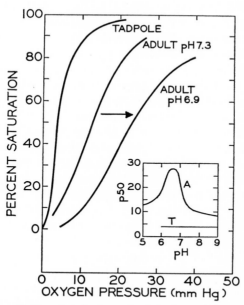

Fig. 8. Oxygen affinity of tadpole and adult hemoglobin of *Rana catesbeiana*. Percent saturation of hemoglobin with oxygen versus oxygen partial pressure in millimeters of mercury. Inset: Oxygen partial pressure in millimeters of mercury to give 50% saturation (p⁵⁰) at various pH values; A = adult, T = tadpole. Adapted from Riggs (1951).

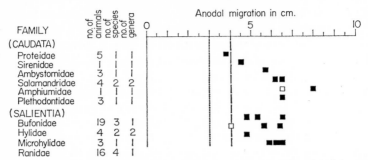

Fig. 9. Electrophoretic migration of amphibian hemoglobins. Solid bars, major fractions; open bars, minor fractions. Dotted line at 3 cm corresponds to reference hemoglobin S; dashed line at 4 cm corresponds to reference hemoglobin A. From Dessauer *et al.* (1957).

Taxonomic groups of Amphibia exhibit variations in electrophoretic mobilities of hemoglobins (Dessauer *et al.*, 1957). This is illustrated in Fig. 9. Except in the case of *Necturus maculosus* (Proteidae) and for the minor component of *Hyla cinerea* (Hylidae), the hemoglobins of Amphibia migrate more rapidly than does normal, human, adult hemoglobin A. The major component of the "Congo eel," *Amphiuma means* (= *Amphiuma tridactylum*), has a greater electrophoretic mobility than the hemoglobins of other amphibians examined, and it is greater than the major components of 69 species of Reptilia. *Bufo valliceps* can easily be distinguished from *Bufo fowlerei* on the basis of the greater migration rate of hemoglobin of the former. The hemoglobin of adult *Rana clamitans* has a greater mobility than the "fetal" hemoglobin taken from larvae.

Herner and Frieden (1961) have clearly shown that the hemoglobins of larval *Xenopus laevis*, *Rana hecksheri*, and *Rana catesbeiana* are replaced by an adult form in the course of metamorphosis (see Fig. 10). The electrophoretically distinct adult hemoglobins of these species all represent slower moving molecules than the larval hemoglobins.

These differences in hemoglobin are obviously of great phylogenetic interest. There appears to be a trend in vertebrate evolution for the appearance of electrophoretically slower moving hemoglobins (Dessauer *et al.*, 1957) which is mimicked by metamorphosing anurans (G. Chieffi *et al.*, 1960, cited in Herner and Frieden, 1961).

Serum proteins differ in species within the same genus. Different electrophoretic patterns were found by Lanza and Antonini (1956) for serum proteins of *Rana esculenta* and *Rana dalmatina* (= *Rana agilis*), and these workers suggest that such differences may be useful in distinguishing between species of the same genus.

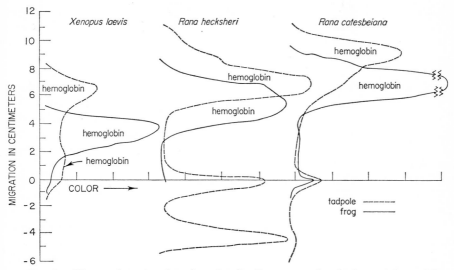

Fig. 10. Electrophoretic migration of red cell extracts of tadpoles and frogs. The curves are densitometer tracings of bromophenyl blue-stained paper after electrophoresis of extracts in veronal buffer, pH 8.6, containing 5% glycerol by volume. From Herner and Frieden (1961).

Specific properties of proteins arise largely by virtue of their amino acid composition and sequence; these are most likely determined by the arrangement of pyrimidine and purine bases in DNA. We see therefore, that in development there is a gradual unfolding of the potentialities of the genetic material, which, mediated by RNA molecules of a new kind, lead to the synthesis of new and distinct proteins. This is clearly shown in the case of enzymes which catalyze the reactions of the urea cycle discussed in the next section, enzymes which appear in increasing amount during the metamorphic crisis. Such appearances (or disappearances) are characteristic of embryonic and larval development until the adult stage is reached, at which point many of the heritable characteristics have been expressed in the form of relatively stabilized metabolic pathways leading to a more or less steady state.

4. Nitrogen Excretion and Urea Biosynthesis

a. During Embryogenesis. The total nitrogen remains nearly constant during embryonic development (Gregg and Ballentine, 1946). Of the 160 μg of total nitrogen other than the vitelline membrane (2 μg) in the fertilized egg of *Rana pipiens*, no more than about 1 μg of nitrogen would seem to be lost (see Barth and Barth, 1954, for discussion of this) by the time of hatching (Shumway stage 20). Only traces of ammonia and urea appear during this time; it is thought that some small amounts of these are excreted during periods of segmentation, gastrulation, and neurulation (Needham *et al.*, 1938; Brachet, 1939; Urbani and de Cesaris-Coromaldi, 1957).

b. During Metamorphosis. Anuran tadpoles have only a limited ability to synthesize urea (for review see Cohen and Brown, 1960). Consequently, prior to metamorphosis, most of the waste nitrogen is excreted in the form of ammonia (Bialascewicz and Mincóvna, 1921; Needham, 1931; Munro, 1939, 1953; Underhay and Baldwin, 1955; Urbani and de Cesaris-Coromaldi, 1957; Brown and Cohen, 1958).

At the onset of crucial metamorphosis (stage XVIII of Taylor and Kollros, 1946) all of the enzymes of the Krebs and Henseleit (1932) ornithine-urea cycle (= urea cycle; depicted in Fig. 11) of *Rana catesbeiana* rapidly increase in activity as shown in Table VII. The metamorphosed anuran is now anatomically equipped for locomotion on land and for air-breathing, and it is moreover fitted out with a biochemical excretory mechanism compatible with a partially terrestrial life.

Vertebrates, in general, are very susceptible to ammonia toxicity, and synthesis and excretion of urea or uric acid instead of ammonia circumvents this situation. Excretion of ammonia such as is found in embryonic and premetamorphic larval Amphibia, in teleosts, and in marine invertebrates

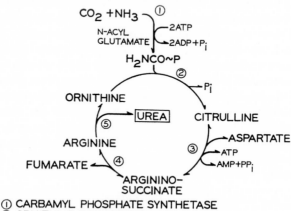

Fig. 11. Krebs and Henseleit (1932) urea cycle as modified and completed by later enzymic studies. From Brown and Cohen (1960).

TABLE VII

SUMMARY OF LEVELS OF UREA CYCLE ENZYMES IN LIVER OF *Rana catesbeiana*[a]

(Representative data)

Enzyme	Stage of development[c]			
	X	XVII–XVIII	XXII–XXV	Adult
Carbamyl phosphate synthetase	55	84	444	1,040
Ornithine transcarbamylase	2320	2480	6660	20,000
Arginine synthetase system[b]	1–2	2.5	10–20	30–50
Argininosuccinate cleavage enzyme	25 (V–X)	>60	—	506
Arginase	1040	2110	2840+	28,900

[a] Values given in terms of μmoles per hr per gm liver wet weight at 38°C. After Brown *et al.* (1959).

[b] In these experiments the activity of arginine synthetase reflects the activity of the condensing enzyme.

[c] Larval stage numbers of Taylor and Kollros (1946).

leads to no difficulties inasmuch as ammonia can be excreted or undergo diffusion into a medium of low ammonia concentration.

During metamorphosis, the excretion ratio, urea-N:ammonia-N, generally increases (Munro, 1939, 1953; Underhay and Baldwin, 1955; Brown *et al.*, 1959; Brown and Cohen, 1958) by virtue of the conversion of ammonia to urea by the urea cycle. That this newly formed urea is indeed synthesized *de novo* was shown in experiments wherein surviving liver slices from tadpoles at different stages of development were allowed to utilize $C^{14}O_2$ (Brown, 1962a). The author found that the incorporation of the radioactive CO_2 into urea-C^{14} markedly increased at the onset of metamorphosis of *Rana catesbeiana*, and that it continued to increase throughout the metamorphic period (see Fig. 12). The kinetic aspects of such incorporation are in harmony with the observed increases in levels of the enzymes of the urea cycle and with the increasing urea-N:ammonia-N excretion ratio.

Increases in both arginase (Dolphin and Frieden, 1955) and carbamyl phosphate synthetase (Brown *et al.*, 1959; confirmed and extended by Paik and Cohen, 1960) have been found in the case of anuran tadpoles undergoing precocious metamorphosis with thyroid-active substances.

The enhancement in activity of the urea cycle enzymes during metamorphosis appears to be due to a net increase in the amount of enzyme proteins catalyzing the reactions of the cycle (Brown *et al.*, 1959). Some recent experiments show that there is indeed a synthesis, *de novo*, of these enzymes rather than merely an unmasking of activity as is the case for

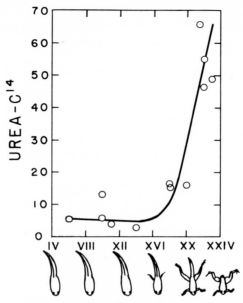

Fig. 12. Incorporation of bicarbonate-C^{14} into urea-C^{14} by tadpole liver slices. Ordinate: thousands of counts per minute incorporated into urea. Abscissa: larval stage number after Taylor and Kollros (1946). Tissue (0.1 gm) from *Rana catesbeiana* tadpoles incubated in buffer medium at pH 7.5 containing 6.8×10^5 counts per minute of bicarbonate-C^{14}. Incubation for 2.0 hr at 37° with oxygen in the gas phase. From Brown (1962a).

many proteolytic enzymes which are "blocked" by a low molecular weight peptide.

Dr. Margaret Marshall in the Wisconsin laboratories was able to obtain an antibody from rabbits which had been immunized with a highly purified carbamyl phosphate synthetase prepared from the liver of the giant bullfrog, *Rana catesbeiana* (see Metzenberg *et al.*, 1961). A close correspondence was found between the increasing enzymic activity of the enzyme in homogenates of tadpoles undergoing thyroxine-stimulated metamorphosis and the amount of precipitin-N obtained when aliquots of the extracts were treated with the antibody.

c. Adults. All adult Amphibia so far examined, and in addition, turtles and mammals (see Cohen and Brown, 1960), and no doubt elasmobranchs (Anderson and Jones, 1959; Baldwin, 1960; Brown, 1962b), are capable of synthesizing urea *de novo* from carbon dioxide and ammonia by the classic Krebs-Henseleit cycle. The over-all reaction with its favorable associated free energy change may be formulated as follows (Brown and

Cohen, 1958):

$$HCO_3^- + NH_4^+ + aspartate^{\pm-} + H_2O + 3\ ATP\ \xrightarrow[\text{Mg}^{++},\ \text{Mn}^{++}]{\substack{N\text{-acetyl-L-glutamate,}\\ \text{ornithine}}}$$

$$urea + fumarate^{--} + 2\ ADP + AMP + 2\ P_i + PP_i + H^+ \quad (40)$$

$$\Delta F^{0\prime} = -10.0\ kcal$$

(Based on $\Delta F^{0\prime} = -7.0$ kcal for ATP hydrolysis)

The liver is the site of urea synthesis from carbon dioxide and ammonia in all animals so far examined which have a ureotelic metabolism. Some enzyme activities of the cycle may be present in other tissues (Brown and Cohen, 1960; Ratner et al., 1960), but the full and functioning complement of enzymes catalyzing urea synthesis de novo has so far been found only in the liver. Some of the levels of these enzymes observed in the liver of various Amphibia are given in Table XI (see Section VI,B).

In vitro, the condensing enzyme of liver exhibits the lowest activity of the enzymes of this cycle in Amphibia so far examined (see Reaction 3 of Fig. 11; see Table VII). The condensation of citrulline and aspartate to yield argininosuccinate is thus thought to be the rate-limiting step of the cycle in the intact organism. In any event, the activity of this enzyme as assayed in vitro appears to be sufficient to account for the rate of urea synthesis and excretion by Rana catesbeiana at all stages of developnent (Brown and Cohen, 1958).

In addition to the values for liver arginase given in Table XIII, the following levels of arginase recently obtained by Balinsky and Baldwin (1962) are cited. In terms of micromoles of urea per hour per gram liver wet weight: Xenopus laevis, 185,000; Rana temporaria ♂, 130,000; Rana temporaria ♀, 133,000. Conditions of incubation were: L-arginine, 0.238 M; Mn^{++}, 0.0017 M; $t = 37°$; pH, 9.55.

d. Relationship of Excretory Nitrogen Partition to Environment. We owe to Delaunay (1931) the suggestion that a relationship exists between the nature of the principal nitrogenous waste product and the habitat of a vertebrate. Generally speaking, the highly toxic ammonia is excreted as the main nitrogenous product only in certain aquatic animals such as teleosts and invertebrates. On the other hand, animals living under conditions of a restricted water supply are able to prevent the serious effects of ammonia accumulation by converting ammonia to urea or uric acid.

Marine fishes do not have a plentiful supply of water (in an osmotic sense). As a consequence, they produce at most a scant flow of urine—insufficient as an excretory route for ammonia. The marine teleosts, none of which is known to possess the urea cycle, dispose of ammonia by excreting it through the gills (H. W. Smith, 1959, p. 256). It is not clear how much of the ammonia so excreted derives from tissues other than the gills, for as Smith points out, the gill is rich in glutaminase and glutamic dehydrogenase. These enzymes produce ammonia from their respective substrates, glutamine and glutamic acid. Ammonia from a variety of sources is readily incorporated into these substrates.

In the case of elasmobranchs, urea is synthesized from ammonia and is maintained at a plasma concentration sufficiently high ($\sim 2\%$) as to provide a slight osmotic advantage with respect to sea water. Fishes have also evolved another mechanism for the removal of ammonia—synthesis of trimethylamine oxide (see H. W. Smith, 1959).

The relationship of the excretory nitrogen product and environment for Chelonia has been demonstrated convincingly by Moyle (1949). She was able to show that, depending upon species and environment, turtles may assume a mode of excretion involving various combinations and ratios of ammonia, urea, and uric acid.

It should be pointed out that Amphibia can convert uric acid to urea (see Section V,C), and we do not as yet know what proportion of the urea excreted has passed through uric acid as an intermediate. Most likely, the major portion of urea excreted by terrestrial amphibians derives, however, from that synthesized via the urea cycle.

Studies on a number of species of Amphibia examined by Munro (1939, 1953) showed that the predominant nitrogenous waste product of Amphibia depended to a great extent upon whether the organism would ultimately be aquatic or terrestrial. Urea was found to be the main excretory product for adult *Rana temporaria* and for *Bufo bufo*, whose environments include the terrestrial habitat. But for the completely aquatic toad, *Xenopus laevis*, ammonia predominated, as with premetamorphic tadpoles.

The question of excretory product and environment in the case of Amphibia has been reexamined in detail by Cragg *et al.* (1961). Some of the findings are given in Table VIII. As shown there, the ratio of urea-N:ammonia-N of urine collected over a period of 24 hours is high (usually >10) for the terrestrial species examined, and it is low (usually <1) for the aquatic species.

The urea-N:ammonia-N excretion ratio of 9.0 observed in a bladder sample of the highly aquatic *Amphiuma* sp. (Brown and Cohen, 1960) appears to be anomalously high. However, when it is recalled that *Amphiuma* deposit and guard their eggs on land, the ability to synthesize urea is clearly of great economy here.

Some interesting questions are raised by Underhay and Baldwin's (1955) observation on the excretory pattern of developing *Xenopus laevis*.

TABLE VIII

PARTITION OF EXCRETORY NITROGEN BY AMPHIBIA[a]

Species	Habitat (non-breeding season)	Microatoms N per gm body weight per 24 hours as		Urea-N / Ammonia-N
		Ammonia	Urea	
URODELA				
Salamandra salamandra	Terrestrial	0.24	4.5	19
Triturus cristatus	Terrestrial	0.20	4.8	24
Ambystoma mexicanum (neotenic larvae)	Aquatic	5.3	3.5	0.66
ANURA				
Pipidae				
Xenopus laevis	Aquatic	12	7.7	0.64
Xenopus tropicalis	Aquatic	9.2	5.7	0.62
Hymenochirus sp. (boettgeri?)	Aquatic	6.9	2.0	0.29
Pipa pipa	Aquatic	7.2	0.54	0.75
Ranidae				
Rana esculenta	Semi-aquatic	0.35	3.2	9.1
Rana temporaria	Terrestrial	0.63	6.6	11
Hylidae				
Hyla arborea	Terrestro-arboreal	0.50	11	22
Bufonidae				
Bufo bufo	Dry terrestrial	0.44	7.6	17
Bufo calamita	Dry terrestrial	0.41	6.1	15

[a] Adapted from Cragg et al. (1961).

This wholly aquatic toad excretes its nitrogen chiefly in the form of ammonia before metamorphosis and switches over to a largely ureotelic mechanism during metamorphosis. However, there is a reversion to a largely ammonotelic mechanism in the adult. Does the toad remain permanently aquatic because of the decreased enzymic ability of the adult to convert its extra ammonia to urea? Or is this extra ammonia excreted as such merely because the habitat is more conducive to doing so? This toad, being aglossal and of somewhat fragile structure, is not anatomically suited for foraging in a terrestrial habitat.

The answer probably lies somewhere between the two questions posed. Measurement of the level of urea cycle enzymes in the liver and measurement of renal and extra-renal methods of disposing of ammonia, from the larval stages to the adult, would provide information which could be brought to bear on this problem.*

A situation similar to that for *Xenopus laevis* exists in the case of the red eft, *Triturus viridescens*, referred to previously in connection with visual pigment reversion (see Section III,C). The eft exhibits a decreased urea-N: ammonia-N excretion ratio upon resumption of the aquatic habitat at the time of spawning (Nash and Fankhauser, 1959).

Interesting questions may be posed with respect to *Eleutherodactylus* which, following a larval development that takes place within an egg deposited *out of water*, hatches as a metamorphosed miniature frog.

In considering mode of excretion and habitat, one must also consider the nature of foodstuffs available and consumed. Changes in the nature of the excretory product can be brought about in compensation for dietary alterations or for maintenance of adequate electrolyte balance. It is known, for example, that the amount of urinary urea in Mammalia is directly related to the amount of protein in the diet. The finding of Schimke (1962), that the levels of urea cycle enzymes of rat liver are markedly increased as the percentage of protein in the diet is increased, further illustrates the complex role of the total environment in the economy of the organism.

The route of excretion must also be considered. In larval or perennibranchiate Amphibia a low level of ammonia may be maintained by its loss from the gills or possibly the integument. In this connection, it is known that minute amounts of ammonia can be excreted by the lungs of rats (Robin *et al.*, 1959).

The influence of environment on excretory mechanisms is illustrated in striking fashion by the African lungfish, *Protopterus aethiopicus*, which excretes ammonia when in the water, but apparently converts this to urea when estivating in its mud cocoon (see H. W. Smith, 1959). It would be of considerable interest to ascertain if the levels of the urea cycle enzymes increase, i.e., whether there is an induction of the cycle, as a result of whatever internal stimulus leads the lungfish to estivate. As an ancillary study

---

* While this chapter was in press, Silver and Balinsky (1961) demonstrated the presence of all of the urea cycle enzymes in the liver of *Xenopus laevis*. However, the activities were below those reported previously for terrestrial frogs and toads. Ammoniotelism in *X. laevis* seems to be due to a decreased rate of hepatic urea synthesis. If *X. laevis* is removed from the water for 1 to 3 weeks, urea accumulates in the blood, liver, and muscle. This urea is excreted upon return to the water (Balinsky *et al.*, 1961). Urea appears to be an emergency waste product which can replace NH_3 during dehydration.

In this connection, several reports have appeared recently on the crab-eating frog (*Rana cancrivora*) of Siam (Gordon *et al.*, 1961a, 1961b; Schmidt-Nielsen and Lee, 1962). This crab survives in full-strength sea water by virtue of the fact that in such a medium its blood is slightly hypertonic, due, in part, to an unusually high concentration of urea in the body fluids ($\cong 0.3\ M$).

in connection with biochemical excretory mechanisms in Amphibia, such information would be extremely valuable.

It appears to the writer that future studies on nitrogenous excretory patterns will have to deal concomitantly with three items: (1) nature of the environment with respect to temperature and water supply; (2) nature of the diet, particularly with respect to the amount or percentage of protein or other nitrogen-containing substances consumed; and (3) the capabilities, in genetic (phylogenetic) terms, of supporting a given level of excretion of a given product. The latter item appears to be best studied through examination, under various experimental conditions, of the enzymes and integrated schemes of intermediary nitrogen metabolism responsible for the formation of such products.

5. Summary of Protein Metabolism during Metamorphosis

An attempt is made in this section to summarize protein changes in the typical anuran during metamorphosis (see Fig. 13). At the onset of metamorphosis, the animal generally stops feeding and energy must be derived from body sources. Since excretion of nitrogen increases during metamorphosis with an attending increase in the urea-N:ammonia-N excretion ratio, it is obvious that a net amount of protein is being degraded at this time. This protein derives from embryonic structures such as the tail, gills, etc., presumably by the action of phagocytes and by the action of cathepsins which have been shown to be increased in activity in the tail during metamorphosis (Weber, 1957a,b).

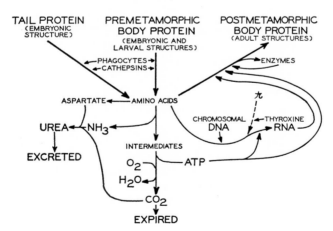

Fig. 13. Summary of protein changes during amphibian metamorphosis showing disposition of ammonia-nitrogen and synthesis of intra- and postmetamorphic protein, including enzymes. The symbol, *ϰ*, represents an unknown factor or metabolic process which is influenced by thyroxine and which accounts for the observed metamorphic changes.

The amino acids resulting from the hydrolysis of protein representing larval structures now can suffer several fates. By well-known enzymic reactions, part of these amino acids can be converted to acetylSCoA and be oxidized via the tricarboxylic acid cycle to yield energy. As a result of the oxidation of a portion of this new amino acid pool there is produced an excess amount of ammonia, most of which is excreted as such in the early stages of metamorphosis. In later stages, however, it is excreted largely as urea. Coupled with this proteolysis is the synthesis of new kinds of RNA, which leads to the synthesis of new types of protein, e.g., proteins of post-metamorphic structures such as legs and lungs, as well as new enzymes.

The whole process of metamorphosis can be initiated by treatment of tadpoles with thyroid-active substances (Allen, 1938). Just how such compounds initiate this is unknown, but it appears to be a "trigger" phenomenon, and an irreversible one. If the phenomenon represents the action of distinct metabolites formed as the result of the presence of thyroxine or one of its analogues, then every cell has the ability to make this metabolite available, as shown by studies whereby thyroxine pellets are implanted in various tissues (for skin of *Rana pipiens* see Kollros and Kaltenbach, 1952). It would seem, rather, that thyroxine is involved in some distinct process depicted as t in Fig. 13, process t affording the synthesis of new types of RNA molecules from chromosomal DNA. To say that the process initiated by thyroxine brings about an "unfolding" of genetic information of DNA may not be inappropriate, even in the physical sense. On the other hand, the process could be one whereby thyroxine alters the permeability or the configuration of microsomal membranes or surfaces permitting new areas of template RNA to be accessible to "transfer-RNA" pools for the first time. In any event, the amino acids of the newly created pool may now be converted to the postmetamorphic type of protein, including new enzymes. Since such new enzymes are used to produce new cells of specific types containing more newly formed enzymes, the process is autocatalytic, which no doubt accounts for the very rapid course of metamorphosis once the event has been initiated.

In a sense, chromosomal information in the form of DNA appears to be transformed largely irreversibly in that information is lost for the synthesis of embryonic and larval structures, but is gained in the form of the ability to synthesize, continuously throughout adult life, the proteins associated with this final phase, for we know the body to be in a Schoenheimer dynamic state. The brief summary presented here in no wise gives a final answer to the events associated with metamorphosis, and further speculation here is unwarranted.

For other discussions of the protein changes and related biological phenomena occurring during amphibian development, the reader is referred to Chapter 8 and various review articles (Etkin, 1955; Bennett and Frieden, 1960; Frieden, 1961, 1963).

V. Nucleic Acids

Nucleic acids are of two types which differ from one another in the nature of the sugar molecules, which, bound to a purine or pyrimidine base and to phosphate, make up the repeating unit of these polymers (Davidson, 1960). A portion of the polynucleotide structure of a nucleic acid is shown here in highly diagrammatic form:

$$
\left[
\begin{array}{cccc}
\text{Pur} & \text{Pyr} & \text{Pur} & \text{Pyr} \\
| & | & | & | \\
\text{S} & \text{S} & \text{S} & \text{S} \\
| & | & | & | \\
\text{U} & \text{U} & \text{U} & \text{U} \\
| & | & | & | \\
\text{G} & \text{G} & \text{G} & \text{G} \\
| & | & | & | \\
\text{A} \quad \text{P} & \text{A} \quad \text{P} & \text{A} \quad \text{P} & \text{A} \quad \text{P} \\
| & | & | & | \\
\text{R} & \text{R} & \text{R} & \text{R}
\end{array}
\right]_n
$$

In the case of DNA the sugar is 2-deoxyribose; in the case of RNA it is ribose. Just how these repeating units, the nucleotide residues, are incorporated into the final RNA or DNA molecule has been the subject of vigorous investigations following the impetus provided by the initial demonstration of the enzymic synthesis of polynucleotides (Kornberg *et al.*, 1956; Grunberg-Manago *et al.*, 1956). While some such mechanism as already proposed probably accounts for the synthesis of nucleic acids in Amphibia, there is yet no direct evidence which can be brought to bear on this. We do know, however, that the synthesis of both DNA and RNA is a property of amphibian cells as it is of all living organisms.

A. DEOXYRIBONUCLEIC ACID (DNA)

1. DNA of Egg and Embryo

There appears to be no net synthesis of purines during about the first 15–20 hr of development of *Rana pipiens* embryos (S. Graff and L. G. Barth, see Hoff-Jørgensen and Zeathen, 1952). This raises the question as to the source of DNA for nuclei of cells formed during early embryogenesis. Hoff-Jørgensen and Zeathen (1952) have found that the mature, unfertilized eggs of *Rana platyrrhina* (= *Rana temporaria*) contain 0.20×10^{-9} moles of total deoxynucleoside (the value probably includes both free and combined deoxynucleotide; Grant, 1958a). If all of this deoxyribonucleoside were in the form of DNA nucleotides it would correspond to 0.065

μg of DNA per egg. This amount of DNA could not possibly fit in the nucleus—each haploid nucleus is known to contain about 12×10^{-6} μg of DNA, based on the value for the spermatozoon. Hence, most of the DNA of the mature, unfertilized egg must be in the cytoplasm in a cytoplasmic: nuclear ratio of about 5000.

Most workers agree that there is an excess of DNA,* but the exact amount of the excess and the time at which new DNA is synthesized during embryogenesis is in dispute. It is clear, however, that there is too much DNA present to be all in the nucleus. According to Grant (1958a), the unfertilized egg of *Rana pipiens* contains 0.023 μg of DNA, and synthesis of DNA probably begins at Shumway stage 8 (18 hr development at 15°). Studies on the incorporation of glycine-2-C^{14} and phosphate-P^{32} into nucleic acids during early embryonic development show no *de novo* synthesis of DNA during the first 12 hr (Grant, 1958b). Grant concludes that the excess DNA of the egg is sufficient to support the demand for new cells up to an early blastula. There appears to be a constant amount of DNA in the embryo until the early blastula stage when there are about 700–800 cells.

The values obtained for the acid-insoluble deoxyribosidic compounds for *Bufo vulgaris* and for *Triturus pyrrhogaster* during early cleavage, i.e., 0.032 and 0.027 μg per egg, respectively (Kuriki and Okazaki, 1959) agree nicely with the value found by Grant above. Acid-soluble deoxyribosidic compounds make up a large portion of the total compounds of this type, as much as 3–5.5 times that of the acid-insoluble compounds.

Recently, Chen (1960) has shown that the DNA (as well as the RNA) content of developing eggs of *Triton alpestris*, *Triton palmatus*, and *Triton cristatus* is constant in amount from fertilization until the end of blastulation. Synthesis of both types of nucleic acids appears to begin at the onset of gastrulation. Studies on the developmental failure of lethal hybrids (Moore, 1941) in connection with changes in levels or nature of DNA and RNA (cf. Chen and Zeller, 1961) offer a fruitful course of research to students of embryology.

2. Evolutionary Considerations of DNA Content

The DNA content of somatic cells of Amphibia is constant for a given species and ranges from 7.3×10^{-12} gm per nucleus in a toad (*Bufo* sp.?) to 168×10^{-12} gm per nucleus in *Amphiuma* sp. (Mirsky and Ris, 1951). With the exception of the Dipnoi (lungfishes) (e.g. *Protopterus* sp.: 100×10^{-12} gm DNA per nucleus), Amphibia possess the highest values tabulated for the vertebrates.

A very striking correlation exists between the DNA content of vertebrate somatic cells and the occurrence of the urea cycle in the liver of the same

---

* The writer is of the opinion that what is termed DNA here may in fact be low molecular weight precursors of nuclear DNA yet to be synthesized.

animal (see Brown, 1962c). This was brought to light through a comparison of those vertebrates possessing urea cycle activity (see Brown and Cohen, 1960; Cohen and Brown, 1960) and the values tabulated for the DNA content per somatic cell nucleus in 73 different species of vertebrates (see Vendrely, 1955). With but few exceptions, which are borderline cases and which include no Amphibia, *the urea cycle as a nitrogen excretion mechanism occurs in, and only in, those vertebrates, having more than about 5×10^{-12} gm of DNA per nucleus of somatic cell.* Exceptions to this rule have values differing from the figure 5.0 by ± 0.1 or less, well within the limit of experimental error in determination of the DNA content. More precise determinations of the borderline values seem to be in order to determine whether the rule can be stated without known exceptions.

The above correlation is consistent with the view that there has been a deletion of some of the urea cycle enzymes during the course of vertebrate evolution (Brown and Cohen, 1960). In this regard, Mirsky and Ris (1951), whose data make up a large portion of the values tabulated by Vendrely (1955), interpret their findings in terms of decreases in the DNA content per cell in the course of vertebrate evolution.

Reduction of cellular DNA content to values below about 5×10^{-12} gm per nucleus of somatic cell and loss of urea cycle activity probably did not occur until after the establishment of the chelonian and mammalian branches of the vertebrate phylogenetic tree, for all turtles and mammals examined to date possess the full complement of urea cycle enzymes. Presumably a reduction in DNA to values below 5×10^{-12} gm had already taken place much earlier in the actinopterygian fishes which led to the urea-cycle-deficient Teleostei.

3. Constancy of DNA in Cells with Respect to Ploidy

England and Mayer (1957) have confirmed the Boivin-Vendrely theory of the constancy of DNA in cells of the same species. As shown in Table

TABLE IX

DNA CONTENT OF CELL NUCLEI OF *Rana pipiens*[a]

Picograms (10^{-12} gm) DNA per nucleus		
Ova nuclei	Spermatozoa	Liver nuclei
13.27 ± 1.0 (diploid)[b]	6.48 ± 1.0 (haploid)	15.76 ± 1.0 (diploid +)[c]

[a] After England and Mayer (1957).

[b] Before reduction division.

[c] Slightly high value for liver nuclei is attributed to the occurrence of some cells with polyploid nuclei.

IX, the theory holds for ova nuclei, spermatozoa, and liver nuclei of *Rana pipiens*, if one takes into consideration diploidy and haploidy of the cells.

About 2 % of the liver cells of *Triturus granulosa* are tetraploid (Truong and Dornfeld, 1955) and presumably contain twice the diploid DNA content. In the case of *T. granulosa*, diploid cells are found only in the kidney, while from 1 to 5 % of the pancreatic cells are tetraploid. The granular glands of the integument exhibit variable ploidy up to the octaploid state. The high degree of ploidy found in some cells may be correlated with secretory activity (Merriam and Ris, 1954).

There probably will always exist uncertainty as to whether cells of the same ploidy of an organism contain *exactly* the same amount of DNA. We are always limited in this regard by the analytical procedures employed.

B. RIBONUCLEIC ACID (RNA)

According to current concepts, RNA is involved in the synthesis of proteins (see Section IV,E,2e). The role of the nucleus in determining the type of protein to be synthesized, protein which is characteristic of a given cell, is indirect. The DNA, which is located entirely within the nucleus some time *after* early embryonic stages, determines a given RNA which in turn determines a given protein. Support of this idea comes from studies on enucleated cells which have been shown to continue to synthesize proteins (see Brachet, 1952) because the actual synthesis is effected by soluble cytoplasmic RNA. Nuclear RNA is thought to be a precursor of cytoplasmic RNA, at least in the salivary gland cells of the fruit fly, *Drosophila melanogaster*.

During early stages of oögenesis the absolute amount of RNA per oöcyte increases, as shown with *Triturus pyrrhogaster* (Ôsawa and Hayashi, 1953). The oöcyte nuclei of Amphibia have been shown to each contain hundreds of nucleoli during most of their development, these finally accumulating about centrally located chromosomes and disintegrating. All nucleoli contain proteins and most of the nucleoli contain RNA, but in all stages of oögenesis one or two large nucleoli do not contain RNA (C. A. Brown and Ris, 1959). DNA has not been found in the nucleoli.

It has been inferred that RNA synthesis occurs directly on unusual structures, the lateral loops of the so-called lampbrush chromosomes (for *Ambystoma tigrinum* see Gall, 1958). These lampbrush chromosomes must possess much coiling for they are thought to have an average total length of about 5 cm. RNA, in addition to being a component of the nucleolus and being associated with chromosomal material, also exists free in the karyoplasm or nuclear sap in amphibian oöcytes (Swift, 1958).

Incorporation of adenine-C^{14} into the nuclear RNA fraction of intact *Triturus viridescens* liver was studied by Swift (1958) who found a high

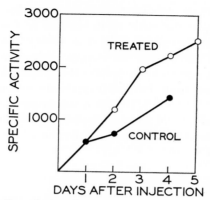

Fig. 14. Incorporation of phosphate-P³² into liver RNA of *Rana grylio* tadpoles previously injected with 3,5,3′-triiodo-L-thyronine. Specific activity in counts × min⁻¹ × (μg P)⁻¹ versus days after injection of phosphate-P³². Control tadpole received only phosphate-P³². Adapted from Finamore and Frieden (1960).

rate of incorporation outside of the nucleolus in the chromosomal RNA. *Triturus viridescens* liver cells are estimated to contain 98×10^{-12} gm DNA per diploid nucleus and 68×10^{-12} gm RNA per nucleus, excluding the nucleolus.

In some striking experiments, Finamore and Frieden (1960) found that the rate of incorporation of phosphate-P³² into RNA, DNA, and protein of liver is increased during induced metamorphosis of *Rana grylio*. These increases were found before any external morphological changes could be noted. The stimulation of incorporation of P³² into RNA is apparent as early as 2 days after the injection of triiodothyronine as shown in Fig. 14. As shown in the last column of Table X, there is an increase in the weight ratio RNA:DNA from 0.86 to 1.7 by the fourth day after injection of the hormone, while the control tadpoles showed little or no change in this ratio. Because treatment with the hormone increases the wet weight of the liver by some 20%, the RNA content on the fourth day of 2.7 mg per gm liver wet weight compared with that of 2.2 mg per gm on the first day, probably reflects a true net synthesis of RNA, and the authors have so interpreted their data. During this metamorphosis the purine and pyrimidine base composition of neither RNA nor DNA changes noticeably. To account for the synthesis of new protein, including enzymes, concomitant with metamorphosis, the conclusion is almost inescapable that template-RNA molecules with new and different sequences of pyrimidines and purines must arise or become exposed in some manner.

Thiouracil-2-C¹⁴ and thiouracil-S³⁵ have been found by Paik and Cohen (1961) to be incorporated into RNA by thyroxine-treated tadpoles of

Rana catesbeiana. They claim that thiouracil "exerts its action on the hormone (thyroxine) as the result of the synthesis of a faulty ribonucleic acid molecule." In another study, Paik *et al.* (1961) found that the amount of liver DNA-P and RNA-P did not change in thyroxine-treated tadpoles during the time that carbamyl phosphate synthetase increased as much as 15-fold. They conclude from this and from the decreased rate of incorporation of adenine-8-C^{14} into RNA, that thyroxine caused a rearrangement of RNA molecules. It will be of great interest to follow investigations in this area, especially those directed toward a demonstration of different base sequences in the newly formed RNA.

C. DEGRADATION OF URIC ACID

Uric acid, an intermediate in the catabolism of purines, is further degraded to glyoxylic acid and urea by the following sequence of enzymic reactions:

The over-all reaction at pH 7 may be written as:

$$\text{Uric acid} + \tfrac{1}{2}O_2 + 4H_2O = 2 \text{ urea} + \text{glyoxylate}^- + HCO_3^- + 2 H^+ \quad (41)$$

$$\Delta F^{0'}_{298} = -56.7 \text{ kcal}$$

Przylecki's (1926) early studies showed that Amphibia (*Proteus, Salamandra, Triton, Rana*) could degrade uric acid to allantoin. Uricase activity

TABLE X

Nucleic Acid Content of *Rana grylio* Liver[a]

Days after injection	Control				Treated[b]			
	Hind limb/tail	RNA (mg/gm)	DNA (mg/gm)	RNA/ DNA	Hind limb/tail	RNA (mg/gm)	DNA (mg/gm)	RNA/ DNA
1	0.08	2.0	2.1	0.98	0.06	2.2	2.5	0.86
4	0.07	2.1	2.3	0.91	0.16	2.7	1.6	1.7
Froglet	∞	2.7	2.9	0.95	∞	3.1	3.9	0.80

[a] Modified from Finamore and Frieden (1960).
[b] 1×10^{-8} moles of 3,5,3'-triiodo-L-thyronine per gm body weight (injected intraperitoneally).

was measured in homogenates of liver and kidney of *Rana esculenta* somewhat later by Truszkowski and Goldanówna (1933), but activity was noticeably absent from skin, muscle, heart, lungs, brain, intestine, spleen, ovary, and testicle. More recently, liver homogenates of *Rana tigrina* and of *Bufo melanostictus* were shown by Friedmann (1954) to possess uricase activity. Surprisingly, no activity could be demonstrated in liver homogenates prepared from eight specimens of *Rana hexadactyla*. Friedmann suggests that the latter frog is an exception to the rule that uricase occurs in livers of animals which are not uricotelic.

A liver homogenate of *Rana viridis* was shown to convert uric acid to allantoic acid (Fosse *et al.*, 1930). It was thus clear that an enzyme acting upon the breakdown product of uric acid, i.e., allantoin, must have been present. This enzyme, allantoinase, was also shown to be present in *Rana temporaria* and numerous fishes. Brunel (1937a, b) finally established the presence of the last enzyme in the series, allantoicase, in liver of various amphibians (*Triton* sp., *Bufo* sp., and *Rana* spp.) and showed that the final products were urea and glyoxylate.

A systematic study of the development in embryonic and/or larval amphibians of the enzymes catalyzing these reactions would be highly informative and would complement the study dealing with urea synthesis in the metamorphosing anuran tadpole.

It should now be clear that excretory urea can arise in Amphibia from ammonia via the urea cycle, by hydrolysis of dietary arginine, and by degradation of purines via uric acid. It would still be of interest, however, to establish the magnitude of each of these routes, in spite of the fact that in the adult amphibian the first route appears to predominate.

VI. Enzyme Studies on Amphibia

A. COMMENT

An upgrading of the field of enzymology of the Amphibia could be achieved if more careful attention were paid to the reporting of enzymic protocols and data. In particular, one of the standard units of enzymic activity should be employed, such as μmoles of product formed or substrate utilized per unit time. Similarly, the specific activity is best reported in terms such as μmoles per minute per milligram protein. Comparisons of relative levels of activity in homogenates of various tissues of the same or different animals also can be made easily when expressed on the basis of μmoles per unit time per wet or dry weight. What should be avoided specifically are the uses of weights or weight concentrations of substrate or product instead of mole quantities in the expression of activity. The practice of reporting enzyme activity in terms of milliliters of some titrant is no longer excusable.

In the past, Q values (μliters per hour per milligram dry weight), have been employed to express enzyme activity even when a solid substance was dealt with. As an aid in comparing such values with newer expressions, the relationship, $10 Q \cong \mu$moles per hour per gram wet weight, can be employed when dealing with soft tissues where the ratio of wet weight:dry weight is $\cong 5$. The expression of activity in an hour time unit, even though the assay may have been carried out over a shorter interval, creates no difficulties if the assay has been shown to be linear with time for the amount of enzyme employed in a given assay.

B. SOME ENZYMES AND THEIR ACTIVITIES IN AMPHIBIA

Some of the enzymes of carbohydrate metabolism were presented in Section IV,C,2. Other enzymes appeared in appropriate sections of the chapter. A brief tabulation of the levels (activities) of a few enzymes, assayed mostly in homogenates, is given in Table XI. In addition to these, mention will also be made below of certain other enzymes studied in Amphibia. Reactions catalyzed by the enzymes appear in parentheses in abbreviated form.

ATPase. (ATP $\rightarrow$ ADP + P$_i$)   Hydrolysis of phosphate from ATP by homogenates of liver, muscle, kidney, lung, and heart (in decreasing order of activity) at an optimal pH of 7.4 and at 45° has been reported by Lipshitz and Frank (1949) for *Rana pipiens*. Barth and Jaeger (1947) assume the presence of three different ATPases in eggs of *Rana pipiens*. ATPase appears to reach a maximum activity early in gastrulation (30–40 hr). Embryos of *Bufo vulgaris* in late gastrula (yolk plug stage) contain an active ATPase which is activated by dinitrophenol (1–1.5 $\times$ 10^{-4} M). Azide (10^{-3} M) reduces the activation produced by dinitrophenol (Maruyama, 1956). Activity for the enzyme increases in liver during normal and induced metamorphosis of *Rana grylio* (Frieden and Mathews, 1958). There is a drop in activity of tail ATPase during spontaneous metamorphosis of this frog, but treatment with L-triiodothyronine leads to an increase in activity.

Catalase. ($H_2O_2 \rightarrow H_2O + \frac{1}{2}O_2$) Many reports have dealt with the catalase activity of tissues of Amphibia. Activity is reported to be highest at the tip of the tail of *Xenopus laevis* tadpoles, decreasing toward the base of the tail (von Hahn, 1958). Mitsuda and Yasumatsu (1955) report the crystallization from toad liver (species not given) of catalase in the form of square, thin plates. Optimal temperature of 15° for the experimental incubation period and a Kat.-*f* of 21,600 (versus 39,500 for cow liver) are reported. An increase in activity of tail-tip catalase was observed in fed but not in fasted larvae of *Xenopus laevis* (see also Serfaty and Louvier, 1942; Katajama, 1954).

Cholinesterase. (Acetylcholine $\rightarrow$ acetate + choline) Numerous reports on this enzyme exist. By manometric and histochemical techniques, Shen and co-workers (1955) found the enzyme to be localized in the brain of adult *Rana pipiens* largely in the well defined neuropils of the isthmic and mesencephalic regions. Only small amounts were found in the cerebral hemispheres and infundibulum. Motor neurons of the cranial nerves showed high concentrations of the enzyme as did the capillary walls in parts of the brain, As in *Ambystoma maculatum*, the enzyme is of the specific type characterized by (1) marked substrate inhibition; (2) relatively high affinity for acetyl-β-choline; (3) inability to hydrolyze benzoyl-choline; and (4) relative resistance to inhibition by diisopropylfluorophosphate (DFP) at a concentration of $10^{-7} M$. Activity of cholinesterase is thought to be an essential part of the sodium pump mechanism. In sartorius muscle of *Rana pipiens*, hexyl tetraphosphate irreversibly inhibits, and physostigmine reversibly inhibits the transport mechanism (van der Kloot, 1956).

DNAase II. (Deoxyribonucleic acid $\rightarrow$ 3'-nucleotides) Tails of *Rana catesbeiana* undergoing precocious metamorphosis with thyroxine exhibit a 2- to 3-fold increase in the activity of this enzyme (Coleman, 1963).

DOPA decarboxylase. (3,4-Dihydroxyphenylalanine $\rightarrow$ hydroxytyramine + CO_2) This enzyme catalyzes one of the reactions in the sequence for the conversion of phenylalanine or tyrosine to noradrenaline and adrenaline. Blaschko (1942) has found this enzyme to be present in liver, but absent from kidney, of *Rana temporaria*. On the other hand, activity of guinea pig kidney is as much as 15 times that of guinea pig liver, and both of these tissues are more active, on a wet weight basis, than is the frog liver described above.

Esterase(s). (Ester $\rightarrow$ acid + alcohol) Glenner and Burstone (1958) give the distribution of esterase, as studied by histochemical techniques, for liver, kidney, and integument. Distribution is quite different from that in various mammals also studied.

Glucose-6-phosphatase. (Glucose-6-P $\rightarrow$ glucose + P_i) This enzyme increases in the liver of *Rana grylio* during both normal and induced metamorphosis (Frieden and Mathews, 1958).

β-Glucuronidase. (β-glucuronide $\rightarrow$ β-glucuronic acid + alcohol) Activity for this enzyme was measured in homogenates of *Xenopus laevis* larvae. Assay was performed at pH 4.5 in the presence of 0.00167 *M* glucuronide of 8-hydroxy-quinoline (Billet, 1957).

Hyaluronidase. (Hyaluronic acid $\rightarrow$ oligosaccharides) The enzyme occurs in frog skin (Akino, 1951). Hyaluronic acid is the term for a mixture of mucopolysaccharides occurring in the ground- or cement-substance of the subcutaneous tissue and of the vitreous body of the eye and synovial fluid.

TABLE XI[a]

Enzyme Levels

Enzyme	Tissue	Species	Temp.	pH	Substrate conc.	μMoles per hr per gm wet weight	Remarks	Reference
Acid phosphatase[b]	Liver	Rana esculenta	37°	5.0	See ref.	409	—	Ponz (1947)
	Pancreas	Rana esculenta	37°	5.0	See ref.	68	—	Ponz (1947)
	Lung	Rana esculenta	37°	5.0	See ref.	42	—	Ponz (1947)
	Intestine	Rana esculenta	37°	5.0	See ref.	26	—	Ponz (1947)
	Serum	Rana esculenta	37°	5.0	See ref.	4.2[c]	—	Ponz (1947)
	Bile	Rana esculenta	37°	5.0	See ref.	1.3–9.7[c]	—	Ponz (1947)
Alkaline phosphatase[b]	Liver	Rana esculenta	37°	9.4	See ref.	361	—	Ponz (1947)
	Pancreas	Rana esculenta	37°	9.4	See ref.	58	—	Ponz (1947)
	Lung	Rana esculenta	37°	9.4	See ref.	39	—	Ponz (1947)
	Intestine	Rana esculenta	37°	9.4	See ref.	116	—	Ponz (1947)
	Serum	Rana esculenta	37°	9.4	See ref.	1.5[c]	—	Ponz (1947)
	Bile	Rana esculenta	37°	9.4	See ref.	4.8–64[c]	—	Ponz (1947)
Amino acid oxidase	Kidney	Rana esculenta	37.5°	8.0	DL-Alanine, 0.033 M	110	—	Krebs (1935)
	Liver	Rana esculenta	37.5°	8.0	DL-Alanine, 0.033 M	37	—	Krebs (1935)
	Liver	Triton cristatus	37.5°	7.4	DL-Alanine, 0.033 M	36	—	Krebs (1935)
	Liver	Ambystoma tigrinum	37°	7.4	DL-Alanine, 0.03 M	17	—	Schooler and Brown (1960)
Arginase	Liver	Rana catesbeiana	38°	9.5	0.00125 M	24,600	(With Mn^{++})	Brown and Cohen (1960)
	Liver	Rana catesbeiana	38°	9.5	0.085 M	60,000 ± 5,880	(With Mn^{++})	Brown (1963)
	Liver	Bufo marinus	38°	9.5	0.0125 M	22,500 ± 3,560	(With Mn^{++})	Brown and Cohen (1960)
	Liver	Necturus maculosus	38°	9.5	0.0125 M	20,000 ± 13,100	(With Mn^{++})	Brown and Cohen (1960)
	Liver	Amphiuma means	38°	9.5	0.0125 M	18,700	(With Mn^{++})	Brown and Cohen (1960)
	Liver	Newt (not identified)	38°	9.5	0.085 M	192,000	(With Mn^{++})	Brown (1963)
Arginine synth. system	Liver	Rana catesbeiana	38°	7	See ref.	46.3 ± 9.9	—	Brown and Cohen (1960)
	Liver	Bufo marinus	38°	7	See ref.	33.2 ± 6.0	—	Brown and Cohen (1960)
	Liver	Bufo americanus	38°	7	See ref.	33.0 ± 13.8	—	Brown and Cohen (1960)
	Liver	Necturus maculosus	38°	7	See ref.	9.1 ± 1.0	—	Brown and Cohen (1960)
	Liver	Amphiuma means	38°	7	See ref.	29.8	—	Brown and Cohen (1960)

Enzyme	Tissue	Species	Temp.	pH	Conditions	Value	Notes	Reference
ASA cleavage enzyme	Liver	*Rana catesbeiana*	38°	7	0.002 M	498	—	Brown and Cohen (1960)
	Liver	*Necturus maculosus*	38°	7	0.002 M	56.1	—	Brown and Cohen (1960)
	Liver	Newt (not identified)	38°	7	0.002 M	>121	—	Brown and Cohen (1960)
	Liver	*Amphiuma means*	38°	7	0.002 M	369	—	Brown and Cohen (1960)
Asp-αKG transaminase	Tail	*Rana japonica* (XVI)	37°	7.4	See ref.	5,700 ± 300	No change upon metamorphosis	Yamamoto (1960)
ATPase	Gastrula	*Bufo vulgaris formosus*	30°	7.2	See ref.	46	With DNP + Mg^{++}	Maruyama (1956)
	Gastrula	*Bufo vulgaris formosus*	30°	7.2	See ref.	14	Without DNP + Mg^{++}	Maruyama (1956)
	Tail	*Rana grylio* (tadpoles)	30°	7.2	0.010 M	4200	Leg/Tail = 0.4	Frieden and Mathews (1958)
	Tail	*Rana grylio* (tadpoles)	30°	7.2	0.010 M	2280	Leg/Tail = 2.5	Frieden and Mathews (1958)
	Liver	*Rana grylio* (premetamorphic)	30°	7.2	0.010 M	~600	Normal metamorphosis	Frieden and Mathews (1958)
	Liver	*Rana grylio* (postmetamorphic)	30°	7.2	0.010 M	1,200–4,200	Normal metamorphosis	Frieden and Mathews (1958)
Carbamyl phosphate synthetase	Liver	*Rana catesbeiana*	38°	7	See ref.	980 ± 120	—	Brown and Cohen (1960)
	Liver	*Bufo fowlerei*	38°	7	See ref.	772	—	Brown and Cohen (1960)
	Liver	*Bufo marinus*	38°	7	See ref.	804 ± 45	—	Brown and Cohen (1960)
	Liver	*Bufo americanus*	38°	7	See ref.	779 ± 56	—	Brown and Cohen (1960)
	Liver	*Necturus maculosus*	38°	7	See ref.	16 ± 4	—	Brown and Cohen (1960)
	Liver	*Ambystoma tigrinum*	38°	7	See ref.	360 ± 80	—	Brown and Cohen (1960)
	Liver	Newt (not identified)	38°	7	See ref.	378	—	Brown and Cohen (1960)
	Liver	*Amphiuma means*	38°	7	See ref.	206 ± 36	—	Brown and Cohen (1960)
Cytochrome oxidase	Liver	*Xenopus laevis* (feeding state, 120 hr)	20°	7.4	Cytochrome c, $5 \times 10^{-4}\ M$	4,760	—	Boell and Weber (1955)
DOPA decarboxylase	Liver	*Rana temporaria*	18.5°–20.5°	7.4	DOPA, 0.05 M	1.4–3.6	—	Blaschko (1942)
Glucose-6-phosphatase	Liver	*Rana grylio* (premetamorphic)	30°	6.5	0.010 M	24	—	Frieden and Mathews (1958)
	Liver	*Rana grylio* (postmetamorphic)	30°	6.5	0.010 M	80–320	—	Frieden and Mathews (1958)

TABLE XI—*Continued*

Enzyme	Tissue	Species	Temp.	pH	Substrate conc.	μMoles per hr per gm wet weight	Remarks	Reference
Glycerophos-phatase (acid)	Tail	*Bufo vulgaris formosus* (XVII)	37°	4.4	See ref.	750 ± 100	—	Yanagisawa (1953)
	Tail	*Bufo vulgaris formosus* (XX)	37°	4.4	See ref.	927 ± 140	—	Yanagisawa (1953)
	Tail	*Bufo vulgaris formosus* (XXI–XXII)	37°	4.4	See ref.	1860 ± 410	—	Yanagisawa (1953)
	Tail	*Bufo vulgaris formosus* (XXIII)	37°	4.4	See ref.	2590 ± 790	—	Yanagisawa (1953)
Glycerophospha-tase (alkaline)	Tail	*Bufo vulgaris formosus* (XVII)	37°	10.1	See ref.	1020 ± 180	—	Yanagisawa (1953)
	Tail	*Bufo vulgaris formosus* (XX)	37°	10.1	See ref.	1390 ± 290	—	Yanagisawa (1953)
	Tail	*Bufo vulgaris formosus* (XXI–XXII)	37°	10.1	See ref.	2390 ± 940	—	Yanagisawa (1953)
	Tail	*Bufo vulgaris formosus* (XXIII)	37°	10.1	See ref.	2900 ± 1200	—	Yanagisawa (1953)
Glycerophospha-tase (acid)	Tail	*Rhacophorus schlegelii arborea* (premetamor-phic)	37°	4.4	See ref.	602 ± 106	—	Yanagisawa (1953)
Glycerophospha-tase (alkaline)	Tail	*Rhacophorus schlegelii arborea* (premetamor-phic)	37°	10.1	See ref.	1470 ± 425	—	Yanagisawa (1953)
Glycerophospha-tase (acid)	Tail	*Rhacophorus schlegelii arborea* (after inducing metamorphosis)	37°	4.4	See ref.	953 ± 490	—	Yanagisawa (1953)
Glycerophospha-tase (alkaline)	Tail	*Rhacophorus schlegelii arborea* (after inducing metamorphosis)	37°	10.1	See ref.	2260 ± 650	—	Yanagisawa (1953)

Enzyme	Tissue	Species	Temp.	pH	Substrate	Value	Notes	Reference
Hexokinase	Brain	Rana temporaria	30°	7.9	Glucose, 0.0277 M	162	with ATP, Mg++, NaF	Kerly and Leaback (1957)
	Brain	Rana temporaria	30°	7.9	Fructose, 0.00277 M	60	With ATP, Mg++, NaF	Kerly and Leaback (1957)
Ornithine transcarbamylase	Liver	Rana catesbeiana	38°	8.3	L-Ornithine, 0.01 M CP, 0.01 M	9,700 ± 2,300	—	Brown and Cohen (1960)
	Liver	Bufo fowlerei	38°	8.3	L-Ornithine, 0.01 M CP, 0.01 M	16,000	—	Brown and Cohen (1960)
	Liver	Bufo marinus	38°	8.3	L-Ornithine, 0.01 M CP, 0.01 M	18,200 ± 2,200	—	Brown and Cohen (1960)
	Liver	Necturus maculosus	38°	8.3	L-Ornithine, 0.01 M CP, 0.01M	2,100 ± 1,000	—	Brown and Cohen (1960)
	Liver	Ambystoma tigrinum	38°	8.3	L-Ornithine, 0.01 M CP, 0.01M	Present	—	Brown and Cohen (1960)
	Liver	Amphiuma means	38°	8.3	L-Ornithine, 0.01 M CP, 0.01 M	10,200 ± 2,500	—	Brown and Cohen (1960)
Phosphoprotein phosphatase	Embryo	Rana pipiens	26°	3.5	?	0.85[d]	Mean, during first 100 hr	Mezger-Freed (1953)
Pseudo-cholinesterase	Brain	Rana temporaria	R.T.?	?	Acetylcholine, 0.01 M	633	Not inhibited by DFP 10^-6 M	Hardwick and Hebb (1956)
	Brain	Rana temporaria	R.T.?	?	Butyrylcholine, 0.01 M	156	Inhibited by DFP 10^-6 M	Hardwick and Hebb (1956)
Rhodanese	Liver	Frog (species not given)	20°	8.3	$Na_2S_2O_3$, 0.005 M NaCN, 0.005 M	1490	—	Lang (1933)
Uricase	Liver	Rana esculenta	18°	8	0.003 M	16	—	Truskowski and Goldanówna (1933)
	Kidney	Rana esculenta	18°	8	0.003 M	13	—	Truskowski and Goldanówna (1933)

[a] Abbreviations used: αKG, α-keto-glutarate; ASA, argininosuccinate; CP, carbamyl phosphate; DFP, diisopropylfluorophosphate; DNP, dinitrophenol. Roman numerals refer to larval stages of Taylor and Kollros (1946).

[b] Average values.

[c] Per milliliter.

[d] Per egg.

Lactic dehydrogenase. (Lactate $\rightleftharpoons$ pyruvate)   Lactic dehydrogenase is reported to decrease rapidly in *Rhacophorus schlegelii* at hatching (Ohara and Suyama, 1952). Depending upon source, it requires either DPN or TPN.

Lipase(s). (Triglyceride $\rightarrow$ 3 fatty acids + glycerol)   Numerous reports have appeared on the hydrolysis of triglycerides during embryonic and larval development of Anura (Kurata and Tanaka, 1953; Urbani, 1956, 1957; Urbani-Mistruzzi, 1957).

Monoamine oxidase. (Monoamine $\rightarrow$ aldehyde + NH_4^+)   Homogenates of *Rana temporaria* liver oxidize tyramine (Smith, 1960). The enzyme in the frog is thought to be important for the inactivation of sympathomimetic amines. A seasonal variation in the level of the enzyme has been observed, highest values occurring from August to November. Amines can arise from the decarboxylation of amino acids. The enzyme yields H_2O_2 as the end product; the prosthetic group has not been clearly established but it is probably FMN.

Nitrate reductase. ($NO_3^- \rightarrow NO_2^-$)   The Japanese workers, Ohara and Suyama (1952) claim to have measured nitrate reductase activity in embryos of *Rhacophorus schlegelii*. This enzyme is considered to be typically of plant and microorganismal origin.

Polyphenyl oxidase = phenol oxidase = tyrosinase. (o-Diphenol $\rightarrow o$-quinone)   An enzyme has been obtained from *Rana nigromaculata* which oxidizes (destroys) adrenaline and noradrenaline (Sato *et al.*, 1954). The enzyme is inhibited by CN^- and is activated by Cu^{++} (as are the polyphenol oxidases from other sources).

Phosphatases, acid and alkaline. More reports on the occurrence of these enzymes have appeared than for any other single amphibian enzyme. Fruton and Simmonds (1958) classify phosphatases into four groups: (1) phosphomonoesterases (e.g., glucose-6-phosphatase [see above]); (2) phosphodiesterases (e.g., glyceryl-phosphorylcholine $\rightarrow$ L-α-glycerophosphate + choline); (3) pyrophosphatases (examples, $PP_i \rightarrow 2 P_i$; $ATP \rightarrow AMP + PP_i$); and (4) metaphosphatases [$(HPO_3)_n \rightarrow nP_i$]. In studies of phosphatase activities in amphibian tissues it is not always clear that the activity measured is on a preferred substrate. Most reports on "alkaline" and "acid" phosphatases deal with the hydrolysis of β-glycerophosphate. Phosphatase activities thus are cited in this section on the basis of the substrate used (see ATPase, glucose-6-phosphatase, metaphosphatase).

Alkaline (pH 9.6) and acid (pH 4.6) phosphatases are present during cleavage stages of *Bufo vulgaris*, and activity increases from embryonic to larval life (de Cesaris-Coromaldi, 1955). Activity of both enzymes is greater in the caudal than in the cephalic regions of embryos at the limb-bud state. Alkaline and acid phosphatase activity occurs in adult *Rana pipiens* kidney, liver, heart, spleen, and muscle (Kind and Macchi, 1952). The alkaline phosphatases are activated by Mg^{++}, Mn^{++}, and Co^{++} and are inhibited by CN^-. Inactivation at temperatures above 50° is rapid. The alkaline phosphatase of *Rana pipiens* kidney is higher than for either the alkaline or acid phosphatase of all other tissues (organs) studied.

Various histochemical demonstrations of acid and/or alkaline phosphatase activities in amphibian tissues have appeared (for *Ambystoma maculatum* see Longley, 1955; for *Rana pipiens* see Burgos, 1955).

Acid (pH 5.3) and alkaline (pH 9.2) phosphatases are present in extracts of the entire integument of larval and adult *Rana esculenta* and of the epidermis and integument of *Triton cristatus* (Cafiero *et al.*, 1950). Alkaline phosphatase (pH 9.6) has also been measured in H_2O extracts of *Ambystoma mexicanum* and *Xenopus laevis* (Krugelis, 1949–1951). There is a steady increase in activity during embryonic development, and the specific activity of the enzyme is greater in the animal than in the vegetal pole of gastrulae.

Phosphorylase. (Glycogen → glucose-1-P) Frog muscle (probably *Rana* sp.) extract contains phosphorylase (Cowgill and Cori, 1955). Inactive phosphorylase is activated by adrenaline to form phosphorylase *b*. The latter, in the presence of AMP is converted to phosphorylase *a*. Phosphorylase converts glycogen to glucose-1-P, and activation by adrenaline can act as a mechanism for rapid mobilization of glycogen reserves as a source of energy for the "fear and flight" phenomenon.

Polyphosphatase. (Polyphosphates → nP$_i$) An enzyme hydrolyzing a linear polymer of phosphoric acid has been demonstrated in homogenates of embryos, larvae, and adults of *Rana pipiens* and of *R. clamitans* (Berg, 1955). The enzyme(s) exhibits two pH optima of 3.9–4.4 and 7.2–7.7, is activated by Mg^{++}, and does not hydrolyze glycerophosphate or phosphoprotein. The significance of this enzyme is unknown.

Pseudo-cholinesterase. (Acylcholine → acid + choline) An enzyme cleaving butyrylcholine occurs in homogenates of brain, spinal cord, and sciatic nerve of the frog (probably *Rana temporaria*) (Hardwick and Hebb, 1956). This enzyme is distinguishable from cholinesterase (which see).

Rhodanese. (Thiosulfate + cyanide → sulfite + thiocyanate) The reaction catalyzed by rhodanese is regarded as a detoxication reaction. Production of thiocyanate from cyanide by frog liver (probably *Rana temporaria*) proceeds more rapidly than in the case of liver from several representative mammals (rabbit > beef > man > cat > dog) and birds (chicken > pigeon) (Lang, 1933). Sánchez and Bertrán (1950) and Bertrán and Sánchez (1951) have measured the rhodanese content of intestine, skin, muscles, and gonads of frogs.

Xanthine oxidase. (Xanthine or hypoxanthine → uric acid) This enzyme is reported to be absent from the liver of the burrowing frog, *Cacopus systoma*, and of *Rana tigrina* (Friedmann, 1954). It is present in liver homogenates of *Bufo melanostictus*. The enzyme is also present in kidney of all these animals. It is reported to be absent from the liver, spleen, pancreas, lung, and ovary of *Rana hexadactyla*, according to Friedmann (1953). Xanthine oxidase generally occurs in the liver of various vertebrates, but there are other known exceptions, e.g., pigeon, dog, hedgehog.

VII. Mineral Metabolism

In addition to C, H, O, and N, the elements thought to be essential to Amphibia are listed in Table XII. As indicated, certain of the elements may be classified as micronutrients and serve largely for the activation of enzymes or for certain prosthetic groups such as the iron-containing heme. Table XII has been adapted from several sources and lists those mineral ions and elements which are considered to be necessary to support certain physiological and enzymic functions of Amphibia. The list does not differ in any known respect from Mammalia nor probably from other vertebrate classes. These elements, with the possible exception of iodine, are generally readily available from dietary sources and to some extent from minerals dissolved in water in the case of aquatic species.

TABLE XII

Element or ion	Role or function
Ca^{++}	Bone formation, blood coagulation, capillary integrity, enzyme activator, permeability, nervous system
Cl^-	Chief anion of extracellular fluid, esophageal or gastric HCl, acid-base balance, blood transport of CO_2 ("chloride shift")
Co (micronutrient)	Stimulation of hematopoiesis, vitamin B_{12}, enzyme activator
Cu (micronutrient)	Erythropoiesis, Cu-flavin enzymes (polyphenol oxidase, etc.)
F^-	Bone formation
Fe^{++} or Fe^{+++} (micronutrient)	Part of heme group in hemoglobin, catalase, cytochromes, Fe-flavins
I_2 or I^-	Metamorphosis via thyroxine, metabolic regulator
K^+	Chief cation of intracellular fluid, nervous system, enzyme activator
Mg^{++}	Neuromuscular system, bone formation, activator for enzymes (especially involving phosphate transfer)
Mn^{++} (micronutrient)	Metal ion activator for enzymes (e.g., arginase)
Mo (micronutrient)	Mo-flavin enzymes (aldehyde oxidase)
Na^+	Chief cation of extracellular fluid, nerve conduction, enzyme activation
P ($HPO_4^=$-$H_2PO_4^-$)	Bone formation, organic phosphates, tissue buffer
S (organic)	Amino acids, proteins, coenzymes, redox reactions
Zn^{++}	Some enzymes (carbonic anhydrase)

The roles of Na^+, K^+, and Cl^- are played largely in connection with water, acid-base balance, and neuromuscular activity, and are more properly discussed in subsequent chapters. Allusion has already been made to the activation of certain enzymes by metal ions. Table XII is largely self-explanatory, but several observations will be appended concerning a few of the minerals:

Calcium. Calcium is stored by Amphibia in unique structures, the paravertebral lime sacs (for literature see Schlumberger and Burk, 1953). These gland-like structures envelop the spinal ganglia and contain calcium to the extent of over 90 % $CaCO_3$ in the form of the mineral, aragonite. As judged by roentgenograms, remarkable amounts of orthorhombic doubly refractile crystals of $CaCO_3$ accumulate in the lime sacs of *Rana pipiens* following immersion in 0.8 % $CaCl_2$ solutions. Calcium released from the bones after injection of vitamin D also appears in the lime sacs. Amphibian bone is similar to that of mammals (see Schlumberger and Burk, 1953). Studies with intact *Bufo bufo* larvae and Ca^{45}-lactate have shown that the calcareous deposits of the lime sacs are used for ossification. A decrease in the $CaCO_3$ in these sacs occurs during growth and mineralization of the skeleton which accompanies metamorphosis (Guardabassi, 1960).

Copper. Copper has been detected in the fat body of *Rana* sp., and the amount decreases during spring, possibly as a result of egg production (Narasaka, 1938). This copper may be in the form of the Cu_2^{++}-flavin compound which is known to be the prosthetic group of butyrylCoA dehydrogenase, one of the enzymes concerned with the oxidation of fatty acids (Mahler, 1954).

Eggs are rather rich in copper content compared with many other tissues. Cupric ion is thought to counteract to some extent the stimulation of metamorphosis of *Rana temporaria* by thyroxine (Sutter, 1941).

Copper occurs in the eyes of fresh-water fishes and frogs (Bownes and Morton, 1952), and along with zinc is thought to be associated with the formation of melanin pigments. In the case of *Rana esculenta*, the amount of copper in the pigment-protein fraction of the choroids is 5 times that of the sclera and 30 times that of the lens (Bownes and Morton, 1952). It is to be recalled that melanins derive from the aromatic amino acids, phenylalanine and tyrosine, and that the enzymes in this sequence (DOPA-oxidase and polyphenyl oxidase) contain copper. The reviewer has noted that homogenates of *Rana catesbeiana* liver which have large amounts of melanin yield upon centrifugation a pellet with a blue-colored substance which may contain copper.

Zinc. Like copper, zinc is in high concentration in the pigment-protein fraction of the choroids. Eye tissue of *Rana esculenta* contains 28.1 mg per gm dry weight of tissue, over 1000 times that of the sclera or of the kidney (Bownes and Morton, 1952).

Iron. Absorption of iron (ferric sulfate) by frogs (*Rana pipiens*) takes place in the duodenal region (McCallion and Scott, 1950). A maximal amount of iron appears in the liver 6 hr after feeding. Iron was taken up by Küpfer cells, sinusoid lining, and by the stellate cells of the pigment patches. Bound forms of iron were found in the nuclei of all cells of liver and spleen. It would seem, as with mammals, that only small amounts of iron are absorbed, and the amount is probably regulated by a mechanism which takes up more iron the greater the requirement.

The iron content of the pigment cells of the liver of *Salamandra maculosa* was found to be higher than for parenchymal cells; iron could not be detected in the pigment cells of a nourished animal in the summer (Meyer, 1934). The iron content of eggs of *Rhacophorus schlegelii* is 1 µg per egg (Hiromatsu, 1959). Radioactive iron (as Fe^{59}-Cl_3) is taken up by red cells of *Rana grylio* and is incorporated into hemoglobin (Herner and Frieden, 1961).

Iodine. The importance of iodine and its uptake for metamorphosis of the tadpole has been recognized since the early observation of Gudernatsch (1913). Osmotic changes in the watery environment of a tadpole may play some part in the retention and metabolism of I^{131} in adult *Triturus viridescens* (Boatman and Sunder, 1955). The ecological significance of seasonal variations in this species is discussed by the authors. Uptake of intraperitoneally injected carrier-free I^{131} was found by Bradley (1953) to be greatest by the thyroid gland, less by liver, and least by striated muscle of *Rana pipiens*. Krogh (1937) believes I^- is not taken up *from solution* by frogs (*Rana esculenta*); surprisingly, in this study the related halide, Br^-, was taken up. However, Dent and Hunt (1952) and others have shown that *molecular* I_2^{131} is taken up from solution (*Hyla versicolor*, *Rana palustris*, and *Bufo americanus*). The iodine content of Detroit tap water was found by Metcalf and Creaser (1936) to be so low that it was insufficient for the metamorphosis of tadpoles. Low iodine contents of the water of glaciated and mountainous regions (endemic goiter areas) may account for observed delays in the metamorphosis of numerous amphibians.

VIII. Concluding Remarks

The facets of metabolism of the Amphibia discussed here show that this class has the same general mechanisms which occur throughout the animal kingdom for the trapping and utilization of energy and for synthesizing, degrading, and interconverting foodstuffs and intermediary metabolites. In addition it is seen that the requirements for specific metabolites, vitamins, cofactors, inorganic salts, and metal ion activators are much the same as found in other classes.

Poikilothermy, while of a disadvantage in some obvious respects, nevertheless serves the economy of Amphibia in numerous ways, including the ability to go for long periods in the absence of food, to minimize radiation heat loss, to tolerate low oxygen tensions, and to be of much smaller size than their warm-blooded cousins.

Amphibia offer themselves as an excellent tool for the study of such basic processes as differentiation, growth, and development, in the form of material which can easily be studied from the egg to the adult. The wide swings in the levels of metabolites experienced by Amphibia in response to environment or other factors afford the opportunity of studying the interaction of the environment with biochemical entities such as enzyme sequences and hormone action.

Moreover, Amphibia are uniquely so placed phylogenetically between the primitive fishes and the homoiothermic vertebrates that they offer unexplored opportunity for studies on evolutionary trends. And, because of the wealth of reproductive and developmental mechanisms exhibited by members of this class, because of variety of habitat and variability in retention of larval characteristics by sexually mature adult forms, the continued study of Amphibia promises to yield biological information of a unique kind.

Acknowledgments

This work was supported, in part, by grants from the National Institutes of Health of the U. S. Public Health Service, and the National Science Foundation. The author is greatly indebted to Susan G. Brown for conceptual and technical aid in the preparation of the manuscript.

References*

Ackerman, J. (1949). Annual rhythm of the fatty metamorphosis of the liver in the frog *Rana esculenta. Bull. Intern. Acad. Polon. Sci. Classe Sci. Math. Nat. Ser.* BII, 145–174.

Afanasyeva, E. M., and Stepanenko, B. N. (1956). Species differences in the chemical constitution of glycogens. *Biokhimiya* 21, 603–611; *Biochemistry (U.S.S.R.) (Engl. Transl.)* 21(5), 624–632 (1957).

Akino, M. (1951). Hyaluronidase activity of frog skin. *Zool. Mag. (Tokyo)* 60, 86–88.

Allen, B. M. (1938). The endocrine control of amphibian metamorphosis. *Biol. Rev. Cambridge Phil. Soc.* 13, 1–19.

Allen, E. H., Glassman, E., and Schweet, R. S. (1960a). Incorporation of amino acids into ribonucleic acid. I. The role of activating enzymes. *J. Biol. Chem.* 235, 1061–1067.

Allen, E. H., Glassman, E., Cordes, E., and Schweet, R. S. (1960b). Incorporation of amino acids into ribonucleic acid. II. Amino acid transfer ribonucleic acid. *J. Biol. Chem.* 235, 1068–1074.

Anciaux, H. (1952). Study of metabolism of lipides of the frog with the aid of C^{14}. *Verhandel. Koninkl. Vlaam. Acad. Wetenschap. Belg. Kl. Wetenschap.* 14(37), 5–46.

Anderson, A. D., and Jones, M. E. (1959). Requirement for an N-acyl glutamate for

* Foreign titles appear in English translation.

84 GEORGE W. BROWN, JR.

84 GEORGE W. BROWN, JR.

carbamyl phosphate synthetase in various animal tissues. *Am. Chem. Soc. (Biol. Div. Abstr.) Abstr. Papers 135th Meeting, Boston*, p. 63c.

Blaschko, H. (1942). The activity of L(−) DOPA decarboxylase. *J. Physiol. (London)* **101**, 337–349.

Bleibtreu, M. (1910). Glycogen in frog ovaries. *Arch. Ges. Physiol. Pflüger's* **132**, 580–599.

Boatman, J. B., and Sunder, J. H. (1955). Salt effect on I[131] metabolism in the salamander. *Science* **122**, 1229–1230.

Boell, E. J. (1948). Biochemical differentiation during Amphibian development. *Ann. N. Y. Acad. Sci.* **49**, 773–800.

Boell, E. J., and Weber, R. (1955). Cytochrome oxidase activity in mitochondria during amphibian development. *Exptl. Cell Res.* **9**, 559–567.

Bownes, J. M., and Morton, R. A. (1952). Distribution of copper and zinc in the eyes of fresh-water fishes and frogs. Occurrence of metals in melanin fractions from eye tissues. *Biochem. J.* **51**, 530–535.

Boyd, E. M. (1938). Lipid substances of the ovary during ova production in *Rana pipiens*. *J. Physiol. (London)* **91**, 394–397.

Boyer, P. D., Lardy, H., and Myrbäck, K., eds. (1959–1963). "The Enzymes," 2nd. ed., 8 volumes. Academic Press, New York (Vols. 7 and 8 in press).

Brachet, J. (1934). Study of the metabolism of *Rana fusca* eggs during development. I. Respiration and glycolysis from segmentation to hatching. *Arch. Biol. (Liege)* **45**, 611–727.

Brachet, J. (1935a). Study of the metabolism of *Rana fusca* eggs during development. II. Respiration of the egg during fertilization and mitosis. *Arch. Biol. (Liege)* **46**, 1–24.

Brachet, J. (1935b). Study of the metabolism of *Rana fusca* eggs during development. III. Respiratory metabolism and the "organizer center" of the gastrula. *Arch. Biol. (Liege)* **46**, 25–45.

Brachet, J. (1939). Study of the metabolism of *Rana fusca* eggs during development. V. Protein and carbohydrate metabolism in relation to organizer problem. *Arch. Biol. (Liege)* **50**, 233–267.

Brachet, J. (1952). The roles of the nucleus and cytoplasm in synthesis and morphogenesis. *Symp. Soc. Exptl. Biol.* **6**, 173–200.

Brachet, J., and Needham, J. (1935). Study of the metabolism of *Rana fusca* eggs during development. IV. Glycogen content of the egg from segmentation to hatching. *Arch. Biol. (Liege)* **46**, 821–835.

Bradley, W. O. (1953). Radioactive iodine as an indicator of the uptake of iodine by the liver, gastrocnemius, and thyroid of *Rana pipiens*. *Science* **117**, 483–484.

Brady, R. O. (1960). Biosynthesis of fatty acids. II. Studies with enzymes obtained from brain. *J. Biol. Chem.* **235**, 3099–3103.

Brecht, K., and Meiners, S. (1941). Spontaneous variations in vascular size in the frog and the effect of choline derivatives and vitamin B_1 on them. *Arch. Ges. Physiol. Pflüger's* **245**, 224–234.

Brody, S. (1945). "Bioenergetics and Growth, with Special Reference to the Efficiency Complex in Domestic Animals." Reinhold, New York.

Brown, C. A., and Ris, H. (1959). Amphibian oöcyte nucleoli. *J. Morphol.* **104**, 377–414.

Brown, F. A., Jr. (1950). Chromatophores and color change. *In* "Comparative Animal Physiology" (C. L. Prosser, ed.), pp. 677–724. Saunders, Philadelphia, Pennsylvania.

Brown, F. A., Jr., Webb, H. M., and Bennett, M. F. (1958). Comparisons of some fluctuations in cosmic radiation and in organismic activity during 1954, 1955, and 1956. *Am. J. Physiol.* **195**, 237–243.

Brown, G. W., Jr (1962a). Comparative biochemistry of urea synthesis. IV. [14C] urea

86   GEORGE W. BROWN, JR.

4GEORGE W. BROWN, JR.

synthesis by liver slices of the metamorphosing tadpole. *Biochim. Biophys. Acta* **60,** 185–186.

Brown, G. W., Jr. (1962b). Urea synthesis in elasmobranchs. *Intern. Conf. Taxonomic Biochem., Univ. Kansas, Lawrence, Kansas, 1962* (in press).

Brown, G. W., Jr. (1962c). Urea cycle and cellular deoxyribonucleic acid content. *Nature* **194,** 1279–1280.

Brown, G. W., Jr. (1963). Unpublished survey.

Brown, G. W., Jr., and Cohen, P. P. (1958). Biosynthesis of urea in metamorphosing tadpoles. *In* "Symposium on the Chemical Basis of Development" (W. D. McElroy and B. Glass, eds.), pp. 495–513. Johns Hopkins Press, Baltimore, Maryland.

Brown, G. W., Jr., and Cohen, P. P. (1960). Comparative biochemistry of urea synthesis. III. Activities of urea-cycle enzymes in various higher and lower vertebrates. *Biochem. J.* **75,** 82–91.

Brown, G. W., Jr., Brown, W. R., and Cohen, P. P. (1959). Comparative biochemistry of urea synthesis. II. Levels of urea cycle enzymes in metamorphosing *Rana catesbeiana* tadpoles. *J. Biol. Chem.* **234,** 1775–1780.

Brunel, A. (1937a). A new enzyme, allantoicase; its presence in the animal kingdom. *Compt. Rend.* **204,** 380–382.

Brunel, A. (1937b). Metabolism of purine nitrogen in fishes and Amphibia. III. Catabolism of purine nitrogen in Amphibia. *Bull. Soc. Chim. Biol.* **19,** 1683–1696.

Bucci, G. (1951). Quantitative changes of ascorbic acid during the metamorphosis of *Bufo vulgaris. Riv. Biol. (Perugia)* **43,** 529–543.

Burgos, M. H. (1955). Histochemistry of the testis in normal and experimentally treated frogs (*Rana pipiens*). *J. Morphol.* **96,** 283–299.

Burton, K., and Krebs, H. A. (1953). The free-energy changes associated with the individual steps of the tricarboxylic acid cycle, glycolysis, and alcoholic fermentation and with the hydrolysis of the pyrophosphate groups of adenosinetriphosphate. *Biochem. J.* **54,** 94–107.

Cafiero, M., Guardabassi, A., and Sacerdote, M. (1950). Phosphomonoesterases of the integument of *Rana esculenta. Boll. Soc. Ital. Biol. Sper.* **26,** 155–157.

Cambar, R. (1953). The evidence of enzymes of hatching in *Rana dalmatina* and their utilization in experimental embryology. *Compt. Rend.* **237,** 355–357.

Cantarow, A., and Schepartz, B. (1962). "Biochemistry," 3rd ed. Saunders, Philadelphia, Pennsylvania.

Catolla-Cavalcanti, A. (1951). Pantothenic acid as a growth factor in *Bufo vulgaris* (anurous amphibians). *Acta Vitaminol.* **5,** 162–164.

Cattaneo, P., and de Sutton, G. K. (1951). Composition of the fat acids of the adipose bodies of the toad *Bufo arenarum. Rev. Brasil. Quim. (Sao Paulo)* **32,** 388.

Cattaneo, P., de Sutton, G. K., and Penhos, J. C. (1951). Fatty acid content of the fat body of spontaneously or force-fed toads. *Anales Asoc. Quim. Arg.* **39,** 206–221.

Chaikoff, I. L., and Brown, G. W., Jr. (1954). Fat metabolism and acetoacetate formation. *In* "Chemical Pathways of Metabolism" (D. M. Greenberg, ed.), Vol. I, pp. 277–347. Academic Press, New York.

Chan, S. K. (1960). Personal communication. (In press, 1963.)

Chang, Y. T., Chen, J. M., and Shen, T. (1943). Induced polycythemia in salamander by Co, ascorbic acid and other water-soluble vitamins. *Arch. Biochem.* **3,** 235–239.

Chen, P. S. (1956). Metabolic changes in free amino acids and peptides during urodele development. *Exptl. Cell Res.* **10,** 675–686.

Chen, P. S. (1960). Changes in DNA and RNA during embryonic urodele development. *Exptl. Cell Res.* **21,** 523–534.

Chen, P. S., and Rickenbacher, J. (1954). Concerning the free amino acids in amphibian development. *Experentia* **10**, 182–183.

Chen, P. S., and Zeller, C. (1961). Changes in DNA (deoxyribonucleic acid) and RNA (ribonucleic acid) during embryonic development of the merogonic combination *Triton palmatus* (female) x *Triton cristatus* (male). *Experentia* **17**, 177–178.

Clayton, R. M. (1953). Distribution of antigens in the developing newt embryo. *J. Embryol. Exptl. Morphol.* **1**, 25–42.

Cohen, A. I. (1954). Glycolysis during the early development of *Rana pipiens*. *Physiol. Zool.* **27**, 128–141.

Cohen, P. P., and Brown, G. W., Jr. (1960). Ammonia metabolism and urea biosynthesis. *In* "Comparative Biochemistry" (M. Florkin and H. S. Mason, eds.), Vol. II, pp. 161–244. Academic Press, New York.

Cohen, S. (1954). The metabolism of $C^{14}O_2$ during amphibian development. *J. Biol. Chem.* **211**, 337–354.

Coleman, J. R. (1963). Acid deoxyribonuclease activity in amphibian metamorphosis. *Biochim. Biophys. Acta* **68**, 141–143.

Collins, F. D., Love, R. M., and Morton, R. A. (1953a). Studies in Vitamin A. 24. Spectroscopic examination of the lipids of two species of newts. *Biochem. J.* **53**, 629–632.

Collins, F. D., Love, R. M., and Morton, R. A. (1953b). Studies in Vitamin A. 23. Vitamin A and its occurrence in *Amblystoma tigrinum*. *Biochem. J.* **53**, 626–629.

Cooper, W. G., and Copenhaver, W. M. (1956). The distribution of succinic dehydrogenase within the heart of urodele amphibians. *Anat. Record* **126**, 503–519.

Cowgill, R. W., and Cori, C. F. (1955). The conversion of inactive phosphorylase to phosphorylase *b* and phosphorylase *a* in lobster muscle extract. *J. Biol. Chem.* **216**, 133–140.

Cragg, M. M., Balinsky, J. B., and Baldwin, E. (1961). A comparative study of nitrogen excretion in some Amphibia and reptiles. *Comp. Biochem. Physiol.* **3**, 227–235.

Davidson, J. N. (1960). "The Biochemistry of the Nucleic Acids," 4th ed. Wiley, New York.

Davison, J. (1955). Body weight, cell surface, and metabolic rate in anuran Amphibia. *Biol. Bull.* **109**, 407–419.

de Cesaris-Coromaldi, L. (1955). Investigation of phosphatases in the embryonic and larval development of *Bufo vulgaris*. *Ric. Sci.* **25**, 2323–2333.

Decker, K. (1959). "Active Acetate. Coenzyme A and its Acyl Derivatives in Cellular Metabolism" (in German). Enke, Stuttgart.

de Graaf, A. R. (1957). A note on the oxygen requirements of *Xenopus laevis*. *J. Exptl. Biol.* **34**, 173–176.

de Groot, N. (1960). Unpublished observations.

Delaunay, H. (1931). The nitrogen excretion of invertebrates. *Biol. Rev. Cambridge Phil. Soc.* **6**, 265–301.

Denis, H. (1960). Electrophoretic pattern during amphibian development. *Nature* **187**, 62.

Dent, J. N., and Hunt, E. L. (1952). An autoradiographic study of iodine distribution in larvae and metamorphosing specimens of Anura. *J. Exptl. Zool.* **121**, 79–97.

de Robertis, E. (1939). Origin and localization of pigment in amphibian liver. *Rev. Soc. Arg. Biol.* **15**, 87–93.

Dessauer, H. C., Fox, W., and Ramírez, J. R. (1957). Preliminary attempt to correlate paper electrophoretic migration of hemoglobins with phylogeny in Amphibia and Reptilia. *Arch. Biochem. Biophys.* **71**, 11–16.

88 GEORGE W. BROWN, JR.

Deuchar, E. M. (1955). Distribution of free amino acids in embryos of *Xenopus laevis*. *Nature* **176**, 258–259.

Deuchar, E. M. (1956). Amino acids in developing tissues of *Xenopus laevis*. *J. Embryol. Exptl. Morphol.* **4**, 327–346.

Dolphin, J. L., and Frieden, E. (1955). Biochemistry of amphibian metamorphosis. II. Arginase activity. *J. Biol. Chem.* **217**, 735–743.

Edlbacher, S. (1926). Concerning the intermediary metabolism of histidine. *Z. Physiol. Chem.* **157**, 106–114.

Edlbacher, S. (1943). Histidase and urocanase. *Ergeb. Enzymforsch.* **9**, 131–154.

Edlbacher, S., and Kraus, J. (1930). Concerning the intermediary metabolism of histidine. II. Communication. *Z. Physiol. Chem.* **191**, 225–242.

England, M. C., and Mayer, D. T. (1957). The comparative nucleic acid content of liver nuclei, ova nuclei, and spermatozoa of the frog. *Exptl. Cell Res.* **12**, 249–253.

Etkin, W. (1934). The phenomena of anuran metamorphosis. II. E. Oxygen consumption during normal metamorphosis. *Physiol. Zool.* **7**, 129–148.

Etkin, W. (1955). Metamorphosis. *In* "Analysis of Development" (B. H. Willier, P. A. Weiss, and V. Hamburger, eds.), pp. 631–663. Saunders, Philadelphia, Pennsylvania.

Evans, G. (1939). Factors influencing the oxygen consumption of several species of Plethodontid salamanders in aerial and aquatic media. *Ecology* **20**, 74–95.

Feinstein, R. N., and Volk, M. E. (1949). Phosphoprotein phosphatase in mammalian tissues. *J. Biol. Chem.* **177**, 339–346.

Finamore, F. J., and Frieden, E. (1960). Nucleic acids and induced amphibian metamorphosis. *J. Biol. Chem.* **235**, 1751–1755.

Fletcher, K., and Myant, N. B. (1959). Oxygen consumption of tadpoles during metamorphosis. *J. Physiol. (London)* **145**, 353–368.

Flickinger, R. A., and Nace, G. W. (1952). An investigation of proteins during the development of the amphibian embryo. *Exptl. Cell Res.* **3**, 393–405.

Fontaine, M., Raffy, A., and Busnel, R. G. (1941). Distribution of riboflavin (vitamin B₂) in the axolotl and Ambystoma. *Compt. Rend. Soc. Biol.* **135**, 251–253.

Fosse, R., Brunel, A., and de Graeve, P. (1930). A new fermentation of uric acid, demonstrated in the liver of various animals. *Compt. Rend.* **190**, 79–82.

Frieden, E. (1961). Biochemical adaptation and anuran metamorphosis. *Am. Zoologist* **1**, 115–149.

Frieden, E. (1963). The chemistry of amphibian metamorphosis. *Sci. Am.* **209**, 110–118.

Frieden, E., and Mathews, H. (1958). Biochemistry of amphibian metamorphosis. III. Liver and tail phosphatases. *Arch. Biochem. Biophys.* **73**, 107–119.

Frieden, E., Herner, A., Fish, L., and Lewis, E. J. C. (1957). Changes in serum proteins in amphibian metamorphosis. *Science* **126**, 559–560.

Friedmann, H. C. (1953). Distribution of xanthine oxidase in organs of the frog (*Rana hexadactyla*). *Biochim. Biophys. Acta* **11**, 585.

Friedmann, H. C. (1954). Xanthine oxidase and uricase in liver and kidney of some amphibians. *Biochim. Biophys. Acta* **13**, 151.

Fromm, P. O. (1956). Heat production of frogs. *Physiol. Zool.* **29**, 234–240.

Fromm, P. O., and Johnson, R. E. (1955). The respiratory metabolism of frogs as related to season. *J. Cellular Comp. Physiol.* **45**, 343–359.

Fruton, J. S., and Simmonds, S. (1958). "General Biochemistry," 2nd ed. Wiley, New York.

Gall, J. G. (1958). Chromosomal differentiation. *In* "Symposium on the Chemical

Basis of Development" (W. D. McElroy and B. Glass, eds.), pp. 103–135. Johns Hopkins Press, Baltimore, Maryland.

Glenner, G. G., and Burstone, M. S. (1958). Esterase and phosphatase activity in *Necturus maculosus*. A study in comparative histoenzymology. *Anat. Record* **130,** 243–252.

Goldfederova, A. (1926). Glycogen during the ontogeny of the frog and the influence of the seasons, *Compt. Rend. Soc. Biol.* **95,** 801–804.

Goldsmith, E. D., Schreiber, S. S., and Nigrelli, R. F. (1950). Folic acid analogs in lower animals. II. The amphibia: *Rana clamitans. Ann. N. Y. Acad. Sci.* **52,** 1346–1348.

Gordon, M. S., Schmidt-Nielsen, K., and Kelley, H. M. (1961a). Osmotic regulation in the euryhaline crab-eating frog (*Rana cancrivora*) of Southeast Asia. *Federation Proc.,* **20,** 208.

Gordon, M. S., Schmidt-Nielsen, K., and Kelley, H. M. (1961b). Osmotic regulation in the crab-eating frog (*Rana cancrivora*). *J. Exptl. Biol.* **38,** 659–678.

Grant, P. (1958a). The synthesis of deoxyribonucleic acid during early embryonic development of *Rana pipiens. J. Cellular Comp. Physiol.* **52,** 227–247.

Grant, P. (1958b). The incorporation of P^{32} and glycine-2-C^{14} into nucleic acids during early embryonic development of *Rana pipiens. J. Cellular Comp. Physiol.* **52,** 249–267.

Green, D. E. (1959). Electron transport and oxidative phosphorylation. *Advan. Enzymol.* **21,** 73–129.

Gregg, J. R. (1948). Carbohydrate metabolism of normal and of hybrid amphibian embryos. *J. Exptl. Zool.* **109.** 119–133.

Gregg, J. R., and Ballentine, R. (1946). Nitrogen metabolism of *Rana pipiens* during embryonic development. *J. Exptl. Zool.* **103,** 143–168.

Gregg, J. R., and Pomerat, C. M. (1942). Glycogen content of the embryo of *Rana pipiens* during development. *Growth* **6,** 231–234.

Grunberg-Manago, M., Ortiz, P. J., and Ochoa, S. (1956). Enzymatic synthesis of polynucleotides. I. Polynucleotide phosphorylase of *Azotobacter vinelandii. Biochim. Biophys. Acta* **20,** 269–285.

Guardabassi, A. (1960). The utilization of the calcareous deposits of the endolymphic sacs of *Bufo bufo bufo* in the mineralization of the skeleton. Investigations by means of Ca^{45}. *Z. Zellforsch. Mikroskop. Anat.* **51,** 278–282.

Gudernatsch, J. F. (1913). Feeding experiments on tadpoles. I. The influence of specific organs given as food on growth and differentiation. *Arch. Entwicklungsmech. Organ.* **35,** 457–481.

Günder, I. (1953). Paper chromatographic and fluorescence microscopic detection of pterin and riboflavin in Amphibia and reptiles. *Naturwissenschaften* **40,** 20–21.

Hall, F. G., and Root, R. W. (1930). The influence of humidity on body temperature of certain poikilotherms. *Biol. Bull.* **58,** 52–58.

Hama, T., and Obika, M. (1958). The nature of some fluorescent substances in the adult skin of the toad *Bufo vulgaris formosus. Experientia* **14,** 182–184.

Hanawa, I., Kuge, K., and Saito, J. (1960). Thioctic acid contained in visual cell. *Science* **132,** 1668.

Hara, T. (1949). Thiamine in frog eyes. II. Thiamine content of retina and chorioidea. *Seiri Seitai* **3,** 102–110.

Hardwick, D. C., and Hebb, C. (1956). Pseudo-cholinesterase in the central nervous system of the frog. *Nature* **177,** 667.

90   GEORGE W. BROWN, JR.

Harris, D. L. (1946). Phosphoprotein phosphatase, a new enzyme from the frog egg. *J. Biol. Chem.* **165**, 541–550.

Hawk, P. B., Oser, B. L., and Summerson, W. H. (1947). "Practical Physiological Chemistry," 12th ed. McGraw-Hill (Blakiston), New York.

Heatley, N. G. (1935). The distribution of glycogen in the regions of the amphibian gastrula, with a method for the microdetermination of glycogen. *Biochem. J.* **29**, 2568–2572.

Heatley, N. G., and Lindahl, E. (1937). Studies on the nature of the amphibian organization center. V. The distribution and nature of glycogen in the amphibian embryo. *Proc. Roy. Soc.* **B122**, 395–402.

Herner, A. E., and Frieden, E. (1960). Biochemistry of anuran metamorphosis. VII. Changes in serum proteins during spontaneous and induced metamorphosis. *J. Biol. Chem.* **235**, 2845–2851.

Herner, A. E., and Frieden, E. (1961). Biochemical changes during anuran metamorphosis. VIII. Changes in the nature of the red cell proteins. *Arch. Biochem. Biophys.* **95**, 25–35.

Hilditch, T. P. (1940). "The Chemical Constitution of Natural Fats." Wiley, New York.

Hill, A. V. (1911–1912a). A new form of differential micro-calorimeter, for the estimation of heat production in physiological, bacteriological, or ferment actions. *J. Physiol.* (*London*) **43**, 261–285.

Hill, A. V. (1911–1912b). The total energy exchanges of intact cold-blooded animals at rest. *J. Physiol.* (*London*) **43**, 379–394.

Hill, R. L., Kimmel, J. R., and Smith, E. L. (1959). The structure of proteins. *Ann. Rev. Biochem.* **28**, 97–144.

Hiromatsu, K. (1959). Embryonic content of iron in amphibia. *Nara Joshi Daigaku Seibutsu Gakkaishi* **9**, 16–17.

Hoff-Jørgensen, E., and Zeuthen, E. (1952). Evidence of cytoplasmic desoxyribosides in the frog egg. *Nature* **169**, 245–246.

Hofmann, K. (1962). Chemistry and function of polypeptide hormones. *Ann. Rev. Biochem.* **31**, 213–246.

Holtzer, H. (1956). Free energy of biochemically important equilibria. *In* "Biochemisches Taschenbuch" (H. M. Rauen, ed.), pp. 668–679. Springer, Berlin.

Hunter, N. W., and Hunter, R., Jr. (1957). The tricarboxylic acid cycle of isolated frog skin. *Physiol. Zool.* **30**, 18–22.

Huxley, T. H. (1868). See "Autobiography and Selected Essays" (A. L. F. Snell, ed.), p. 114. Houghton Mifflin (Riverside Press, Cambridge, Massachusetts, 1909).

Imai, A. (1959). Metabolism of amino acids in the brain. VI. Transamination in the brain of frog. (*Rana nigromaculata.*) *Okayama Igakkai Zasshi* **71**, 1651–1654.

Iosifova, M. A. (1939). Effect of the season on the phosphatide content of frog muscles. *Biochem. J.* (*Ukraine*) **13**, 495–513.

Jaeger, L. (1945). Glycogen utilization by the amphibian gastrula in relation to invagination and induction. *J. Cellular Comp. Physiol.* **25**, 97–120.

Janosky, I. D., and Wenger, B. S. (1956). A histochemical study of glycogen distribution in the developing nervous system of *Ambystoma. J. Comp. Neurol.* **105**, 127–150.

Jones, M. E., Spector, L., and Lipmann, F. (1955). Carbamyl phosphate, the carbamyl donor in enzymatic citrulline synthesis. *J. Am. Chem. Soc.* **77**, 819–820.

Jordan, H. E., and Speidel, C. C. (1923a). Studies on lymphocytes. I. Effect of splenectomy, experimental hemorrhage, and a hemolytic toxin in the frog. *Am. J. Anat.* **32,** 155–188.

Jordan, H. E., and Speidel, C. C. (1923b). Blood cell formation and distribution in relation to the mechanism of thyroid-accelerated metamorphosis in the larval frog. *J. Exptl. Med.* **38,** 529–541.

Katajama, H. (1954). Catalase activity of the organizer in the toad gastrula (*Bufo vulgaris formosus*). *Rept. Liberal Arts Sci. Fac. Shizuoka Univ. Nat. Sci.* (5) 29–32.

Kato, K. (1910). Concerning the glycogen content of frog ovaries at different times of the year. *Arch. Ges. Physiol. Pflüger's* **132,** 545–579.

Kavanau, J. L. (1953). Metabolism of free amino acids, peptides, and proteins in early sea urchin development. *J. Exptl. Zool.* **122,** 285–337.

Kennan, A. L. (1961). Unpublished observations.

Kennedy, E. P. (1957). Metabolism of lipids. *Ann. Rev. Biochem.* **26,** 119–148.

Kerly, M., and Leaback, D. H. (1957). The hexose specificity of hexokinase in brain from various species. *Biochem. J.* **67,** 250–252.

Kind, C. A., and Macchi, M. E. (1952). Phosphatase activity in the tissues of the frog, *Rana pipiens. J. Cellular Comp. Physiol.* **39,** 153–159.

Kleiber, M. (1947). Body size and metabolic rate. *Physiol. Rev.* **27,** 511–541.

Klotz, I. M. (1957). "Some Principles of Energetics in Biochemical Reactions." Academic Press, New York.

Knoop, F. (1904–1905). The degradation of aromatic fatty acids in the animal body. *Beitr. Chem. Physiol. Pathol.* **6,** 150–162.

Koller, M. (1941). Distribution of free thiamine and cocarboxylase in the metazoa. *Boll. Soc. Ital. Biol. Sper.* **16,** 718–719.

Kollros, J. J., and Kaltenbach, J. C. (1952). Local metamorphosis of larval skin in *Rana pipiens. Physiol. Zool.* **25,** 163–170.

Kornberg, A., Lehman, I. R., Bessman, M. J., and Simms, E. C. (1956). Enzymic synthesis of deoxyribonucleic acid. *Biochim. Biophys. Acta* **21,** 197–198.

Krebs, H. A. (1935). Metabolism of amino acids. III. Deamination of amino acids. *Biochem. J.* **29,** 1620–1644.

Krebs, H. A. (1954). The tricarboxylic acid cycle. In "Chemical Pathways of Metabolism" (D. M. Greenberg, ed.), pp. 109–171. Academic Press, New York.

Krebs, H. A., and Henseleit, K. (1932). Studies on the formation of urea in animals. *Z. Physiol. Chem.* **210,** 3–66.

Krebs, H. A., and Kornberg, H. L. (1957). Energy transformations in living matter (with an Appendix by K. Burton). *Ergeb. Physiol. Biol. Chem. Exptl. Pharmakol.* **49,** 212–298.

Krebs, H. A., Gurin, S., and Eggleston, L. V. (1951). The pathway of oxidation of acetate in baker's yeast. *Biochem. J.* **51,** 614–628.

Krehl, L., and Soetbeer, F. (1899). Investigations concerning the heat economy of poikilothermic vertebrate animals. *Arch. Ges. Physiol. Pflüger's* **77,** 611–638.

Krogh, A. (1916). "The Respiratory Exchange of Animals and Man," Monographs on Biochemistry. Longmans, Green, New York.

Krogh, A. (1937). Osmotic regulation in the frog (*Rana esculenta*) by active absorption of chloride ion. *Skand. Arch. Physiol.* **76,** 60–73.

Krugelis, E. (1949–1951). Properties and changes of alkaline phosphatase activity during amphibian development. *Compt. Rend. Trav. Lab. Carlsberg. Ser. Chim.* **27,** 273–290.

Kurata, Y., and Mukawa, A. (1955). The presence of formaldehyde during the embryonic development of the frog. *Exptl. Cell Res.* **9**, 588–589.

Kurata, Y., and Tanaka, T. (1953). Lipase activity during embryonal development of the frog. *Igaku To Seibutsugaku* **27**, 108–109.

Kurata, Y., Yamamoto, A., and Mizukami, T. (1954). Aldolase activity during the embryonic development of the frog. *Igaku To Seibutsugaku* **33**, 263–264.

Kurata, Y., Maeda, S., Iwata, T., and Mizukama, T. (1955). Phosphorylase, phosphoglucomutase, and phosphohexoisomerase activity during embryonal development of the frog. *Igaku To Seibutsugaku* **36**, 154–156.

Kuriki, Y., and Okazaki, R. (1959). Deoxyribonucleic acid and acid-soluble deoxyribosidic compounds in amphibian embryos. *Embryologia (Nagoya)* **4**, 337–348.

Kutsky, P. B., Eakin, R. M., Berg, W. E., and Kavanau, J. L. (1953). Protein metabolism of amphibian embryo. IV. Quantitative changes and non-protein amino acids. *J. Exptl. Zool.* **124**, 263–277.

Lang, C. A., and Grant, P. (1961). Respiratory enzyme changes during frog embryogenesis. *Proc. Natl. Acad. Sci. U.S.* **47**, 1236–1244.

Lang, K. (1933). The formation of thiocyanate in the animal body. *Biochem. Z.* **259**, 243–256.

Lanza, B., and Antonini, F. M. (1956). Possibility of distinguishing different (animal) species by means of serum proteinograms. A study on *Rana esculenta* and *Rana dalmatina. Monit. Zool. Ital.* **63**, 293–299.

Lardy, H. A. (1960). Personal communication.

Latimer, W. M. (1938). "Oxidation Potentials. The Oxidation States of the Elements and their Potentials in Aqueous Solutions." Prentice-Hall, Englewood Cliffs, New Jersey.

Lester, R. L., and Crane, F. L. (1959). The natural occurrence of coenzyme Q and related compounds. *J. Biol. Chem.* **234**, 2169–2175.

Levin, E. (1955). The amylase content of the toad. *Bufo arenarum. Rev. Asoc. Bioquim. Arg.* **20**, 79–83.

Lewis, G. N., and Randall, M. (1923). "Thermodynamics and the Free Energy of Chemical Substances." McGraw-Hill, New York.

Li, C. H., Schnabel, E., Chung, D., and Lo, T.-B. (1961). Synthesis of L-methionyl-L-glutamyl-L-histidyl-L-phenylalanyl-L-argininyl-L-tryptophyl-glycine and its melanocyte-stimulating and corticotropin-releasing activity. *Nature* **189**, 143.

Lindahl, P. E., and Lennerstrand, A. (1942). Cozymase in amphibian development. *Arkiv Kemi Mineral. Geol.* **15B** (13), 1–6.

Lipshitz, R., and Frank, S. (1949). Apyrases in adult frog tissues. *J. Cellular Comp. Physiol.* **33**, 27–40.

Longley, J. B. (1955). Alkaline phosphatase in the kidneys of aglomerular fish. *Science* **122**, 594.

Løvtrup, S. (1953a). Energy sources of amphibian embryogenesis. *Compt. Rend. Trav. Lab. Carlsberg. Ser. Chim.* **28**, 371–399.

Løvtrup, S. (1953b). Changes in the content of peptidase during amphibian embryogenesis at different temperatures. *Compt. Rend. Trav. Lab. Carlsberg. Ser. Chim.* **28**, 426–443.

Lusk, G. (1928). "The Elements of the Science of Nutrition," 4th ed. Saunders, Philadelphia, Pennsylvania.

Lynen, F. (1955). Lipide metabolism. *Ann. Rev. Biochem.* **24**, 653–688.

McCallion, D. J., and Scott, J. L. (1950). A cytochemical study of the absorption and distribution of iron in the frog, *Rana pipiens. Can. J. Res.* **28D**, 119–125.

McCutcheon, F. H. (1936). Hemoglobin function during the life history of the bull-frog. *J. Cellular Comp. Physiol.* **8,** 63–81.

Mahler, H. R. (1954). Studies on the fatty acid oxidizing system of animal tissues. IV. The prosthetic group of butyryl coenzyme A dehydrogenase. *J. Biol. Chem.* **206,** 13–26.

Maruyama, K. (1956). Antagonistic effect of 2,4-dinitrophenol and sodium azide on the apyrase action of a cell-free extract of the toad embryo. *Arch. Biochem. Biophys.* **60,** 74–81.

Merriam, R. W., and Ris, H. (1954). Size and DNA content of nuclei in various tissues of male, female, and worker honeybees. *Chromosoma* **6,** 522–538.

Metcalf, J. L., and Creaser, C. W. (1936). Iodine and the production of permanent tadpoles in the frog (*Rana pipiens*). *Papers Mich. Acad. Sci.* **22,** 661–663.

Metzenberg, R. L., Marshall, M., Paik, W. K., and Cohen, P. P. (1961). The synthesis of carbamyl phosphate synthetase in thyroxin-treated tadpoles. *J. Biol. Chem.* **236,** 162–165.

Meyer, R. (1934). Spark spectrographic identification of iron in animal tissue. Investigation of the liver of *Salamandra maculosa*. *Protoplasma* **22,** 34–43.

Mezger-Freed, L. (1953). Phosphoprotein phosphatase activity in normal, haploid, and hybrid amphibian development. *J. Cellular Comp. Physiol.* **41,** 493–517.

Minganti, A., and Azzolina, G. (1955). Proteolytic activity of the hatching enzyme of *Bufo* and *Discoglossus*. *Ric. Sci.* **25,** 2103–2108.

Mirsky, A. E., and Ris, H. (1951). The desoxyribonucleic acid content of animal cells and its evolutionary significance. *J. Gen. Physiol.* **34,** 451–462.

Mitsuda, H., and Yasumatsu, K. (1955). Crystallization of animal catalase and studies on its optimum temperature. *Bull. Agr. Chem. Soc. Japan* **19,** 200–207.

Moore, J. A. (1941). Developmental rate of hybrid frogs. *J. Exptl. Zool.* **86,** 405–422.

Morton, R. A., and Rosen, D. G. (1949). Carotenoids, Vitamin A, and 7-dehydro-steroid in the frog (*Rana temporaria*). *Biochem. J.* **45,** 612–627.

Moyle, V. (1949). Nitrogenous excretion in chelorian reptiles. *Biochem. J.* **44,** 581–584.

Munro, A. F. (1939). Nitrogen excretion and arginase activity during amphibian development. *Biochem. J.* **33,** 1957–1965.

Munro, A. F. (1953). Ammonia and urea excretion of different species of amphibia during their development and metamorphosis. *Biochem. J.* **54,** 29–36.

Mustakallio, K. K., and Telkkä, A. (1954). Effect of aureomycin, vitamin B_{12}, folic acid, and aminopterin on the metamorphosis of tadpoles. *Ann. Med. Exptl. Biol. Fenniae (Helsinki)* **32,** 9–14.

Nachmansohn, D., and Wilson, I. B. (1951). The enzymic hydrolysis and synthesis of acetylcholine. *Advan. Enzymol.* **12,** 259–339.

Narasaka, S. (1938). Studies in the biochemistry of copper. XXX. Seasonal changes in the amount and distribution of Cu in the tissues of the cultivated bull-frog. *Japan. J. Med. Sci. II.* **4,** 65–69.

Nash, G., and Fankhauser, G. (1959). Changes in the pattern of nitrogen excretion during the life cycle of the newt. *Science* **130,** 714–716.

Needham, J. (1931). "Chemical Embryology," Vol. II. Cambridge Univ. Press, London and New York, and Macmillan, New York.

Needham, J., Boell, E. J., and Rogers, V. (1938). Measurement of the anaerobic glycolysis of the regions of the amphibian gastrula by the Cartesian diver ultra-micromanometer. *Nature* **141,** 973.

Needham, J., Rogers, V., and Shen, S. C. (1939). Morphogenesis and metabolism:

Studies with the Cartesian diver ultramicromanometer. V. Aerobic glycolysis measurements on the regions of the amphibian gastrula. *Proc. Roy. Soc.* **B127**, 576–583.

Nespor, E. (1936). Seasonal variations in the ascorbic acid of the various organs of the frog, *Rana temporaria*. *Compt. Rend. Soc. Biol.* **123**, 928–929.

Newbold, S. G. (1960). Unpublished observations.

Noble, G. K. (1931). "The Biology of the Amphibia." McGraw-Hill, New York.

Nollet, H., and Raffy, A. (1940). Riboflavin (vitamin B_2) content of some organs of the frog *(Rana viridis)*. *Compt. Rend.* **210**, 269–270.

Nowiński, W. W. (1939). Intermediary carbohydrate metabolism in amphibia. I. Carbohydrate breakdown before metamorphosis. *Biochem. J.* **33**, 978–983.

Ohara, M., and Suyama, T. (1952). Nitrate reductase activity during the embryonal development of the frog. *Nature* **169**, 285–286.

Ohnishi, T. (1951). The changes in sugar content of frog skin as influenced by the adaptation to the background. *Zool. Mag. (Tokyo)* **60**, 63–64.

Ôsawa, S., and Hayashi, Y. (1953). Ribonucleic acid and protein in the growing oöcytes of *Triturus pyrrhogaster*. *Science* **118**, 84–86.

Paik, W. K., and Cohen, P. P. (1960). Biochemical studies on amphibian metamorphosis. I. The effect of thyroxine on protein synthesis in the tadpole. *J. Gen. Physiol.* **43**, 683–696.

Paik, W. K., and Cohen, P. P. (1961). Biochemical studies on amphibian metamorphosis. II. The effect of thiouracil on thyroxine-stimulated protein synthesis in tadpole liver. *J. Biol. Chem.* **236**, 531–535.

Paik, W. K., Metzenberg, R. L., and Cohen, P. P. (1961). Biochemical studies on amphibian metamorphosis. III. Metabolism of nucleic acids and nucleotides in the tadpole liver during thyroxine-induced metamorphosis. *J. Biol. Chem.* **236**, 530–541.

Pardee, A. B., and Ingraham, L. L. (1960). Free energy and entropy in metabolism. *In* "Metabolic Pathways" (D. M. Greenberg, ed.), Vol. I, pp. 1–40. Academic Press, New York.

Parks, G. W., and Huffman, H. M. (1932). "The Free Energies of Some Organic Compounds." Am. Chem. Soc. Monograph Ser. Chemical Catalog, New York.

Peters, J. P., and Van Slyke, D. D. (1932). "Quantitative Clinical Chemistry," Vol. II. Williams & Wilkins, Baltimore, Maryland.

Petrucci, D. (1955). Metabolism of α-keto acids in embryogenesis of *Bufo bufo*. I. Quantitative study on cocarboxylase. *Ric. Sci.* **25**, 3096–3101.

Petrucci, D. (1957). Cytochrome oxidase and respiration in embryogenesis of anuran amphibians. I. Cytochrome oxidase content and O_2 consumption velocity in the embryogenesis of *Bufo bufo*. *Acta Embryol. Morphol. Exptl.* **1**, 105–117.

Petrucci, D. (1959). Cytochrome *c* oxidation and respiratory metabolic changes in the embryonal development of Amphibia. *Arch. Sci. Biol. (Bologna)* **43**, 25–32.

Ponz, F. (1947). Digestive phosphatases in the amphibians. II. Liver, bile and pancreas. *Rev. Espan. Fisiol.* **3**, 311–315.

Przylecki, S. J. (1926). The degradation of uric acid by vertebrates. III. The distribution of uricase and allantoinase in poikilothermic vertebrates. *Arch. Intern. Physiol.* **26**, 33–53.

Ranzi, S., and Citterio, P. (1955). The proteins in the *Rana esculenta* embryo in normal development and in experimental conditions. *Exptl. Cell Res.*, Suppl. **3**, 287–293.

Ratner, S., Morell, H., and Carvalho, E. (1960). Enzymes of arginine metabolism in brain. *Arch. Biochem. Biophys.* **91**, 280–289.

Recknagel, R. O. (1950). Localization of cytochrome oxidase on the mitochondria of the frog egg. *J. Cellular Comp. Physiol.* **35**, 111–129.

Regnault, V., and Reiset, J. (1849). "Chemical Studies on the Respiration of Animals." Buchelier, Imprimeur-Libraire, Paris.

Reichard, P. (1959). The enzymic synthesis of pyrimidines. *Advan. Enzymol.* **21**, 263–294.

Riggs, A. (1951). The metamorphosis of hemoglobin in the bull frog. *J. Gen. Physiol.* **35**, 23–40.

Robin, E. D., Travis, D. M., Bromberg, P. A., Forkner, C. E., Jr., and Tyler, J. M. (1959). Ammonia excretion by mammalian lung. *Science* **129**, 270–271.

Rondell, P. A., and Wright, P. A. (1958). Metabolic studies of ovulation in the frog. *Physiol. Zool.* **31**, 236–243.

Roy, R. N., and Guha, B. G. (1958). Species difference in regard to the biosynthesis of ascorbic acid. *Nature* **182**, 319–320.

Rubner, M. (1883). Concerning the influence of body size on energy metabolism. *Z. Biol.* **19**, 535–562.

Rubner, M. (1924). Concerning the life of cold blooded animals. II. Amphibia and reptiles. *Biochem. Z.* **148**, 268–307.

Sánchez, F. S., and Bertrán, E. (1950). Enzymes in the frog. Rhodanese, alkaline and acid phosphomonoesterases. *Farmacoterap. Actual (Madrid)* **7**, 17–22.

Sato, S., Yoshimura, K., Kita, T., Takana, R., and Yagi, H. (1954). o-Polyphenolase in tadpole muscle. III. Nature of the enzyme and its effects on various substances. *Osaka Daigaku Igaku Zasshi* **6**, 285–289.

Saunders, J. F., and Friess, S. L. (1959). Tracer studies on the biosynthesis of cholesterol from 2-carbon precursors in active bullfrog sciatic nerve. *Arch. Biochem. Biophys.* **85**, 234–244.

Saxén, L. (1955). The glycogen inclusion of the visual cells and its hypothetical role in the photomechanical responses. Histochemical investigation during frog ontogenesis. *Acta Anat.* **25**, 319–330.

Schimke, R. T. (1962). Adaptive characteristics of urea cycle enzymes in the rat. *J. Biol. Chem.* **237**, 459–468.

Schlumberger, H. G., and Burk, D. H. (1953). Comparative study of the reaction to injury. II. Hypervitaminosis D in the frog with special reference to the lime sacs. *A.M.A. Arch. Pathol.* **56**, 103–124.

Schmidt-Nielsen, K., and Lee, P. (1962). Kidney function in the crab-eating frog, *Rana cancrivora*. *J. Exptl. Biol.* **39**, 167–177.

Schoenheimer, R. (1942). "The Dynamic State of Bodily Constituents." Harvard Univ. Press, Cambridge, Massachusetts.

Schooler, J. M., and Brown, G. W., Jr. (1960). Unpublished observations.

Serfaty, A., and Gueutal, J. (1943). The resistance of the frog to asphyxiation during prolonged immersion. *Compt. Rend. Soc. Biol.* **137**, 154–156.

Serfaty, A., and Louvier, R. (1942). Catalase activity of organs from *Rana esculenta*. *Bull. Biol. France Belg.* **76**, 222–225.

Shen, S. C., Greenfield, P., and Boell, E. J. (1955). The distribution of cholinesterase in the frog brain. *J. Comp. Neurol.* **102**, 717–737.

Shumway, W. (1940). Stages in the normal development of *Rana pipiens*. I. External form. *Anat. Record* **78**, 139–147.

Silver, I., and Balinsky, J. B. (1961). A comparison of Krebs-ornithine cycle enzymes in *Xenopus laevis* and *Bufo carens*. *S. African J. Med. Sci.* **26**, 99.

Slome, D. (1936). The diabetogenic hormone of the pituitary gland. *J. Exptl. Biol.* **13**, 1–6.

Smith, C. L. (1950). Seasonal changes in blood sugar, fat body, liver glycogen, and gonads in the common frog, *Rana temporaria*. *J. Exptl. Biol.* **26**, 412–429.

Smith, C. L. (1953). Action of insulin on the frog (*Rana temporaria*). *Nature* **171**, 311–312.

Smith, C. L. (1954). The relation between seasonal hyperglycemia and thyroid activity in the frog (*Rana temporaria*). *J. Endocrinol.* **10**, 184–191.

Smith, C. L. (1960). Monoamine oxidase, thyroid activity and hyperglycemia in the frog. *J. Endocrinol.* **19**, 295–302.

Smith, H. W. (1959). "From Fish to Philosopher." Little, Brown, Boston, Massachusetts.

Spar, I. L. (1953). Antigenic differences among early developmental stages of *Rana pipiens*. *J. Exptl. Zool.* **123**, 467–497.

Spector, W. S., ed. (1956). "Handbook of Biological Data." Saunders, Philadelphia, Pennsylvania (also WADC Tech. Report 56–273).

Spiegel, M., and Frankel, D. L. (1961). Role of enzyme induction in embryonic development. *Science* **133**, 275.

Stearns, R. N., and Kostellow, A. B. (1958). Enzyme induction in dissociated embryonic cells. *In* "A Symposium on the Chemical Basis of Development" (W. D. McElroy and B. Glass, eds.), pp. 448–454. Johns Hopkins Press, Baltimore, Maryland.

Steenholt, G. (1944). On the distribution of asparaginase. *Acta Physiol. Scand.* **8**, 342–347.

Štefl, J. (1937). Effect of feeding vitamin D on frog larvae. *Arch. Exptl. Pathol. Pharmakol. Naunyn-Schmiedeberg's* **185**, 81–84.

Stumpf, P. K. (1960). Lipid metabolism. *Ann. Rev. Biochem.* **29**, 261–294.

Stumpf, P. K., and Barber, G. A. (1960). Comparative mechanisms for fatty acid oxidation. *In* "Comparative Biochemistry" (M. Florkin and H. S. Mason, eds.), Vol. I, pp. 75–105. Academic Press, New York.

Sutter, J. (1941). Antagonistic action of thyroxine and copper salts in experiments on metamorphosis of *Rana temporaria*. *Compt. Rend. Soc. Biol.* **135**, 827–829.

Swift, H. (1958). Cytoplasmic particulates and basophilia. *In* "Symposium on the Chemical Basis of Development" (W. D. McElroy and B. Glass, eds.), pp. 174–210. Johns Hopkins Press, Baltimore, Maryland.

Takahashi, I. (1935). Chemical embryology of Amphibia. VII. The enzymes of the giant salamander. *J. Japan. Biochem. Soc.* **22**, 45–47.

Taylor, A. C., and Kollros, J. J. (1946). Stages in the normal development of *Rana pipiens* larvae. *Anat. Record* **94**, 7–24.

ten Cate, G. (1953). Formation of enzymes during embryogenesis. *Arch. Neerl. Zool.* **10** (Suppl. 1), 108–126.

ten Cate, G. (1959). The citric acid content of embryos of *Rana esculenta*. *Experientia* **15**, 57–59.

Tindal, J. S. (1956). Glycogenolysis in the liver of the common frog, *Rana temporaria*. *J. Exptl. Biol.* **33**, 196–210.

Truong, S. T.-H., and Dornfeld, E. J. (1955). Desoxyribose nucleic acid content in the nuclei of salamander somatic tissues. *Biol. Bull.* **108**, 242–251.

Truszkowski, R., and Goldanówna, C. (1933). Uricase and its action. VI. Distribution in various animals. *Biochem. J.* **27**, 612–614.

Tsukamoto, T., and Ohtaki, T. (1949a). Fatty substances from the adipose tissues of *Bufo melanostictus*. *J. Pharm. Soc. Japan* **69**, 221–223.

Tsukamoto, T., and Ohtaki, T. (1949b). Fatty substances from the adipose tissues of Chúi-Koe. *J. Pharm. Soc. Japan* **69**, 217–221.

Underhay, E. E., and Baldwin, E. (1955). Nitrogen excretion in the tadpoles of *Xenopus laevis* Daudin. *Biochem. J.* **61**, 544–547.

Urbani, E. (1955a). The proteolytic enzymes in cells and embryos. *Experientia* **11**, 210–218.

Urbani, E. (1955b). Enzymatic aspects of embryonic and larval development. Essay of a physiological zoology of Amphibia. *Ric. Sci.* **25**, 2258–2289.

Urbani, E. (1956). Lipases and lipides in the embryonic and larval developments of *Bufo vulgaris* and *Rana esculenta*. *Atti Accad. Nazl. Lincei Rend. Classe Sci. Fis. Mat. Nat.* **21**, 498–503.

Urbani, E. (1957). The enzymatic activity in the metamorphosis of *Bufo vulgaris*. *Atti Accad. Nazl. Lincei Rend. Classe Sci. Fis. Mat. Nat.* **23**, 86–89.

Urbani, E., and de Cesaris-Coromaldi, L. (1954). Study of proteinases in the embryonic and larval development of *Rana esculenta*. *Ric. Sci.* **24**, 2364–2374.

Urbani, E., and de Cesaris-Coromaldi, L. (1955). Proteinases in the embryonic and larval development of *Bufo vulgaris*. *Atti Accad. Nazl. Lincei Rend. Classe Sci. Fis. Mat. Nat.* **18**, 341–347.

Urbani, E., and de Cesaris-Coromaldi, L. (1957). Elimination of ammonia and urea in the embryonal and larval development and during metamorphosis of *Bufo vulgaris*. *Acta Embryol. Morphol. Exptl.* **1**, 1–11.

Urbani, E., and Scollo-Lavizzari, G. (1955). Lipase activity of *Rana esculenta* during embryonic and larval development. *Ric. Sci.* **25**, 2119–2221.

Urbani-Mistruzzi, L. (1957). The behavior of lipases in the embryonal development of *Bufo vulgaris* at different temperatures. *Ric. Sci.* **27**, 2786–2794.

van der Kloot, W. G. (1956). Cholinesterase and sodium transport by frog muscle. *Nature* **178**, 366–367.

Vendrely, R. (1955). The deoxyribonucleic acid content of the nucleus. *In* "The Nucleic Acids" (E. Chargaff and J. N. Davidson, eds.), Vol. II, pp. 155–180. Academic Press, New York.

Vernberg, F. J. (1952). The oxygen consumption of two species of salamanders at different seasons of the year. *Physiol. Zool.* **25**, 243–249.

von Hahn, H. P. (1958). Regional distribution of catalase activity in the tails of starved and fed *Xenopus* tadpoles. *Experientia* **14**, 67–68.

Waddington, C. H., and Sirlin, J. L. (1954). The incorporation of labelled aminoacids into amphibian embryos. *J. Embryol. Exptl. Morphol.* **2**, 340–347.

Wagner-Jauregg, T., Rauen, H., and Möller, E. F. (1934). *Z. Physiol. Chem.* **228**, 273–276.

Wagner-Jauregg, T., Möller, E. F., and Rauen, H. (1935). "Zwischenferment" from frog muscle. *Z. Physiol. Chem.* **231**, 55–61.

Wald, G. (1942). Visual systems and the vitamins A. *Biol. Symp.* **7**, 43–72.

Wald, G. (1945). Chemical evolution of vision. *Harvey Lectures* Ser. **41**, 117–160.

Wald, G. (1955). Visual pigments and vitamins A of the clawed toad, *Xenopus laevis*. *Nature* **175**, 390–391.

Wald, G. (1958). The significance of vertebrate metamorphosis. *Science* **128**, 1481–1490.

Weber, R. (1957a). On the biological function of cathepsin in tail tissue of *Xenopus* larvae. *Experientia* **13**, 153–155.

Weber, R. (1957b). The cathepsin activity in tails of *Xenopus* larvae during growth and metamorphosis. *Rev. Suisse Zool.* **64**, 326–336.

West, E. S., and Todd, W. R. (1961). "Biochemistry," 3rd ed. Macmillan, New York.

White, A., Handler, P., Smith, E. L., and Stetten, DeW., Jr. (1959). "Principles of Biochemistry," 2nd ed. McGraw-Hill, New York.

Williams, R. T. (1949). "Detoxication Mechanisms," pp. 1601–62. Wiley, New York.

Wilt, F. H. (1959). The differentiation of visual pigments in metamorphosing larvae of *Rana catesbeiana*. *Develop. Biol.* **1,** 199–233.

Woerdemann, M. W. (1933). Concerning the chemical processes of embryonic induction. *Proc. Koninkl. Akad. Wetenschap. Amsterdam* **36,** 842–849.

Wolken, J. J., and Schwertz, F. A. (1956). Molecular weight of algal chloroplastin. *Nature* **177,** 136–138.

Wood, H. G. (1955). Significance of alternate pathways in the metabolism of glucose. *Physiol. Rev.* **35,** 841–859.

Wright, P. A. (1959). Blood sugar studies in the bullfrog, *Rana catesbeiana. Endocrinology* **64,** 551–558.

Yagi, K. (1950). Riboflavin in the eyeball of frogs. *J. Japan. Biochem. Soc.* **22,** 143–147.

Yamamoto, K. (1960). Changes in activities of succinic and glutamic dehydrogenases, aspartic-α-ketoglutaric transaminase and proteolytic enzyme in tadpole tail tissue of *Rana japonica* during induced metamorphosis. *Endocrinol. Japon.* **7,** 8–12.

Yanagisawa, T. (1953). Alkaline and acid glycerophosphatase activities in the tail during metamorphosis of *Bufo vulgaris formosus* and *Rhacophorus schlegelii arborea. Rept. Liberal Arts Fac. Shizuoka Univ. Nat. Sci.* **4,** 20–26.

Ziegler-Günder, I. (1956). Investigations concerning the photolabile pterines of frog skin and of the eyes of *Drosophila melanogaster. Z. Naturforsch.* **11b,** 493–500.

Zimmet, D., and Dubois-Ferrière, H. (1936a). Ascorbic acid and reduced glutathione in the venom of the common toad, *Bufo vulgaris. Compt. Rend. Soc. Biol.* **123,** 654–656.

Zimmet, D., and Dubois-Ferrière, H. (1936b). Distribution of ascorbic acid in the common toad. *Compt. Rend. Soc. Biol.* **123,** 798–800.

THE DIGESTIVE SYSTEM

William G. Reeder

I. Introduction

For a group of such notable diversity and whose members have evolved in different lines for vast lengths of time, it is impressive that all known members of the Class Amphibia, at least as adults, are primarily carnivorous. Moreover, although hampered or inactivated by low temperatures, they usually feed only on live prey, actively sought, pursued, and captured. Adult urodeles feeding on land will take prey of any appropriate size, including worms, frogs, or other salamanders and, in larger species, even small mammals. The capture results from very slow approach of predator, culminating in a short leap and seizure in the mouth. Under water, adult salamanders have developed a snapping behavior by which the mouth is brought close to the small prey animal and is very rapidly opened. Water, presumably carrying with it the prey, rushes into the mouth, which is then snapped shut (Matthes, 1934). The smaller neotenic urodeles, for example *Necturus*, feed on frogs, small fishes, and fish eggs. Small larval urodeles will take arthropods or soft-bodied invertebrates of appropriate size.

Adult frogs and toads usually capture prey on land by flicking contact with a sticky and adhesive tongue, which, being attached anteroventrally, is often capable of surprisingly great protrusion. Feeding under water, the anuran may either seize an animal directly or utilize the snapping process described for the salamander. Anuran larvae or tadpoles appear in nature to be omnivores, gaining foods in a variety of ways. Using the horny teeth of the lips they may graze, taking particles from dead or soft plants and animal carrion in the water. In addition, they concentrate bacteria, protozoans, small animals, and organic detritus by filtration of water that is being pumped through the branchial apparatus in the respiratory currents. Since small animals and plants aggregate at or near the surface of the water, this is one of the most common feeding localities of the tadpole.

Caecilians appear also to devour suitably sized animal prey within their particular habitat, discriminating largely on the basis of size. These forms possess a tongue which is basally adherent but which can be slightly protruded during capture. The teeth are sharp, relatively long, and point rearward.

Sensory apparatus utilized in feeding behavior includes vision, the vibratory sense, and olfaction (Matthes, 1924). For example, it is suggested by W. Schultze (1937) that larval *Triturus vulgaris* feed for the first time on the third day after hatching, utilizing initially only sight and vibratory sense. *Triturus* has demonstrated alarm reaction to an unfamiliar chemical stimulus from the fourth day after hatching, thereby making probable the presence of an olfactory sense at that time. At metamorphosis, however, the young animals move onto land and are at first incapable of picking up odors. About 6 days after the change of medium the possibility of olfaction on land, or at least suitable reaction thereto, has become established.

Structurally, in comparison with teleost fishes, the Amphibia have evolved greater specialization and localization of function within the gut. Multicellular buccal glands are well developed, although primarily mucogenic rather than zymogenic. This buccal mucus contributes to lubrication of food, a matter of concern in forms having assumed a terrestrial existence. In addition, the pancreas has developed as a discrete organ, arising as a dorsal outgrowth of the duodenum and joined thereto by one or more patent ducts (Buddenbrock, 1956). Dentition is weakly developed in all living amphibians, which utilize teeth not for comminution or for infliction of injury, but rather for maintenance of grasp on prey (Partsch, 1877).

II. Buccal Cavity and Pharynx

The mouth of the adult amphibian is simple in form, with lips, supported by cartilage, providing extradental closure. The palate is gently curvate, with paired longitudinal supralingual folds defining the position of the intermaxillary gland. The internal choanae may open directly to the palatal surface (e.g., *Salamandra*) or may exit deeply within a narrow crescentic depression separating the marginal and palatal teeth in certain genera (e.g., *Siredon, Proteus*). Epithelial flaps provide closure of the internal choanae in *Siren* (Barge, 1937). Position of the inner choanal aperture varies rather widely in both Anura and Urodela; within both groups, however, a posterior position facilitates air passage lateral to the tongue and an evolutionary trend to such position has been postulated (Fahrenholz, 1937).

Thus, the buccal cavity functions in conducting air from the internal choanae to the glottis, as well as in the capture and reception of foods. Live prey or other food items ordinarily do not undergo comminution here but are lubricated and positioned preparatory to passage into the digestive regions of the gut. Secretions of the several buccal glands contain either insignificant concentrations of digestive enzymes or none at all; thus digestive breakdown is not here initiated.

A. TONGUE

With some exceptions, (e.g., *Xenopus* and *Pipa*) adult amphibians possess a well developed tongue, the form of which, however, may be varied and specialized. In most terrestrial urodeles, the tongue is strongly attached in the ventral midline, maintaining free anterior and lateral margins. In these forms the tongue is not important in seizure of prey; rather, by appressing the prey to the palate, the tongue functions as a retentive mechanism. Exceptional structure is noted in *Aneides* and *Batrachoceps*, wherein the tongue is attached anteriorly and along the ventral midline, and in *Chiroglossa* and *Hydromantes*, in which the ovate tongue is pedunculate.

The peduncle, protruding from a ventral sheath, permits extension of the strongly adhesive tongue (Hoffmann, 1873–1878; Herter, 1941).

In most Anura the tongue acts as an organ of seizure and is attached anteroventrally, thus permitting eversion of the lingual flap, which is flattened and often incipiently bifurcate. Within the Discoglossidae, in contrast, the tongue is enlarged, almost filling the buccal cavity, and is non-eversible, having attachment around the entire margin.

The body and horns of the hyoid support the elaborate glossal musculature, which is variable among amphibian groups. In general, the genioglossus controls lingual protraction or dorsal appression. In the more elaborate development of the anuran feeding behavior the posterior flap of the tongue is thereby rolled anteriad, causing the tip to pass along the palatal depression of the intermaxillary gland, from which mucoid adhesive is transferred to the lingual surface. Continuation of the movement everts the tongue from the mouth and applies the sticky surface to the prey animal. Contraction of the hypoglossus retracts the tongue, which rolls back into the mouth carrying adherent prey.

B. TEETH

The small teeth of modern Amphibia function primarily to retain a grasp on prey or to position the latter for swallowing. Even in *Aneides*, with enlargement of certain teeth, laceration or wounding of prey is not normally the primary dental function (Peyer, 1937). The use of procumbent premaxillary teeth of certain male urodeles (e.g., *Hydromantes*) in courtship behavior has been discussed by Noble (1931). Within the mouth, distribution of the teeth may be quite variable, even among closely related groups. Marginal dentition may be present on the premaxillary and maxillary as well as on the dentary and larval coronoid, whereas palatal dentition, when present, may be found in paired, usually longitudinal groups, on the parasphenoid or prevomer. Pseudodental projections of the prearticular have been described by Noble (1922, 1931) in *Dimorphognathus, Hemiphractus*, and *Amphodus*.

All amphibian teeth are roughly conical, with a single principal body or pedestal and cusp, of which the apical acuity may be variable. The pedestal is derived from bone and ossifies separately, while the apical section is composed primarily of dentine surrounding a pulp cavity and often capped by enamel. The plane of conjunction is marked by a circumferential ring in the adult tooth. A single short secondary cusp protrudes labially on most teeth, although this structure may be absent, as in *Leptopeltis, Phrynopsis*, and *Ceratophrys* (Noble, 1931) or, as in *Alytes* (Oltmanns, 1952), two may be observed. Sexual differences in dental distribution or morphology have been described, but appear not to be correlated directly with food habits. For example, in *Desmognathus quadramaculatus*, vomerine teeth are absent in males; maxillary and premaxillary teeth are monocuspidate in males, bicuspidate in females (Noble, 1931).

In his extensive review of amphibian dentition, Oltmanns (1952) has segregated, described, and carefully exemplified three primary dental types, on the basis of micromorphology and the mode of attachment to the dentigerous bone.

Type I (e.g., *Amphiuma, Salamandrina, Alytes*); pedestal with patent and simple vacuity continuous with dentinal pulp cavity; dentine of simple hollow conical or subconical shape, unsupported internally; pleurodont attachment.

Type II (e.g., *Proteus*); pedestal with internal bony trabeculae forming a supportive reticulum within internal cavity, but with central axis clear of obstruction; supportive bony struts penetrate pulp cavity giving support to dentinal sheath; pleurodont attachment.

Type III (e.g., *Ceratophrys*); pulp cavity nearly obliterated by bony trabeculae of basal pedestal; lines of force and bony supports appear to run centrifugally to support sheathing dentine at nearly a right angle; dentine strongly plicate (a condition otherwise known in fossil Stegocephalia); acrodont attachment.

The functional significance of these groups has not been tested.

C. BUCCAL MUCOSA AND GLANDS

The buccal cavity is lined by oral mucosa, variously elaborated as uni- and multicellular glands (Seifert, 1932). The microscopic anatomy of this membrane is complex and varies markedly, even among closely related species (Fahrenholz, 1937; Elkan, 1955). Nonsecretory areas of the palate, the roof and walls of the pharynx are lined by ciliated epithelium which transports epimucosal fluid and entrapped detritus posteriorly at a rate which is, at least in part, controlled by temperature (Herter, 1941).

The buccal and pharyngeal walls are heavily vascular, with elaborate capillary beds which provide for rapid subsurface perfusion of blood. Indeed in certain forms, e.g., *Salamandra, Triturus, Ensatina, Pseudotriton, Desmognathus*, capillaries penetrate not only the submucosa but into the deeper layers of the stratified epithelium. As specializations in other genera, e.g., *Schistometopum, Amphiuma*, large venous sinuses occur in the dermis of anterior mandibular and maxillary regions (Elkan, 1958). Previously postulated as a specialized accessory mechanism for respiratory exchange, it is now largely conceded that these elaborations function principally in the nutrition of the rich glandular beds, some of which secrete almost constantly.

The oral mucosa is richly beset with mucogenic gland cells in all investigated amphibians except *Pipa, Siren,* and *Amphiuma* (Fahrenholz, 1937). Indeed, in some forms, dense aggregations of these mucous cells form broad secretory surfaces.

As innovation over the fishes, multicellular buccal glands occur in most Amphibia. Absence of such glands in certain highly aquatic forms suggests secondary suppression and loss, for example in *Pipa,* or a failure to complete development in several neotenic urodeles. Effluent secretions appear to be expressed under pressure of the oral contents and contraction of surrounding musculature (Lundberg, 1958).

The intermaxillary gland or group of glands is formed of alveoli or tubules which interpenetrate the tissues between and often posterior to the nasal capsules, with collecting ducts opening to the anterior palatal surface. In caecilians, the alveolar organs open separately anterior and medial to the internal choanae. In other Amphibia this glandular region is more extensive, penetrating in anurans to a point near the corner of the mouth. In the latter group the secretory tubules have become discretely encapsulated as a single glandular system, proliferating fluid to the palatal surface at or near the midline as a compact series of openings. The mucoid secretion is often extremely sticky and, when applied to the tongue, may serve in entrapment of prey.

Amphibians with a well developed muscular tongue possess numerous tubular or alveolar glands which deeply penetrate the lingual muscle masses but whose distribution on the tongue is quite variable. *Pipa* and *Xenopus,* having but feeble lingual development, lack these glands, as do also a number of the neotenic urodeles (Fahrenholz, 1937). Deep epithelial crypts lined with Becker cells represent the lingual glands in *Cryptobranchus* and *Megalobatrachus.* The caecilians possess few but simple lingual glands having true alveolar form; these have been described in *Geotriton* as serous in nature.

Forming a part of the palatal surface, but opening within the choanae, the palatal or choanal glands are distributed throughout the Amphibia. In the Anura the glands are large, growing occasionally nearly to occlude the lumen of the nasal canal. The choanal glands of the caecilians, of dubious homology, consist of a discrete group of secretory tubules, encapsulated in a deep vomerine fossa and opening collectively to the inner margin of the choanae. In contrast, the structures in urodeles, although morphologically similar, open deep within the choanae on the margin of the olfactory epithelium. Secretory effluents are thence conducted through the choanae to the mouth.

Digestive Enzymes

Lepine and, more recently, J. Junold (cited by Fahrenholz, 1937; Vonk, 1941) have demonstrated a low concentration of a diastatic amylase in the intermaxillary, lingual, and paired pharyngeal glands of *Rana esculenta, R. temporaria, Bufo,* and *Pelobates,* listed in order of decreasing enzymic activity. These species as adults feed solely on small animals or organic remains which are rather promptly swallowed whole. The utility of this enzyme is therefore obscure, although slight progress in surface amylytic digestion before acidification of the prey might be made in the fundus of the stomach.

D. LARVAL ANURAN BRANCHIAL FILTER

Feeding in anuran larvae is brought about by the filtration within the pharynx of a stream of water pumped from the mouth through the pharynx to emerge laterally from the gill slits into the atrium, thence through the asymmetrical spiracle. Nutritive material extracted, depending on the specific feeding habit, may be planktonic or suspended animals and plants, bacteria, detritus, or material removed from a larger organic mass by abrasion of the horny denticles. Fragments entrapped by the mucus-covered filter are transferred, usually by ciliary action, to the esophagus. This branchial sieve with ciliary transportation system, coupled with the apparent absence of esophageal peristalsis, has been suggested as a specific adaptation to microphagy (Barrington, 1946). It should be emphasized, however, that the mechanism is not equivalent to that demonstrated in the cephalochordate *Amphioxus* or the larval lamprey, since active gulping of water, utilizing masticatory muscles, is the prime mover of water within the buccal cavity, cilia acting only in the directed transfer of the mucous layer.

The filter is formed within the branchial basket by a series of closely opposed filter plates which extend from the sequent branchial arches. Each single arch supports a filter plate which itself is made up of a series of 10 or more transverse, zig-zag epithelial folds, upon each of which are situated additional epithelial ridges or flaps of secondary and tertiary order (F. E. Schultze, 1892; Kratochwill, 1933; Buddenbrock, 1956). When appropriately positioned by the circumpharyngeal musculature, the filter plates form a narrow-mesh reticulum covered by a layer of mucus which functions in actual entrapment.

A series of ciliated pharyngeal grooves has been demonstrated along the outer margin of the branchial arches in *Rana, Bufo,* and *Xenopus* (Bles, 1905; Kratochwill, 1933; Barrington, 1946). In *Xenopus* a midventral pharyngobranchial tract was described by Weisz (1945) although reexamination by Dodd (1950) did not confirm its presence. Ciliary currents in these tracts and subsidiary adducent channels in the branchial chamber are directed posteriorly, carrying the mucous layer, with entrapped filtrational residue, spirally into the esophagus.

Elaborate masticatory musculature of larval anurans functions primarily to bring water and suspended materials into the mouth and to provide positive pressure to assure movement of water through the branchial filter. The pumping action which provides unidirectional water flow is biphasic, being tied to the respiratory function. At inspiration the mouth is opened, the hypopharyngeal musculature lowers the floor of mouth and pharynx, increasing the buccopharyngeal volume. At expiration the mouth is closed, the buccopharyngeal floor raised, and water expressed from the pharynx through the filter, out through the gill slits and spiracle. Rhythmic pharyngeal movements in the ventral midline direct the stream of water into the branchial pouches.

Bles (1905) using *Xenopus* and Barrington (1946) with *Rana* and *Bufo*, have tested the effectiveness of the branchial sieve by allowing the larvae to feed in water containing a suspension of carmine or graphite particles of 0.2 to 2.0 μ diameter. These particles were then recovered from mucous bands removed from pharynx, esophagus, and "stomach" or manicotto. The ability of tadpoles to live and develop in a bacterial suspension is also tribute to the elegance of this nutritive structure.

Many tadpoles supplement the filtrable suspended organic materials by rasping the surface layer of submerged plants and dead animals. In the larva of *Bufo regularis* elaborate musculature operates upper and lower jaws, producing an alternate movement of anterior and posterior horny blades on the lip margins toward and away from each other. Resultant particles are then conducted to the esophagus by the ciliary system (Sedra, 1950).

The microphagous microhylid tadpoles appear to be exceptional in that the circular branchial basket and filter are not ciliated. Mucus is said to be carried to the esophageal entry by swirling water currents (Savage, 1952, 1955).

Direct Absorption of Nutrients

A number of attempts have been made experimentally to demonstrate that aquatic animals, including vertebrates, can be nurtured by absorption of nutrient materials dissolved in water. A. Pütter (cited by Křiženecký, 1924) postulated that a large biomass could be supported in small ponds by inoculating the water with dissolved nutrients which could then be absorbed through the skin. With the hope of verifying this theory, Křiženecký (1924, 1925a,b,c) raised tadpoles of *Rana temporaria* in various nutrient solutions but without a supply of particulate food. In each case comparison was made with a similar group of larvae, part of which were maintained in tap water and starved, the remainder being kept in tap water and fed particulate food. Results of a large series of experiments appeared to demonstrate the verity of Pütter's theory, since the experiments showed that individuals starved of natural particulate food but living in a nutrient medium not only survived but increased in size and began to metamorphose in manner similar to but slower than the normally fed controls.

Bock (1924, 1925) attempted duplication of the Křiženecký experiments, using *Siredon* and *Salamandra*. Those urodeles raised in nutrient solution but without supplementary feeding died, as did those starved in tap water, but contrary to the group being fed usual particulate food. It was further shown that even *Rana temporaria*, raised this time in sterile nutrient media, die before metamorphosis, and show no evidence for external absorption of nutrients. In commenting on the poorly controlled experiments of Křiženecký, Bock suggested the tadpoles to have been feeding upon a flourishing colony of bacteria in the nutrient medium, rather than by direct absorption, thus hypothesizing the elegant performance of the branchial filters of the anuran larvae. Bock demonstrated moreover that the concentration of bacteria within a nutrient solution was strongly reduced by the presence of *Rana* tadpoles. The interesting but rather vitriolic exchange of papers between the workers involved served, however, to focus attention upon the general problem of amphibian feeding and nutrition and resulted in further experimentation.

III. Esophagus

A. HISTOLOGY

The esophagus is a muscular, extensible tube of thin wall, the function of which is to conduct food materials from the pharynx to the stomach, or upon occasion, in the reverse direction. At both upper and lower ends, sections of circularly directed muscle fibers, slightly increased in thickness, act to prevent the entry of water or air from the mouth or regurgitation of gastric contents (Ingelfinger, 1958). Form of the amphibian esophagus varies from a short structure with relatively large cross section in the anurans to a more linear and elongate tube in *Amphiuma* and *Proteus*. In the inactive state, the esophagus is of uniform diameter, except for a flaring dilatation at the junction with the stomach. In cross section, the esophagus has a rosette appearance, with the lining thrown into a series of 6 to 8 longitudinal folds which gradually continue into the stomach before being suppressed in the fundic wall (Pernkopf and Lehner, 1937).

The mucosal epithelium consists of one to several layers of cuboidal or columnar ciliated cells (cilia absent in *Proteus*) interspersed frequently with goblet cells, which are, however, more densely distributed anteriorly. Near the junction with the stomach, the ciliated mucosa grades into characteristic fundic structure. The muscularis mucosae may be virtually absent, as in *Triturus*, weakly present as a series of single smooth muscle fibers running in various directions as observed in *Proteus* and *Necturus*, or more commonly, is represented by minute bundles of longitudinal smooth muscle. This layer, as well as the underlying, heavily muscular submucosa, appears to become better organized and more strongly developed in the highly glandular region near the stomach. The tunica muscularis is formed principally of a well developed layer of circular smooth muscle fibers. An outer component of longitudinal fiber bundles is irregularly present and is sparse anteriorly, but increases in importance posteriorly to form a much stronger layer near the stomach. Fibers of connective tissue have invaded the layer providing thin sheathing for the bundles. The protective adventitia, where present, is fibrous and heavy.

The presence and variable distribution within the esophageal wall of glands which proliferate pepsinogen has been documented for many amphibian genera (Swiecicki, 1876; Langley, 1881; Kingsbury, 1894; Bensley, 1900; Biedermann, 1911; Herter, 1941; Eksaeva, 1958). Absence of esophageal peptic glands has been demonstrated in the urodeles *Siredon* and *Salamandra* and in the anurans *Cystignathus*, *Bombinator*, and *Pipa* (Pernkopf and Lehner, 1937). These structures, believed by Kingsbury (1894) to be true homologues of the gastric glands of the stomach, are concentrated in the posterior portion of the esophagus, from whence they form a continuous series in the stomach with the gastric chief glands of the fundus. The form taken by these glands may be variable, but they appear most often, as in *Rana*, as a series of plaques of compound glands with tubular acini, increasingly large and concentrated near the gastric end of the esophagus. *Proteus* and *Necturus* possess 20 to 30 such discrete plaques within which are elaborated pepsinogen and, from interspersed goblet cells, mucus. Effluence to the esophageal lumen from each glandular complex is by way of a single duct lined with mucous neck cells. In *Rana temporaria*, a continuous secretory layer, formed by the confluence of glandular plaques in the last 2 or 3 mm of esophagus and the first 1 or 2 mm of the stomach, proliferates proteolytic enzyme in alkaline medium. Here a well distributed mixture of simple and complex tubular glands suggests transition from characteristic esophageal to a gastric structure. Gross structure and size of the secretory granules are also transitional from the large esophageal to the smaller, more densely concentrated gastric types (Langley, 1881; Machan, 1935). More pepsinogen is produced within the esophagus than within the stomach in *Rana*, *Hyla*, *Bufo*, *Pelobates*, and *Triturus* (Jordan, 1927).

B. TRAVERSAL OF ESOPHAGUS

A food bolus, formed as an aggregation of small prey in the pharynx, is forced into the esophagus against the resistance of the rather feeble anterior esophageal sphincter by pressure exerted by the tongue and the circumpharyngeal musculature (Bosma, 1957). The food mass, compacted to nearly spherical shape, slowly traverses the esophagus propelled by a sequence of peristaltic waves. Such contractile sequence of the tunica muscularis, originating at the pharyngoesophageal junction, passes at nearly uniform rate down the esophagus to the stomach.

Local movements within the esophagus, peristaltic in effect but initiated posterior to the usual position, often appear to be stimulated by local irritants, such as food particles remnant within the tube (Ingelfinger, 1958).

As the bolus traverses the esophagus, mucus and pepsinogen are expressed in quantity from the respective glands and accrete around the food mass; there is little or no mixture of the secretions with the food before reaching the stomach. Buccal and esophageal mucus, alkaline in reaction, prohibits proteolytic digestion before gastric acidification.

IV. Stomach

It is suggested by Barrington (1942) that the original function of the stomach was that of storage, thus permitting active feeding during brief periods of activity or of optimal thermal condition, and subsequent more leisurely but continuous processing of the stored foods. Since such aggregations of dead food would tend to undergo bacterial disintegration, with production of toxic by-products, hydrochloric acid secretion may have evolved early as an inhibitor of such bacterial activity (Jordan, 1929). In addition, the presence of acid in the stomach would hasten the death of prey taken alive (Dorris, 1935) and would decalcify ingested skeletal materials. Thus it is perhaps subsequent to the development of a strongly acid storage chamber that peptic proteolysis evolved. So far as known, pepsin occurs only in vertebrates, and its precursor, pepsinogen, is elaborated from the chief glands or their homologue in the stomach or lower esophageal lining (Vonk, 1937; Yonge, 1937; Barrington, 1942).

A. HISTOLOGY

Separation of stomach from esophagus in the Amphibia is largely a definitional convenience, since both have been shown to differentiate from the larval or embryonic foregut, but with great variation in process and form among the separate phyletic groups. The adult stomach is inflated and of relatively thin wall, consisting of a strongly glandular mucosa, a thin submucosa, and a well organized tunica muscularis. In amphibians, as in fishes, the stomach is lined by a series of slender, spindle-shaped mucogenic cells (Tschassownikow, 1927); the goblet cells and ciliated epithelium of the esophageal lining are absent. The chief glands are present in the corpus, which comprises the anterior-most 70 to 80% of the stomach in *Bufo* and *Necturus* (Kingsbury, 1894; Barrington, 1942); those near the esophagus are described as being transitional between the esophageal gland and the mucoid glands of the pyloric region. The characteristic branched tubular gland consists of finely granular basal zymogen cells, followed, approaching the lumen, by large mucous neck cells and a discrete duct, the lining of which is provided by an ingrowth of surface epithelium (Lim, 1922; Barrington, 1946). The basal finely granular zymogen cells in *Rana* appear to be responsible for secretion of both small amounts of pepsinogen and important amounts of acid. The mucous neck cell, absent in fishes, is large and filled with secretory precursor. In the frog, Langley (1881) and Machan (1935) have demonstrated the concentration of pepsinogen to be greater in the anterior-most chief glands; secretory granules are somewhat smaller in the more posterior chief glands. In *Bufo* (Biedermann, 1911; Barrington, 1946) the differential distribution of granule size appears to be of lesser prominence. That the mucous neck cell is the homologue of the pyloric mucogenic cell has been suggested by Langley.

The characteristic pyloric glands in *Rana* extend 3 to 4 mm anterior from the duodenum and are entirely mucogenic. The morphology appears similar in *Bufo* and *Triton*.

The tunica submucosa is well represented. The muscularis consists of a strong layer of circular fibers and a somewhat thinner and more feeble set of longitudinal strands (Grützner, 1901; Kuntz, 1924).

B. GASTRIC CONTRACTION

Spontaneous muscular movements of the stomach walls have been studied in detail, although with considerable conflict of conclusion, for over a century. The older literature is summarized by Goltz (1872) and is not further cited here. Contrary to the situation in mammals, the "hunger contraction" or contraction of the wall in the unfilled stomach, cannot be differentiated physiologically from gastric peristalsis as observed in the stomach of a well fed and active frog (Patterson, 1916). Roux and Balthazard (1898) initially described stomach movements of the intact frog using roentgenographic observation of barium-filled stomachs. Gastric peristalsis is a tonic contraction of a limited section of circular musculature, which moves very slowly, by relaxation of anterior fibers and contractile involvement of additional posterior fibers, from anterior cardiac to pyloric region, deforming the stomach to an hour-glass shape. As in the dog and man, two types of stomach movement have been discerned, each of which is inferred to be of specialized value in food manipulation and transport. Fundic movement consists of relatively weak contractions which do not obliterate the gastric lumen but transport soft fluid and largely peripheral food materials to the pyloric region. Movements within the pyloric region, on the contrary, are very strong peristaltic contractions, at times nearly obliterating a section of the gastric lumen. The function of these rather rapid and regular movements is the kneading of chyme and, finally, its movement to and through the pyloric sphincter (Vonk, 1941).

While the pyloric region is very active in contraction, with waves ascending and descending, the majority of contractile waves are initiated in the cardiac or prepyloric region and slowly progress posteriad. However, initiation of the formation of a contractile peristaltic ring may take place anywhere on the stomach and may progress in any direction over the stomach (Babkin, 1924). The regularity of this contraction has been disputed by Dixon (1902) and by Morishima and Fujitani (1908), but the large number of controlled experiments appears to validate the position of Patterson (1916).

Characteristics of the gastric contraction may be described using a gastric balloon, inserted at stomastomy and attached to a recording manometer. The "hunger contraction" continues with regularity day after day at a rate which varies with temperature and with the quantity of food in the stomach or extent of starvation, but the muscular tonus remains quite constant under the variant conditions. On the basis of an unstated number of observations the average duration of contraction is 96 sec and the alternating period of relaxation is between 16 and 33 sec (Patterson, 1916). These automatic movements function to empty the stomach at a rate which is temperature dependent.

In the fasting frog the gastric contractions increase markedly in amplitude, but show no increase in tonus (Dixon, 1902). As the amplitude increases, the contractions become more lengthy (e.g., to 4 min duration, with 3.5 to 4 min relaxation, after 9 weeks fast) and the rate is retarded. That a period of fasting occasions aberrant gastric contraction in frogs has been disputed by Babkin (1924), who maintains a normal contractility to be characteristic even in variant nutritional state, if the animals are maintained with great care in the experimental situations.

Rate of automatic contraction is subject to modification by thermal changes. Within the range 13° to 35° C in *Rana catesbeiana* rates of gastric contraction have been demonstrated to follow the van't Hoff relationship (Table I) as ambient temperature is raised or lowered at a rate of about 3° C per hour. Abruptly at an upper limit of 35° and a lower of 13° C or within 0.5° thereto, automatic contraction is completely suppressed. Thus thermal inhibition of this regular contractility should be quite common at the lower temperatures often experienced in nature. The intensity of contraction is maximal between 15° and 32° C and is reduced outside these limits (Patterson, 1916).

TABLE I

INFLUENCE OF TEMPERATURE ON GASTRIC CONTRACTION IN *Rana catesbeiana*[a]

N	At T_h	N	At T_l	Thermal coefficient[b]
(5)	23.5°C	(9)	32.5°C	2.00
(6)	25. °	(10)	32.8°	2.15
(6)	24.5°	(10)	32.3°	2.15

N	At T_l	N	At T_h	Thermal coefficient
(7)	20°C	(5)	14°C	2.33
(4)	19°	(3)	14°	2.66
(6.5)	21°	(4)	14°	2.32

[a] Data from Patterson (1916). Number of contractions (N) per 12-min interval as temperatures are changed from high temperatue (T_h) to low temperature (T_l) or the reverse.

[b] The thermal coefficient has been calculated $10(N_{T_h})/N_{T_l}$ $(T_h - T_l)$, where N_{T_h} is rate of contraction at high temperature, N_{T_l} is rate at lower temperature.

Gastric contractility may be weakened or inhibited completely by the direct introduction to the stomach of small quantities of water, weak acid, or base. In the normal bullfrog with empty stomach or, interestingly, in well fed bullfrogs with filled stomach, introduction of 5 to 10 ml water will weaken, but not completely inhibit, the contraction. Weakening of the contraction for a period of about 2 min is occasioned by introduction of 5 ml of 1% solution of Na_2CO_3. Inflating the stomach with 5 ml of 0.5% HCl causes complete inhibition for 17 to 25 min. Duration of modification or inhibition depends upon the concentration of chemical agents as well as upon the quantity injected; onset of inhibition is less rapid than in higher vertebrates. Complete suppression is seen only after 4 or 5 very strong contractions (Patterson, 1916). Similar chemical inhibition is described in *Necturus* (Patterson, 1928).

Hopf (1911) presented experimental data which do not entirely agree with those of Patterson and which suggest, in summary, that both acid and base, under some circumstances, stimulate contraction rather than inhibit it.

Necturus was studied with techniques similar to those applied to *Rana* and *Bufo*, but using a lower esophageal fistula for insertion of the gastric balloon. Contractions are similar to, but somewhat weaker than, those of the bullfrog; intervals between contractions are 5 to 9 times as long (Patterson, 1928). No change in tonus was observed in fasting animals, although gastric contractions appeared to be nearly continuous. At environmental temperature of 18° C the duration of contraction was about 45 sec; intervals between contractions varied from 80 sec to 5 min. As in the frog, introduction of weak alkali or acid directly to the stomach caused inhibition of automatic contraction. The lower thermal limit for spontaneous contraction was 7° C. Handling of individual *Necturus* or manipulation of the head or gills brought about gastric inhibition.

Spontaneous contraction of musculature of the excised stomach wall has been investigated in *Rana esculenta* by Gellhorn and Budde (1923). Contraction of fundic muscle has been shown to be more regular, of higher frequency and greater amplitude than pyloric sections. The smooth curve of fundic contraction shows rapid rise and fall, whereas the pyloric contractions consist of aggregations of superimposed small partial contractions. Fundic musculature is more elastic than that of the pyloric region and, in both, circular muscle is more easily stretched than the longitudinal muscle (Budde and Gellhorn, 1924). These authors have shown experimentally that loading of the stomach reduces the frequency of spontaneous contraction in the fundus, while the pyloric region proceeds with strong contractions. Thus, assuming a similar effect in nature, the pyloric mixing would continue unabated, while the body of newly ingested food, stored in the fundus, was undergoing a lowering of pH preparatory to moving gradually into the pyloric region and more active mixing.

As HCl is proliferated into the stomach and becomes mixed with the food mass, there is observed in the intact animal a further reduction in rate of fundic contraction, thus allowing food to remain for a longer period. As the acidified food mass moves through the actively contracting pyloric section toward the prepyloric sphincter, these circular muscle bands as well as the pyloric sphincter relax, allowing penetration of the orifice by the food mass (Babkin, 1924; Vonk, 1941). The acid food mass then, in contrast, promotes energetic contraction of the small intestine.

Separated muscle layers of the *Necturus* stomach contract spontaneously and rhythmically *in vitro* (Friedman, 1935). Automatic contractions of circular muscle strips are more frequent (average 8.5 per 10 min) than are those of longitudinal sections (average 4.5 per 10 min); the amplitude is usually equivalent from cardium and the pyloric regions.

C. GASTRIC INNERVATION

In *Rana* and *Bufo*, while spontaneous gastric contractions may occur in the absence of motor innervation, it is the concensus that the regular sequence observed *in vivo* is the direct outcome of neuromotor stimulation, and that the larger and more regular waves are of neurogenic origin (Dixon, 1902; Langley and Orbeli, 1910; Patterson, 1916; Tschermak, 1919; Itagaki, 1930; Vonk, 1941). In the absence of gastric contraction, electrical stimulation of the communicating ramus of the 4th spinal nerve will initiate peristalsis. If the gastric musculature is contracting automatically, stimulation of the 4th nerve augments the contractions, increasing their regularity and tonus. A similar but less pronounced effect is observed with stimulation of the 3rd and 5th spinal rami. Stimulation of the sympathetic trunk was without effect (Barbéra, 1898).

Stimulation of the parasympathetic vagus results often in brief inhibition of peristaltic movement, followed by an augmentation of contraction (Hopf, 1911), but with reduction in tonus. Thus the vagus appears to contain tonic inhibitory fibers, but in addition motor fibers, stimulation of which initiates or augments peristaltic contraction of the stomach (Waters, 1885; Steinach and Wiener, 1895; Dixon, 1902; Patterson, 1916; Friedman, 1935). The pharmacological studies of Epstein (1931, 1932a, 1932b) are generally, although not completely, in agreement with this model of gastric innervation in *Rana*.

Innervation of the gastric wall of *Necturus* has been described by L. Drüner and later by H. W. Norris and M. Buckley (cited by Patterson, 1928) as a complex mixed system deriving principally from the glossopharyngeal and vagus trunks, but emerging from three branchial nerves. As summarized by Patterson (1928) the innervation of respiratory and gastric organs is intimately linked, through confluent rami of these three nerves. It is suggested that conditions affecting respiratory function secondarily exert at least partial reflex control over gastric musculature through this complex. For example, mechanical stimulation of the *Necturus* gill usually leads to reflex inhibition of movements of the external gills as well as suppression of gastric contraction of the empty stomach during the period of stimulus. Section of the branchial nerves, transection of the vagi, or pithing of the medulla terminates these reflex effects.

Section of the vagi produces marked amplitude enhancement after brief initial inhibition while maintaining about the same frequency. Electrical stimulation of the intact vagus or peripheral section of the transected nerve immediately inhibits spontaneous gastric contraction. No motor effects have been found despite repeated attempts at vagal stimulation by variant means and various workers (Luckhardt and Carlson, 1921; Patterson, 1928). Unilateral vagotomy followed by stimulation of the proximal nerve segment results in reflex inhibition of gastric movement. Thus it is concluded that the action of the vagus in *Necturus* is largely, if not entirely, inhibitory.

In three of four test animals, stimulation of splanchnic nerves of intact *Necturus* by rapid electrical shock induced peristaltic activity which progressed slowly from cardium to pylorus, but no farther (Patterson, 1928).

Autonomic drugs and related compounds have been shown to affect the frequency, the amplitude, and degree of tonus of strips of gastric musculature in the frog (Gruber, 1923). Longitudinal muscle strips are markedly less sensitive to chemical stimulation than are circular sections from the same area. With application of adrenaline in concentrations between 5×10^{-5} and 1×10^{-9}, stimulation of the cardiac and fundic circular strips is effected. The tonus of contraction rises markedly; frequency increases from an average of 8.5 to 13 per 10 min. Concentrations of adrenaline in excess of 1×10^{-5} are distinctly inhibitory, however, with reduction of tonus and decrease of frequency to 4 per 10 min. The effect on automatic contraction of excised strips from the three stomach regions is summarized in Table II. A synergistic effect has been described (Friedman, 1935) wherein acetylcholine, following a low stimulatory concentration of adrenaline, enhances the action of the latter, whereas, if adrenaline is applied in concentration sufficient to inhibit contraction, acetylcholine, acting as antagonist, will stimulate contraction and bring its frequency to near normal.

Inoculation of excised gastric wall sections with acetylcholine increased the tonus in pyloric and fundic regions; there is increase in frequency of contraction as well as decrease in amplitude. With similar concentration of acetylcholine, stimulation of the fundus continues appreciably longer than does that of the pyloric region. The same reaction to electrical stimula-

TABLE II

Effect of Drugs on Automatic Contraction of Excised Gastric Musculature in *Necturus maculosus*[a]

	Cardium		Fundus		Pylorus	
	Circular	Longitudinal	Circular	Longitudinal	Circular	Longitudinal
Adrenaline 5×10^{-5} to 1×10^{-9}	Stimulation	No effect or inhibition	Stimulation	Inhibition	Stimulation	Inhibition
Adrenaline $>5 \times 10^{-5}$	Inhibition	Inhibition	Inhibition	Inhibition	Inhibition	Inhibition
Acetylcholine	Stimulation	Stimulation	Stimulation	Stimulation	Stimulation	Stimulation
Pilocarpine	Stimulation	Inhibition	Stimulation	Inhibition	Stimulation	Inhibition

[a] Compiled from Friedman (1935).

tion is shown. Threshold for chemical excitors such as acetylcholine, morphine, $CaCl_2$, and $BaCl_2$ is markedly lower in the fundus. A higher concentration of adrenaline, which can be shown to debilitate the fundic tissue may still actively stimulate the pyloric tissue (Gellhorn and Budde, 1923). Reaction of the gut to stimulus by autonomic drugs appears to be independent of season, period of captivity, sex, modest fluctuations of temperature, and pH (Epstein, 1931).

Pieces of gastric wall from the same areas, but which had no automatic contractility, were stimulated electrically. Length of latent period, duration of contraction, and other characteristics of the contractile sequence depend on strength of stimulus, age of the preparation, and nutritional state. Great variability in results is seen in the literature. Despite variant results, with given stimulus, a contractile sequence of the fundus persists longer than that of the pyloric region and the amplitude is greater. Latent period averages 2.6 sec in fundic musculature and 4.4 sec in the pyloric. Absolute figures vary with experimental conditions but their relative magnitude is of significance.

It is suggested (Friedman, 1935) that, with relaxation and inhibition of the longitudinal musculature of *Necturus* under mild adrenaline stimulation, length of the organ is thereby increased and capacity for holding food is usefully amplified. Circular muscle then, stimulated to an increased frequency of contraction, churns food materials and propels them toward the pyloric orifice. Reaction to drugs by the pyloric sphincter is similar to that of adjacent circular gastric muscle (Gruber, 1923).

Reaction to mechanical stimulus, however, shows reverse characteristics. In response to a mechanical stimulus which was insufficient to initiate contraction of a fundic fragment, the pyloric section contracted strongly.

Analyzing the clear differences in frequency and amplitude between spontaneous fundic and pyloric contraction, Hecht (1920) demonstrated that, in the fundic region, spontaneous movement and excitability to electrical stimuli were high when intact stomach wall was used, but when mucosa and submucosa were stripped from the underlying muscularis the spontaneous contractility was lost or heavily suppressed and there was but weak response to electrical stimulation. It is suggested by Mangold (1920) and Hecht (1920) that the ganglionate plexus of Meissner, ramifying in the submucosa, controls the automaticity and is itself excited by electrical stimulation. In the pyloric section, stimulation of the intact pyloric wall provoked but feeble response. The latter could be amplified several fold, however, by removal of the mucosa and submucosa, whereupon the muscularis also became active in spontaneous contraction. Hecht has suggested as a model that Auerbach's plexus, which runs within the muscularis itself is stimulated to initiate contraction by filling of the intact stomach and the stretching of appropriate receptors. It is postulated that this excitation may be inhibited by submucosal nervous stimulation.

Principal control of the magnitude and regularity of gastric contraction is exerted in the midbrain or medulla, as decerebration fails to affect appreciably the amplitude or rate of automatic contraction, but total pithing or vagal section terminates these regular movements (Goltz, 1872; Patterson, 1916). Strong electrical stimulus to various skin areas in *Rana* adversely affects the medulla, resulting in vagal inhibition. Increase of gastric motility and tonus are a secondary result (Goltz, 1872; Steinach, 1898).

Epstein (1931) and Buddenbrock (1956) have drawn attention to the vast body of conflicting experimental testimony concerning innervation of gastric musculature in Amphibia. Information has derived from electrophysiological and pharmacological experiment; some investigators have used the intact animal, others the excised organs or tissue fragments of various types. Experimental work has been carried out on a number of genera and occasionally unwarranted inferences have been carried from one such study to another. That this may lead to serious error has been shown by Epstein (1931) and Patterson (1916, 1920, 1928). It must be emphasized that care need be exercised in evaluation of evidence in this area. Since unimpaired structure is demanded for delicate coordinated activity in the frog stomach, further experimentation using the intact animal is desired (Klee, 1927b).

D. SECRETION OF GASTRIC JUICE

Gastric juice is secreted from esophageal and gastric glands 40–50 min after food is swallowed by the frog (A. J. Smirnov, cited by Vonk, 1941). The concentration of active pepsin increases for 6 to 10 hr, then slowly declines to about the twentieth hour after feeding, when a minimum is reached; the concentration then increases to resting level (Biedermann, 1911). Proteolysis proceeds most rapidly where pepsin and food are most completely intermixed. Thus there is considerable disparity in the contents of the fundus and the pyloric region. Peptides may be found in the latter section while yet a part of the food mass remains unmodified in the fundus, being released gradually to be mixed with the gastric juice. Esophageal pepsinogen, upon entry into the stomach, becomes effective rapidly, since fluids are briskly propelled into the pyloric region (Jordan, 1927; Babkin, 1928, 1950).

The normal digestive sequence in *Rana esculenta* has been described by Wolvekamp and Tinbergen (1942). The esophageal wall of the fasting animal was pale in color until about 30 min after ingestion of an earthworm, when marked vasodilatation, indicative of the secretory state, was observed in the reddened mucosa. The stomach of the same frog before feeding contained a small quantity of mucus at pH above 5. Within the first hour after ingestion of the worm, the stomach accumulated a quantity of secreted fluid, still at pH greater than 5. The duodenum remained pale and empty for about an hour, at which time the small intestine contained a brownish fluid and the mucosa was flushed with blood. After about 6 hr the stomach contents had become more acid. Within 24 hr the earthworm was digested but the stomach still contained a fluid of pH 3. After 48 hr, the mucosal surface had returned to the nonsecretory resting state with pale color and a higher pH of epimucosal fluid.

1. Pepsin

Pepsinogen is a proteinaceous enzyme precursor which is spontaneously and autocatalytically converted to the active proteinase pepsin at a pH of less than 6 (Hirschowitz, 1957). At 25° C, this conversion is almost instantaneous at pH 2, but requires about 12 hr at pH 4.6. Molecular configuration of pepsin is somewhat variable, since species differences in molecular activity have been described (Langley and Edkin, 1886; Vonk, 1929). At low temperatures, for example, pepsin from *Rana* is destroyed more slowly in bicarbonate solution than is mammalian pepsin. Pepsinogen in dilute alkaline solution is quite stable. Müller (1922) has demonstrated pepsin to be thermally stable at temperatures within the range normally encountered by amphibians in nature; denaturation of *Rana* pepsinogen and pepsin occurs above 55° C. Production of pepsin from gastric mucosa *in vitro* requires rather specific chemical environment, within which calcium and bicarbonate ions are especially important. The work of Delrue (1933) and Gray and Adkison (1941) gives entry to the literature in this specialized area.

2. Gastric pH

The gastric proteolytic enzyme, pepsin, found only in vertebrates, functions only in rather strongly acid medium. Tests of hydrogen ion concentration optimum for activity of pepsin from a number of vertebrates were made by Vonk. He found the pH optima of pepsins from the several vertebrate classes to be approximately equivalent. For *Rana*, pH ranges of 1.40 to 1.71 (Vonk, 1929) and 1.6 to 1.9 (Pjatnitzky, 1931) have been determined to be optimum for maximum proteolysis. It must be emphasized that these figures do not reflect actual ranges of intragastric pH, but rather the chemical optimum. At higher pH, compensation for decreased enzymic effectiveness may be brought about by the production of increased amount of the enzyme, relative to the mass of food to be broken down.

Initially, the pH is lowered only at the surface of the food introduced into the stomach. Later, depending on the nature of the prey, the acid and enzyme penetrate more deeply and the rate of total proteolysis is increased; the total stomach contents may come to have low and more or less uniform pH. Wolvekamp and Tinbergen (1942) have further pointed out that abundant secretion of gastric juice with pepsin in normal concentration may not always be combined with a strongly acid reaction. Thus the stimulus to acid secretion and that controlling production of pepsin appear to be separate.

Actual pH within the active frog stomach was investigated by A. M. W. Mennega (dissertation cited by Vonk, 1941). After the frog had been fed bread, the relatively uniform gastric pH reached 2.18, whereas, with a food mass of ground meat, there was considerable difference between the center and the surface of the mass. Measurements of Mennega at the cardiac (pH 3.25), fundic (pH 2.31), and pyloric (pH 2.20) surfaces demonstrate that at least at the surface of an unmixed food mass the reaction is relatively close to the optimum for pepsin. Vonk (1929) lists variant pH measurements (from 2.2 to 3.7 in the frog during November) but he later (1941) stated technical dissatisfaction with these measurements. Delrue (1930) has presented measurements (pH 4.2–4.8) which, on the basis of the careful and more recent determinations, appear to be erroneous. Penetration of acid through the experimental food mass of ground meat was perhaps slower than normal, leading to excessive pH gradient. Particulate foods such as are frequently taken in nature will allow maximum penetration of gastric juice with but limited peristaltic churning (Grützner and Swiecicki, 1891).

Early experiments of Grützner (1905), in which the food mass consisted of bread soaked in milk and penetrated with litmus, neatly described the progressive reduction in pH with progress through the stomach from esophageal entrance (blue) to pylorus (red), and also the radial fundic gradient from peripheral (red) to central (blue). In the pyloric region of the intestine the contents were well mixed and apparently nearly uniform in reaction.

3. Hydrochloric Acid Secretion

The mechanism whereby hydrochloric acid is produced in quantity at the gastric mucosal surface is complex and not completely known. Secretion of gastric acid in Amphibia, as in other vertebrates, implies the accumulation at the mucosal surface of hydrogen ions, likewise a movement of chloride ions to this surface; simultaneously observed is the generation of an electromotive force (EMF) across the mucosal membrane (Crane et al., 1948a; James, 1957; Durbin and Heinz, 1958). Active chloride transfer has been identified and described; since the rate of such transfer across the mucosa has been measured as electrochemically equivalent to the generated EMF, it has been assumed that both resultants reflect operation of the same, or closely allied, physiological processes (Hogben, 1955).

Excised fragments of gastric mucosa or, in other experiments, the entire stomach, were suspended separating two chambers of appropriate trophic substrate, one bathing the serosal or muscular surface, the other the mucosal. Such tissues, removed from summer or active anurans very often continue secretion of their normal products (Langley, 1881, 1882; Gray et al., 1940; Davies and Longmuir, 1948). Indeed, in unbuffered substrate, the isolated gastric mucosa of Rana will secrete acid, rapidly lowering the substrate pH to an average of 2.5; secreting into buffered substrate, mucosal sheets, normal or everted gastric bags may show prolonged and intense activity. Gray et al. (1940) postulated that, as HCl was produced at the mucosal surface, "alkali" was being elaborated at the muscularis of his preparation. Using closed gastric bags of Rana temporaria and Bufo bufo, Davies (1948, 1951) obtained experimental verification; furthermore, he was able to show equimolar ($\pm 1\%$) production of acid and base from opposite surfaces. Given excess of CO_2 bubbled through the system, the hydroxyl ion was apparently neutralized to bicarbonate (HCO_3^-) which passed freely into the medium. With rapid secretion of acid and production of OH^-, an external source of CO_2 was required to maintain conversion to bicarbonate.

The electrical properties of isolated digestive mucosa were also described by Crane et al. (1948a); their preparations produced potential differences, measured across the membranes tested averaging as follows: across "corpus" of stomach, -30 mv; rectal mucosa, -16 mv; pyloric mucosa, -5 mv; esophageal, duodenal, and ileal mucosa, -2 mv. In all cases the mucosal surface was negative with respect to the nutrient surface. During active secretion of HCl the transmembrane resistance rose sharply, while the potential difference decreased.

Proposing a hypothetical inorganic model, Crane et al. (1948a) calculated that, within the small groups of secreting cells in the frog gastric mucosa, the potential difference, maintained at equilibrium in a non-stimulated stomach, would result in current flow in an external circuit maintaining power output of about 1 microwatt per milligram dry weight. The model, not here detailed, further proposes that HCl is produced by a process of electron cycling among inorganic intracellular components; this position is disputed by Heinz and Durbin (1957).

A series of experiments, entry into the literature of which is provided by Durbin and Heinz (1958; also Heinz and Durbin, 1957), argues that acid secretion and electromotive chloride transport involve two different and independent mechanisms. The use of specific inhibitors has demonstrated that the rate of electromotive chloride transport was affected neither by changes in the rate of acid secretion nor by thiocyanate inhibition of acid secretion. Several inhibitors of carbonic anhydrase fail to block the secretion of acid by the mucosa *in vitro* but depress the rate of total chloride flux and may also reduce or eliminate the gastric EMF. Thus these authors infer that carbonic anhydrase is required in the mechanism of active chloride transport but is probably not important in the production of acid at the mucosal surface.

Heinz and Durbin (1957) also propose a model which describes movement of Cl^- across the mucosa, but seems not to be concerned directly with active secretion of HCl at the secretory surface. Since application of metabolic inhibitors does not affect appreciably the movement of Na^+ from nutrient to mucosal surface, but the Cl^- flux is strongly reduced, it is inferred that under conditions of experimental inhibition, Cl^- moves across the membrane as a free ion, while in the normal membrane Cl^- travels across the mucosa combined with a carrier, the latter requiring active metabolic machinery for maintenance of concentration or appropriate activity. It has at least been shown that the Cl^- does not simply follow a positive ion across the membrane, since the polarity of the structure is of inappropriate sign.

Enhancement of the potential difference by application of an EMF across the secreting isolated frog mucosa resulted in increased rate of HCl secretion (Durbin and Heinz, 1958) or if impressed with opposing polarity the elaboration of HCl was diminished (Crane *et al.*, 1948b). No significant secretion of acid was obtained *in vitro* in the absence of the EMF.

While Durbin and Heinz (1958) conclude the EMF to be a direct manifestation of the active chloride pump it has not been possible to determine whether or not the chloride secreted as the acid has in fact been moved by this mechanism, although with increased secretion of acid, Cl^- flux from nutrient to secretory surface also rose sharply. Carbonic anhydrase was shown by Davenport (1946) to be present in quantity within the frog gastric mucosa. It is inferred that carbonic anhydrase is important in the function of the chloride pump, since its inhibition by Diamox® suppresses the EMF. Acid secretion is reduced but not eliminated by such treatment. Davies (1948) has calculated that the minute quantity of carbonic anhydrase remaining after treatment with Diamox probably would permit sufficient conversion to bicarbonate ion.

Without an external source of CO_2, at times of moderate secretion of HCl, the isolated gastric bag of *Rana temporaria* is subject to severe lesions and perforation. Such consequences are avoided if the $CO_2 : HCO_3^-$ buffer is maintained. Failure of a phosphate buffer to prevent tissue damage suggests the hydroxyl ion to be neutralized within the secretory cells. Since pepsinogen or pepsin occurs only in very low concentration in the anuran stomach after isolation from the secreting esophagus it is probable that the gastric acid or one of the concomitants of its production is responsible for the described lesions.

Results of these experiments are thus consistent with the postulated model of electrochemical production of HCl. That the gastric mucosa is unique in its ability to elaborate relatively large amounts of acid was established on the basis of chemical evidence and histochemical examination (Langley, 1881; Gray *et al.*, 1940) and is further evidenced by uniform failure to stimulate the secretion of acid from any other digestive membrane by experimental means.

4. Gastric Urease

Urease has been demonstrated *in vitro* in the gastric mucosa of *Rana catesbeiana, Rana pipiens,* and *Bufo* in addition to a variety of mammals (Glick, Zak, and von Korff, 1950; von Korff and Glick, 1951; Kornberg and Davies, 1955). The urease is located within the wall of the stomach where protected from the action of pepsin and HCl, by either of which it may be inactivated. In mammals, the urease has been shown histochemically to be concentrated in the surface layers of mucosa in the body of the stomach and to be found only in much lesser degree either deeply situated in the base of gastric glands or distributed through the pyloric antrum. Thus the urease appears to be located in the section of the stomach wherein concentration of oxyntic cells is greatest, but appears not to be present within them. In cats, the action of the urease was highest when gastric juice was being secreted actively by the mucosal cells, thus passing fluids outward into the gastric lumen.

A theory of Mathews (1920), reviewed by Kornberg and Davies (1955) suggested that secretion of HCl by the gastric mucosa was dependent upon the action of gastric urease, which provided ammonium ions by the breakdown of urea. Hydrogen ions were thought to be derived from the ammonium ions, either by the reaction $NH_4^+ = NH_3 + H^+$, ammonia then being absorbed or converted to ureido or carbamido compounds, or by the exchange of NH_4^+ and H^+ between mucosal cells and the blood during acid secretion. That this hypothesis is incorrect has been shown by a series of experiments using frog gastric mucosa *in vitro* (Davies, 1948; Davies and Kornberg, 1950, 1951; Glick, Zak, and von Korff, 1950). The rate of acid production in isolated frog gastric mucosa can be more than 500 times as great as the rate of urea breakdown and, indeed, more than 30 times the total urea content of the sample. Conversely, the amount of acid secreted by the isolated frog stomach is neither stimulated nor increased by addition of ammonia or urea; indeed, the urea added in several experiments was recovered quantitatively after incubation (Davies and

Kornberg, 1950). Thus, the extensive literature to the contrary, it is concluded by Kornberg and Davies (1955) that gastric urease plays no role in the mechanism of HCl production by the stomach. Further, in mammals, the presence of urease has been drastically inhibited by the use of antibiotics, both *in vivo* and *in vitro*. It is concluded that gastric urease is of bacterial origin and plays no essential part in gastric physiology.

5. Gastric Mucus

The lavish secretion of alkaline mucus in the esophagus and stomach protects the gastric mucosa from severe mechanical damage by abrasive gut contents. Also it acts to neutralize HCl at the beginning and end of a secretory period, when the flow is meager and the concentration of food and pepsinogen uncertain. Perhaps most importantly, the presence of mucus protects the mucosa from autodigestion by reducing the rate of diffusion of HCl and pepsin, thus roughly controlling the relative concentrations of active ions in the food mass (Babkin and Komarov, 1932).

When mucus secretion is suppressed or inadequate, severe lesions may occur in the stomach wall. Such autoproteolysis may be observed experimentally. An excised stomach of *Xenopus*, filled artificially with gastric acid and suspended in the same solution or Ringers solution, rather quickly perforates due to local action of activated pepsin on the gastric mucosa. The lesion penetrates the thin wall near the cardiac end, usually on or near the lesser curvature of the stomach; the pylorus is not usually affected. Similarly in *Rana*, the perforation occurs very rapidly; at 40°C, intragastric pH 1.0, an average of 2.4 min is required. Raising the pH to 2.8, an average of 11.7 min are required for full proteolytic perforation. There appeared to be no seasonal variation in susceptibility to autoproteolysis (Zwarenstein, 1953).

E. TEMPERATURE

Effect of temperature and season on peptic digestion was studied in *Rana* and *Necturus* by Riddle (1909), using Mett tubes. Although the method is not sensitive, relative rates of proteolysis may be established. However, the method does not discriminate between thermal effect on enzyme activity and the rate of enzyme secretion (Vonk, 1941). The rate of digestion as determined by this method is controlled and limited by (a) the available surface area of undigested protein; (b) differential diffusion of enzyme and acid through the nonhomogeneous medium; (c) length of experiment, with exchange at surface being reduced as the undigested protein recedes from the orifice of the tube.

Many individual experiments concerning peptic digestion at different temperatures, carried out during two or more seasons and with several

TABLE III

THERMAL COEFFICIENTS OF PEPTIC DIGESTION[a]

Species	Month	Run #1		Run #2		Thermal coefficient[c]
		Temp.	Digestive power[b]	Temp.	Digestive power[b]	
Rana	Nov.–Dec.	8.8°C	0.0167	23.1°C	0.1204	5.71
	March	10.6°	0.0249	24.7°	0.0927	1.94
	March–April	10.6°	0.0249	29.8°	0.1510	3.16
	March–April	24.7°	0.0924	29.8°	0.1510	3.20
	July	18.2°	0.1642	27.7°	0.1807	1.19
Necturus	Nov.–Dec.	8.7°	0.0358	23.0°	0.0474	0.93
	March	10.0°	0.0197	24.8°	0.0389	1.62

[a] Data from Riddle (1909).

[b] In Mett units; of relative, not absolute, value.

[c] Thermal coefficient defined: $C_t = 10 \ R_h/R_l \cdot x$, where R_h = digestive power at higher temperature; R_l = digestive power at lower temperature; x = difference between temperatures.

different species are recorded (Joly, 1958). They lack uniformity of protocol, however, which makes quantitative summary difficult. Calculation of thermal coefficient for a number of runs through the season have been presented (Table III).

Lowest temperature at which peptic proteolysis may take place *in vitro* varies from one animal group to another. Riddle has suggested that pepsin from *Amia* functions down to about 3° C, and that of *Rana* to about 10° C. It is implied that the turtle has an even higher thermal minimum for peptic digestion, but the published data do not substantiate the statement.

There appears to be some reduction in the digestive power of *Necturus* between November and March, although that of *Rana* remains nearly constant. In July, digestive power is observed to have increased about 3-fold over March and April. The species tested are shown to be capable of digestion at any season, provided a reasonable temperature be maintained. Thus the period of lowest digestive power appears to coincide with the fasting period of many of the animals. Maximum digestive power is found in the months in which feeding is most active.

Since pepsin is chemically still slightly active at 0° C, termination of proteolytic digestion at a higher temperature is apparently due to cessation of enzyme proliferation. Herter (1941) asserts that the gastric wall in *Rana* is nonsecretory at temperatures below 5° to 10° C. Amphibians maintained in captivity over winter often eat little and if fed artificially may digest ineffectively. Biedermann (1911) suggests this behavior to stem from inactivity of the gastric glands.

F. CONTROL OF GASTRIC SECRETION

A very large body of contradictory literature is concerned with those factors which initiate and control secretion of the gastric glands (Buddenbrock, 1956). Higher vertebrates, most especially the mammals, have been shown to effect secretion of gastric juice in reflex response to sight or odor of an experienced food item or a stimulus associated therewith, and also in response to mechanical stimulation of food within the stomach. Although of undoubted importance in initiating capture of prey, careful behavioral experiments of Wolvekamp and Tinbergen (1942) make convincing their conclusion that neither visual, olfactory, nor gustatory stimuli directly influence gastric secretion in tested amphibians. In the frog, physical contact of food materials on the gastric epithelium initiates and continues to stimulate proliferation of mucus, pepsinogen, and HCl (Friedman, 1934, 1937). In one series of experiments (Table IV) continuous mechanical stimulation of the stomach of sympathectomized frogs was provided by intragastric sponges. After 1 hr, pH had changed little and peptic activity was relatively low; whether feeble activity is due to absence of pepsin, lack of HCl, or both is not known. After a second hour's intragastric mechanical stimulation, the pH had dropped markedly and relative peptic activity was much higher (Wolvekamp and Tinbergen, 1942).

Insertion of glass beads in the stomach of *Rana* resulted in continuous secretion from esophageal and gastric glands for a period of about 2 months, at which time the irritants were removed. Decrease in rate of pepsin production after long-term secretion, may be due to inability of the chief cell to produce pepsinogen at the demanded rate.

TABLE IV

PEPTIC SECRETION AND DIGESTION AFTER SYMPATHETIC SECTION AND
MECHANICAL STIMULATION IN *Rana esculenta*[a]

Animal number	Initial pH	After first hour's mechanical stimulation		After second hour's mechanical stimulation	
		pH	Peptic activity	pH	Peptic activity[b]
1	>6.2	?	3–4.5	1.2	192
2	>6.2	?	51–60	1.2	252–264
3	3.0	?	1.5–6	1.2	114
4	4.4–6.2	4.4–6.2	30–36	1.2	90–132
5	4.4	4.4–6.2	9–12	1.2	132–150
6	1.2	>6	54–60	3.0	108–126
5	Empty	4.0–6.2	12	1.2	48–54
6	<4.0	?	9	1.2	24

[a] From Wolvekamp and Tinbergen (1942).
[b] Measured in arbitrary units.

Gastric acid secretion has been observed about an hour after natural or artificially induced vigorous activity. Friedman (1934) postulates a reflex, mediated by sympathetic fibers, in which the receptors are located in a strongly active organ, such as a limb. For example, if spinal and splanchnic innervation is intact, such reflex secretion will occur when the proximal section of a severed sciatic nerve is stimulated. Whether this response is due to direct reflex or is secondarily produced by adrenaline production is not known. Secretion subsequent to activity and handling has been indicated as a major source of potential error in digestive experimentation (Wolvekamp and Tinbergen, 1942).

Friedman (1934) has described secretion of pepsinogen and HCl to be controlled by the sympathetic system through the splanchnic nerve and, further, that the parasympathetic does not participate in this control. Wolvekamp and Tinbergen (1942) however, on the basis of a careful sequence of experiments, have demonstrated the ability of mechanical stimulus of an earthworm in the stomach to provoke secretion of pepsinogen and HCl in *Rana*, after section of all sympathetic connections to the stomach. There is agreement that the vagus is not involved in gastric secretion in this genus. Distention or loading of the denervated stomach will also result in gastric secretion (Crombach *et al.*, 1958). Friedman (1939) has demonstrated that the gastric glands of *Necturus* are not under nervous control. The mechanism of stimulation may thus be similar in *Rana* and *Necturus;* both may resemble that in fishes (Buddenbrock, 1956). O. Yamamoto, however (cited by Buddenbrock), has shown gastric secretion in *Bufo* to be controlled by the parasympathetic, with acetylcholine effecting secretion and adrenaline acting to depress secretion.

Application of drugs may modify behavior of the gastric glands. In *Rana*, small doses of adrenaline stimulate the secretion of HCl and pepsinogen in the stomach and highly concentrated pepsinogen in the esophagus, whereas larger doses inhibit this production. Small adrenaline dosage in *Necturus* results in the secretion of a highly acid gastric juice, with low pepsin concentration. Acetylcholine and pilocarpine fail to stimulate acid secretion in either genus (Friedman, 1934, 1937, 1942). In *Rana*, however, a viscous neutral or slightly alkaline gastric juice with little digestive power may be elaborated.

Since a number of amphibians have been shown to lack nervous control of gastric secretion, it is particularly crucial to examine evidence concerning hormonal influences. Extract of the stomach wall of the pig, as well as that of the bullfrog, provoke gastric secretion when injected into the dorsal lymph sinus (Keeton *et al.*, 1920; Popielski, 1929; Delrue, 1930, 1933). As a manifestation of increased HCl production, histamine raised the chloride content of the gastric mucosa from 0.06 to 0.23% in 5 hr (Hogartz, 1932).

N. W. Timofeev and co-workers (1936–1939, cited by Buddenbrock, 1956) injected extracts of stomach linings, peptones, and a variety of additional digestive extracts, stimulating gastric secretion. They demonstrated, furthermore, that blood from an animal actively secreting gastric juice, when injected into a second individual, provoked secretion therein. Thus, although suggesting the hormonal mechanism as probable, the experiments have not demonstrated thus far unequivocally the hormonal influence and control of gastric secretion in the normal, unaltered, amphibian.

G. VOMITING

Retrograde expulsion of stomach contents may be brought about by vomiting in at least some species of all vertebrate classes, but character- istics of the action and its physiological background vary from one group to another and in lower vertebrates are little known (Klee, 1927b; Borison and Wang, 1953). While in the higher vertebrates control of vomiting lies apparently in the medulla, the anurans (at least *Rana* and *Bufo*) are able to regurgitate the stomach contents and expel them from the mouth after extirpation of the brain and spinal cord (Mellinger, 1881). Also, mammals characteristically rely on back-pressure generated by contraction of the abdominal musculature and the diaphragm to propel the gastric contents through the esophagus, whereas in the anurans this is clearly not required. Mellinger described his controlled experiments, since duplicated under the direction of Thumas (1891), in which the entire process of vomiting was successfully completed in the fully pithed frog after opening of the ab- dominal cavity.

Subcutaneous or intragastric injection of 0.05 gm of tartar emetic into frogs well fed with meat resulted in antiperistaltic contractions within 5 min. Repeatedly, for 10 min or more, these reverse movements recurred, visibly moving stomach contents into the cardium, thence from the body through the esophagus and mouth. Similar antiperistalses resulted from apomorphine injection, but the gastric contents came to lie in the mouth, since the buccal region had become paralyzed before gastric evacuation. Using the same drugs, however, Mellinger was unable to bring about vomit- ing in *Triturus*.

Capacity to vomit appears to vary with season in *Rana* (Mellinger, 1881). Spring- and summer-captured individuals characteristically exhibit the reaction; the ability lessens in October and November animals, while it appears no longer present in January and February. That various workers have declared anurans unable to vomit, Mellinger suggests to be due to use of either winter animals or those kept in fasting condition in the laboratory.

V. Larval Foregut

A. ANURA

Barrington (1946), emphasizing and extending suggestions of Machan (1935), details the observation that in anurans, the larval foregut differentiates at metamorphosis into the ciliated esophagus and inflated stomach, within which proteolysis occurs in acid medium.

The precursorial foregut runs posteriad on the right side of the tadpole body cavity, loops about the pancreas, with some inflation to form the "stomach," thence runs to join with the midgut. This normally unelaborated tube is nondigestive, but serves only for food transportation from the pharynx to the midgut. Abrupt change in histological anatomy and the entrance of the bile duct just posterior to this junction, added to actual observation of the gut in metamorphosis, evidences the foregut to be embryological precursor to both adult stomach and esophagus, while the larval midgut, surrounding and posterior to the bile duct, differentiates to the adult small intestine.

Peristaltic movements have not been observed in the short esophagus. Thus the rich foregut ciliation is principal agent transporting mucus to the larval stomach, where the thin mucous strings become tightly packed (Dodd, 1950). The foregut in the microhylid *Hypopachus* exhibits exceptional form in being vertically divided almost to its ventral wall by a ciliated longitudinal septum, which forms as a continuation of the pharyngeal vela which direct right and left mucous cords into the foregut. Thus each cord maintains its own duct to the "stomach" (Savage, 1952).

The term "manicotto" has been usefully introduced by Lambertini (1929) to designate the larval anuran stomach, which has been demonstrated to be a storage organ, in position similar to a true stomach, but without proteolytic function. The manicotto is very weakly muscular.

1. Histology

Principal cell types of the larval foregut include a ciliated and a mucogenic epithelial cell, both of which follow definite patterns of distribution in the mucosa. The anterior foregut of *Bufo bufo* and *Rana temporaria* is strongly ciliated, but is separated from the larval stomach by a brief nonciliated area. Bounding the unciliated mucosa of the manicotto both anteriorly and posteriorly are narrow ciliated bands. In the unciliated posterior foregut of *Rana* and *Bufo*, the presence of well developed muscle in the gut wall suggests a presumptive pyloric sphincter, although it is probably rarely, if ever, functional in the tadpole. In *Bufo* the larval stomach is absent and the cilia in the lower foregut are confined to the outer side of the pancreatic loop. Distribution of the cilia appears not to change markedly through larval life (Barrington, 1946).

The mucus-secreting cell is important in forming the whole of the unciliated foregut mucosa, as well as being interspersed among the ciliated cells. Anterior to the manicotto, rarely within, and never behind it, goblet cells may develop from the more typical cell type which has a striated border and distal aggregations of mucin within the cell. Mucous neck cells, present in adult gastric glands, are absent as are all indications of structures similar to the adult esophageal glands (Machan, 1935; Barrington, 1946). Actual production of mucus diminishes posteriorly in the foregut as the striated epithelial border becomes more prominent.

2. Metamorphosis

In *Bufo* at metamorphosis the definitive esophagus and stomach differentiate from the larval foregut. Barrington (1946) has described the growth of a novel cell type beneath the base of the larval columnar epithelium. As the larval epithelium sloughs away to the lumen, these new cells proliferate to form the definitive adult epithelium. In the toad a number of changes of physiological importance may be noted. The midgut is reduced in length and is increased markedly in width; the shortening structure moves across to the left side of the body cavity. The tubular esophagus becomes externally differentiated from the inflated stomach; within the esophageal mucosa the ciliated and goblet cells differentiate from surface epithelium while the mucous and zymogen cells develop within the expanding esophageal glands. The posterior heavily muscular section of foregut develops to the pyloric region, shortly posterior to which the bile duct enters the small intestine. Throughout the gut ciliated epithelium degenerates at metamorphosis to be replaced with the adult cells. The new gastric epithelium appears, gastric glands develop, with cells differentiating to form mucous neck and basal cells (Duesberg, 1907; Bowers, 1909).

In comparison, the pattern of change is similar in *Rana temporaria* except for detail involving the larval stomach. At metamorphosis the manicotto becomes progressively less distinct externally and finally cannot be discerned. The tissue differentiates to a position in the stomach just anterior to the pyloris. The observation of Janes (1934) that all glandular vestiges have not been lost at metamorphosis but rather re-form or at least contribute to glandular re-formation in the adult, has been tentatively confirmed by Barrington (1946).

B. URODELA

Larval urodeles are carnivorous, feeding by predation upon small animals. As particulate feeders they have not evolved the elaborate branchial filter of the anuran tadpole but rather possess well developed buccal apparatus, as in the adult. Food accumulated in the pharynx is swallowed and is carried by peristalsis to the stomach, where peptic proteolysis is

TABLE V

RELATIVE PEPTIC POWER IN DEVELOPING *Ambystoma*[a]

Stage of development	Column (in mm) of egg albumen digested in 24 hr	Relative peptic power[b]
Premetamorphic	3.5	1.0
Early metamorphic	0.8	0.052
Late metamorphic	1.2	0.117
Postmetamorphic	4.5	1.64

[a] Data from Kuntz (1924).
[b] Rate of premetamorphic digestion chosen as unity.

initiated. At metamorphosis, as in the Anura, the foregut undergoes radical change, in which all layers of the gut experience autolysis, phagocytosis, and reorganization. There is gross reduction in length of gut and, by aggregation of the muscle, a thickening of the walls. Definitive gastric glands arise earliest in the pyloric region, advancing to the cardiac end.

The power of peptic digestion changes markedly during metamorphosis. Kuntz (1924), using Mett tubes in the stomach of *Ambystoma*,* measured the relative capacity to digest albumen in a sequence of developmental stages (Table V). Throughout the metamorphic period proteolytic digestion is severely retarded. The data suggest more effective digestion at the standard Mett tube surface in the postmetamorphic adult than in the larva.

VI. Small Intestine

The small intestine of the adult anuran is elongate and thrown into folds within the abdominal cavity; in urodeles this structure runs directly posteriad to join the large intestine, from which it is often separated by a valve and is clearly differentiated by structure. In amphibians, as in the remaining vertebrate classes, the principal processes of digestion take place in this section of the gut. Acid chyme is received from the stomach through the pylorus into the duodenum, which also receives effluents of the pancreatic and bile ducts. Churned by controlled contraction and propelled slowly, at controlled rate, through the small gut, digestive enzymes are mixed with the chyme, molecular fragmentation is brought about, with active absorption of final digestive products.

A. HISTOLOGY

The interspecifically variable mucosa of the small intestine may be simple and confined to the principal curvature of the small intestine, or

* The preferred spelling *Ambystoma*, rather than *Amblystoma*, is used throughout this volume.

may be variously elaborated. In *Rana esculenta*, the anterior duodenal wall is expanded as a series of longitudinal leaf-like ridges, which are grouped irregularly just behind the pyloric sphincter. Posteriorly these ridges aggregate to become more clearly organized, forming a series of flexible, valvular, crescentic folds, enclosing deep crypts which open to the rear, thereby inhibiting intestinal regurgitation. In the posterior half of the small intestine, the diagonal crescents are superseded by longitudinal folds which expand the effective surface area to the end of the gut. Crypts of the small intestine function in *Proteus*, *Salamandra*, and *Necturus* as proliferative areas within which epithelial cells differentiate, mature, and migrate to the surface (Biedermann, 1911).

The entire mucosa is richly vascular; lymphatic vessels are concentrated beneath the epithelial ridges, where present, with lacteal extensions penetrating from the submucosa toward the lumen. The intestinal villi with central lacteal ducts, lacking entirely in *Rana*, are present in *Salamandra maculata*; in *Bufo laurentii* the anterior third of the duodenum is described as villous. The epithelial surface itself is formed primarily of columnar cells with striated border, richly interspersed with mucoid goblet cells (Herter, 1941) which increase in number posteriorly. The muscularis is heavily developed in the mature small intestine, most especially in the duodenum, where elaborately innervated circular musculature controls intestinal movement.

The modified Brunner's glands and epithelial mucous cells elaborate mucus for protection from mechanical and autoproteolytic damage (Florey and Harding, 1933). These mucoid cells exist in a number of defined stages (Fischer and Ritter, 1953) as follows: (1) storage cells with coarse mucous plug, (2) cells in process of secretion, (3) empty cells, (4) resting cells, (5) new mucus-forming cells, (6) nearly filled cells. It is described that the cells pass sequentially through the stages as listed, rotating back to secretory utility. The ratios of cell numbers among the types are quite fixed. About 10 min after feeding, the storage cells are strongly depleted. The actively secreting cells effect maximum concentration of mucus in about 50 min, but secretion persists at decreasing rate for several hours (Buddenbrock, 1956).

The mucoid secretion of the anterior duodenum, with high concentration of bicarbonate, is strongly alkaline in reaction (pH 7.5 to 9.0). Triggered to secrete by the acid reaction of duodenal contents, the fluid produced acts rapidly, in company with bile, to raise the pH of the chyme to an optimum for intestinal enzymes.

Elaborate multicellular digestive glands appear lacking in most amphibians, but crypts of Lieberkühn have been described in *Salamandra* and certain other urodeles (Biedermann, 1911; Vonk, 1941).

Acid reaction of chyme entering from the stomach (Thomas, 1957), as well as the presence of bile, stimulates initial peristaltic contraction of the duodenum (Babkin, 1924). The functional operation of the contractile small gut, especially the duodenal section, is quite similar to that of the stomach and will not be detailed here. Innervation and pharmacological stimulation have been little investigated.

B. PANCREAS

The pancreas exists as a discrete structure of variable external form, situated between the duodenum and the stomach, and enclosed in the hepato-gastric ligament (Broman, 1937). Development usually follows from three rudiments, one dorsal and two ventral (Siwe, 1927 gives extensive literature survey). External secretion from the anuran pancreas usually passes directly to the small intestine in a single duct; in some urodeles, however, two pancreatic ducts enter the duodenum. The more posterior duct runs to the small intestine variously combined with the bile duct (Göppert, 1891). In other forms, few to many ducts may run between pancreas and duodenum, e.g., 7 small openings in *Cryptobranchus* (Broman, 1937) and 19–47 in *Proteus* (Oppel, 1889).

Secretion of pancreatic juice is intermittent, depending upon food intake. Between periods of secretory flow, zymogen granules accumulate within the secretory cells. At the entry of an acid food mass from the stomach, the intestinal mucosa is stimulated to secrete mucus, enzymes, and secretin. This hormone is elaborated into the capillaries within the intestinal submucosa; it circulates to the pancreas and stimulates that gland to secrete pancreatic juice.

The complex pancreatic secretion, little investigated in the amphibia, includes three classes of enzymes—tryptic protease, lipase, and amylase.

At metamorphosis, the pancreas undergoes only slight and short-term changes. Total size of the organ is initially reduced. Zymogen granules are lost from the acinous cells and production of the digestive secretion is but briefly interrupted.

Secretin

The hormone secretin is produced within the mucosa of the small gut at the time of entry of acid chyme from the stomach. It functions in stimulating the secretion of pancreatic juice, which provides the more active enzymes of intestinal digestion. The hormone has been recovered from extracts of the duodenal mucosa in a number of amphibians and has been tested by autostimulation and by successful initiation of pancreatic secretion in dogs. Secretins from all tested vertebrate species appear equivalent in their capacity to influence pancreatic production (Bayliss and Starling, 1902, 1903; Koschtojanz *et al.*, 1933). Distribution of secretin production in the duodenum is variable, but species specific. In the frog, only that section of the duodenum directly posterior to the pyloric sphincter produces secretin, while it is secreted the length of the duodenum in "the salamander" (Koschtojanz *et al.*, 1933).

C. LIVER

The liver and attached gall bladder are uniformly present and discrete within amphibians. The anuran liver is usually bilobate; urodeles and apodans have a single, undivided, but sometimes emarginate liver. Of excessive complexity, this organ is here of concern as the source of bile, which, after production, is stored in the gall bladder. Upon reception in the duodenum of acid chyme released by the pyloric sphincter, bile is discharged from the gall bladder to flow through the bile duct into the small intestine.

Bile itself is a complex mixture of manifold function. When flowing into the acid chyme, bile neutralizes a part of the remaining HCl, raising the pH of the duodenal contents. Presence of bile in the lumen of the small intestine may initiate or amplify peristaltic contractions, thereby mixing rapidly the contents of the upper small intestine. Bile acts as an inhibitor of growth in a number of bacteria, which may exist at moderate population level with slight benefit, or at least no detriment, to the host. These same bacteria, however, unchecked, may build up population size and simultaneously accumulate detrimental concentrations of metabolites (Herter, 1941). Perhaps of greatest significance is the facilitation of fat digestion and absorption by the presence of bile with the enzyme lipase.

Bile

Bile enters the small intestine through the *ductus choledochus*, having been stored in the gall bladder from the time of its elaboration within the secretory cords of the liver. The bile is a most complex mixture, only certain components of which are of interest in the present connection. The term "bile salt," used in the sense of Haslewood (1955) as "those substances which have a special function as an aid in the digestion of fats and their absorption into tissue fluids," generally indicates several groups of molecules secreted within the bile. Although many variant steroid molecules qualify within the sense of the term, it is notable that the characteristic composition of bile salts is species specific; from one taxonomic group to another, a variety of bile salts is present, but within a species the component salts apparently are altered only in relative proportion, not in kind, by disparity in state of nutrition, temperature, or particular endocrine level.

Evidence is quite conclusive (Haslewood and Wooten, 1950; Haslewood, 1955) that in most vertebrates the bile acids exist as conjugated salts and that naturally occurring unconjugated acids are very rare. The latter have been found, however, as a minor but significant part of the biliary secretion of frogs and a toad (Kazuno, 1940). The rarity of appearance of unconjugated bile acids would suggest scrutiny where reported, for the possibility of splitting of the conjugated salt by microorganisms, either within the animal, or later, *in vitro*.

Three general types of bile salts have been described from amphibians. The first includes esters, which at biological pH exist as ions, formed by conjugation of sulfate with alcohols of **27**, **28**, or **29** carbon atoms. The examples ranol sulfate from *Rana* and pentahydroxybufostane sulfate from *Bufo* have a general formula $R \cdot O \cdot SO_3H$.

The second generic group of compounds are carboxylic hydroxyacids with **27**, **28**, or **29** carbon atoms, which are conjugated with taurine to form molecules of the formula $R \cdot CO \cdot NH \cdot CH_2 \cdot SO_3H$ which actually exist in ionic form within the animal. As examples, trihydroxybufosterocholenic and trihydroisosterocholenic acids (probably $C_{28}H_{46}O_5$) from *Bufo* and trihydroxycoprostanic acid ($C_{27}H_{46}O_5$) from *Rana* may be cited (Haslewood, 1952, 1955).

Third, a group of hydroxylated cholanic acids with **24** carbon atoms, conjugated with glycine, result in substances of the general formula $R \cdot CO \cdot NH \cdot CH_2 \cdot COOH$, for example isohydroxycholene (probably $C_{24}H_{40}O_3$) from *Bufo vulgaris* (Shimizu, Kazuno, and Tsuboi, 1953; Haslewood, 1955).

Bile of the newt *Diemyctylus pyrrhogaster* (100, 200 specimens yielding 1.5 liters of bile) was shown by careful analysis to contain cholic acid (0.27 gm), deoxycholic acid (20 gm), and a crude bile alcohol (11.5 gm) named tetrahydroxyisohomocholane (probably $C_{25}H_{44}O_4$) with small amounts of other alcohols (Okasaki, 1944; Haslewood, 1955).

A detergent fat-emulsifying molecule will include a portion which attracts fats and, usually distant on the molecule, another part which is attractive to water. On the one hand the methyl and the —CH_2— groups of bile salts have affinity for fats and concentrate centripetally in a micelle about dissolved fat, whereas peripheral hydrophylous parts of the molecule (the hydroxyl, carboxyl, and sulfate groups) hold the micelle in suspension in aqueous medium. Thus within such a medium many loose chemical complexes may form and be suspended.

Lipase, acting to facilitate the hydrolysis of fats to fatty acids and glycerol, apparently does not require the presence of bile salts. However, emulsification of the fat increases markedly the effective enzyme-fat interface at which reaction occurs, thus increasing its rate. There has been suggestion that taurocholate acts as a specific lipase stimulator, but evidence is inconclusive (Haslewood, 1955).

D. ENZYMES ACTIVE IN SMALL INTESTINE

The digestive enzymes which act in the small intestine derive from secretory glands in the intestinal wall or from the pancreas. As a diverse group these enzymes are most active in a slightly acid medium, although the optimum pH in any case depends not only upon the specific enzyme but upon precise characteristics of substrate. Up to the limit at which they are thermally denatured, i.e. 50° to 60° C, these enzymes improve their rate of substrate hydrolysis with increased temperature. In all cases within the Amphibia, the optimum performance temperature of the individual enzyme is well above body temperature normally attained by a living individual. Thermal coefficients have not been calculated from the literature as many of the measures of enzymic activity have been inaccurate and insufficiently controlled (Kenyon, 1925; Chesley, 1934; Vonk, 1941).

No known amphibians possess enzymes which facilitate breakdown of keratin, chitin, or cellulose. While occasional members of the intestinal flora may utilize these compounds, it is doubtful if bacterial breakdown, with secondary use of the products by the host, normally provides significant nutrient in Amphibia. Extreme length of the mid- and hindgut in anuran larvae has been suggested as an adaptation to permit utilization of bacterial hydrolysis as a nutritional mode. But this potential source appears unnecessary and its postulation is not demanded by evidence (see Section VII).

The pH of the small intestine in *Rana* has been measured by A. M. W. Mennega (cited by Vonk, 1941) as averaging 7.84 ± 0.26 for the duodenum and 7.89 ± 0.28 for the postduodenal gut. The slight difference appears to be insignificant.

1. Trypsin

The pancreatic proteinase trypsin is secreted as a zymogen which is activated rapidly in the duodenum in the presence of enterokinase, a secretory product of the intestinal glands. In amphibians this is perhaps the principal proteolytic enzyme series, as it is able to hydrolyze protein as well as the intermediate breakdown products in a slightly alkaline medium.

2. Erepsin

Erepsin, in reality a series of peptidases, is produced by the intestinal glands. Experimentally it occurs in greater concentration in extracts of the intestinal mucosa than in the secreted juice. This hormone does not attack the unbroken protein molecule but hydrolyzes peptones and proteoses to amino acids.

3. Amylase

Amylase is secreted principally as a component of pancreatic juice and functions in the hydrolysis of glycogens, starches, or intermediate hydrolytic products to simple sugars, which then may be absorbed in the small intestine. As secreted in pancreatic juice of *Rana*, amylase is very active (Kuntz, 1924); amylytic activity of a pancreatic extract was found to be about 50 times that of an extract of the intestinal wall (Jordan, 1927), verifying the relative insignificance of the latter source. Similarly in *Necturus* the pancreatic extract far surpasses intestinal extract in amylytic activity (Kenyon, 1925). There has been little attempt systematically to identify the number of types of amylytic enzymes acting in amphibians. Maltase, in small amount, has been identified in pancreatic, but not intestinal, extracts of *Rana* (Herter, 1941; Vonk, 1941). Diastase and glucosidase also have been specified in pancreatic juice. Invertase and lactase were absent in gut extract of *Necturus* (Kenyon, 1925). Since most adult amphibians are carnivorous, the utility of a large flow of active amylase has properly been questioned by Herter (1941), who has postulated its utility in completing digestion of the gut contents of the prey animals.

4. Lipase

Pancreatic lipase is also apparently secreted as a zymogen and may be activated by calcium or bile salts, protein in alkaline medium, or magnesium chloride (Vonk, 1937). This enzyme facilitates hydrolysis of fats and glycerides to fatty acids and glycerol and in addition participates in the breakdown of lipoprotein. The presence of lipase also makes possible the opposite reaction, of importance in fat absorption, in which fats are reconstituted from glycerol and available fatty acids in the absorbing epithelial cell. Simultaneous presence of bile salts increases the efficiency of lipase; the bile component emulsifies fat, thereby providing much greater reaction area. Fatty acids are transported as a finely dispersed colloid in the presence of bile salts (Vonk, 1937).

E. ABSORPTION

Very few investigations have been made concerning the absorption of nutrients in amphibians. True absorption, involving expenditure of energy and active movement of molecules against a concentration gradient, was early established in the frog (Jordan and Begemann, 1921; Jordan, 1927; Houssal *et al.*, 1941). The gut of operated animals, filled with isotonic or hypotonic solutions of NaCl or glucose was emptied in 2 to 3 days. *In vitro* studies of excised gut bags verified rapid absorption of glucose and relative permeability to disaccharides. Westenbrink and Gratama (1937) examined absorption of various monosaccharides, which were found to vary in rate of uptake. Galactose and glucose were rapidly absorbed; fructose and L-arabinose were taken up, but at much lower rate.

Expenditure of energy in absorption of nutrients is verified by increased O_2 consumption of tissue in the intestinal wall. In a detailed set of experiments, Weel (1938) pipetted 5% solutions of monosaccharide, glucose, and peptone into the stomach of the frog; the oxygen consumption of sample sections of gut from a series of experimental animals was followed for 24 hr (Fig. 1). Oxygen consumption rose strongly in the first 3 hr, evidencing the initiation of absorption. More total energy is required for uptake of glucose and peptone than for the monosaccharide. Initial uptake of glucose

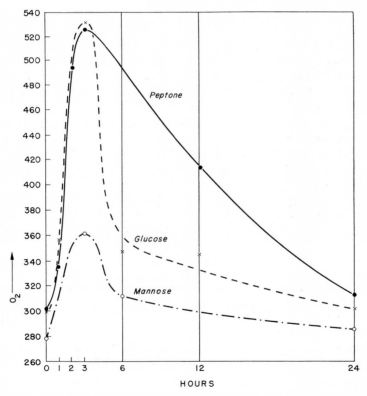

Fig. 1. Oxygen consumption of intestinal tissue during active absorption of nutrients. Ordinate: oxygen utilization in cubic centimeters per gram dry tissue per quarter hour. Abscissa: time in hours after feeding. Redrawn from Weel (1938).

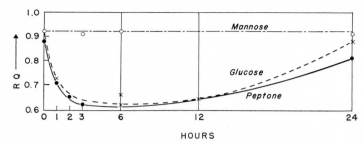

HOURS

Fig. 2. Change of respiratory quotient (RQ) of intestinal tissue during active absorption of nutrients. Ordinate: respiratory quotient. Abscissa: time in hours after feeding. Redrawn from Weel (1938).

and peptone was rapid; glucose absorption was readily completed whereas the process was much slower for the peptone.

In the same experiments the respiratory quotient (RQ) during the absorption of monosaccharide did not change, but in both glucose and peptone uptake the RQ decreased rapidly during the first 3 hr (Fig. 2), only slowly approaching again the level of the starving animal (shown at time 0 hr). The low RQ values typify those observed in fat metabolism; it is assumed that lipids are being oxidized in the absorptive cells during uptake of glucose and peptone.

Fatty acids may be absorbed against a concentration gradient, but the rate is reduced in the absence of glucose and the process is abolished in the absence of oxygen, thus documenting the energy requirement for intracellular reconstitution of fat in the presence of lipase (Gordon and Csáky, 1942; Frazer, 1946).

Severe oxygen deficiency diminishes sharply the rate of intestinal absorption of glucose and galactose in *Rana* (Table VI) but does not affect the rate for fructose and xylose, as anoxia retards the process of intracellu-

TABLE VI

EFFECT OF OXYGEN TENSION ON SUGAR ABSORPTION[a]

Sugar	Number individuals	O_2 (parts per 100)	Per cent sugar absorbed in 8 hr
Glucose	15	21 (normal)	34
	12	3.3–3.9 (anoxia)	24
Galactose	13	21 (normal)	37
	9	3.0–3.7 (anoxia)	29

[a] Data from Cordier and Worbe (1955).

lar phosphorylation. It is suggested that resistance to anoxia varies with the season (Cordier and Worbe, 1955). Hypoxia has little effect on the rate of glucose uptake down to a concentration of 6 parts per 100 of O_2. Beneath this O_2 concentration, absorption rate very rapidly drops off to a low level at 3 or 4 parts per 100 of O_2, in which concentration the frog can exist for at least 10 hr (Cordier and Worbe, 1956b, c).

Glucose absorption in the frog is sensitive to hyperconcentration of CO_2. An inhibitory effect is noted at 5 parts per 100 of CO_2; the rate of absorption diminishes to 50% normal at 12 to 15 parts per 100 of CO_2 (Cordier and Worbe, 1956a). The same authors have demonstrated an increased rate of hexose absorption (Q_{10} of 1.5 to 2.0) with higher temperatures in *Rana esculenta*, arguing in favor of glucose phosphorylation in the course of intestinal absorption.

Elaborate studies concerning water and salt balance in amphibians, but verifying the transfer of water and NaCl across the membrane of the small intestine, have been discussed by Cooperstein and Hogben (1959; this paper provides entry to a vast literature).

VII. Larval Mid- and Hindgut

The mid- and hindgut of anuran larvae together have a length somewhat greater than the total length of the animal. The long but rather delicate tube is coiled within the abdominal cavity forcing the stomach and duodenum to the right side of the body. Maximum gut length is reached at the stage when hind legs are well developed. Herter (1941) cites the ratio of small intestine to total body length as averaging 1.9 to 1 in *Rana esculenta* and 1.02 to 1 in *Rana temporaria*.

There is great variability in this ratio within species which have apparently similar food habits; the adaptive importance to the species of particular ratio thus remains obscure (Schmidt, 1935). However, that the length of intestine may be controlled, within limits, by the larval diet, is well established. Literature concerning this nutritional problem is well reviewed by Babak (1903, 1906) and Herter (1941). In a very general way, among amphibians, relative gut length increases as a function of the body mass. Young individuals have relatively larger small intestines than do older. In those fed a vegetable diet the small intestines are relatively longer than in those fed on meat. Although there has been criticism of Babak's experiments, it remains probable that this hyperextension is due to chemical influence rather than to the processing of extra bulk.

At metamorphosis the anuran gut, posterior to the manicotto, becomes much shorter; the reduction in length apparently takes place at both ends through the gradual tonic contraction of circular and longitudinal muscle.

This contraction and reorganization of the gut requires about 24 hr in *Bufo* and occurs about 10 days before the front limbs break through (Bowers, 1909).

Histological changes in *Rana* include a thickening of the gut wall, which is then mostly composed of submucosa and muscularis. The mucosal epithelium is replaced by cells migrating from underneath and the definitive intestinal glands are formed. In *Ambystoma*, the cells of the gut wall aggregate to become more compact and specifically organized (Kuntz, 1924).

Metamorphic reorganization of the mid- and hindgut in *Rana temporaria* involves quantitative change in proteolytic enzyme concentration and activity (Blacher and Liosner, 1930). With initiation of change from the larval state, enzymic strength is briefly increased until the gut lining itself is destroyed, at which time the enzymes disappear, and feeding and digestion cease. After intestinal changes have been completed, proteolysis again becomes possible, although the relative concentration of enzymes and, therefore, the activity, is modified.

Absence of peptic digestion and a true stomach in amphibian larvae is said by Kuntz (1924) to be due to herbivorous food habit. Herbivorous vertebrates are uniformly incapable of cellulase production and rely upon bacterial fermentation for whatever breakdown of large carbohydrate molecules may occur. As an adaptation in larval anurans to increased total fermentation within the gut it is suggested that increased time is allowed within the digestive tract by the marked elongation of the midgut. Likewise, since an acid medium inhibits fermentation, elimination of the gastric acid would allow advantageous pH. Although the importance of bacterial fermentation in reduction of cellulose and consequent increase in the relative nutrient value of vegetable foods is unknown, there at least exists the possibility of bacterial breakdown of complex carbohydrates and their partial utilization in tadpoles. That most tadpole larvae are omnivorous rather than strictly herbivorous appears to weaken Kuntz' hypothesis concerning utility of the lengthened gut (Barrington, 1946).

In order to reduce stagnation, movement of chyme through the gut near the larval stomach is improved by the presence of cilia on the outer curvature of each bend.

A. PROTEOLYTIC ACTIVITY

Histological evidence has suggested the absence of peptic proteolysis in larval anurans. A number of workers have tested extracts of the several regions of the larval gut for digestive power. Using Mett tubes, Kuntz (1924) examined the relative peptic potency at various developmental stages in *Rana pipiens* and *Ambystoma tigrinum*. No peptic activity was shown either before or during the period of metamorphosis in *Rana*. As soon as the tadpoles emerged to land and resumed feeding as adults, the 1.5-mm Mett tube of albumin was digested in 24 hr.

Barrington (1946) reports results of *in vitro* experiments on digestion of casein by foregut extracts from tadpoles of *Rana temporaria* and *Bufo bufo*, at pH 2.2. Before the metamorphic stage at which the gut is reduced in length, no evidence for the presence of pepsin or peptic digestion was found. However, in either genus, with the appearance of detectable rudiments of the definitive glands (e.g. in *Rana*, when limbs are visible and tail is shortening) peptic activity may be verified experimentally. It is suggested thus that the active enzyme precursor appears within gland cells before the glands are fully differentiated. It is quite clear that the larval stomach is not in fact a true stomach and that neither that structure nor any part of the larval foregut is capable of the production of pepsin or the digestion of protein.

The manicotto was also tested by Barrington (1946) for the presence of amylase, with negative results.

VIII. Large Intestine

The hindgut is usually differentiated from the small intestine by abruptly increased cross section. At that transition a flap-like valve, absent in most Amphibia, prevents retrograde movement of the gut contents in *Rana*. The mucosal lining is of columnar epithelium with interspersion of goblet cells, which become more densely distributed posteriorly. The hindgut participates in no principal digestive function, although the pH is appropriate—8.05 ± 0.27—(cited by Vonk, 1941, from Mennega) for lingering continuation of certain of the small intestinal processes. Also possible here is bacterial breakdown of otherwise inaccessible compounds, such as cellulose. Some products of this hydrolysis might be absorbed in the hindgut.

Water and salts are absorbed in the large intestine. In isolated large gut of *Rana catesbeiana*, the mucosa is negative in electrical potential (45 mv) with respect to the serosa. The potential difference is concomitant of the active sodium pump which provides the mechanism for salt resorption from the hindgut of this species, which invariably lives in a hypotonic environment. Chloride ion is moved by passive flux in the direction of the electrical gradient, thus away from the gut lumen (Cooperstein and Hogben, 1959). The $HC_3^-:CO_2$ system, acting as a unit, also moves across the membrane in the direction of the serosa. *In vitro*, this reduction of HCO_3^- concentration within a closed bag of large intestine, has been demonstrated in *Rana* (Cooperstein *et al.*, 1957).

A. DEFECATION

As water and salts are absorbed from the contents of the hindgut, the remnant mass is converted to a semisolid consistency. The feces are usually gray or blackish in color and contain indigestible materials, such as chitin, soil particles from oligochaete gut contents, and plant materials, as well as incompletely digested products. In addition, parasites, commensals, and large masses of bacteria are all held together in a mucoid matrix. In adult anurans, a fine membrane, consisting primarily of mucus and cellular detritus is separated from the gut epithelium and surrounds the bolus as a delicate bag. This bag and its contents are extruded in a spiral fashion, as determined by spiral rugosities of the hindgut, thus giving a screw-shaped form to the feces. This neat disposal acts to prevent contamination of the cloaca and its other orifices (Herter, 1941). Such mechanism appears to have achieved antiquity as the spirally decorate coprolites of the Stegocephalia suggest that those individuals, also, avoided cloacal contamination.

References

Babak, E. (1903). Ueber den Einfluss der Nahrung auf die Länge des Darmkanals. *Biol. Zentr.* **23**, 477–483, 519–528.

Babak, E. (1906). Ueber die morphogenetische Reaktion des Darmkanals der Froschlarve auf Muskelproteine verschiedener Tierklassen. *Beitr. Chem. Physiol. Pathol.* **7**, 323–330.

Babkin, B. P. (1924). The influence of natural chemical stimuli on the movements of the frog's stomach. *Quart. J. Exptl. Physiol.* **14**, 259–277.

Babkin, B. P. (1928). The digestive work of the stomach. *Physiol. Rev.* **8**, 365–392.

Babkin, B. P. (1950). "Secretory Mechanism of the Digestive Glands," 1027 pp. Hoeber, New York.

Babkin, B. P., and Komarov, S. A. (1932). The influence of gastric mucus on peptic digestion. *Can. Med. Assoc. J.* **27**, 463–469.

Barbéra, A. G. (1898). Ueber die Reizbarkeit des Froschmagens. *Z. Biol.* **36**, 239–258.

Barge, J. A. J. (1937). Mundhöhlendach und Gaumen. *In* "Handbuch der vergleichenden Anatomie der Wirbeltiere" (L. Bolk, E. Göppert, E. Kallius, W. Lubosch, eds.), Vol. III, pp. 29–48. Urban and Schwarzenberg, Berlin and Vienna.

Barrington, E. J. W. (1942). Gastric digestion in the lower vertebrates. *Biol. Rev. Cambridge Phil. Soc.* **17**, 1–27.

Barrington, E. J. W. (1946). The delayed development of the stomach in the frog (*Rana temporaria*) and the toad (*Bufo bufo*). *Proc. Roy. Soc.* **116**, 1–21.

Bayliss, W. M., and Starling, E. H. (1902). The mechanism of pancreatic secretion. *J. Physiol. (London)* **28**, 325–353.

Bayliss, W. M., and Starling, E. H. (1903). On the uniformity of the pancreatic mechanism in Vertebrata. *J. Physiol. (London)* **29**, 174–180.

Bensley, R. R. (1900). The oesophageal glands of Urodela. *Biol. Bull.* **2**, 87–104.

Biedermann, W. (1911). Die Aufnahme, Verarbeitung und Assimilation der Nahrung. *Handb. Vergleich. Physiol.* **2**, 1–1563.

Blacher, L. J., and Liosner, L. D. (1930). Veränderung der proteolytischen Funktion des Darmes im Prozess der Metamorphose bei *Rana temporaria* L. *Biol. Zentr.* **50**, 285–292.

Bles, E. J. (1905). The life history of *Xenopus laevis*. *Trans. Roy. Soc. Edinburgh* **41**, 789–822.

Bock, F. (1924). Zur Frage der Ernährung von Amphibienlarven durch im Wasser gelöste Nährstoffe. *Zool. Anz.* **61**, 171–177.

Bock, F. (1925). Weiterer Beitrag zur Frage der Ernährung von Amphibienlarven durch im Wasser gelöste Nährstoffe. *Zool. Anz.* **64**, 261–276.

Borison, H. L., and Wang, S. C. (1953). Physiology and pharmacology of vomiting. *Pharmacol. Rev.* **5**, 193–230.

Bosma, J. F. (1957). Deglutition: pharyngeal stage. *Physiol. Rev.* **37**, 275–300.

Bowers, M. A. (1909). Histogenesis and histolysis of the intestinal epithelium of *Bufo lentiginosus*. *Am. J. Anat.* **9**, 263–280.

Broman, I. (1937). Das Pankreas. *In* "Handbuch der vergleichenden Anatomie der Wirbeltiere" (L. Bolk, E. Göppert, E. Kallius, W. Lubosch, eds.), Vol. III, pp. 775–796, Urban and Schwarzenberg, Berlin and Vienna.

Budde, W., and Gellhorn, E. (1924). Beiträge zur Physiologie der Magenmuskulatur. *Arch. Ges. Physiol. Pflueger's* **203**, 170–185.

Buddenbrock, W. von. (1956). "Vergleichende Physiologie," Vol. III, pp. 1–677. Birkhäuser, Basel and Stuttgart.

Chesley, C. (1934). The influence of temperature upon the amylase of cold- and warm-blooded animals. *Biol. Bull.* **66**, 330–338.

Cooperstein, I. L., and Hogben, C. A. M. (1959). Ionic transfer across the isolated frog large intestine. *J. Gen. Physiol.* **42**, 461–473.

Cooperstein, I. L., Chalfin, D., and Hogben, C. A. M. (1957). Ionic transfer across the isolated bullfrog large intestine. *Federation Proc.* **16**, 24–25.

Cordier, D., and Worbe, J. F. (1955). Étude sur l'absorption intestinale des hexoses et des pentoses chez la Grenouille (*Rana esculenta*). *Compt. Rend. Soc. Biol.* **149**, 110–112.

Cordier, D., and Worbe, J. F. (1956a). Influence de la tension de l'anhydride carbonique dans l'air sur la vitesse de l'absorption intestinale des solutions isotoniques de glucose chez la Grenouille (*Rana esculenta*). *J. Physiol. (Paris)* **48**, 465–468.

Cordier, D., and Worbe, J. F. (1956b). Recherches sur la vitesse de l'absorption intestinale du glucose chez la Grenouille (*Rana esculenta*) en fonction de la tension de l'oxygène dans le milieu extérieur. *Compt. Rend. Soc. Biol.* **150**, 1204–1205.

Cordier, D., and Worbe, J. F. (1956c). Modifications de l'absorption intestinale du glucose chez la Grenouille (*Rana esculenta*) sous l'influence de mélanges gazeux pauvres en oxygène et enrichis en anhydride carbonique. *Compt. Rend. Soc. Biol.* **150**, 1960–1963.

Crane, E. E., Davies, R. E., and Longmuir, N. M. (1948a). Relations between hydrochloric acid secretion and electrical phenomena in frog gastric mucosa. *Biochem. J.* **43**, 321–336.

Crane, E. E., Davies, R. E., and Longmuir, N. M. (1948b). The effect of electric current on HCl secretion by isolated frog gastric mucosa. *Biochem. J.* **43**, 336–342.

Crombach, J. J. M. L., de Jong, M. I. C. P., and Wolvekamp, H. P. (1958). Quelques expériences sur la sécrétion de pepsine de la grenouille verte (*Rana esculenta* L.) et de la grenouille rousse (*Rana temporaria* L.) *Acta Physiol. Pharmacol. Neerl.* **7**, 78–92.

Davenport, H. W. (1946). Carbonic anhydrase in tissues other than blood. *Physiol. Rev.* **26**, 560–573.

Davies, R. E. (1948). Hydrochloric acid production by isolated gastric mucosa. *Biochem. J.* **42**, 609–621.

Davies, R. E. (1951). Mechanism of hydrochloric acid production by the stomach. *Biol. Rev. Cambridge Phil. Soc.* **26**, 87–120.

Davies, R. E., and Kornberg, H. L. (1950). Gastric urease and HCl secretion. *Biochem. J.* **47**, II–III.

Davies, R. E., and Kornberg, H. L. (1951). The role of gastric urease in acid secretion. *Biochem. J.* **50**, 119–122.

Davies, R. E., and Longmuir, N. M. (1948). Production of ulcers in isolated frog gastric mucosa. *Biochem. J.* **42**, 621–627.

Delrue, G. (1930). Étude de la sécrétion acide de l'estomac I. *Arch. Intern. Physiol.* **33**, 196–216.

Delrue, G. (1933). Étude de la sécrétion de l'estomac II. *Arch. Intern. Physiol.* **36**, 129–136.

Dixon, W. E. (1902). The innervation of the frog's stomach. *J. Physiol. (London)* **28**, 57–75.

Dodd, J. M. (1950). Ciliary feeding mechanisms in Anuran larvae. *Nature* **165**, 283.

Dorris, F. (1935). The development of structure and function in the digestive tract of *Amblystoma*. *J. Exptl. Zool.* **70**, 491–527.

Duesberg, A. (1907). Contribution à l'étude des phénomènes histologique de la métamorphose chez les amphibiens anoures. *Arch. Biol. (Liege)* **22**, 163–228.

Durbin, R. P., and Heinz, E. (1958). Electromotive chloride transport and gastric acid secretion in the frog. *J. Gen. Physiol.* **41**, 1035–1047.

Eksaeva, V. A. (1958). The histological structure of the esophagus of certain cold-blooded vertebrates. *Dokl. Biol. Sci. Sect. (English Transl.)* **118**, 42–46.

Elkan, E. (1955). The buccal and pharyngeal mucous membrane in urodeles. *Proc. Zool. Soc. London* **125**, 685–710.

Elkan, E. (1958). Further contributions on the buccal and pharyngeal mucous membrane in urodeles. *Proc. Zool. Soc. London* **131**, 335–355.

Epstein, D. (1931). The responses of the excised batrachian alimentary canal to autonomic drugs I. *J. Pharmacol. Exptl. Therap.* **43**, 653–675.

Epstein, D. (1932a). The responses of the excised batrachian alimentary canal to autonomic drugs. Ephedrine. *Quart. J. Exptl. Physiol.* **21**, 281–287.

Epstein, D. (1932b). The response of the batrachian alimentary canal to autonomic drugs. *J. Physiol. (London)* **75**, 99–111.

Fahrenholz, C. (1937). Drüsen der Mundhöhle. *In* "Handbuch der vergleichenden Anatomie der Wirbeltiere" (L. Bolk, E. Göppert, E. Kallius, W. Lubosch, eds.), Vol. III, pp. 115–210. Urban and Schwarzenberg, Berlin and Vienna.

Fischer, M. H., and Ritter, U. (1953). Die Funktion der Becherzellen des Froschdarms bei der Verdauung. *Arch. Ges. Physiol. Pflueger's* **257**, 161–168.

Florey, H. W., and Harding, H. E. (1933). The functions of Brunner's glands and the pyloric end of the stomach. *J. Pathol. Bacteriol.* **37**, 431–453.

Frazer, A. C. (1946). The absorption of triglyceride fat from the intestine. *Physiol. Rev.* **26**, 103–119.

Friedman, M. H. F. (1934). The nervous control of gastric secretion in the frog (*Rana esculenta*). *J. Cellular Comp. Physiol.* **5**, 83–95.

Friedman, M. H. F. (1935). A study of the innervation of the stomach of *Necturus* by means of drugs. *Trans. Roy. Soc. Can. V* **29**, 175–186.

Friedman, M. H. F. (1937). Oesophageal and gastric secretion in the frog. *J. Cellular Comp. Physiol.* **10**, 37–50.

Friedman, M. H. F. (1939). Gastric secretion in *Necturus. Am. J. Physiol.* **126**, 495–496.

Friedman, M. H. F. (1942). Gastric secretion in *Necturus. J. Cellular Comp. Physiol.* **20**, 379–384.

Gellhorn, E., and Budde, W. (1923). Beiträge zur Physiologie der Magenmuskulatur I. *Arch. Ges. Physiol. Pflueger's* **200**, 604–619.

Glick, D., Zak, E., and von Korff, R. W. (1950). Role of urease in gastric mucosa. *Am. J. Physiol.* **163**, 386–393.

Göppert, E. (1891). Die Entwicklung und das spätere Verhalten des Pankreas des Amphibien. *Morphol. Jahrb.* **17**, 100–122.

Goltz, F. (1872). Studien über die Bewegungen der Speiseröhre und des Magens des Frosches. *Arch. Ges. Physiol. Pflueger's* **6**, 616–642.

Gordon, H., and Csáky, T. (1942). Ueber die Durchlässigkeit der Darmepithelzellen von *Rana fusca. Arch. Exptl. Zellforsch. Gewebezuecht.* **24**, 233–240.

Gray, J. S., and Adkison, J. L. (1941). The effect of inorganic ions on gastric secretion in vitro. *Am. J. Physiol.* **134**, 27–31.

Gray, J. S., Adkison, J. L., and Zelle, K. (1940). The in vitro secretion of acid by the gastric mucosa of the frog. *Am. J. Physiol.* **130**, 327–331.

Gruber, C. M. (1923). The effect of epinephrine on excised strips of frogs' digestive tracts. *J. Pharmacol. Exptl. Therap.* **20**, 321–357.

Grützner, P. (1901). Ueber die Muskulatur des Froschmagens. *Arch. Ges. Physiol. Pflueger's* **83**, 187–198.

Grützner, P. (1905). Ein Beitrag zum Mechanismus der Magenverdauung. *Arch. Ges. Physiol. Pflueger's* **106**, 463–522.

Grützner, P., and Swiecicki, H. von (1891). Bemerkungen über die Physiologie der Verdauung bei den Batrachiern. *Arch. Ges. Physiol. Pflueger's* **49**, 638–642.

Haslewood, G. A. D. (1952). Bile salts of Crocodylidae. *Biochem. J.* **52**, 583–587.

Haslewood, G. A. D. (1955). Recent developments in our knowledge of bile salts. *Physiol. Rev.* **35**, 178–196.

Haslewood, G. A. D., and Wooton, U. (1950). Comparative studies of bile salts. *Biochem. J.* **47**, 584–597.

Hecht, P. (1920). Automatie und Totenstarre am Magen des Frosches. *Arch. Ges. Physiol. Pflueger's* **182**, 178–204.

Heinz, E., and Durbin, R. P. (1957). Studies on the chloride transport in the gastric mucosa of the frog. *J. Gen. Physiol.* **41**, 101–117.

Herter, K. (1941). Die Physiologie der Amphibien. *In* "Handbuch der Zoologie" (W. Kükenthal, ed.), Vol. VI, Pt. 2, pp. 1–252. Gruyter, Berlin.

Hirschowitz, B. I. (1957). Pepsinogen: its origins, secretion and excretion. *Physiol. Rev.* **37**, 475–511.

Hoffmann, C. K. (1873–1878). Amphibia. *In* "Klassen und Ordnungen des Thier-Reichs" (H. G. Bronn, ed.), Vol. VI, pt. 2, pp. 1–726. Winter'sche Verlagshandlung, Leipzig and Heidelberg.

Hogartz, W. (1932). Beiträge zur Physiologie der Verdauung. IX. Ueber Chlorspeicherung in der Magenschleimhaut des Frosches. *Arch. Ges. Physiol. Pflueger's* **230**, 668–673.

Hogben, C. A. M. (1955). Active transport of chloride by isolated frog gastric epithelium. *Am. J. Physiol.* **180**, 641–649.

Hopf, H. (1911). Studien über antagonistische Nerven VII. Ueber den hemmenden und erregenden Einfluss des Vagus auf den Magen des Frosches. *Z. Biol.* **55,** 409–459.

Houssay, B. A., Foglia, V. G., and Fustinoni, O. (1941). Intestinal absorption of sugars in the toad with hypophyseal or adrenal insufficiency. *Endocrinology* **28,** 915–922.

Ingelfinger, F. J. (1958). Esophageal motility. *Physiol. Rev.* **38,** 533–584.

Itagaki, M. (1930). On the innervation of the stomach of the Japanese frog. *Japan. J. Med. Sci. III* **1,** 105–108.

James, A. H. (1957). "The physiology of gastric digestion," 192 pp. Arnold, London.

Janes, R. G. (1934). Histological changes in the alimentary tract of anuran larvae during involution. *J. Exptl. Zool.* **67,** 73–91.

Joly, J. (1958). Influence des basses températures sur le cycle alimentaire de quelques tritons français. *Bull. Soc. Zool. France* **1958,** 128–131.

Jordan, H. G. (1927). "Uebungen aus der vergleichenden Physiologie," 272 pp. Springer, Berlin.

Jordan, H. J. (1929). "Allgemeine vergleichende Physiologie der Tiere," 761 pp. Gruyter, Berlin and Leipzig.

Jordan, H. J., and Begemann, H. (1921). Über die Bedeutung des Darmes von *Helix pomatia. Zool. Jahrb. Abt. Allgem. Zool. Physiol. Tiere* **38,** 565–582.

Kazuno, T. (1940). Untersuchung der Krötengalle VII. Pentaoxybufostan, $C_{28}H_{50}O_5$. *Z. Physiol. Chem.* **266,** 11–30.

Keeton, R. W., Koch, F. C., and Luckhardt, A. B. (1920). Gastrin studies III. The response of the stomach mucosa of various animals to gastrin bodies. *Am. J. Physiol.* **51,** 454–468.

Kenyon, W. A. (1925). Digestive enzymes in poikilothermal vertebrates: an investigation of enzymes in fishes with comparative studies on those of amphibians, reptiles, and mammals. *U. S. Fish Wildlife Serv. Fishery Bull.* **41,** 179–200.

Kingsbury, B. F. (1894). The histological structure of the enteron of *Necturus maculosus. Proc. Am. Microscop. Soc.* **16,** 19–64.

Klee, P. (1927a). Die Magenbewegungen. *In* "Handbuch der normalen und pathologischen physiologie" (A. Bethe, G. V. Bergmann, G. Embden, and A. Ellingen, eds.), Vol. III, pp. 398–440. Springer, Berlin.

Klee, P. (1927b). Der Brechakt. *In* "Handbuch der normalen und pathologischen physiologie" (A. Bethe, G. V. Bergmann, G. Embden, and A. Ellingen, eds.), Vol. III, pp. 441–451. Springer, Berlin.

Kornberg, H. L., and Davies, R. E. (1955). Gastric urease. *Physiol. Rev.* **35,** 169–177.

Koschtojanz, C. S., Iwanoff, I., Mujeeff, W., Korjuieff, P., and Otschakowskaja, S. (1933). Zur Frage der Spezifität des Secretiṇs. *Z. Vergleich. Physiol.* **18,** 112–115.

Kratochwill, K. (1933). Zur Morphologie und Physiologie der Nahrungsaufnahme der Froschlarven. *Z. Wiss. Zool. Abt. A.* **144,** 421–468.

Křiženecký, J. (1924). Experimentelle Untersuchungen zur Frage nach der Ernährung der Wassertiere durch gelöste Nährstoffe. *Zool. Anz.* **58,** 187–194.

Křiženecký, J. (1925a). Untersuchungen über Assimilationsfähigkeit der Wassertiere für im Wasser gelöste Nahrstoffe. *Biol. Generalis (Vienna)* **1,** 79–149.

Křiženecký, J. (1925b). Ueber eine wachstumsteigernde Wirkung der im Wasser gelösten Nährstoffe bei den Wassertieren. *Biol. Generales (Vienna)* **1,** 279–297.

Křiženecký, J. (1925c). Zur Frage der Ernährung von Amphibien-Larven durch im Wasser gelöste Nährstoffe. *Zool. Anz.* **62,** 65–71.

Kuntz, A. (1924). Anatomical and physiological changes in the digestive system during metamorphosis in *Rana pipiens* and *Amblystoma tigrinum*. *J. Morphol.* **38**, 581-598.

Lambertini, G. (1929). Il manicotto glandulare di *Rana esculenta*. *Ric. Morphol.* **9**, 71-88.

Langley, J. N. (1881). On the histology and physiology of pepsin-forming glands. *Phil. Trans. Roy. Soc. London* **B172**, 663-711.

Langley, J. N. (1882). On the histology of the mammalian gastric glands, and the relation of pepsin to the granules of the chief-cells. *J. Physiol. (London)* **3**, 269-291.

Langley, J. N., and Edkins, J. S. (1886). Pepsinogen and pepsin. *J. Physiol. (London)* **7**, 374-415.

Langley, J. N., and Orbeli, L. A. (1910). Observations on the sympathetic and sacral autonomic system of the frog. *J. Physiol. (London)* **41**, 450-482.

Lim, R. K. S. (1922). The gastric mucosa III. The gastric mucoid cells in man, dog, rabbit and frog. *Quart. J. Microscop. Sci.* **66**, 205-212.

Luckhardt, A. B., and Carlson, A. J. (1921). Studies on the visceral sensory nervous system VI. Lung automatism and lung reflexes in *Cryptobranchus*, with further notes on the physiology of the lung of *Necturus*. *Am J. Physiol.* **55**, 212-222.

Lundberg, A. (1958). Electrophysiology of salivary glands. *Physiol. Rev.* **38**, 21-40.

Machan, B. (1935). Ueber Oesophagusdrüsen und Magenhauptdrüsen einheimischer Anuren. *Z. Mikroskop.-Anat. Forsch.* **39**, 344-372.

Mangold, O. (1920). Ueber Automatie. Erregbarkeit und Totenstarre in verschiedenen Teilen des Froschmagens. *Deut. Med. Wochschr.* **46**, 447-448.

Mathews, A. P. (1920). "Physiological Chemistry," 3rd ed., 1154 pp. Wood, New York

Matthes, E. (1924). Die Rolle des Gesichts-, Geruchs- und Erschütterungssinnes für den Nahrungserwerb von *Triton*. *Biol. Zentr.* **44**, 72-87.

Matthes, E. (1934). Bau und Funktion der Lippensäume wasserlebender Urodelen. *Z. Morphol. Oekol. Tiere* **28**, 155-169.

Mellinger, C. (1881). Beiträge zur Kenntnis des Erbrechens. *Arch. Ges. Physiol. Pflueger's* **24**, 232-245.

Morishima, K., and Fujitani, J. (1908). Zur Untersuchungsmethode der spontanen Bewegung des Froschmagens. *Arch. Exptl. Pathol. Pharmakol. Naunyn-Schmiedeberg's, Suppl. Vol. Schmiedeberg Festschr.* pp. 407-414.

Müller, H. (1922). Bestehen Unterschiede in der Pepsinverdauung des Frosches und der Warmblüter? *Arch. Ges. Physiol. Pflueger's* **193**, 214-224.

Noble, G. K. (1922). The phylogeny of the Salientia; I. *Bull. Am. Museum Nat. Hist.* **46**, 1-87.

Noble, G. K. (1931). "The Biology of the Amphibia," 577 pp. McGraw-Hill, New York.

Okasaki, Y. (1944). Bile acids of aquatic salamanders I. *J. Biochem. (Tokyo)* **36**, 65-76.

Oltmanns, E. (1952). Zur Morphologie der Zähne rezenter Amphibien. *Anat. Anz.* **98**, 369-389.

Oppel, A. (1889). Beiträge zur Anatomie des *Proteus anguineus*. *Arch. Mikroskop. Anat. Entwicklungsmech.* **34**, 511-572.

Partsch, C. (1877). Beiträge zur Kenntniss des Vorderdarmes einiger Amphibien und Reptilien. *Arch. Mikroskop. Anat. Entwicklungsmech.* **14**, 179-203.

Patterson, T. L. (1916). The physiology of the gastric hunger contractions in the Amphibia and the Reptilia. *Am. J. Physiol.* **42**, 56-88.

148   WILLIAM G. REEDER

Patterson, T. L. (1920). Vagus and splanchnic influence of the gastric hunger movements of the frog. *Am. J. Physiol.* **53**, 293–306.

Patterson, T. L. (1928). The influence of the vagi on the motility of the empty stomach in *Necturus*. *Am. J. Physiol.* **84**, 631–640.

Pernkopf, E., and Lehner, J. (1937). Vergleichende Beschreibung des Vorderdarms bei den einzelnen Klassen der Kranioten. *In* "Handbuch der vergleichenden Anatomie der Wirbeltiere" (L. Bolk, E. Göppert, E. Kallius, and W. Lubosch, eds.), Vol. III, pp. 349–476. Urban and Schwarzenberg, Berlin and Vienna.

Peyer, B. (1937). Zähne und Gebiss. *In* "Handbuch der vergleichenden Anatomie der Wirbeltiere" (L. Bolk, E. Göppert, E. Kallius, W. Lubosch, eds.), Vol. III, pp. 49–114. Urban and Schwarzenberg, Berlin and Vienna.

Pjatnitzky, N. P. (1931). Zur Kenntniss der Proteasenatur IX. Bestimmung des Optimums der Wasserstoffionenkonzentration bei Verdauung von Eiereiweiss durch Froschpepsin bei 38°. *Z. Physiol. Chem.* **199**, 231–242.

Popielski, B. (1929). Influence de l'histamine sur le sécrétion de suc gastrique chez la grenouille. *Compt. Rend Soc. Biol.* **100**, 295–296.

Riddle, O. (1909). The rate of digestion in cold-blooded vertebrates.—The influence of season and temperature. *Am. J. Physiol.* **24**, 447–458.

Roux, J. C., and Balthazard, V. (1898). Étude du fonctionnement moteur de l'estomac a l'aide des rayons de Röntgen. *Arch. Physiol. Norm. et Pathol.* [v] **10**, 85–94.

Savage, R. M. (1952). Ecological, physiological and anatomical observations on some species of anuran tadpoles. *Proc. Zool. Soc. London* **122**, 467–514.

Savage, R. M. (1955). The ingestive, digestive and respiratory systems of the microhylid tadpole, *Hypopachus aguae*. *Copeia* **1955**, 120–127.

Schmidt, W. (1935). Beiträge zur vergleichenden Untersuchungen der heimischen Schwanzlurche. *Zool. Jahrb. Abt. Anat. Ontog. Tiere* **59**, 277–332.

Schultze, F. E. (1892). Ueber die inneren Kiemen der Batrachierlarven II. *Abhandl. Kaiserliche Akad. Wiss. Berlin (Physik.-Math. Kl.)* Pt. III, **1892**, 1–66.

Schultze, W. (1937). Ueber das Riechvermögen und den Bau des Geruchsorgans von *Triton vulgaris* vor und nach der Metamorphose. *Z. Morphol. Oekol. Tiere* **32**, 463–491.

Sedra, S. N. (1950). The metamorphosis of the jaws and their muscles in the toad, *Bufo vulgaris* Reuss, correlated with the changes in the animal's feeding habits. *Proc. Zool. Soc. London* **120**, 405–449.

Seifert, H. (1932). Untersuchungen über die Mundhöhlendrüsen der urodelen Amphibien. *Morphol. Jahrb.* **70**, 173-216.

Shimizu, T., Kazuno, T., and Tsuboi, S. (1953). Bile acids in toad bile VIII. *Proc. Japan Acad.* **29**, 466-470.

Siwe, S. A. (1927). Pankreasstudien. *Morphol. Jahrb.* **57**, 84–307.

Steinach, E. (1898). Ueber die viscero-motorischen Functionen der Hinterwurzeln und über die tonische Hemmungswirkung der Medulla oblongata auf den Darm des Frosches. *Arch. ges. Physiol. Pflueger's* **71**, 523–554.

Steinach, E., and Wiener, H. (1895). Motorische Functionen hinterer Spinalnervenwurzeln. *Arch. Ges. Physiol. Pflueger's* **60**, 593–622.

Swiecicki, H. von (1876). Untersuchung über die Bildung und Ausscheidung des Pepsins bei den Batrachiern. *Arch. Ges. Physiol. Pflueger's* **13**, 444–452.

Thomas, J. E. (1957). Mechanics and regulation of gastric emptying. *Physiol. Rev.* **37**, 453–474.

Thumas, L. J. (1891). Ueber das Brechcentrum und über die Wirkung einiger pharmakologischer Mittel auf dasselbe. *Arch. Pathol. Anat. Physiol. Virchow's* **123**, 44–69.

Tschassownikow, N. (1927). Ueber den Gang des Sekretionsprozesses in den Zellen des Magendeckepithels bei einigen Amphibien und Säugern. *Z. Zellforsch. Mikroskop. Anat.* **5**, 680–703.

Tschermak, G. (1919). Bioelektrische Studien an der Magenmuskulatur I. Das Elektrogastrogramm (EGG) bei Spontanrhythmik des isolierten Froschmagens. *Arch. Ges. Physiol. Pflueger's* **175**, 165–186.

Vonk, H. J. (1929). Das Pepsin verschiedener Vertebraten I. Die pH-Optima und die Wasserstoffionenkonzentration des Mageninhaltes. *Z. Vergleich. Physiol.* **9**, 685–702.

Vonk, H. J. (1937). The specificity and collaboration of digestive enzymes in Metazoa. *Biol. Rev. Cambridge Phil. Soc.* **12**, 245–284.

Vonk, H. J. (1941). Die Verdauung der niederen Vertebraten. *Advan. Enzymol.* **1**, 371–417.

von Korff, R. W., and Glick, D. (1951). Role of urease in the gastric mucosa II. *Am. J. Physiol.* **165**, 688–700.

Waters, W. H. (1885). Some vaso-motor functions of the spinal nerves in the frog. *J. Physiol. (London)* **6**, 460–463.

Weel, P. B. van. (1938). Beiträge zur Histophysiologie des Dünndarms II. *Z. Vergleich. Physiol.* **26**, 35–66.

Weisz, P. B. (1945). The development and morphology of the larva of the South African clawed toad, *Xenopus laevis. J. Morphol.* **77**, 163–217.

Westenbrink, H. G. K., and Gratama, K. (1937). Ueber die Spezifität der Resorption einiger Monosen aus dem Darme des Frosches. *Arch. Neerl. Physiol.* **22**, 326–331.

Wolvekamp, H. P., and Tinbergen, L. (1942). Recherches sur la sécrétion de la pepsine par les glandes oesophagéales de la grenouille verte (*Rana esculenta* L.). *Arch. Neerl. Physiol.* **26**, 435–456.

Yonge, C. M. (1937). Evolution and adaptation in the digestive system of the Metazoa. *Biol. Rev. Cambridge Phil. Soc.* **12**, 87–113.

Zwarenstein, H. (1953). A demonstration of the secretion of pepsin by the isolated frog stomach. *Quart. J. Exptl. Physiol.* **38**, 217–223.

3

BLOOD AND RESPIRATION

G. E. H. Foxon

I. Introduction

It is generally agreed that the evolutionary origin of the Amphibia is to be sought among the Osteolepid fish of the Devonian period. At that time, apparently, conditions of life in fresh water were such as to place at an advantage those fish which, like the lungfish of to-day, were able to respire by means of lungs rather than by gills. The lung method of breathing enabled fish first to overcome the rigors of dry seasons and second to forsake the aquatic habitat and thus to become the first land-living vertebrates. In such a way it is presumed that the Amphibia arose. With a return of less arid conditions in the Carboniferous period, fresh water again provided a favorable habitat and while some vertebrates continued as terrestrial forms giving rise, among their descendants to Reptilia, others reverted to a more aquatic existence. From these arose the Amphibia of today.

A detailed discussion of these matters is outside the scope of this chapter; reference should be made to the work of Watson (1925) and to the account given by Romer (1945). The principal point of importance here is that when the conditions changed in such a way as to make life in fresh water easier than in Devonian times, tetrapod vertebrates immediately began to repopulate such habitats. As a consequence it has come about that many recent Amphibia are, so far as can be judged, much more adapted to an aquatic environment than were their Palaeozoic ancestors. Thus recent Amphibia cannot be regarded as representing an evolutionary stage intermediate between fish on the one hand and reptiles on the other. They are to be looked upon as a group which has reverted to a more aquatic mode of life and this reversion has resulted in an increased use of water as a respiratory medium. In this way the reversion of the Amphibia to an aquatic habitat differs markedly from the conditions seen in the other vertebrate groups where, although some members, such as whales, have become thoroughly aquatic they exhibit only pulmonary respiration. Many amphibians on the other hand carry out respiratory exchange through gills and the skin and the moist membrane lining the buccal cavity as well as through the lungs. The lungs may be of little importance in respiratory exchange and may be used as hydrostatic organs or even be lost.

The variation of methods of gaseous exchange met with in Amphibia is one of the most noteworthy features exhibited by the group. These methods may be correlated with habits and habitat on the one hand and with structural and physiological adaptations on the other hand. The adaptations may be very far reaching, extending to the skin, and buccal cavity, the lungs, the heart, the course of the circulation and even to the composition of the blood itself. In this chapter the more important aspects of these variations will be discussed; special attention will be paid to the physiological problems raised but it is not possible to include every specialization that has been reported. It is hoped that all important recent references on the subject are included but no attempt has been made to provide a full bibliography of works published before Noble's (1931) "Biology of the Amphibia."

II. Respiratory Exchange

The epithelia of the lungs, the skin, and the buccal cavity are the respiratory surfaces of Amphibia. The relative importance of these surfaces has often been the subject of study, for the amount of gaseous exchange which takes place through any one of them relative to the others may show great variation. Such variation exists between species, between adult and developing stages of one species, and even in one individual in differing environmental conditions.

It is proposed to discuss these variations as they are met with in Anura and Urodela. It is convenient to consider conditions obtaining in developmental and adult stages separately. The Apoda, about whose respiration comparatively little is known, will also be dealt with separately.

A. RESPIRATORY EXCHANGE IN ADULT ANURA AND URODELA

1. The Respiratory Surfaces and Their Comparative Importance

Evidence as to the parts played in respiratory exchange by the skin, lungs, and lining of the buccal cavity may be sought in two ways. First by a detailed study of the respiratory membrane itself, second by direct physiological experiment. The results of both methods of inquiry will be discussed in turn. In such discussions a point of anatomy which should not be overlooked is that although cutaneous respiration is important in both Anura and Urodela, in the former group a special blood supply to the skin is found which the latter lacks. In Anura the skin of a large area of the body receives blood through the left and right cutaneous arteries which originate, along with the pulmonary arteries, from the hindmost of the arterial arches (the pulmocutaneous) on each side as it leaves the heart. In Urodela no comparable vessels exist; the blood is supplied to the skin from underlying vessels of the particular area. In the venous return Anura are again different in that blood from much of the skin is returned through the left and right musculocutaneous veins which drain into the subclavian veins. In Urodela venous drainage is by local underlying veins.

a. *Skin Structure.* A method of estimating the relative importance of the various respiratory surfaces is that of a detailed study of their histology and vascularization. The capillary network is injected with a suitable dye so that the number of capillary meshes per square millimeter of surface can be counted, the capillary diameter measured, and the total length of capillaries present in the surface estimated. The thickness of the skin and its layers is also noted and the frequency of the occurrence of glands recorded.

Using such methods Szarski, Czopek, and co-workers have obtained considerable information relating to many species. The interpretation of this is somewhat complicated. As Szarski (1955) has pointed out, the data, much of which is of a numerical nature, has to be considered as a whole. Thus the figures for capillary length, which often show striking differences between species, have to be interpreted in the light of those for skin thickness and also those relating to the numbers of glands present. Habit and habitat differences too, cannot be forgotten. Breathing habits are particularly important as unless the air in the lungs can be renewed the lung capillaries will be useless for oxygen absorption if no oxygen remains in the lungs. Evidence that this may happen will be quoted in Section II, A, 1b.

Counts of the capillary meshes have shown (Szarski, 1955) that in

Rana esculenta while the average count for the whole surface is 220 meshes per mm² of skin, on the back and on the thighs, which are normally well exposed to the air, the count rises to 300. While the index of the number of meshes per unit area is very useful in comparing one part of an animal with another part it may show wide differences between species. For comparisons between species the estimated length of all the capillaries present, expressed in meters per gram body weight, provides a useful measure. Comparing the skin of *Bombina bombina* with that of *Rana esculenta* the average count of capillary meshes per mm² is 68 in the former and 220 in the latter. The figures for the total length of capillaries per gram body weight are 7.85 meters and 6.14 meters respectively.

When the length of the capillaries in the lungs and the buccal membrane is also estimated it is possible to express the length of the capillaries of each surface as a percentage of the total. If this is done for *Bombina bombina* and *Rana esculenta* the percentages as shown in Table I (Czopek, 1955b):

TABLE I

PERCENTAGES OF TOTAL CAPILLARY LENGTH IN RESPIRATORY SURFACES

Species	Skin	Buccal membrane	Lungs
Bombina bombina	53.7	1.1	45.2
Rana esculenta	34.3	0.9	64.8

Table II shows the comparative abundance of capillaries in the various respiratory surfaces of a number of anurans and urodeles. Szarski and Czopek are of the opinion that these figures give, at least, a general indication of the relative importance of the respiratory surfaces. Inspection of this table immediately suggests that the buccal membrane is unimportant as a respiratory surface. Evidence that the so-called "buccopharyngeal" respiration of amphibians in which air is constantly being drawn into the mouth cavity through the nares and immediately expelled again is really "sniffing" and concerned with olfaction will be mentioned later. Another generalization which the table permits is that among the urodeles the newts (*Triton*) carry out respiratory exchange mostly through the skin, whereas in Anura lung respiration is more important, *Leiopelma hochstetteri*, *Pelobates fuscus*, and *Bombina bombina* being the only species recorded as having less than 50% of their total respiratory capillaries in the lungs.

More detailed comparisons can be made and a clearer picture of the significance of the figures obtained if the total length of all capillaries per gram body weight is taken in conjunction with other data. For example, *Hyla arborea* has 11.14 meters per gram body weight of capillaries in the

TABLE II

PERCENTAGE OF TOTAL CAPILLARIES FOUND IN THE VARIOUS RESPIRATORY SURFACES
OF SOME ADULT ANURA AND URODELA[a]

Species	Skin	Buccal cavity	Lungs	Reference
Anura				
Leiopelma hochstetteri	65.1	3.0	31.9	Czopek (1955a)
Bombina variegata	41.6	1.2	57.2	Czopekowa and Czopek (1955)
Bombina bombina	53.7	1.1	45.2	Czopek (1955b)
Xenopus laevis	33.9	0.2	65.9	Czopek (1955a)
Pelobates fuscus	48.3	2.4	49.3	Czopek (1955b)
Bufo cognatus	20.5	1.7	77.8	Bieniak and Watka (1962)
Bufo compactilus	21.2	1.0	77.8	Bieniak and Watka (1962)
Bufo bufo	27.6	0.9	71.5	Czopek (1955b)
Bufo viridis	34.2	1.6	64.2	Czopek and Czopek (1959)
Bufo calamita	35.4	1.6	63.0	Czopek and Czopek (1959)
Hyla arborea	24.2	1.1	74.7	Czopek (1955b)
Rana temporaria	36.6	0.9	62.5	Czopek (1955b)
Rana terrestris	32.4	0.7	66.9	Czopek (1955b)
Rana esculenta	34.3	0.9	64.8	Czopek (1955b)
Urodela				
Ambystoma mexicanum (metamorphosed)	50.0	1.1	48.9	Czopek (1957)
Salamandra salamandra	41.4	1.3	57.3	Czopek (1959a)
Triton vulgaris	74.0	1.5	24.5	Czopek (1959b)
Triton cristatus	73.7	3.0	23.3	Czopek (1959b)
Triturus alpestris	75.6	1.6	22.8	Brodowa (1956)
Amphiuma means	—	—	68.2	Czopek (1962)
Siren intermedia	—	—	58.16	Czopek (1962)

[a] In preparing this table the figures given by the various authors have been approximated to one significant figure.

skin and the newt *Triton cristatus* 11.666 (Czopek, 1959b). At first sight these figures seem similar but for all respiratory surfaces *T. cristatus* has 15.57 and *Hyla arborea* 45.99 (Czopek, 1955b) (see Table I). The high figure for *H. arborea* is accounted for by the extreme vascularity of the lungs where there are many well developed vascularized partitions. The great difference between the total length of capillaries present in these two species and the fact that this difference is accounted for by the vascularity of the lungs in *H. arborea*, emphasizes the importance of habits and habitats. Putting the matter in very general terms it can be said that 11.6 meters per gram body weight of skin capillaries form three-quarters of all respiratory capillaries in the newt and subserve its respiratory needs, but in the active tree-frog the same quantity of skin capillaries forms only one-quarter of its total respiratory capillaries and here lung respiration must be largely relied upon.

So far it has been assumed that the total length of capillaries per gram body weight and their proportional distribution between the respiratory surfaces is constant throughout adult life. Neither of these suppositions is strictly true. As will be made clear when the developmental stages are discussed, respiratory exchange through the body surface of the embryo is, at first, the only method. Later gills and lungs are developed. As this happens so the proportional distribution of the capillaries changes. At metamorphosis the respiratory methods are stabilized but changes in the degree of vascularization of surfaces continue to take place. These soon cease in Anura but in Urodela they may continue for a considerable time during growth and also may show seasonal influences.

Studying the newt *Triton cristatus* Czopek (1959b) found that when, in the breeding season, the "breeding dress" was assumed the number of skin capillaries significantly increased. This condition, particularly well seen in males, involves the enlargement of the tail fin with the development of numerous extra capillaries. The skin also becomes thinner. It has been shown (Bannikov, 1948) that breeding newts placed in water, but deprived of atmospheric oxygen, survived considerably longer than did non-breeding specimens under the same conditions. Czopek likens this breeding dress to the well known case of the "hairy-frog," the male of *Astylosternus robustus* reported on by Noble (1925). A similar instance of a "hairy-frog" has been described by Parker (1936); the male of *Trichobatrachus robustus* lives in mountain streams in the Cameroons (West Africa) and is apparently dependent on cutaneous respiration; the female lives in holes in the ground. A male specimen which measured 130 mm from snout to vent had approximately 2560 "hairs" with a total surface area of 80 square centimeters, nearly equal to the area of the remainder of the frog's surface. The lungs of the males and females of this species also exhibit differences. In the males the posterior part of the lung is without alveoli and forms a diverticulum enclosed by a muscular sheath. Parker suggested that this is a hydrostatic mechanism and only necessary in the aquatic males.

The hydrostatic function of lungs, which does not strictly fall within the purview of this chapter, is obviously important in many lake-living urodeles. That it is important so far as mountain stream forms are concerned has been disputed (Dunn, 1928). On the contrary it has been suggested that the possession of organs of flotation is a disadvantage in fast rocky streams and that the lunglessness exhibited by some species inhabiting such localities is an adaptation to be correlated with the disadvantage of being buoyant in such surroundings rather than with the high oxygen content of swiftly flowing upland waters.

Noble (1931, p. 167) discussing the simplicity of lung structure in Amphibia points out that it can be explained either as a larval feature carried over into the adult stage or as a secondary degeneration; it is not primitive.

In some salamanders (Plethodontidae) the lungs are completely lacking. Figures for the comparative development of the capillaries of the skin and buccal membrane have been given by Czopek (1961). A distinctive feature of these figures is that they show that as growth proceeds the total length of capillaries present per gram body weight declines remarkably. As previously remarked, in most amphibians a definite relationship between the development of the capillaries and the body weight is established fairly soon after metamorphosis (apparently earlier in anurans than in urodeles) ; this relationship is achieved by increase in body weight being accompanied by an increase in capillaries per unit area. In Plethodontidae small specimens of *Aneides lugubris* which weighed between 1 gm and 3 gm and whose length ranged from 65 to 88 mm had about 12 meters per gram body weight of skin capillaries whereas a large female weighing 13.6 gm and measuring 140 mm in length had only about 4.4 meters per gram. Similar variations were shown in the other genera studied.

These low figures obtain because as weight increases with growth the number of capillaries does not increase as it does in most amphibians. Yet this length of capillaries must suffice for the respiratory needs of the animal. Bernstein (1953) pointed out that the epidermis of these lungless salamanders is extremely thin, but it does not seem to be thinner than in some species of both urodeles with lungs (*Triton* spp.) and some anurans (*Bombina bombina*) (Czopek, 1961). The particular adaptation which allows this small capillary length to be sufficient is that as the animals grow larger so the diameter of the capillaries increases. In some instances the increase exceeds 50%. Czopek believes that this may compensate, at least partly, for the unfavorable length:weight ratio. This compensation is accomplished by the slower flow of blood which results from the larger capillary diameter and which thus increases the efficiency of respiratory exchange. This increase of efficiency is also desirable as larger specimens have a thicker epidermis than do small ones. Buccopharyngeal respiration may be of some importance in some lungless salamanders. The figures in Table III show that up to just over 10% of the respiratory capillaries may be in the mouth. In two species (*Eurycea bislineata* and *Pseudotriton*

158 G. E. H. FOXON

TABLE III

RELATIVE DISTRIBUTION OF RESPIRATORY CAPILLARIES OF SOME PLETHODONTIDAE[a]

Species	Skin[b]	Buccal cavity[b]
Eurycea longicauda	95.47	4.53
Desmognathus fuscus	89.15	10.85
Plethodon glutinosus	92.73	7.27
Plethodon jordani metcalfi	92.64	7.36
Batrachoseps attenuatus	94.70	5.30
Aneides flavipunctatus	92.89	7.11
Aneides lugubris	94.69	5.31

[a] Data from Czopek (1961). The figures given are for the largest specimens irrespective of sex.
[b] The length of the capillaries of the skin and buccal cavity are given as percentages of the total.

ruber) Elkan (1958) has described modifications which could be associated with respiration. Both species have capillaries evaginated into the epithelium; this intra-epithelial network is particularly well developed in *P. ruber*. The buccopharyngeal breathing movements are also said to be very frequent (Noble, 1931, p. 173), *Aneides lugubris* being credited with a rate of vibration of the floor of the mouth of 120 to 180 per minute. Adaptation of the erythrocytes of these animals which have to do with their oxygen carrying capacity will be discussed in Section III,A,1.

Evagination of capillaries into the epidermis is not limited to the mouth region or to this group. Noble (1931) shows (in his Fig. 62b) how the capillaries are evaginated into the epidermis of *Cryptobranchus alleganiensis*. Bernstein (1953) who repeated this observation, and found a similar state to exist in *Ambystoma tigrinum*, also pointed out that in both *Necturus maculosus* and *Siren lacertina* the Leydig cells of the larval skin, which are thought to increase permeability to water, are retained in the fully grown condition.

The species of lungless salamanders just mentioned are the only instances where a modification of the buccopharyngeal epithelium which can be looked upon as a respiratory adaptation has been described. Table III shows the very small proportion of total capillary length can be attributed to the mouth cavity. While respiratory exchange must of necessity take place to some extent through any thin, moist, vascularized epithelium such considerations as those just noted have encouraged the growth of the view (Vos, 1936; Elkan, 1955, 1958) that the primary purpose of the movements of the floor of the mouth in amphibians is not to renew the air in the mouth for respiratory purposes but to carry air over the sensory cells of the olfactory organs. In other words movements of the floor of the mouth are to be correlated with "sniffing" rather than breathing. In some species the movements are very rapid. Spurway and Haldane (1953) recorded *Triturus* sp. as having a rate of 60–200 per minute in air which fell to 4–8 per minute under water. It is only in some urodeles that the movement continues under water; in Anura the movements cease when the animals are submerged.

b. Physiological Experimental Evidence. We now turn to the evidence concerning the respiratory functions of the skin, lungs, and lining of the buccal cavity based on physiological experiments.

Our basic knowledge of the respiratory physiology of frogs is due to the work of Krogh (1904) who worked on *Rana temporaria* (as *R. fusca*) and *R. esculenta*. His work has been confirmed and to some degree extended by Dolk and Postma (1926). Krogh showed that in *R. temporaria* the lungs and skin are both important in respiratory exchange but in somewhat different ways. Carbon dioxide is excreted mainly through the skin whereas the lungs are the main site for the intake of oxygen. Elimination of carbon dioxide is at a constant rate through the skin during the greater part of the year but rises in spring during the spawning season in response to an increase in metabolic activity. The intake of oxygen through the skin is determined solely by physical limitations. As the partial pressure of oxygen in the atmosphere remains constant throughout the year, the diffusion of oxygen through the skin continues at an even rate. Dolk and Postma (1926) found that, under experimental conditions, the rate of diffusion of oxygen was lowered at low oxygen tensions (e.g., 8%) and that under such conditions the pulmonary intake of oxygen increased. Normally the pulmonary intake of oxygen increases in response to increased metabolic activity in the spring.

The output of carbon dioxide through the lungs varies with the oxygen intake. If a greater quantity of oxygen is absorbed through the lungs there is a tendency for a greater quantity of carbon dioxide to be eliminated through the lungs, but this tendency is not as marked as is the change in oxygen intake, for most of the increased carbon dioxide produced by the increase in metabolism is eliminated through the skin.

Considering the relative importance of lung and skin respiration as studied by the usual physiological methods, Krogh concluded that in *Rana fusca* (now *R. temporaria*) the lungs predominate in oxygen intake over the skin in the ratio 3:1. The parts played by the two surfaces in *R. esculenta* are equal 1:1. Charles (1931) has estimated that in *Xenopus laevis* the ratio of lung to skin intake of oxygen is 3–2.5:1.

These differences between *R. temporaria* and *R. esculenta* reported by Krogh are greater than might have been expected from the studies on the capillaries quoted above. These suggested that the lungs and skin might be of equal importance in the two species or, indeed, that *R. esculenta* might be slightly more dependent on its lungs than *R. temporaria*. The explanation of this apparent contradiction would appear to lie in the habits of these two frogs. It is well known that *R. esculenta* is a more aquatic animal than is *R. temporaria*, and Krogh's findings are more easily related to this than to the figures for the numbers of respiratory capillaries. This must not be taken to indicate that such figures are without significance, this would be manifestly incorrect in such instances as those of *Triturus cristatus* and *Hyla arborea*.

In view of the fact that so much respiratory exchange goes on through the skin, a question that is often posed in various ways is "How essential are the lungs in respiratory exchange in frogs?" An attempt to assess the relative importance of pulmonary and cutaneous respiration by direct experiment on the blood supply to the two surfaces has been made by Jullien and others (1958). Using "la Grenouille" they ligated the pulmonary and cutaneous arteries. Some times both were ligated simultaneously. Some experiments were unilateral and some bilateral. Survival time was longest with one pulmocutaneous trunk ligated, then in decreasing order, two cutaneous arteries ligated, two pulmonary arteries ligated, and least when the two pulmocutaneous trunks were ligated. Survival was slightly longer with elimination of the pulmocutaneous circulation on one side than when either both pulmonary or both cutaneous arteries were ligated.

It was concluded that pulmonary and cutaneous respiration were of approximately equal importance but that there might perhaps be a slight emphasis on pulmonary respiration.

It has long been known that some frogs cannot survive indefinitely if deprived of lung breathing. Serfaty and Gueutal (1943) investigated this using male *Rana esculenta*. It was found that the survival time in well aerated water and without access to atmospheric air depended on temperature. The frogs were acclimatized to the experimental temperature for 5 days before being deprived of air. Once under water the frogs made no attempt at buccopharyngeal breathing. Survival was as follows:

14–15°C	2 to 3 weeks
19–20°C	10 to 15 days
26–27°C	36 to 48 hours

It was calculated that a motionless frog did not use more than 90 cubic centimeters of oxygen per kilogram of skin per hour so long as the temperature was below 19–20°C.

This result suggests that the lungs may be used as an oxygen reserve when the animals are under water for long periods, and Bastert (1929) has produced evidence to show that the lungs of *Rana esculenta* and *R. temporaria* can act as oxygen stores under such conditions. She points out that in diving animals, such as these frogs, the decrease of oxygen tension in the lungs does not necessarily bring about the normal respiratory reflexes of land animals and that the oxygen content of the gas in the lungs of frogs can be reduced to zero. Absorption of the oxygen from the lungs, can, she maintains, be regulated by the numbers of lung capillaries open at any given time. This regulation is under the control of the central nervous system and disappears if the frog is pithed. Some further details of this control have been added by H. J. Jordan (1929) who has shown that, if the oxygen tension of the lungs falls below a critical level, the walls of the capillaries relax and allow further oxygen to be absorbed by a more copious flow of blood. The number of capillaries in the skin that are open at any time is subject to a similar form of control (Poczopko, 1957; Szarski, 1959). This will be discussed in Section V.

In concluding this survey of the importance of the respiratory surfaces of adult Urodela and Anura little generalization is possible, except to point out that most probably Amphibia do not meet any great physiological difficulties in eliminating carbon dioxide, which mostly passes out through the skin. The great variety of adaptations met with would seem to have to do with oxygen intake. In Anura the lungs are usually important in this respect (Table II), but not so much so in "hairy-frogs." In Urodela the skin may take over the whole of this function, the lungs being suppressed or used as hydrostatic organs. So-called "buccopharyngeal" respiration is probably "sniffing" in connection with the sense of smell.

2. The Mechanism of Ventilation of the Lungs

The respiratory movements of the floor of the mouth and their correlation with lung breathing are not so well understood as most accounts given in elementary textbooks of zoology would seem to suggest. In particular the amount of mixing that takes place in the buccal cavity of air from the lungs with that drawn in from the outside, which must occur on expiration, is a matter of some dispute. Also differing views are held on the contribution, if any, made to the emptying and filling of the lungs by active movements of the flank muscles. The reason for these differences of opinion lies in the practical impossibility of conducting experiments under anything approaching "normal" conditions. It is difficult to believe that experiments under anesthetics, such as those of Gnanamuthu (1936), bear a very close resemblance to what goes on in the conscious animal.

Some experiments on unanesthetized *Rana temporaria* and *R. esculenta* have been made by Scholton (1942), who has also reviewed previous work. The movement of the flanks and of the buccal floor were recorded with the glottis (a) functioning normally and (b) held open by a small glass canula. It was found important to distinguish between true movements of

the flanks caused by inflation or deflation of the lungs and passive movements due to transmitted pressure originating from movement of the
hyoid. Conclusions were: with the nares open and the glottis closed, lowering of the floor of the buccal cavity draws air in through the nares. The
air is then forced out again as the floor rises. (This renewal of air in the
buccal cavity draws air over the olfactory organ and, as has already been
pointed out above, is probably best described as "sniffing" and not "breathing"; the latter term will, however, be retained as it is the customary
usage.) Air is passed to the lungs when the nares are closed and the glottis
opened and the raising of the buccal floor forces air into the lungs. At this
stage the glottis is closed and buccal "breathing" normally resumed. The
air in the lungs can be added to by a further supply being forced down into
them. As is well known, some species of toads can so inflate themselves
as a defense mechanism.

Neil and co-workers (1950) have suggested that a function of the
fibers of the vagus nerve, which terminate in the lungs, is to convey information to the respiratory centers concerning the state of inflation of the
lungs so that there is no possibility of overinflation. Exactly how the lungs
are deflated is a matter on which varying opinions have been expressed.
Muscular movements of the flanks of the body wall have been suggested
as actively forcing the air out. The lungs of many frogs have elastic fibers
which suggest a simple elastic recoil. Finally the air may be "sucked" out
by closing the nares and opening the glottis and lowering the floor of the
mouth which draws air into the mouth. This air is then expressed through
the nares by opening them, closing the glottis, and raising the floor of the
mouth.

Scholton concludes that the flanks "co-operate actively during the lung
expiration," also that at the beginning of the expiration the lowering of
the floor of the buccal cavity (the nares being closed) is an active movement but as soon as the glottis opens the pressure in the lungs forces the
floor of the mouth downward. He is very doubtful as to whether the pumping movements of the buccal floor with both nares and glottis open ever
takes place in an unanesthetized frog. He also regards as of doubtful
validity the suggestion which has been made that the lungs may be emptied
if both glottis and nares are open simultaneously. Cherian (1956) confirmed the importance of the flanks in deflating the lungs of *Rana hexadactyla* but also stated the opinion that in this species the glottis is never
completely closed. He also did not observe "buccopharyngeal" respiration
taking place separately from lung breathing and remarked (pp. 165–166)
"But there is no experimental proof for the buccopharyngeal ventilation
nor is there any necessity for separately ventilating the mouth cavity
because each time the lungs are ventilated air passes through the mouth,

and therefore, the buccal cavity is also ventilated." Whatever may happen in this species independent buccal breathing can be observed in most frogs. According to Das and Srivastava (1957) in *Rana tigrina* there is a constant relation between the movements of the mouth and the filling of the lungs. They state that in this species whatever the actual respiratory rate may be, and this will depend on temperature, activity, etc., the number of buccal movements if divided by the lung inspirations observed in the same time will always give a constant dividend (K). For *R. tigrina*, $K = 4$. I think it extremely unlikely that such a constant relationship could be demonstrated in many species.

It seems strange that in discussing the breathing mechanism "croaking" is never mentioned. Yet the mechanisms involved must be very similar. Noble (1931) pointed out that in croaking air is forced from one part of the body to another. In male *Rana esculenta* air is forced by contractions of the flank muscles from the lungs into the mouth, the nares being closed. The mouth cannot hold all the air and some passes into the croaking sacs (which are said to act as resonators) which are diverticula of the floor of the mouth. During this act the croak is emitted. The air is then passed back to the lungs; this involves the expansion of the lungs, the relaxation of the flanks, the raising of the floor of the mouth, and the collapse of the sacs. The flanks are extremely active during croaking and that they are active during lung breathing cannot be doubted. The movements of the floor of the mouth cannot be responsible for the whole process.

It may be remarked that if an active animal, largely dependent on pulmonary respiration, is to use the "force-pump" method of ventilating its lungs there must be, presumably, a limit to the difference in volume between the bellows (buccal cavity) and the lungs. Also that bellows pumping equal quantities of air may take either of two forms they can be deep and narrow or wide and shallow; if the latter, a small excursion of the movable side of the bellows will suffice to fill and empty them. This is what appears to have happened in the Anura, in the great majority of which the head is large in relation to the body (as compared with the proportions found in a newt for example) ; it is dorsoventrally flattened so that the comparatively small excursion of the floor of the mouth will suffice to pump the air into the lungs. The fact that frogs have large flat heads compared with some other amphibians is, then, probably not due to chance but related to the force-pump method of filling the lungs (Schmalhausen, 1957; Czopek, 1962).

The evolutionary aspect of the respiratory movements is not without interest, for it may be assumed either that the force-pump method of filling the lungs is a relic of some ancestral habit or that it is derived from the larval method of passing the water over the gills.

Willem (1931) has suggested that in the Stegocephalia both the amphibian (force-pump) and the reptilian (rib movement) methods of filling the lungs were present and it was his opinion that the structure of the ribs of Stegocephalia supported this suggestion. The force-pump method is to be correlated with the loss of ribs. Willem states that in the fish *Protopterus* and probably also in *Polypterus* air is helped into the lungs by rib action. Many reptiles seem to retain traces of the force-pump method along with the rib method. Such views as have been expressed on the origin of the force-pump method of inflation of the lungs, are based on the assumption that the buccopharyngeal movements of amphibians are primarily respiratory in function, but this seems doubtful. Also none of the air-breathing fishes uses the nares for breathing (Atz, 1952; Greenwood and Oliva, 1959). The nares of fish, even if internal, are apparently always olfactory organs. If Willem is correct in thinking that the early amphibians used their ribs to fill their lungs they probably also used the buccal floor movement to ventilate the nares. They thus had currents of air passing into and out of the mouth produced by two mechanisms. Evolution then proceeded so that these two mechanisms became integrated and this probably happened in several different ways. One of these ways is the complete domination of the buccal method, as seen in the Anura, which obviously cannot be an intermediate stage between fish on the one hand and terrestrial vertebrates on the other. The big evolutionary advance shown by the Amphibia is the use of the nares for breathing. *Cryptobranchus* and *Amphiuma* breathe through the nostrils, but *Siren* and *Necturus* take in air through the mouth (Atz, 1952). Spurway and Haldane (1953) state that newts (*Triturus* sp.) usually fill the lungs through the nostrils by movements of the hyoid—the mouth remaining closed—and usually a bubble of air is discharged through the mouth as the animal withdraws its head under water after filling the lungs. Noble (1931, p. 173) suggests that newts rising to the surface can fill their throats more quickly through the mouth than through the nares. Czopek (1962), who in a preliminary communication has drawn attention to the fact that in *Amphiuma means* and *Siren intermedia* the lung capillaries constitute 68.2 and 58.16% of all respiratory capillaries, has pointed out that the buccal method of breathing could not be expected efficiently to ventilate these lungs. He draws attention to the great development of smooth muscles in these lungs and suggests that further work might show that these muscles are responsible for the ventilating mechanism.

B. RESPIRATORY EXCHANGE IN DEVELOPMENTAL STAGES

The majority of Amphibia lay their eggs in water and development proceeds through an aquatic larval stage before metamorphosis into the adult. In this sequence of events respiratory exchange takes place first by way of the egg surface, second through the body surface, and finally through the lungs (except in lungless species). Although the gills generally, but in urodeles by no means always, disappear in the adult, cutaneous respiration remains important in all recent Amphibia.

Some species are extremely selective as regards their spawning sites, the basis of this selection is not well understood but is obviously directed toward ensuring that the minimum requirements for the successful development of the spawn are present. Savage (1939) observing *Rana temporaria* in England concluded that there is a significant correlation between the potassium content of the water and the presence or absence of spawn and also that dissolved carbonates may affect spawn distribution. He considered it unlikely that the effects of the dissolved salts are directly on the frogs, but that the salts may affect the microflora and that the presence or absence of particular elements in the microflora may be the factor which determines whether or not a particular pond is selected for spawning.

However this may be, it is essential that the ponds selected should have sufficient oxygen content to support the development of both eggs and larvae.

The oxygen needs of developing amphibian eggs are best known for urodeles, and Hopkins and Handford (1943) have given an account of the respiratory metabolism of two species of *Ambystoma*. Both as embryos and as larvae a considerable difference in oxygen consumption between the species was found. At metamorphosis *A. punctatum* (= *A. maculatum*) larvae consumed 1225 μliters per gram dry weight per hour as against 1919 μliters consumed by larvae of *A. tigrinum*. These authors report that the respiratory rate of these larvae rises during the embryonic period and then tends to fall during the larval stages but that in *A. tigrinum* it rises again at metamorphosis. [This rise is probably to be associated with the release of thyroxine into the blood system; see Wills (1936).]

From this work on *Ambystoma* larvae and that of Helff (1926) on *Rana pipiens*, Atlas (1931) on *R. pipiens* and *R. sylvatica*, and Etkin (1934) on *R. catesbeiana* it is clear that although the oxygen needs of larvae are considerable, specific variation occurs.

Rana temporaria lays its eggs in large masses and Savage (1935), who measured the oxygen content of the water inside and outside the spawn masses, concluded that when they hatch the tadpoles must be subject to great oxygen deficiency. In water of 12°C he found that the oxygen content, some 50 cm outside the egg masses, might be as high as 14.5 ml O_2 per liter (136% saturated), whereas inside the spawn masses the percentage saturation was much less, varying between 3 and 16%. Hydrogen-ion concentration also showed variation. In the open water a pH of 7.6 was recorded, near the spawn masses it fell to 7.0, and among tadpoles it was 6.8. Tadpoles of this species tend to aggregate. Experiments have provided a possible explanation. Thus a lack of oxygen causes tadpoles to swim upward but in well oxygenated water there is not such a great tendency to swim, thus tadpoles on the outside of a mass, being in water of higher oxygen content, tend to stop moving and so keep the periphery of the colony intact.

The degree of vascularization of the respiratory surfaces of *Rana esculenta* during its ontogenetic development has been studied by Strawinski (1956). The density of the capillary network of the epidermis goes on increasing in the developing larva until it reaches a maximum at the stage when the forelimbs break through the operculum and this density is maintained in the adult. Just before this density is reached, that is in the two-legged tadpole, the metamorphosis of the skin takes place. At this time the larval capillaries in the corium of the dermis are replaced by the subepidermal capillaries of the adult (see also Chapter 8). Although respiratory exchange takes place through both external and internal gills and the vascularized surface of the filtering apparatus Strawinski does not seem to think that exchange in these sites is of major importance. Most of the exchange takes place through the skin and the vascularization of the internal surface of the operculum is also important. Some of the accessory respiratory structures may be more important in respiration at night, when some fresh-water environments are low in oxygen content; these structures may be of more importance in other species which habitually live in water of low oxygen concentration. (That these accessory respiratory surfaces must have some significance is suggested by the fact that in the Microhylidae the filtering apparatus has the appearance of internal gill which it completely replaces.) As the lungs develop they quickly account for an increasing percentage of the total capillaries and by the late tadpole stage, just at metamorphosis, the final percentages of capillary distribution (Table II) are achieved.

The stage at which the lungs are first used varies considerably. *Rana esculenta* and *R. temporaria* gulp air quite early. In *Bufo* sp. the lungs are not used until metamorphosis (Savage, 1952) and these species are restricted in their spawning to waters which are sufficiently oxygenated to support all the larval modes of respiration. Tadpoles of *Rana catesbeiana* are primarily water breathers, which gulp air only occasionally (Etkin, 1934) and which can live without access to air. *Rana pipiens* tadpoles presumably gulp air, for Helff and Stubblefield (1931) found that while in water of oxygen tension between 108% and 22% saturation oxygen consumption was completely independent of oxygen tension, at and below

22% saturation the tadpoles frequently released oxygen to the water; this oxygen must have been obtained by lung breathing.

In urodeles details of capillary distribution during the development of *Ambystoma mexicanum* and *Salamandra salamandra* have been studied (Czopek, 1957, 1959a). As with all early stages the high surface:mass ratio produces high figures for the degree of vascularity.

A late larva of *Ambystoma* (weight 17 gm) was recorded as having approximately the following distribution of respiratory capillaries: skin 40%, gills 31%, lungs 29%. On metamorphosis the final relative distribution is not at once attained (cf. *Rana esculenta* above). With the disappearance of the gills there is a great increase in the length of capillaries found in the lungs. Then as growth proceeds the skin network intensifies. In a specimen which had been 4 weeks on land the skin had 36% and the lungs 62%; another specimen which had been 9 weeks on land showed skin 50%, lungs 44%. Czopek points out that these variations take place despite the fact that the total length of capillaries per gram body weight remains almost constant.

In *Ambystoma* many larvae do not metamorphose but become neotenous. Here the capillary pattern of the larval skin is retained with much fewer meshes than in the adult but the vessels undergo enlargement, their diameter varying from 20 to 65 μ as against 12–32 μ in metamorphosed individuals. Although neotenic individuals retain their gills the length of gill capillaries per gram body weight is small; for example a larva of 17 gm had 3.877 meters per gram and a neotenic individual of 76 gm had 0.025 meter per gram. Czopek (1959a) points out that if it is assumed that the length of respiratory capillaries per gram body weight is an indication of the gas exchange of an animal the gas exchange of the neotenic form of *A. mexicanum* has the lowest exchange so far found.

The larvae of *Salamandra salamandra* are of interest as they are retained in the oviduct of the female where the skin and gill capillaries carry out their gas exchange with the maternal tissues. According to Czopek "Larvae removed from the egg sheaths weighed on the average 0.220g." In his table, larvae of this weight are accorded the following percentages of capillaries: skin 54.32, lungs 6.03, gills 37.77, palate 1.88. As the lungs and palate are presumably not respiratory surfaces before the young are released into the water the respiratory exchange must take place through the skin and gills only. Whether these surfaces play the relative parts shown by the figures is not indicated; it may be suggested that the details of the relative arrangements of gills and maternal tissues might be of interest.

Close correlation between gill development and oxygen concentration has been described in salamander larvae by Drastich (1927). His photographs of specimens reared in water (a) deficient, and (b) rich, in oxygen show remarkable differences in the degree of development of the gills. Gills of larvae from water poor in oxygen are much larger.

Drastich also drew attention to differences in the histology of the gill filaments. This observation was followed up by Bond (1960) who has concluded that in *Salamandra maculosa, S. salamandra,* and *Ambystoma jeffersonianum* both the size and the structure of the gills are influenced by the oxygen concentration of the water. Enlargement of the gills and more especially of the filaments, is found in animals subjected to oxygen deficiency. Alternatively if the medium is rich in oxygen the surface area of the gills is reduced. These gross changes are the result of changes both in the number of cells in the filaments and in the shape of the cells. Enlarged filaments have flattened epidermal cells, distended blood vessels, and a greater blood volume; the smaller filaments of the animals reared in well oxygenated water have smaller blood vessels and cuboidal cells in the epithelium. It is suggested that the primary effect of reduced oxygen tension is to increase the blood pressure of the larvae. This leads to increased turgidity and so to elongation of the gills and thence to the flattening of the epithelium. High oxygen concentration in the water leads to a low blood pressure, which accounts for the smaller blood vessels, smaller filaments, and cuboidal epithelium. Investigation of mitotic activity gave evidence of the stimulation, by oxygen lack, of cell division and thus to an absolute increase in the number of cells comprising the gills. This result, which was obtained for *Salamandra maculosa* could not be confirmed in *Ambystoma jeffersonianum* where any increase in the numbers of cells was offset by the necrosis of older cells.

C. RESPIRATION IN APODA

The foregoing account of the respiratory methods of Anura and Urodela exemplifies the variety of adaptations to cutaneous respiration shown by amphibians. The Apoda have not so far been mentioned and this is because comparatively few studies have been made on members of this group. In recent years some information has been obtained, which forms the basis of the following summary.

A general description of the lungs of apodans and their development has been given by Noble (1931, pp. 165–166). Baer (1937) has given further details for some species, reporting that *Uraeotyphlus oxyurus* has unequally developed lungs, the right being larger than the left in the proportion 28:5. Similar disproportion is met with in some other genera but in *Typhlonectes* the lungs are equally developed. *Chthonerpeton* spp. have unequally developed lungs as also do some species of *Ichthyophis* but Iyer (1943) found that *I. monochrous* has equally developed lungs while *I.*

glutinosus, Siphonops annulatus, Dermophis gregorii, and *Gegenophis carnosus* have the left lung much smaller than the right. *Uraeotyphlus narayani* has only one lung.

In all species the trachea is supported by hoops of cartilage, which are incomplete on the ventral side. From the trachea a tracheal "lung" is developed. Baer (1937) records that in a specimen of *Uraeotyphlus oxyurus*, in which the trachea measured 25 mm from the glottis to the point of bifurcation of the bronchi, the first 8 mm were trachea proper and the remainder tracheal lung. This lung is served by the tracheal artery. The tracheal lung is formed by the evagination of the ventral wall of the trachea, the cavity within the evagination being divided by complicated folds, the smaller cavities thus formed communicating with the lumen of the trachea. The ciliated mucosa of the trachea proper is replaced in the lung portion by a respiratory epithelium. The walls of the ventral diverticulum contain elastic fibers which cross in all directions and are said to ensure that on inspiration the tracheal lung can expand like a normal lung. The walls of these "lungs" are infiltrated with cartilage.

The ribs are said to play no part in the filling and emptying of the lungs; this is done by movements of the laryngeal cartilages and of the glottis. These movements are also concerned with drawing air into the mouth cavity; the floor of the mouth cavity is very small and is thought to play a very insignificant part, if any part at all, in these movements. Mendes (1941, 1945) has described beating movements of the gullet of *Siphonops annulatus* which are thought to help in tracheal and esophageal respiration; they may be as rapid as 200 per minute. It is not thought that they could be responsible for filling the lungs.

The circulatory system of Apoda (so far as it has a bearing on respiratory exchange) will be discussed later but it may be mentioned here that the circulatory arrangements strongly suggest that, as in other Amphibia, the skin plays a dominant part in respiratory exchange. Mendes (1945) has measured the carbon dioxide output and the respiratory quotient in *Siphonops annulatus*. He obtained suppression of pulmonary respiration both by partial tracheotomy and by anesthesia, and as a result of such experiments found that both methods interfered with oxygen uptake and carbon dioxide output, but concluded that normally the greater part of the carbon dioxide is eliminated through the skin.

III. Blood

A. CONSTITUENTS OF THE BLOOD

The blood of amphibians is typical of nonmammalian vertebrates in that it is composed of a plasma in which are found nucleated erythrocytes, leucocytes, and thrombocytes. Some constituents of the blood pass out from the vessels as lymph and, as is well known, the lymph circulation of amphibians as a whole and of the Anura in particular is copious and rapid. For a consideration of the blood of Amphibia in comparison with that of other vertebrates, reference should be made to Jordan's (1938) article in Downey's "Handbook of Hematology."

1. Erythrocytes

As in the adults of all nonmammalian vertebrates the erythrocytes are typically nucleated; they are generally of large size, the genus *Amphiuma* having the largest erythrocytes known. The greatest diameter of the elliptical disk is stated to be: in *Amphiuma* sp. 70 μ (Noble, 1931), in *Amphiuma means* 60 μ (Smith, 1925), and in *Amphiuma tridactylum* "one third larger than that of *Proteus*" (Schafer, 1912). As *Proteus* is stated to have erythrocytes with the greatest diameter of 62.5 μ this statement indicates that those of *A. tridactylum* must measure approximately 83 μ. Large erythrocytes are also present in other perennibranchiate urodeles; *Necturus* has red cells which measure 54 μ in greatest diameter and *Cryptobranchus* 41 μ. Harris (1953) who found the average dimensions of the erythrocytes of *Necturus* to be 54.4 × 28.2 μ records that one cell he measured was 80 × 34 μ. The Anura have smaller but still elliptical red cells. In both *Rana pipiens* and *R. palustris* the corresponding measurement is 20 μ approximately. The actual size attained by the majority of corpuscles may vary slightly in an inverse direction with the metabolic activity of the animal of which they form a part (Smith, 1925).

That nucleated erythrocytes consume considerably greater quantities of oxygen than do non-nucleate erythrocytes (Scott, 1931) is to be noted if the blood is to be stored for experimental purposes. The presence of the nucleus causes the cell to bulge around it. Harris (1953) found that even the large erythrocytes of *Necturus* were, on an average, 2.1 μ thick but that the nucleus caused an increase in thickness of at least 2 μ. The ratio of the nucleus to cytoplasm in the erythrocytes of salamander larvae has been found to vary with the oxygen tension of the water (Drastich, 1927): normal water, 1:2.09; oxygen-poor water, 1:3.43.

The origin of erythrocytes will be discussed later, but it may be remarked that during its development the cell loses the power of producing pseudopodia and changes from a spherical shape to that of a nearly flattened disk as well, of course, as producing hemoglobin. Some of the physicochemical aspects of the changes in the cell membrane have been discussed by Holtfreter (1947).

Erythrocytes without nuclei (erythroplastids) are found in the circulating blood of several amphibians. The most noted instance is that of the lungless salamander *Batrachoseps attenuatus* where nearly all the red cells are erythroplastids. While it is not unusual for some lungless urodeles to have up to 5% non-nucleated red cells, *Batrachoseps* spp. may have as many as 95% (Emmel, 1924). It has been suggested that, whereas other lungless salamanders show marked adaptations to lunglessness in the form of the gills, tail, or skin, which permit of greater gaseous exchange, *Batrachoseps* does not show such specialization. In this genus adaptation to lunglessness has been adaptation of the erythrocyte, for such cells having no nucleus are flatter than the normal corpuscles and therefore their numbers can be increased in any given volume; also lack of a nucleus means that they do not consume so much of the oxygen they carry. Erythroplastids arise from erythrocytes by budding.

Vacuoles are a conspicuous feature of the erythroplastid of *Batrachoseps* (Dawson and Charipper, 1929) ; also it has been pointed out that in *Triturus viridescens* when the blood is infected with *Trypanosoma* or *Dactylosoma* the erythrocytes frequently become abnormal, the nucleus breaks down, and the cell comes to resemble an erythroplastid (Nigrelli, 1929). Vacuolated red cells are found in frogs suffering from "red-leg" disease (Kaplan, 1952a).

In anurans, erythroplastids are not so well known but in *Rana pipiens* and *Rana catesbeiana* considerable numbers of non-nucleated erythrocytes are found in the spleen and a few may circulate in the blood (Jordan and Speidel, 1923). Most, however, would appear never to leave the spleen but be destroyed there. The budding of erythrocytes of *Xenopus laevis* after splenectomy has been described (Jacobson, 1953) but the buds do not separate from the parent cell.

2. Thrombocytes

Thrombocytes or "spindle cells" take the place of platelets in the nonmammalian vertebrates. They have a nucleus and their relationship with the other cells of the blood has been a matter of some dispute. In urodeles thrombocytoplastids (i.e., thrombocytes without nuclei) have been described (Emmel, 1925; Slonimski, 1935). According to Emmel there is no sharp demarcation between mammals and lower vertebrates with regard to non-nucleated elements in the blood; they are to be looked upon as portions of the cytoplasm detached by a process of segmentation from the nucleated progenitor and liberated into the blood stream. As mentioned below several types of non-nucleated leucocytes have been described, but non-nucleated thrombocytes clearly resemble platelets.

3. Leucocytes

Agranular leucocytes (lymphocytes and monocytes) and granular leucocytes (basophils, neutrophils, and eosinophils) make up the white cells of amphibian blood. The ratio of white cells to red in amphibians has been given as from 1 white to 20 red, to 1 white to 70 red (Stephan, 1954).

It is beyond the scope of this chapter to give a detailed account of the leucocytes of amphibians. Reference should be made to the work of H. E. Jordan (1925, 1932, 1933, 1938), Jordan and Speidel (1923, 1929, 1930), and also to Loewenthal (1929). The last dealt in some detail with the white cells of *Bombinator* and *Salamandra* spp. It is notable that the large size of the erythrocytes of Amphibia is not paralleled to anything like the same extent by the leucocytes. Thus the largest monocytes of both *Bombinator* and *Salamandra* have a diameter of about 30–32 μ.

Just as erythrocytes and thrombocytes without nuclei have been described, so have various of the white cells, and in urodeles basophiloplastids, lymphoplastids, megakaryocytoplastids, and eosinophiloplastids have been described (Emmel, 1925; Slonimski, 1935).

B. BLOOD COUNTS

1. *Erythrocytes*

As may well be imagined in those urodeles where the erythrocytes are very large there are, compared with other amphibians, fewer cells per volume of blood. Thus, *Proteus anguinus*, with the greatest diameter of the cell approximately 58 μ, is reported to have a blood count of 36,000 per mm³; for *Rana temporaria* the corresponding figures are 22 μ and 400,000 (Stephan, 1954). Well fed *Necturus* (greatest diameter of cell about 54 μ) would seem to have a count of about 51,000 per mm³ (Harris, 1953).

There are however many causes of intraspecific variation in number. One of these is sex. It has been reported that, while in *Bufo vulgaris* there was little sex difference, in *Rana temporaria* females gave an average count of 300,000 per mm³, while males gave an average of 450,000 per mm³ (Arvy, 1947). Leucocytes and thrombocytes did not show similar variation. Kaplan (1952a), working on *Rana pipiens*, has recorded differences in count with respect to sex but in a reverse direction; in males the count was 480,000 per mm³ and in females 512,000. These figures are for normal frogs. In frogs affected by "red-leg" disease there was a similar difference although the total count was lower in both sexes.

Variation with season has been shown in *Bufo arenarum* (Varela and Sellarés, 1938) which, in Brazil, gave a count of 1,000,000 per mm³ in July and August (this is the end of the winter). Breeding starts in September and continues in October and there is a rapid decrease in the blood count. From the stages found circulating it is concluded that hematopoiesis is intense so that very rapid destruction of blood cells must be taking place. The count rises again from November through January to diminish again in February and March and then it rises again in the period May to July. The number of both leucocytes and thrombocytes follows the same pattern.

The state of nutrition of the animal must also have a profound effect on the blood picture. There is little information about this, but in *Bufo viridis* starvation leads to an increase in the number of immature red cells in the blood and also to an increase in the number of lymphocytes together with a lowering of the numbers of neutrophils and monocytes (Churý 1952). Starvation has also been found to result in a fall in the red cell numbers in *Necturus* (Harris, 1953).

In man it is well known that acclimatization to life at high altitudes results in an increase in the erythrocyte numbers. An attempt to find similar differences between specimens of *Ambystoma* living in Colorado at heights between 6,000 and 10,000 feet above sea level proved abortive as the variation between individuals living at the same height was so wide as to make no comparison between averages for different heights possible (Myers and Alexander, 1945). As mentioned elsewhere in this chapter, some correlation of hemoglobin content with altitude of habitat has been obtained.

2. *Leucocytes*

Variation of leucocyte numbers with season and with the state of nutrition has already been mentioned in the preceding paragraph.

Detailed comparison of specimens of *Bombinator pachypus* taken in May and June (Loewenthal, 1929) may indicate a seasonal rise in neutrophils at the expense of eosinophils and basophils (neutrophils rise from 6% of the total leucocyte count to 16.4%), but the large numbers of specimens needed to overcome individual variations do not appear to have been studied in this investigation. A large difference in the granulocyte: nongranulocyte ratio was found between *B. pachypus* and *Salamandra atra*; in *B. pachypus* the granulocytes accounted for 25% of the white cell count and the nongranulocytes 75%; whereas in *S. atra* the granulocytes accounted for 65% and the nongranulocytes 35%. Before accepting these figures as typical for anurans and urodeles, a considerably larger number of observations is needed.

Bacterial infection has been shown to have an influence on the differential white cell count. Kaplan (1952b) found that in "red-leg" disease the total white cell count was reduced; in the acute stage of the disease there was a rise in the number of lymphocytes and a significant decrease in the numbers of neutrophils and a slight decrease in eosinophils. In the terminal stages of the disease there was a complete suppression of all granulocytes.

C. HEMATOPOIESIS

1. *General*

Hematopoiesis in amphibians has been much studied. Among accounts that have been given of the origin of the various corpuscles, those of

Jordan (1925, 1932, 1933, 1938) and of Jordan and Speidel (1923, 1929) must be specially mentioned.

In the development of the blood cells of Amphibia nothing has been found which cannot be harmonized with the theory that all blood cells spring from a primitive stem cell. The stem cell, by a series of modifications, gives rise to all the varieties of corpuscle found in the circulation as well as to certain cells of the tissues, e.g., macrophages, lymphocytes. The nomenclature of the stem cells of the blood elements is extremely confused. These indifferent mesenchymal stem cells which may act as progenitors of the various types of cell just mentioned are sometimes termed "primitive reticular cells" but as so much of the work on amphibian blood has been done by Jordan and his collaborators it seems desirable to use his nomenclature so far as possible. Jordan (1933, 1938) uses the term "hemocytoblast" or "lymphoid hemoblast" to cover the progenitor or stem cell. He points out that, in hagfish, which appear to show the most primitive condition, perivenous myeloid cells in the submucosa of the gastrointestinal tract represent a diffuse spleen in which hemocytopoietic activity takes place. In the vertebrate series the separation of the functions of erythrocytopoiesis, granulocytopoiesis, and lymphocytopoiesis, which in lower forms are inextricably intertwined, can be traced. Exactly how the stem cells differentiate, Jordan points out, depends on a number of factors, particularly their location. Thus in higher vertebrates lymphoid hemoblasts of bone marrow differentiate into granulocytes if they are extravascular and into erythrocytes if they are intravascular; in the lymph nodes they will develop into lymphocytes.

It is not proposed to give here any detailed description of the hemocytoblasts or stem cells and the changes that they undergo in order to take on their definitive form; for such accounts, reference may be made to the various authorities cited. A matter of more general interest, however, is the site or sites of hematopoiesis found in various Amphibia. These centers vary with age and systematic group and can be altered by experimental procedures. In the account which follows a summary of such findings is attempted.

The first blood cells to appear in amphibians are in the blood islands of the blastopore-liver area, and tissue culture experiments (Finnegan, 1953) suggest that the development of hemoglobin in erythrocytes is dependent on the presence of the metabolic products of the hemoblasts together with diffusible substances from the endoderm. The floor of the archenteron apparently acts as an organizer of the developing hypomere in the sense that it prevents this portion of the mesoderm from assuming an organization characteristic of more dorsal mesoderm. This is the only source of erythrocytes in the embryo and if this is removed the blood vascular system develops almost normally but there are no red cells.

Later hemocytopoietic activity takes place in various organs or in certain parts of such organs. Jordan (1933) in reviewing this field has drawn attention to the fact that blood formation appears to take place in certain situations which seem to favor this activity and which are found in various parts of the body. Erythrocytopoiesis tends to take place in situations where there are blood sinuses in which the blood flow is slow but also where there is a copious blood supply, also a lack of oxygen, and probably an increased carbon dioxide tension. Such situations occur in Amphibia in the kidney of larvae as well as in the spleen and bone marrow of adults. However, under certain circumstances erythrocytopoiesis seems to take place in the circulating blood and hemoblasts may be found in the endothelial lining of many organs. The fact that erythrocytopoiesis takes place at times in the long bones of some amphibians can be explained simply along the functional lines suggested by Jordan. To attempt to attach any evolutionary significance to this betrays a misunderstanding of the course of vertebrate evolution.

The conditions under which granulocytopoiesis takes place are somewhat different as here a poor blood supply would seem to be one of the requisites. Thus in the kidney of the larvae this function is found in the intertubular connective tissue; in many Amphibia it is found in certain areas of the liver; the pericardium and the thymus have also been suggested as sites. It is convenient to deal with Anura and Urodela separately.

a. *Hematopoiesis in Anura.* In Anura the site of blood formation varies with the age of the animal. The first blood cells are derived from the mesenchyme of the embryo. Then in tadpole larvae they are formed in the kidney (mesonephros). As the spleen develops it also takes on, in many instances, a hematocytopoietic, mainly erythrocytopoietic, function but this does not become important until after metamorphosis when the main function of the spleen is the production of new blood cells and the removal of senile cells. Jordan and Speidel (1923) give a description of hematopoiesis in the frogs *Rana pipiens* and *R. catesbeiana* where in the spleen small lymphocytes give rise to spindle cells and the large lymphocytes to both erythrocytes and granulocytes. [In a later paper (1929) these authors appear to revise their conclusions that spindle cells are derived from small lymphocytes and suggest that at least in the urodele *Triturus* they are descended from large lymphoid hemoblasts.] In the spleen of both frogs numerous erythroplastids are seen. Some hemopoietic activity continues in the kidney of the adult frogs but it is predominantly granulocytopoietic. Lymphocytes also develop into granulocytes in the wall of the intestine and this has been likened to the condition seen in the fishes and cyclostomes where all the splenic tissue is in the intestinal wall. Numerous eosinophils are found to migrate through the intestinal walls into the lumen of the intestine; they would appear to have a close connection with immunity to the bacterial content of the intestinal mucosa.

At metamorphosis, and also for a few days in spring after awakening from hibernation each year, there is erythrocytopoietic activity in the marrow cavity of the long bones, but this is short lived in *Rana catesbeiana* and *R. pipiens*.

In early tadpoles of *Rana temporaria* there is no splenic hematopoietic activity (Maximow, 1910), the kidney being the center of all forms of hematopoiesis. In later larvae lymphocytes accumulate in the blood sinuses of the liver and differentiate into thrombocytes and erythrocytes. Granular and nongranular leucocytes are still formed in the extravascular areas of the kidney. In the fully metamorphosed frogs all varieties of hematopoiesis pass over to the bone marrow where it is a permanent function.

The fact that erythrocytes and thrombocytes differentiate in the same locus might suggest that these two types of cell have a closer connection with each other than with the granular and nongranular leucocytes. But Pinner (1950), who studied hematopoiesis in the tadpoles of *Rana esculenta*, with particular reference to the development of the spindle cells, found that the blood cells of the later tadpoles were derived from the kidney and liver, which can be called lymphoreticular organs. These organs give rise to prothrombocytes. At a still later stage the spindle cells are directly derived from the endothelium, the prothrombocyte stage being omitted. Apparently the spindle cell can also arise directly from the hemocytoblast and thus come from any or all of the hematopoietic organs which Pinner lists as the bone marrow, endothelium, liver, spleen, kidney, postbranchial body, adenolymphoid tissue, etc. Thus it is concluded that there is no closer connection between the stem cells of the erythrocyte and either the prothrombocyte or spindle cell than the hemocytoblast.

Mylius (1952) also studied hematopoiesis in the tadpole and again came to the conclusion that all the varieties of blood cell came from an indifferent mesenchyme cell.

[Jordan and Speidel (1929) as a result of experiments on splenectomized *Triturus viridescens* concluded that in urodeles the thromboblasts, which they found in the circulating blood and which divided by mitosis and gave rise to thrombocytes, were descended from the large lymphoid hemoblast and were not closely related to erythrocytes or lymphocytes.]

  b. Hematopoiesis in Urodela. In Urodela the kidney, spleen, and liver are variously involved in hemocytopoiesis. In the *Plethodontidae* the bone marrow is also involved.

It is only in the Proteidae that the kidney is an important site of hemo-poietic activity. In *Proteus* (Jordan, 1932) the kidney (mesonephros) is the site of granulocytopoiesis and the spleen produces lymphocytes or lymphoid hemoblasts, which enter the circulation and differentiate into erythrocytes and thrombocytes. Except for a small number of basophils, the spleen does not give rise to granulocytes. A few macrophages are said to develop directly from hemocytoblasts. In *Proteus* the liver is not an important site of hematopoiesis although it appears to have the potenti-ality of erythrocytopoiesis and thrombocytopoiesis but not granulocy-topoiesis. The intestinal wall lacks both granulocytes and lymphocytes.

In *Triturus* (Salamandridae), *Amphiuma* (Amphiumidae), and to a lesser degree in *Necturus* (Proteidae) the liver is an organ of granulocy-topoiesis, this activity taking place in the subcapsular region. This region of the liver is the main center of granulocytopoiesis in *Triturus viridescens* (Jordan and Speidel, 1930) while erythrocytopoiesis and thrombocy-topoiesis take place chiefly in the spleen. In *Necturus* not all the granu-locytopoiesis takes place in the liver; the intertubular areas of the mesonephros are also important loci.

The Plethodontidae have a hematopoietic bone marrow which has been described in some detail and compared with that of other urodeles. It is the seat of origin of leucocytes only; it is not erythropoietic (Schaefer, 1935).

Whether the other sites of lymphogranulocytopoiesis are retained in addition to the bone marrow varies with the species. In *Hydromantes italicus* this function is found in certain areas of the liver as well as in the bone marrow but it is not found in the kidney (Barrett, 1947).

Variation of hematopoietic locus is also seen in Salamandridae for, whereas in *T. viridescens* (mentioned above) the liver is the main center of granulocytopoiesis, in *Hynobius retardatus* (Ouji, 1950) the anterior two-thirds of the kidneys is active in this way. In many urodeles the epi-cardium is also a center of blood cell production (Dawson, 1933). Although the spleen is the center of erythropoiesis throughout the urodeles it will be clear from the examples given above that the centers of granulocy-topoiesis are restricted and at the same time varied.

This variation is not, apparently, haphazard and Barrett (1947) pointed out that in some urodeles the granulocytopoietic function of the liver is restricted to certain areas: (1) Perihepatic, subcapsular tissue; (2) In-terstitial tissue; (3) Periportal tissue. He went on to give it as his opinion that restriction to some or other of these areas is a systematic character which can be of assistance in evaluating the relationships of the members of a group.

Erythrocytopoiesis is not entirely confined to the spleen for immature erythrocytes are often to be found in the circulating blood of urodeles. It has been reported that at times (Dawson, 1930) all stages in the formation of the erythrocytes from the lymphoid hemoblast onward can be demonstrated in the circulating blood. In such cases mitotic division only is found and the general blood picture has been likened to that seen in some instances of pernicious anemia in warm-blooded animals. Thrombocytopoiesis does not normally seem to take place in the blood but after splenectomy it has been recorded in Salamanders (Jordan and Speidel, 1929) when the thrombocytes differentiated from lymphocytes which entered the blood stream and divided mitotically. Not all nuclear division seen in the blood of amphibians is mitotic. Braungart (1950) states that amitosis has been described in *Necturus* and records both mitosis and amitosis in the circulating blood of *Rana pipiens*.

The foregoing account of the centers of hematopoiesis gives some impression, if nothing more, of the varied sites of blood formation that are scattered in a number of organs of the body in a seemingly haphazard and unordered manner. An attempt to list some of the principal centers is made in Tables IV and V. A consideration of these sites indicates that the factors suggested by Jordan as controlling the development of the lymphoid hemoblast into either erythrocytes or thrombocytes on the one hand and granulocytes on the other hand, namely the relative amounts of blood flow, oxygenation, and carbon dioxide supply would indeed appear to be operative. At the same time one cannot fail to be impressed with the manner in which all the available sites appear to have been exploited in the various systematic groups in varying permutations and combinations. Inability to reduce the matter to any real logical order tempts one to write, perhaps rather facetiously, that the Amphibia go about their blood-forming activity by "hole and corner" methods, where the erythrocytes and thrombocytes are produced in the holes and the various leucocytes in the corners.

2. Hematopoiesis under Experimental Conditions

Attempts have been made to change the centers of hematopoiesis experimentally. Whereas in frogs, reaction to splenectomy may be one of regeneration of the spleen, or of production of red bone marrow, or of transfer of erythrocytopoiesis to the kidney or even no response at all, in Urodeles the spleen is not regenerated and erythrocytopoiesis and thrombocytopoiesis take place in the blood. This process can be increased in speed by inducing lead poisoning by adding soluble lead salts to the water. Lead has a deleterious effect on the red blood corpuscles, which are then phagocytosed in the blood by macrophages derived from monocytes. Under the conditions of severe anemia produced by these methods it has been found (Dawson, 1933) that for some time the lymphoid hemoblast

TABLE IV

SITES OF ERYTHROPOIESIS IN THREE SPECIES OF *RANA* AT DIFFERENT STAGES OF THE
LIFE HISTORY

Site	Stage in *Rana pipiens* and *Rana catesbeiana*	Stage in *Rana temporaria*
Blood islands	Embryo	Embryo
Mesonephros	Tadpole	Early tadpole
Spleen	Late tadpole (but not important) Adult	—
Liver	—	Later tadpole
Marrow cavity of long bones	Adult (for limited periods of the year)	Adult

TABLE V

PRINCIPAL SITES OF HEMATOPOIESIS IN SOME ADULT URODELA

Genus	Liver	Kidney	Spleen
Proteus	Not important in erythrocytopoiesis. No granulocytopoiesis.	Granulocytopoiesis	Lymphoid hemoblasts differentiate into erythrocytes and thrombocytes in the blood; a few macrophages are found
Triturus	Granulocytopoiesis	—	Erythrocytopoiesis
Amphiuma	Granulocytopoiesis	—	Erythrocytopoiesis
Necturus	Some granulocytopoiesis	Granulocytopoiesis	Erythrocytopoiesis

will serve as a progenitor for both red cells and thrombocytes, but eventually if the condition persists the definitive lymphocyte will act as a progenitor. These cells differentiate in the blood stream and eventually restore the red cell count to normal proportions. Although the other centers of hematopoiesis do not take over the function of the spleen which has been removed yet they seem to be involved in the production of hemoblasts and lymphocytes which, on entering the blood, differentiate into erythrocytes. Thus it may be said that under these conditions the reticuloendothelial system provides progenitor cells for the erythrocytes.

It must be pointed out that these findings are difficult to correlate with the results of those workers who have studied the development of the blood cells in the early embryology of the amphibians. The following account is based on the work of Dawson (1933).

As mentioned above the primitive blood islands of amphibian embryos are the primary source of erythrocytes and it has been found possible to remove these islands and produce embryos in which at least the anterior part of the blood vascular system is developed almost normally, including the possession of reticuloendothelial tissue. Such embryos, however, lack erythrocytes which apparently cannot be derived from the reticuloendothelial tissue; they also lack leucocytes (Fernald, 1943).

In an adult such tissues can give rise to erythrocytes. To explain how the endothelium and reticuloendothelial cells of an adult can produce, under experimental conditions, hemoblasts and lymphocytes which on becoming free in the blood produce hemoglobin, whereas those in the embryo cannot, it has to be imagined either: (a) that at an early stage of development some hemocytoblasts, which possessed the power of hemoglobin production did not manifest it but migrated through the circulation to populate the endothelium and reticuloendothelial tissue with cells indistinguishable from other hemocytoblasts but which differed from them in being able to produce hemoglobin under certain conditions; or (b) that the process of erythrocyte production, found in the adult, is not strictly comparable with that of the early stages and that a new method of erythrocytopoiesis has superseded that found in the embryo.

Hemoglobin production in the early stages of embryonic development, as has been noted above, may depend on the conjoined presence of the metabolic products of the hemoblasts and substances diffusing from the endoderm. There is also evidence that at a slightly later stage the presence of the liver is necessary for hemoglobin production. The liver need not necessarily be in its normal position for although when the rudiment is removed anemia supervenes, this can be prevented by implanting a liver rudiment under the skin at the same time as the liver is removed from its normal position; under such conditions normal erythrocytes are produced. By such experiments as these it can be shown that for the first red cells to appear endoderm must be present either as archenteron or as liver.

That there is a difference between the primary erythrocytes and later ones there is no doubt, for the primary ones contain yolk platelets. According to Cameron (1941) in *Ambystoma jeffersonianum* each of the original cells of the ventral blood island contains 128 yolk plates, and the cells become free and so are corpuscles with 128 yolk plates each. These corpuscles then undergo mitotic division and each daughter cell has 64 yolk plates and the process is repeated giving cells with 32 yolk plates and then 16, 8, 4, 2 and finally cells with 1 yolk plate each; these final cells quickly disintegrate and are replaced by secondary erythrocytes from the new hematopoietic centers which are now established. This event takes place about the time of hatching.

Similar results have been obtained by Fujiwara (1950, 1952, 1953) working on *Rana japonica* and *Rhacophorus schlegelii* who found that there were two distinct sources of erythrocytes in these frogs. First, erythrocytes which contain yolk globules are derived from the ventral blood island of the embryo. Second, others are derived from centers in the sinuses of the mesonephros and replace the first kind. If the ventral blood island tissue is removed before the circulation has started, no erythrocytes are formed at all and the larva dies after about 2 weeks. If the circulation is allowed to start and then the ventral blood island tissue removed, the tadpole proceeds to develop normally until the time comes for the second variety of erythrocytes, formed in the mesonephros, to succeed them. These erythrocytes, however, fail to appear and the tadpole then dies. If these findings are confirmed in other species it seems that the contradiction pointed out above could be explained by supposing that after the original ventral yolk-containing cells had become erythrocytes a second generation of cells was produced in morphologically the same area as the first and that it is this second generation which, migrating through the blood system, populates the erythropoietic centers.

D. PHAGOCYTOSIS

Phagocytosis is the uptake by cells of particulate matter; it was formerly regarded as a somewhat ameboid process of engulfment of solid material, organic or inorganic, which had obtained entrance to the body and which was to be disposed of. In more recent years the term has been extended to include the uptake of all particulate matter irrespective of size and irrespective of the exact mechanism by which it passes into the cell, and no account of the blood of amphibians would be complete without some reference to the phagocytic activity of certain cells. It is customary to regard some of these cells, such as the Kupffer cells of the liver, as fixed macrophages and others as wandering cells which can be produced in various centers of hematopoiesis.

Macrophages can be detected (Clark and Clark, 1930a) in the tails of early amphibian larvae before there are any blood vessels present in that region. Such macrophages are derived directly from the mesenchyme of the embryo. With the appearance of blood vessels various wandering cells arrive in the tail, the first of these are monocytes. Later come small lymphocytes and polymorphs. However, it is from the monocytes (Clark and Clark, 1930b) that further macrophages develop. At first such cells can be distinguished from the fully developed macrophages, but as they become large and ingest cell debris and other such material they become more pigmented and eventually the macrophages from both sources of origin are indistinguishable. Of all the wandering cells macrophages are the only ones which accumulate neutral red; polymorphs and lymphocytes do not. The macrophages may be stimulated to migrate by various factors such as the presence of fat or as a response to injury. Under such conditions they migrate out of the capillaries and later return to the blood stream; while in the tissues the macrophages may divide. If, as in the case of a slight injury, red blood corpuscles have escaped into the tissues, they are engulfed by macrophages which seem to be alerted by chemical stimulation. Macrophages approach the red cells and after sufficient time has elapsed for some alteration in the surface of the red blood cell to occur they are phagocytosed. Other injured cells are also ingested. When a cell dies the cytoplasm begins to swell and to show increased granulation and the nucleus becomes more opaque. Later degenerative changes include vacuolization, with the onset of Brownian movement, followed by complete disintegration. Such a dying cell may be phagocytized before the stage of vacuolization takes place; in fact vacuolization may be seen to take place after ingestion by the phagocyte. The macrophage is described by the authors as undoubtedly a very hardy cell and macrophages can be seen phagocytizing other cells even when they are dying so rapidly that the animal itself is moribund.

Damaged red blood corpuscles are phagocytized not only in the tissues but in the blood stream itself. This is a reminder of what may be considered as the chief biological problem associated with phagocytosis; namely the recognition by the phagocytic cells, of material to be phagocytized, particularly when that material consists of cells of the animal itself. How does the phagocyte distinguish between "worn out" cells and cells which are healthy? There must be some alteration of the surface of the erythrocyte.

Changes in the external medium can bring about marked changes in the surface of erythrocytes, such as those which take place when mammalian blood corpuscles are studied on a slide, when the disklike corpuscle may be transformed into a sphere. Somewhat similar changes resulting in "banding" of the corpuscles have been described in the blood of salamanders (Trotter, 1956).

The relationship between free and fixed macrophages is of some interest. Lehman (1953), working on *Xenopus* larvae by hormone treatment, made the pigment cells expand; he then cut out the melanophores and observed the ingestion of the melanin granules and the cell fragments by both fixed macrophages and others which migrated from the blood stream. The conversion of free macrophages to fixed ones was observed but the change in the reverse direction was not so clear. Although some stellate cells migrated into the capillaries, usually it was the cells with the largest numbers of inclusions which migrated into the blood stream which carried them away.

The radio-opaque colloid "Thorotrast" injected into the dorsal lymph sac of frogs (*Rana temporaria*) passes into the blood stream from which it is removed by the activities of the phagocytic cells of the liver and spleen (Foxon and Rowson, 1956). When the quantity injected is large, Thorotrast particles are found in many other organs of the body, such as kidney and intestinal wall. Evidence has been obtained that macrophages, which ingested the foreign colloid in such situations, eventually pass into the blood stream and so to the liver where the Thorotrast accumulates. It may also be that not only macrophages from the intestinal wall pass to the liver by way of the portal system but that over a long period phagocytic cells may migrate from the spleen to the liver.

The most detailed studies of the phagocytic activity of the fixed cells of the liver of frogs are those of Kniseley and co-workers (1948). It is quite impossible to deal adequately with their results here, but two important ideas which they have enunciated are, first, that all cells lining the sinusoids of the liver are potentially phagocytes (Kupffer cells), whether a cell acts as a phagocyte or not at any given moment, depending on its physiological condition; second, that in order to be phagocytosed a particle must be "coated" by a protein present in the blood. If this coating material is temporarily exhausted phagocytosis ceases until a new supply is available. When a coated particle touches a phagocytic cell it is immediately taken in. There is no prolonged process of engulfment by pseudopodia; it is a process of contact phagocytosis.

According to Lison (1948) and to Lison and Smulders (1949a) there are two types of Kupffer cell in the liver of frogs. These types are distinguishable by their phagocytic activity, type "G" having a preference for particles which carry a negative charge and have a diameter of 80 Å or more; type "F" cells phagocytize particles of a smaller size. Similarly distinguishable phagocytic cells are found in other organs of the body, notably the spleen, and indeed throughout the reticuloendothelial system where they occur in varying proportions. In experiments colored particles were used, and when mixtures of Soluble Blue (230 Å) and Black (27 Å) dyes were injected intraperitoneally and the organs examined after 48 hours it was found that the two dyes had been selectively absorbed into the two types of cell. In the liver, "G" cells were found to be slightly less numerous than the "F" cells. Type "G" cells were seen to be slightly larger than "F" and also to have a more compact shape.

It has also been found (Lison and Smulders, 1949b) that after injection of histamine there was an alteration in the numbers of the two types which were found in various organs. Thus after injection the number of "F" cells in the liver increased while the number of "G" cells remained the same. In the spleen there was an apparent reversal of this but for technical reasons it could not be determined if this increase of "G" cells was absolute or only relative. In various other tissues which were examined there appeared to be a net increase in the "F" cells; particularly this was noted in the endo-thelium of the lymphatic vessels of the alimentary canal. No satisfactory solution of how these changes are brought about has been suggested but the fact that the "F" cells increase everywhere except in the spleen at least suggests that migration in the blood stream of a mobile reserve of "F" cells from the spleen to other sites is a possible explanation.

That leucocytes which have ingested melanin particles and other cell debris do wander about the body in the blood stream appears to account for the reports, for various species, of leucocytes containing pigment granules being found in the circulating blood but forming less than 1% of the total leucocytes. The origin of these cells and the accounts of their occurrence have been discussed by Zylbersac (1946), and this interpreta-tion of these cells seems to fit well with the known facts. Liebman (1945) has described a rather different aspect of the life of the wandering cells in regard to the egg of *Triturus*. Sometimes healthy eggs are seen to attract and ingest lymphocytes. On the other hand neutrophils were sometimes seen to phagocytize the yolk platelets of larger atretic ova. The neutro-phils die out within the egg and phagocytosis is continued by the follicle cells, the last traces of the corpus atreticum being removed by lymphocytes.

E. THE CLOTTING MECHANISM OF THE BLOOD

The clotting mechanism of the blood appears to be similar to that found in warm-blooded animals but it is adjusted to working at lower and more variable temperatures.

Spitzer and Spitzer (1952) found that if thrombin is injected into the heart in frogs, which of course decreases the clotting time, the blood re-gains its normal clotting time more speedily than does that of mammals. These authors also found that both the clotting and prothrombin times were more prolonged in the winter than in the summer and that also in the winter the effectiveness of intracardiac thrombin was lessened. They suggested that the prolongation of clotting time in the winter might be due to some unexplained alteration in the thrombin-fibrinogen reaction which occurs *in vivo* and is not yet understood. Anstall and Huntsman (1960) have compared the clotting times (calcium clotting time) and thrombo-plastin times of *Xenopus laevis* and of man at various temperatures. They point out that the effect of low temperatures on amphibian blood is much less marked than is a fall of temperature on human blood and that the clotting mechanism of the amphibian is well adapted to its normal environmental temperature.

Blood coagulation is brought about by enzyme action and it would seem that the amphibian enzymes are adapted to working over a greater range of temperatures (usually lower) than are those of man.

IV. Transport of the Respiratory Gases

The function of the blood in the transport of oxygen and carbon dioxide throughout the animal kingdom has been surveyed by Redfield (1933), and his review points out the chief peculiarities exhibited by the Amphibia. This section deals mainly with the results obtained since Redfield's review.

Much may be learned concerning the properties of any particular blood from a study of its dissociation curves. Redfield made it clear that in amphibians two rather dissimilar types of oxygen dissociation curve are found.

The first type is the rectangular hyperbola (see Fig. 1a), which is met with in the more aquatic forms and the tadpole larvae of some anurans; it indicates a high capacity of combining power on the part of the hemoglobin and of the necessity for the partial pressure of oxygen to fall to a very low level before the oxyhemoglobin dissociates. This type of curve has been found in many invertebrates (Barcroft, 1934) and has been held to be indicative that the function of the blood is mainly that of providing a store of oxygen which is only drawn upon in very adverse circumstances.

The second type of dissociation curve, the sigmoid curve (see Fig. 1b) is typical of land-living vertebrates, including man. Here loading is, perhaps, never as high as in blood with the rectangular hyperbola but dissociation occurs much more readily when the oxygen tension in the tissues

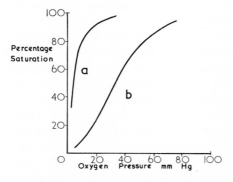

Fig. 1. Diagram to show the form of: curve a, the rectangular hyperbola and b, the sigmoid curve typical of the oxygen dissociation curves of tadpoles and of adult frogs respectively. For full description see text. (Based on curves given by McCutcheon, 1936; McCutcheon and Hall, 1937; Wolvekamp, 1932.)

falls. This type of curve is found in many amphibians particularly in anurans and the more terrestrial urodeles.

The carbon dioxide dissociation curves of the Amphibia, so far as is known, are all of one type which is very much flatter than that of higher vertebrates and indicates that the blood parts only rather slowly with its carbon dioxide and indeed it is found that amphibian blood carries a rather surprisingly high amount of carbon dioxide. It seems as though, because carbon dioxide is so extremely soluble in water and the amphibian skin is so permeable, that amphibians living in water or visiting water temporarily have a physiological problem in retaining sufficient carbon dioxide for their needs.

It is convenient to consider oxygen transport first and it has been shown by Macela and Seliškar (1925), that the affinity for oxygen of a dilute solution of the hemoglobin of the frog *Rana esculenta* at 15°C is almost the same as that for human hemoglobin at 35°C. This at once suggests that frogs' hemoglobin is adapted for carrying out its functions at a lower temperature than is that of a mammal and that this is so can be seen from a consideration of the point of half-saturation. At 35°C with a partial pressure of oxygen of 40 mm Hg frogs' hemoglobin is only half saturated whereas under these conditions human hemoglobin is 75% saturated.

The oxygen dissociation curve for the blood of a European species of *Rana* has been given by Wolvekamp (1932) who pointed out that the curve for the frog at 20°C was like that of man at 38°C. Wolvekamp and Lodewijks (1934) investigated the oxygen dissociation curves of *Rana temporaria* and *R. esculenta* with respect to the influence of carbon dioxide tension. They found that increase of carbon dioxide resulted in easier unloading by the shift of the curve to the right. In *R. temporaria* at 20°C the point of half-saturation of the hemoglobin occurred at 10 mm partial pressure of oxygen in the absence of any carbon dioxide; but if about 16.5–18 mm partial pressure of carbon dioxide was present then the point of half-saturation occurred at 22 mm partial pressure of oxygen.

The fact that amphibians live in a variety of situations and that temperature conditions in one situation may themselves vary, is to be correlated with the fact that the oxygen affinity of the blood can be altered by adaptation to different temperatures. Frogs (*Rana esculenta*) were adapted to the following temperatures, 25°C, 13–15°C, and 3°C (Kirkberger, 1953). If these were all suddenly transferred to a temperature of 25°C and a partial pressure of 19.4 mm HgO_2 the blood was found to hold the following volumes per cent of oxygen:

25°C frogs	2.06 ± 0.03%
13–15°C frogs	1.66 ± 0.04%
3°C frogs	1.64 ± 0.056%

If frogs were acclimatized at the same three temperatures and then transferred to 15°C the following volumes percent were obtained:

25°C frogs	5.1 ± 0.11%
13–15°C frogs	4.41 ± 0.06%
3°C frogs	4.27 ± 0.06%

Kirkberger points out that, if frogs are suddenly placed at a higher temperature than that to which they have been acclimatized, the oxygen dissociation curve is moved to the right. However, acclimatization at the new temperature results in the dissociation curve returning to its normal place by alteration in the hemoglobin content of the blood for example:

25 frogs kept at 25°C	11.4 ± 0.46 gm Hb per 100 cc blood
28 frogs kept at 13–5°C	11.5 ± 0.37 gm Hb per 100 cc blood
26 frogs kept at 3°C	9.84 ± 0.36 gm Hb per 100 cc blood.

These figures may be compared with that of about 15 gm Hb per 100 cc blood given for the normal healthy person (Best and Taylor, 1940).

Redfield quotes other authors as giving the blood of *Amphiuma tridactyla* an oxygen carrying capacity of 2.5–8.4 volumes percent, a cell volume of 14–28%, and an oxygen capacity for 100 cc of cells as 25 volumes percent; and *Rana esculata* oxygen capacity as 13.5–23.0 volumes percent, cell volume 41%, and oxygen capacity per 100 cc cells 33%. These figures are lower than in mammals, as would be expected. In considering Kirkberger's findings relating to acclimatization by a change in the hemoglobin content of the blood, it would be extremely interesting to know whether this is brought about by changes in the hemoglobin itself or in the numbers of red cells present.

That the nature of the hemoglobin present in amphibian blood can change has been demonstrated by McCutcheon (1936) who investigated the oxygen dissociation curve during the life history of the bullfrog (*Rana catesbeiana*). He found that the tadpole had a dissociation curve in the form of a rectangular hyperbola. This form of curve is suitable where unloading is required only at very low oxygen tensions and is typical of animals living in conditions of oxygen scarcity; however, the adult bullfrog has a curve of the sigmoid type typical of air-breathing land-living vertebrates. The tadpole blood had an oxygen capacity of 7.85 volumes percent and the adult blood 11.02.

McCutcheon points out that the hemoglobin present changes in its affinity for oxygen with age and that this change can be correlated with change of habitat. The type of difference is indicated by the fact that the young tadpoles' hemoglobin is 50% saturated at 5 mm Hg partial pressure, whereas at this pressure the adult blood is only 5% saturated. He noted also a slight decrease in the size of the erythrocytes in the adult as compared with the tadpole, yet the oxygen capacity of the blood increased; therefore there was an increase in the hemoglobin content of each cell. It would be tempting to correlate the difference in hemoglobin with the difference found in the site of erythropoiesis (see below) but McCutcheon concluded that this was difficult.

McCutcheon and Hall (1937) have given dissociation curves for various amphibians including *Triturus* and *Cryptobranchus* which are strictly aquatic, *Desmognathus* and *Amphiuma* which are largely aquatic, and *Ambystoma opacum*, a terrestrial salamander found in very moist situations. They also studied tree frogs from South America, *Hyla*, also *Hypopachus inguinatus, Bufo volliceps*, and *B. marinus*. They concluded not only that the aquatic frogs have dissociation curves more the shape of rectangular hyperbolas than do the terrestrial frogs (which have sigmoid curves and which show an increased unloading power at the expense of loading), but that the affinity of the blood for oxygen can be correlated with the respiratory mechanism, the conditions of the environment, and the rate of metabolic activity. They also suggest that the erythrocytopoietic apparatus comes into the story and that the three centers of erythrocytopoiesis found in amphibians, namely kidney, spleen, and bone marrow, produce different kinds of hemoglobin. The bone marrow is only a site in the anurans and then only at certain times; this would apparently produce the hemoglobin found in adult anurans which typically has a sigmoid dissociation curve. The kidney would produce the hemoglobin of the tadpole and the spleen that of later stages in development; in those amphibians which did not get beyond an aquatic stage (urodeles) this would be the ultimate stage. However there are difficulties in the way of the hypothesis: for one thing *Cryptobranchus*, although being aquatic has something of a sigmoid dissociation curve; second, the bone marrow is not the source of red cells in all Anura throughout the year; again, as just mentioned, frogs living in aquatic surroundings tend to have the rectangular hyperbola. No difference in the site of erythropoiesis in these frogs has apparently been recorded.

The transport of carbon dioxide in the blood of amphibians has certain characteristics which differentiate it from that of mammals. As has been mentioned above carbon dioxide is eliminated mainly through the skin and very little by way of the lungs. Carbon dioxide is carried in blood as a small but important amount of carbonic acid and as bicarbonate with base derived from several buffers particularly the serum proteins and the hemoglobin of red blood corpuscles. In man and other mammals, the concentration of red corpuscles is such that a large amount of carbon dioxide transport is attributed to the red cells. It would be expected that in animals with a smaller number of corpuscles per volume the carrying power of the blood would not be so great. However, Redfield (1933) has pointed out that some amphibians (he gives as examples *Amphiuma* and *Rana catesbeiana*) have carbon dioxide dissociation curves which show that the blood retains more carbon dioxide than does that of most vertebrates. This is due to the ability of the blood to combine with more carbon dioxide than would be expected from its hemoglobin content. This condition can be explained by the retention in the blood of an unusually large concentration of bicarbonate; this seems to be brought about by a peculiarity in the electrolyte balance.

Scott (1931) working on *Amphiuma tridactylum* found that if 34% of the blood was cells then carbon dioxide was given up at low oxygen tension, but if only about 20% of the blood was cells and the carbon dioxide tension in the atmosphere fell to 0 mm Hg then 30–40 volumes percent of carbon dioxide still remained. He also found that the difference in carbon dioxide carried by oxygenated and reduced blood was small and that it probably had little physiological significance although this "chloride shift" was in the same direction as that found in mammalian physiology.

Wastl and Seliškar (1925) gave figures for the carbon dioxide tension of blood in *Rana catesbeiana* as follows: at 16°C arterial blood from aorta 58.2 volumes percent = 22 mm Hg CO_2; blood from abdominal vein 70.1 volumes percent = 29 mm Hg CO_2. These figures have been quoted by Prosser (1950) but they have been questioned by Campbell (1926) as being too high because the frogs were anesthetized for the withdrawal of the samples. Campbell had found that urethane caused increased venous tension in rabbits and suggested that this was probably also true in other animals. He also found that carbon dioxide tension under the skin of the toad *Bufo vulgaris* was 4 mm Hg at 3°C, 12 mm Hg at 17°C, and 14 mm Hg at 23°C. In *Rana temporaria* the carbon dioxide tension of the body cavity was 14 mm Hg at 17°C. The blood would presumably be in equilibrium with the tension in the body cavity and these figures are certainly much lower than those of Wastl and Seliškar.

Capraro (1948) has studied the transport of carbon dioxide in the newt *Triton cristatus* and found that at a minimum carbon dioxide tension there was always an appreciable amount of carbon dioxide in the blood. The plasma of the newt tends to behave like a simple solution of bicarbonates.

Throughout the foregoing account the adaptation of the transport system to the method of respiratory exchange has been stressed. All Amphibia face physiological problems different from those of mammals and engendered by the cutaneous elimination of carbon dioxide.

In mammals venous blood is stated to be a better buffer than arterial blood on account of reduced hemoglobin being a weaker acid than oxyhemoglobin, and this of course is significant in the transport of carbon dioxide. When the evolution of the blood system of the vertebrates is discussed, emphasis is usually placed on the importance of an exact division of the arterial and venous systems with very precise control of the distribution of the oxygenated blood. But it must be realized that this strict division into arterial and venous circuits has also made possible many refinements in the carriage of carbon dioxide which are well known to students of mammalian respiratory physiology. In amphibians, however, the use of the skin for respiratory exchange affects not only the site of oxygen uptake but also that of carbon dioxide elimination. In many amphibians, as we have seen, the skin plays an all important part in both functions; in others the lungs are important mainly as a site of oxygen uptake. Thus it is hardly surprising to find specializations of gas transport which cannot be correlated with conditions found in mammals.

An example of adaptation of hemoglobin content of the blood to habitat has been provided by Stuart (1951) who studied the toads *Bufo marinus* and *B. bocourti* in Guatemala. *Bufo marinus* is a lowland form (upper limit 1500 meters), *B. bocourti* an upland form (1700–3600 meters); both species are nocturnal in habit. *Bufo marinus* becomes helpless to escape enemies below 15°C and changes set in which lead to death at 41°C. The corresponding figures for *B. bocourti* are 3°C and 34–35°C. These temperatures are important, for an investigation of the hemoglobin content of the blood of the two species gives the following mean figures expressed in grams of hemoglobin per 100 cc of blood: *Bufo marinus* 8.66 (±0.128); *B. bocourti* 10.57 (±0.153). The figure for *B. bocourti* is higher than that for *B. marinus* but not as much as might be expected. *Bufo bocourti* showed no difference over the height range of 2200–3200 meters, a distance over which man would have shown a 6% increase.

Stuart points out that if the hemoglobin of the two species had identical dissociation curves then more hemoglobin would benefit *B. bocourti*, but this would seem unnecessary on account of the differences in temperature where the animals live. In cold-blooded animals the increase which is necessary is that required to balance the reduced oxygen tension in saturated arterial blood. Whereas in man at high altitudes an increase in both percentage saturation (the amount of oxygen available) and in oxygen tension (which gives the availability of the gas to the tissues) is found to take place (Best and Taylor, 1940, p. 578).

The question of the necessity for the presence of hemoglobin in the blood of amphibians has been raised by de Graaf (1957b) who recorded the occurrence of a specimen of *Xenopus laevis* which had apparently lived a normal life until required for experimental purposes and which was devoid of hemoglobin and indeed of erythrocytes. He then made experiments upon other specimens of this species in which he blocked the hemoglobin with carbon monoxide and found that such action did not have the marked effects expected. He concluded that under certain circumstances *Xenopus* could withstand a nearly complete elimination of its hemoglobin. He suggested that in amphibians the oxygen content of the blood was perhaps to be looked upon more as a store of oxygen than as oxygen under transport. Ewer (1959) who found a similar specimen of *Xenopus laevis* noted that the condition of the gall bladder suggested recent destruction of the hemoglobin. He surmised that de Graaf's toad may not, as de Graaf apparently thought, have been without hemoglobin all its life. It is pointed out by Ewer that to attempt to draw conclusions as to the survival value of the possession of hemoglobin from a few isolated specimens may be misleading, for conditions might occur, perhaps only rarely, in the life of an animal when its ability to survive depended on the presence of hemoglobin.

V. The Circulation of the Blood

In the earlier parts of this chapter the varied methods of respiratory exchange, with greater or less emphasis on the skin as a respiratory surface, have been surveyed and the respiratory functions of the blood discussed. We now survey the course of the circulation of the blood, since without circulation the blood would be valueless and the respiratory surfaces isolated from the remainder of the body. In a typical fish where respiratory exchange is by means of the gills the blood is driven in a logical manner from heart to gills thence to the body and so back to the heart. In a mammal, breathing through lungs, the circulation also follows a logical course, heart to lungs then back to heart and thence to body and back to heart, and because the heart is completely divided into left and right sides containing oxygenated and deoxygenated blood respectively no mixing of the two kinds occurs.

In the amphibians blood leaves a single ventricle by routes which may take it to the head or body or skin or lungs (except in lungless forms). The blood which comes from the head, body, or skin returns to the heart by way of the sinus venosus to the right atrium and that from the lungs by way of the pulmonary vein to the left atrium. In amphibians the skin is an important respiratory surface, yet blood which has been oxygenated there is mixed with blood from the body as it returns to the right atrium; thus this blood cannot properly be described as oxygenated or deoxygenated. Similarly blood returning from the lungs may not always be fully oxygenated if, as some maintain, the lungs of a frog can be used as stores of oxygen which are gradually used up. Thus the circulatory arrangement of the amphibians may be expected to show marked specialization correlated with their peculiar respiratory methods. Unfortunately this state of affairs has not always been realized and by some nineteenth century zoologists the heart of modern amphibians, especially the anuran type of the genus *Rana*, was taken as representative of the amphibian heart and put into the series of hearts of the comparative anatomists and regarded as an "amphibian stage" in the evolutionary history of this organ. It is now realized that the recent amphibians show many specializations which depart widely from what may be regarded as the main line of vertebrate descent—that which gave rise to the reptiles, birds, and mammals; the respiratory skin is such a specialization. The question which now arises is how far is the heart of modern amphibians specialized and how far is it primitive? It has generally been held that the possession of a divided atrium and a single ventricle is a primitive feature but this view has been questioned (Foxon, 1955), and it has been suggested that perhaps the early amphibians had hearts more like those of some extant lungfish, particularly *Lepidosiren*, where partitions, nearly complete, are found in both atrium and ventricle. Other evidence supplementing this contention has been brought forward (Foxon, 1955) both from the field of embryology and from a study of the coronary system. The points of origin of the coronary arteries and their distribution in reptiles and higher vertebrates can be directly related to the anatomical arrangements seen in lungfish whereas the anatomical arrangements seen in Amphibia (see below) are highly anomalous. That the interatrial septum may become fenestrated in some urodeles is well known (Noble, 1931, p. 192) and it is absent in lungless forms.

The statement by Goodrich (1930) to the effect that the similarity in septation between lungfish hearts and those of higher vertebrates is probably due to convergence as an interventricular septum "is not found in any modern Amphibian" has carried great weight. But it does not seem to have been realized that, as pointed out by Marcus (1935), some Apoda have very curious trabeculae in the ventricle which in some species appear to form a septum dividing the ventricle into two parts. I have dissected the ventricles of specimens of *Ichthyophis* and *Hypogeophis* myself and although I am not convinced of the presence of a true septum in either genus, the trabeculae in both are quite unlike anything I have seen in anurans and might possibly be explained as vestiges of a solid interventricular septum which has become widely fenestrated to permit of mixing of the blood in correlation with cutaneous respiratory exchange. In a detailed study of the heart of *Rana tigrina* Sharma (1957) has described a ridge-like structure in the posterior part of the ventricle which he compares with the muscular ridge of reptiles.

However, it is not intended to pursue these evolutionary speculations; rather the point is that just as the respiratory methods of the amphibians are varied so are the circulatory methods and that it is impossible to speak of a generalized scheme for the mode of action of "the amphibian heart."

The action of the heart of the European frog *Rana temporaria* will first be described. For many years it had been thought that in the frog a selective distribution of the blood from the two atria, so-called "arterial" blood from the left atrium and "venous" blood from the right atrium, is brought about as the blood passes through and leaves the heart. An account of this "classic hypothesis" of blood distribution is included in almost every elementary textbook of biology and zoology. Although the accounts given vary as to detail they are based on the following premises: (1) the blood from the two atria remains to a large extent unmixed in the single ventricle; (2) that on ventricular systole the "venous" blood leaves first, and partly by the directive influence of the spiral valve in the conus and partly by a supposed lower blood pressure in the pulmocutaneous arch this first blood passes up this arch to the lungs and skin; (3) that in the middle phase of ventricular systole the more mixed blood from the center of the ventricle is expelled and that this passes mainly up the other side of the spiral valve of the conus whence it is distributed to the systemic arches; (4) this mixed blood does not obtain access to the carotid arches because the function of the carotid "gland" or labyrinth is to ensure a high blood pressure in the carotid vessels so that only the blood under greatest pressure, i.e., the last to leave the ventricle which is the "oxygenated" blood, is sent to the brain. It is unnecessary to repeat here a summary of all the work done on the heart of this frog, which was designed to show that the blood was distributed either in a selective manner or in a nonselective manner (for such a summary see Foxon, 1955).

The most recent account is that of Simons (1957, 1959), who replaced the blood of a decerebrate or anesthetized frog by means of perfusion of Ringer's solution through the abdominal vein. Then by microinjection he introduced into veins returning blood to the heart very exactly measured quantities of an intense dye (Evans blue) and followed its passage through the heart, using both visual methods and cinematography. He found that despite a certain amount of variation there was a very general pattern of distribution of the blood from the ventricle which depended very closely on the volume of the dye injected.

It had previously been established by using radiography (Foxon, 1951) that when the blood passed from the atria into the ventricle little mixing took place and not a great deal as supposed by Vandervael (1933). What had not previously been shown adequately is that this separation is not followed by considerable mixing as the blood leaves the heart. Simons showed that the destination of any particular blood corpuscle on leaving the ventricle is determined very largely by the position it occupies while in the ventricle. Thus blood from the left of the ventricle passes up one side of the spiral valve of the conus into the carotid arteries and the right systemic arch. While blood from the right of the ventricle passes mainly up the other side of the spiral valve into the pulmocutaneous arteries and also into the left systemic arch. During the early part of ventricular systole a stream of blood flows over the spiral valve from the cavum aorticum into the cavum pulmocutaneum and on into the left systemic arch, thus ensuring that some "arterial" blood does find its way into the left systemic arch (Fig. 2A).

The following points should be particularly noted in Simons's account:

a. Blood flows up the two sides of the spiral valve simultaneously and not first up one side and then the other as has often been stated. This fact was established both by visual observations and by simultaneous condenser-manometer pressure recording.

b. Wide differences of pressure between the carotoid, systemic, and pulmocutaneous arteries do not exist.

The average of the pressures found in all three arterial arches in the frog (*Rana temporaria*) are given by Simons (1957) as systolic 15/diastolic 8 mm Hg, and in the toad (*Bufo bufo*) as 26/19. (These figures for *R. temporaria* are lower than those Simons quotes from other authors for a variety of frogs. In general it may be said that the systolic pressure of anurans in good physiological condition may be as much as 30 mm Hg but is often considerably less.)

While the distribution of blood from the ventricle of *Rana temporaria* does show a considerable amount of selection, this selection is not brought about by the methods of pressure differences and sequential passage up the two sides of the conus as has often been supposed.

A point which has been consistently overlooked is that the arteries show considerable asymmetry, the right systemic being associated with left and right carotoid arteries, the left systemic arising separately (see Fig. 2A). Attention has also been directed to this point by Frechkop (1955) who emphasizes the resemblance in both the origin of the left systemic arch and the manner in which it joins the right arch to form the median dorsal aorta to the similar anatomical disposition of the left systemic arch of recent reptiles. In the frog *Rana temporaria* and its allies, the left systemic arch leads directly to the origin of the celiaco-mesenteric artery and its connection with the right systemic arch and dorsal aorta are by way of a somewhat narrow passage (Fig. 2C).

Simons' work has clarified our views on the course of the circulation in *Rana temporaria* but it must not be thought that these findings can be

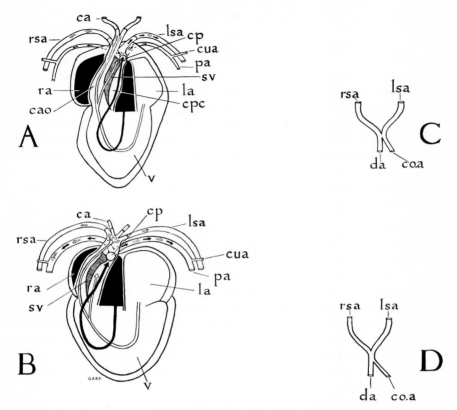

Fig. 2. Diagrams to show the distribution of the blood from the heart in: A. *Rana temporaria*; B. *Xenopus laevis*; also diagrams of the origin of the celiaco-mesenteric artery from the dorsal aorta in C. *Rana temporaria* and D. *Xenopus laevis*. The hearts are shown with the ventral wall removed.

KEY TO LABELS: ca, carotid artery; cao, cavum aorticum; co.a, coeliac artery; cp, common aperture of the pulmocutaneous arches from the cavum pulmocutaneum; cpc, cavum pulmocutaneum; cua, cutaneous artery; da, dorsal aorta; la, left atrium; lsa, left systemic arch; pa, pulmonary artery; ra, right atrium; rsa, right systemic arch; sv, spiral valve of conus; v, ventricle.

applied to all Anura. This is quite definitely not so, for de Graaf (1957a) working on the arterial circulation of *Xenopus laevis* found a different mode of distribution.

Important anatomical differences are seen as between *Xenopus laevis* and *Rana temporaria*. First, the two atria of equal size, not as in *Rana* where the left is approximately only half the size of the right (Fig. 2A and B).

Second, the left and right systemic arches originate symmetrically from the conus arteriosus (Fig. 2B).

Third, the two systemic arches at their distal ends unite to form the unpaired dorsal aorta and contribute equally to it, the celiaco-mesenteric artery (Fig. 2D) arises from the dorsal aorta posteriorly to the junction of the systemic vessels (Millard, 1941).

De Graaf injected small quantities of fluorescine into the circulation of *Xenopus* and, observing with ultraviolet light, found that blood returning from the lungs to the left atrium passed to all parts of the ventricle; then, on contraction of the ventricle it was distributed to carotid, systemic, and pulmocutaneous arteries. It thus appeared that there was no selective distribution. However, injection into a vein returning blood to the right atrium showed that this blood was excluded from the carotid and systemic circulations and was sent through the pulmocutaneous arch. From this vessel most of the blood reached the lungs for, as de Graaf notes, the cutaneous arteries in *Xenopus* are very small compared with those of *Rana*, and in fresh preparations they have about one-ninth of the cross-sectional area of the pulmonary arteries. It was also found that the blood pressures in the carotid and systemic vessels were approximately equal and that the higher pressure envisaged in the carotid vessels by the "classic hypothesis" of heart action in the Anura did not exist. Systolic pressures in the carotid and systemic arches were about 25–27 mm Hg and the diastolic pressures 20–23. However, unlike Simons in studying *Rana*, de Graaf found a much lower diastolic pressure in the pulmocutaneous artery than in carotid and systemic arteries and deduced that the circulation through the lungs is very rapid. He observed that blood corpuscles could be seen passing through the pulmonary circulation at a greater pace than through the systemic circulation; he concluded that at each heart beat the pulmo-cutaneous vessels were passing a greater volume of blood than were the carotid and systemic vessels together. In the pulmocutaneous arch the systolic pressures which were measured averaged about 24 mm Hg and the diastolic 13–14.

We have, therefore, two accounts of the mode of action of the heart in Anura. In both a selective distribution is seen. In both this distribution is brought about by the relative anatomical arrangements of the principal vessels leaving the heart. In both the destination of a corpuscle on leaving the heart depends on its situation while in the heart. But as is obvious from Fig. 2 the destination of some corpuscles varies in the two species. It should be noted that both Simons and de Graaf point out that some mixing of the blood from the two atria must take place in an undivided ventricle. According to Simons the amount of mixing in *Rana* is small. According to de Graaf in *Xenopus* blood from the left atrium obtains access to most of the ventricle but that from the right atria is confined more or less to the right part of the ventricle.

Both modes of action and of distribution show a very close degree of correlation with the respiratory habits of the animal concerned. It has already been stated in the first part of this chapter that *Xenopus laevis* is more dependent on its lungs for its oxygen supply than is *Rana temporaria* and the circulatory arrangements are to be correlated with this view. As a result of detailed anatomical study it has been deduced that in *Rana tigrina* (Sharma, 1957) and *R. pipiens* (Sharma, 1961), blood from the right of the ventricle (the least oxygenated) is sent to the pulmocutaneous arteries and blood from the left (the most oxygenated) is sent to the carotid and systemic vessels. No difference between carotids and systemics is envisaged. However, DeLong (1962) reports that gas analysis of *R. pipiens* blood shows a gradient which, in view of great differences between individuals, is best expressed in arbitrary units as follows: right atrium 1, pulmocutaneous artery 1.25, left systemic arch (right not investigated) 1.75, carotid artery 2.25, left atrium 3.4. DeLong (1962) points out that his experiments support the views of Simons (1959) and not those of Sharma (1961) on the genus *Rana*.

Reverting to *Rana temporaria* and *Xenopus laevis* the question may now be asked as to whether it is more likely (a) that these two differing patterns have arisen in the course of evolution from a heart in which the atrium was divided but the ventricle remained undivided, or (b) whether they have evolved from a heart which had a divided atrium and a partially divided ventricle, and as the animals became differently adapted to cutaneous respiration the ventricular septum disappeared and allowed differing patterns of distribution to arise. This question is easier to ask than to answer; indeed such an attempt would be beyond the scope of this chapter.

Before leaving this subject of distribution it may be pointed out that it is possible to imagine that the exact pattern of distribution may vary from time to time according to physiological conditions, such as the degree of expansion or contraction of various capillary networks in the respiratory surfaces. These in turn would depend on the mode of life being pursued at any given moment—for example, a frog might be leaping on land, or swimming in a pond, or hibernating. During each of these activities it is likely that the amount of respiratory exchange and also the way in which it is achieved will vary.

Poczopko (1957) and Szarski (1959) have shown that in intact frogs under experimental conditions variations in the oxygen and carbon dioxide content of the surrounding atmosphere can bring about variation in the number of skin capillaries open. Poczopko by preventing pulmonary breathing produced variations in the state of the capillary network which he thought might be similar to those taking place when the frog was under water. Szarski found that the reactions of the skin capillaries vary with the season of the year, the highest reactivity of the capillaries being found in the spawning season and the lowest at the end of September (Northern Hemisphere). The conditions under which these results were obtained involved very unusual concentration of the gases but Szarski points out that the experiments show that a reflex mechanism for the control of capillary circulation in the skin exists and that probably, in nature, a rise in carbon dioxide content of the blood causes more skin capillaries to open. The experiments of H. J. Jordan (1929) on the pulmonary circulation of *Rana* spp. mentioned above (Section II,A,1,*b*) also suggest that increase in carbon dioxide in the lungs would bring about a similar dilatation. (Jordan, however, correlated his findings with oxygen lack rather than to increase of carbon dioxide.) He has also drawn attention to the fact that the absence of an interventricular septum in the heart allows of varying volumes of blood being sent to the various respiratory surfaces in a manner which would not be possible with a completely divided ventricle.

The general control of lung respiration in *Rana esculenta* has been reported on by Smyth (1939). He found that excess of carbon dioxide in the surroundings produces an initial inhibiting effect and then a general stimulating effect which has its origin in the central nervous system. Oxygen lack produces an increased rate of lung breathing (hyperpnoea) and this comes about, at least partly, from reflexes originating from the carotid gland. Under natural conditions the frog would be able to eliminate all its carbon dioxide cutaneously and therefore the depth and frequency of lung respiration would probably be regulated by the oxygen requirements of the animal and not, as is the case in mammals, by the amount of carbon dioxide produced.

The function of the carotid gland in Anura has been the subject of some discussion. It used to figure prominently in the accounts of distribution of arterial blood from the heart, where according to the "classic hypothesis" the carotid labyrinth was supposed to play an important part as a mechanical obstruction in the carotid pathway which ensured that only blood under high pressure could proceed by this route to the brain.

In the light of the pressure measurements made by Simons (1957) on *Rana temporaria* and de Graaf (1957a) on *Xenopus laevis* already quoted, it is not necessary to pursue this point further except to say that such is obviously not the function of the carotid gland.

Carman (1955) has suggested that these "glands" do have a mechanical function in diverting blood into the external carotid arteries which in Anura and Urodela take their origin at such awkwardly obtuse angles to the direction of flow of the blood that some control of the speed of this flow would appear necessary to ensure that the vessels receive an adequate supply. He has pointed out that in Apoda, where these vessels take their origin from the carotid arch quite differently, no carotid glands are present.

The innervation of the carotid gland of *Rana temporaria* has been studied by Neil and Zotterman (1950) and by Neil *et al.* (1950). They found that the carotid bifurcation and the carotid gland are sites from which stretch receptor fibers of the glossopharyngeal (IXth) nerve originate. The pulmo-cutaneous trunk has stretch receptor fibers which join the laryngeal branch of the vagus (Xth) nerve, and fibers run from stretch receptors in the lung to the pulmonary branch of the vagus. Afferent fibers from stretch receptors in the atrium run in the vagus nerve, but no fibers have yet been demonstrated originating from the aortic arch. These observations, based on recordings of electrical activity of the fibers, suggest that one function of the carotid gland has to do with blood pressure. These authors could not detect any chemoreceptor activity in the carotid area of the frog.

The mode of action of the heart of Urodela can be dealt with comparatively briefly. Noble (1925) maintained that where there is a complete interauricular septum and a spiral valve in the conus some degree of separation of blood from the auricles was maintained in its distribution to the body. Lüdike (1955) has correlated the degree of development of the septation of the heart with the mode of respiration possessed by the animals and has dealt with this matter at considerable length. Simons (1959), however, concluded that in both *Triturus cristatus* and *Salamandra maculosa* no differential distribution of the blood is demonstrable by injection of dye.

Recently (Johansen, 1962) blood-gas estimations have been made using specimens (500–800 gm) of *Amphiuma tridactylum*. From these large animals blood for analysis has been taken simultaneously from the pulmonary artery and aortic arch and immediately afterward from the sinus venosus and pulmonary vein. It is stated that in most of the experiments the lung was inflated with pure oxygen some time previous to the experiment. In one animal the following result was obtained: oxygen (as estimated by the Scholander method in volumes per cent) in the pulmonary vein 8.5, sinus venosus 5.0, aortic arch 8.5, pulmonary artery 6.9. A second animal gave pulmonary vein 10.2, sinus venosus 7.9, aortic arch 10.2, and pulmonary artery 8.2. These figures indicate that the blood returning from the lungs had the highest oxygen content and apparently was sent without dilution to the aortic arch. The blood returning from the body through the sinus venosus has apparently some of the oxygenated blood added to it. In a third specimen where the blood from the lungs had 10.5 (volumes of O_2 percent) and the sinus venosus 6.8, the figure for the aortic arch was 10.0 and for the pulmonary arch 9.0. These results indicate a considerable separation of the blood during its passage through the heart, and while the aortic arch always gave a figure in close relation to that for the pulmonary vein the blood going to the lungs appear to receive some oxygen in its passage through the heart (a shunt from the arterial to the venous side.) The difference was enhanced when, to reduce cutaneous respiration, the skin of the animal was kept dry. It was found however that the selective process was "easily disturbed and abolished." Normal blood pressures in the great vessels seemed to be essential for the normal operation of the selective mechanism.

It seems that under certain circumstances some selective distribution of blood takes place in some species of urodeles. Obviously such selection cannot take place in lungless forms. The figures given by Johansen show that differences in oxygenation between "oxygenated" and "deoxygenated" blood are slight and, as he points out, selection is easily disturbed. It would appear just as likely in Urodela as in Anura that the conditions seen are secondary in as much as they are more easily considered as adaptations to skin respiration of a physiologically divided circulation than as early stages in the progressive divison of the circulation into arterial and venous sides.

It is now necessary to say something of the heart in Apoda. Here the general arrangements of the heart and great vessels have been reviewed by Ramaswami (1944) and the departure from both anuran and urodele conditions is wide. The sinus venosus is large and appears subdivided. Lawson (1959) describes it in *Hypogeophis* as having a uniform muscular wall and in ventral view it is conspicuous on the animal's right. The sinus venosus principale receives the right jugular, hepatic (postcaval), and renal veins; the sinus venosus sinistra receives the left juglar vein (no left renal) through which most of the blood from the body musculature returns. The two parts of the sinus venosus are bound to the atrium and ventricle by cardiac ligaments. The interatrial septum is perforated (this does not agree with the accounts of Marcus and Schilling) and in the ventricle there are numerous muscular trabeculae which are more massive than the corresponding structures in either anurans or urodeles. According to Schilling (1935) and to Marcus (1935) it is possible in *Hypogeophis* to recognize one of these trabecular ridges as much larger than the others and these authors maintain that it is the vestigial remains of an ancestral interventricular septum. According to Ramaswami (1944) in *Ichthyophis* there are two such enlarged trabecular ridges. These ridges, however, are by no means complete and it would seem that they are not likely to be efficient in keeping separate blood from the two atria. However, the course of the circulation in apodans is obscure. If in *Hypogeophis* it is imagined that arterial and venous blood are kept separate in the ventricle it would seem that on systole arterial blood would be conveyed by one carotid artery and venous blood by the other. However, Lawson does not accept Marcus's account of the origin of the right and left carotid arteries from the truncus and it would seem best to regard the ventricle as most probably delivering a mixture of blood from both auricles into all the arteries. In the absence of physiological experiments, however, this must remain a surmise. One piece of evidence that the blood in the ventricle is in all probability well oxygenated is provided by the extraordinary arrangement of the coronary vessels.

As in Anura and Urodela the heart is supplied with nutriment and oxygen by the blood passing through it. Unlike the Anura (where a coronary artery runs over the conus arteriosus but does not supply the ventricle) there is no trace of any coronary artery originating from either carotid arch. The ventricle, however, is covered with a network of coronary vessels which on inspection are found to be veins. These open into the two ends of the elongated sinus venosus. The blood filling these veins is derived directly from the cavity of the ventricle where, between the bases of the trabeculae, it passes through the spongy myocardium and so into the vessels. This remarkable arrangement is reported in various Apoda by Sawaya (1941), Schilling (1955), and Lawson (1959) and I have confirmed it myself by means of serial sections. The fact that these coronary veins originate from all parts of the ventricle suggests that the blood which passes into them through the muscular wall carries a sufficient supply of oxygen for the respiratory needs of the ventricular muscle. That is to say the blood in the ventricle, irrespective of whether it has entered from the right atrium or the left and irrespective of the degree of mixing in the ventricle, probably cannot properly be referred to as "oxygenated" and "deoxygenated" blood from the left and right atria respectively.

In Apoda, asymmetry of the systemic vessels is frequently found as is also asymmetry of the pulmonary vessels which are modified according to the degree of development of the lungs.

Usually two systemico-carotid and two pulmonary arteries arise from the long truncus. The two systemic arteries may unite anteriorly to the heart to give rise to the median dorsal aorta as in *Dermophis*. In *Herpele* and *Chthonerpeton* only the right systemic arch persists and in *Hypogeophis* only the left systemic is found but in the majority of genera, both systemic arteries are present. In some genera, such as *Ichthyophis*, the right pulmonary artery is larger than the left but in the genus *Gegenophis* a single right pulmonary artery gives a small branch to the reduced left lung. All these specializations can be accounted for by the elongated snake-like form of the body together with the fact that the heart is situated well behind the head; the region in front of the heart can be likened to a "neck" region such as is found in lizards.

It is obvious that the circulatory physiology of the apodans is far from well known and statements concerning the possible course of the circulation are all based on deductions from anatomy.

In concluding this section of the chapter it must again be pointed out that the circulation of the blood from the heart is carried out in different amphibians in very varied ways; these appear to be well adapted to the physiological needs of the animals. The one common factor possessed by all amphibians is cutaneous respiration and this alone makes possible all the variations seen.

VI. Conclusion

In this chapter some account of the respiratory and circulatory physiology of the Amphibia has been given. The extreme specializations shown by these animals have precluded the obvious method of describing a "typical" example first and then surveying the variations met with. The fact that respiration and circulation are so closely interconnected that one cannot be written of without the other in mind has made impracticable the strictly logical description of each topic under a specific heading; it has also led to certain inevitable repetitions which, it is hoped, have been kept to a minimum.

Many groups of evolutionary importance have, after giving rise to more perfectly adapted animals, become extinct or lingered on as "living fossils." The Amphibia have not suffered this fate. The early members of the group not only gave rise to forms more perfectly adapted to life on land and thus to amniotes, but also to the "modern" Amphiba. These, with all their numerous specializations for their peculiar mode of life, must be considered a "successful" evolutionary group. The basis of this success has, I believe, been the use of the skin as a surface of respiratory exchange. It is for that reason that "cutaneous respiration" has been the central idea of this chapter.

References

Anstall, H. B., and Huntsman, R. G. (1960). Influence of temperature upon blood coagulation in a cold- and warm-blooded animal. *Nature* **186**, 726.

Arvy, L. (1947). Le dimorphisme sexuel sanguine chez *Rana temporaria* L. et *Bufo vulgaris* Laur. *Compt. Rend. Soc. Biol.* **141**, 457–459.

Atlas, M. (1931). The rate of oxygen consumption of frogs during embryonic development and growth. *Physiol. Zool.* **11**, 278–291.

Atz, J. W. (1952). Narial breathing in fishes and the evolution of internal nares. *Quart. Rev. Biol.* **27**, 366–377.

Baer, J.-G. (1937). L'appareil respiratoire des gymnophiones. *Rev. Suiss Zool.* **44**, 353–377.

Bannikov, A. G. (1948). O sezonnom izmenenii dychatel' noj funkcii koži utritonov. *Dok. Akad. Nauk SSSR* **59**, 1121–1124.

Barcroft, J. (1934). "Features in the Architecture of Physiological Function," 368 pp. Cambridge Univ. Press, London and New York.

Barrett, W. C. (1947). Hematopoiesis in the European plethodontid, *Hydromantes italicus*, with reference to phylogeny. *Anat. Record* **98**, 127–136.

Bastert, C. (1929). Respiration and circulation of the blood of *Rana esculenta* and *Rana fusca* in connection with their diving habits. *Tijdschr. Ned. Dierk. Ver.* **1**, 98–104.

Bernstein, H. (1953). Structural modifications of the amphibian skin. *Proc. Acad. Nat. Sci. Phila.* **27**, 204–211.

Best, C. H., and Taylor, N. B. (1940). "The Physiological Basis of Medical Practice," 2nd ed., 1872 pp. Ballière, Tindall & Cox, London.

Bieniak, A., and Watka, R. (1962). Vascularization of respiratory surfaces in *Bufo cognatus* Say and *Bufo compactilis* Wiegman. *Bull. Acad. Polon. Sci. Ser. Sci. Biol.* **10**, 9–12.

Bond, A. N. (1960). An analysis of the response of salamander gills to changes in the oxygen concentration of the medium. *Develop. Biol.* **2**, 1–20.

Braungart, D. C. (1950). Mitosis of the erythrocytes in the circulating blood of *Rana pipiens. J. Heredity* **41**, 203–204.

Brodowa, G. (1956). The vascularization of the respiratory surfaces of the alpine newt (*Triturus alpestris* Laur.). *Studia Soc. Sci. Torun. (Zool.)* **3**, 1–9.

Cameron, J. A. (1941). Primitive blood-cell generations in *Amblystoma. J. Morphol.* **68**, 231–248.

Campbell, J. A. (1926). The normal CO_2- and O_2-tensions in the tissues of various animals. *J. Physiol. (London)* **61**, 248–254.

Capraro, V. (1948). La curva di assorbimento per il CO_2 del sangue di '*Triton cristatus*'. *Atti Accad. Naz. Lincei. Rend. Classe Sci. Fis. Mat. Nat.* [8] **4**, 752–754.

Carman, J. B. (1955). The carotid labyrinth in *Hyla aurea*, with a note on that in *Leiopelma hochstetteri. J. Anat.* **89**, 503–525.

Charles, E. (1931). Metabolic changes associated with pigmentary effector activity and pituitary removal in *Xenopus laevis*. I. Respiratory Exchange. *Proc. Roy. Soc.* **B107**, 486–503.

Cherian, A. G. (1956). The mechanism of respiration in the frog. *Acta Physiol. Pharmacol. Neerl.* **5**, 154–168.

Churý, Z. (1952). Some hematologic data in the fasting green toad (*Bufo viridis*). *Scripta Med. Fac. Med. Univ. Brun. Palackyanae* **25**, 23–30.

Clark, E. R., and Clark, E. L. (1930a). Observations on the macrophages of living amphibian larvae. *Am. J. Anat.* **46**, 91–148.

Clark, E. R., and Clark, E. L. (1930b). Relation of monocytes of the blood to the tissue macrophages. *Am. J. Anat.* **46**, 149–186.

Czopek, G., and Czopek, J. (1959). Vascularization of respiratory surfaces in *Bufo viridis* Laur. and *Bufo calomita* Laur. *Bull. Acad. Polon Sci. Ser. Sci. Biol.* **7**, 39–45.

Czopek, J. (1955a). Vascularization of respiratory surfaces in *Leiopelma hochstretteri* Fitzinger and *Xenopus laevis* (Daudin). *Acta Anat.* **25**, 346–360.

Czopek, J. (1955b). The vascularization of the respiratory surfaces of some Salientia. *Zool. Polon* **6**, 101–134.

Czopek, J. (1957). The vascularization of respiratory surfaces in *Ambystoma mexicanum* (Cope) in ontogeny. *Zool. Polon.* **8**, 131–149.

Czopek, J. (1959a). Vascularization of respiratory surfaces in *Salamandra salamandra* L. in ontogeny. *Bull. Acad. Polon. Sci. Ser. Sci. Biol.* **7**, 473–478.

Czopek, J. (1959b). Skin and lung capillaries in European common newts. *Copeia* pp. 91–96.

Czopek, J. (1961). Vascularization of respiratory surfaces in some plethodontidae. *Zool. Polon.* **11,** 131–148.

Czopek, J. (1962). Smooth muscles in the lungs of some urodeles. *Nature* **193,** 798.

Czopekowa, G., and Czopek, J. (1955). The vascularization of the respiratory surfaces in *Bombina variegata* (L.) *Bull. Acad. Polon. Sci. Ser. Sci. Biol.* **3,** 313–318.

Das, S. M., and Srivastava, V. K. (1957). On the mechanism of respiration in *Rana tigrina* Daud. with a note on its respiratory muscles. *Zool. Anz.* **154,** 202–214.

Dawson, A. B. (1930). Differentiation and multiplication by mitosis of cells of the erythrocytic series in the circulating blood of several normal urodeles. *Anat. Record* **45,** 177–188.

Dawson, A. B. (1933). An experimental study of hemopoiesis in *Necturus*, Effects of lead poisoning on normal and splenectomized animals. *J. Morphol.* **55,** 349–385.

Dawson, A. B., and Charipper, H. A. (1929). A comparative study of the amount and distribution of the neutral-red bodies in the erythrocytes of urodeles. *Anat. Record* **43,** 299–316.

de Graaf, A. R. (1957a). Investigations into the distribution of blood in the heart and aortic arches of *Xenopus laevis* (Daud.). *J. Exptl. Biol.* **34,** 143–172.

de Graaf, A. R. (1957b). A note on the oxygen requirements of *Xenopus laevis*. *J. Exptl. Biol.* **34,** 173–176.

DeLong, K. T. (1962). Quantitative analysis of blood circulation through the frog heart. *Science* **138,** 693–694.

Dolk, H. E., and Postma, N. (1926). Über die Haut- und Lungenatmung von *Rana temporaria*. *Z. Vergleich. Physiol.* **5,** 417–444.

Drastich, L. (1927). Über das Leben der Salamanderlarven bei hohem und niedrigem Sauerstoffpartialdruck. *Z. Vergleich. Physiol.* **2,** 632–657.

Dunn, E. R. (1928). The habits of Plethodontidae. *Am. Naturalist* **62,** 236–248.

Duran-Jorda, F. (1951). Haemopoesis as seen in *Batrachoseps attenuatus*. *Acta Med. Scand.* **140,** 183–192.

Elkan, E. (1955). The buccal and pharyngeal mucous membrane in urodeles. *Proc. Zool. Soc. (London)* **125,** 685–710.

Elkan, E. (1958). Further contributions on the buccal and pharyngeal mucous membrane in urodeles. *Proc. Zool. Soc. (London)* **131,** 335–355.

Emmel, V. E. (1924). Studies on the non-nucleated elements of the blood: II. The occurrence and genesis of non-nucleated erythrocytes or erythroplastids in vertebrates other than mammals. *Am. J. Anat.* **33,** 347–406.

Emmel, V. E. (1925). Studies on the non-nucleated cytoplasmic elements of the blood: III. Leucoplastids or non-nucleated leucocytic derivatives in vertebrates other than mammals. *Am. J. Anat.* **35,** 33–62.

Etkin, W. (1934). The phenomena of anuran metamorphosis II. *Physiol. Zool.* **7,** 129–148.

Ewer, D. W. (1959). A toad (*Xenopus laevis*) without Haemoglobin. *Nature* **183,** 271.

Fernald, R. L. (1943). The origin and development of the blood island of *Hyla regilla*. *Univ. Calif. (Berkeley) Publ. Zool.* **51,** 129–148.

Finnegan, C. V. (1953). Studies of erythropoiesis in salamander embryos. *J. Exptl. Zool.* **123,** 371–395.

Foxon, G. E. H. (1951). A radiographic study of the passage of blood through the heart in the frog and the toad. *Proc. Zool. Soc. (London)* **121,** 529–538.

Foxon, G. E. H. (1955). Problems of the double circulation in vertebrates. *Biol. Rev. Cambridge Phil. Soc.* **30,** 196–228.

Foxon, G. E. H., and Rowson, K. E. K. (1956). The fate of 'Thorotrast' (Thorium dioxide) injected into the dorsal lymph sac of the frog, *Rana temporaria*. *Quart. J. Microscop. Sci.* **97**, 47–57.

Frechkop, S. (1955). Le coeur de la grenouille et l'origine du cercel double de la circulation sanguine. *Inst. Roy. Sci. Nat. Belg. Bull.* **31**, 1–23.

Fujiwara, M. (1950). On the erythrocytes of the larval stage of a tree frog, *Rhacophorus schlegelii schlegelii* Guenther. *Dobytsugaku Zasshi* **59**, 242–245.

Fujiwara, M. (1952). Experimental removal of the yolk sac in *Rana* embryo. *Dobytsugaku Zasshi* **61**, 221–224.

Fujiwara, M. (1953). On the origin of erythrocytes of amphibian larvae. *Dobytsugaku Zasshi* **60**, 74–78.

Gnanamuthu, C. P. (1936). The respiratory mechanism of the frog. *J. Exptl. Zool.* **74**, 157–165.

Goodrich, E. S. (1930). "Studies on the Structure and Development of Vertebrates," 837 pp. Macmillan, New York.

Greenwood, P. H., and Oliva, O. (1959). Does a lungfish breath through its nose? *Discovery* **20**, 18–19.

Harris, J. P. (1953). Note on the blood of *Necturus*. *Field Lab.* **21**, 147–148.

Helff, O. M. (1926). Studies on amphibian metamorphosis II. The oxygen consumption of tadpoles undergoing precocious metamorphosis following treatment with thyroid and di-iodotyrosine. *J. Exptl. Zool.* **45**, 69–93.

Helff, O. M., and Stubblefield, K. I. (1931). The influence of oxygen tension of the oxygen consumption of *Rana pipiens* larvae. *Physiol. Zool.* **4**, 271–286.

Holtfreter, J. (1947). Morphogenesis, crenation and cytolytic reactions of the erythrocytes of amphibians. *J. Morphol.* **80**, 345–367.

Hopkins, H. S., and Handford, S. W. (1943). Respiratory metabolism during development in two species of *Amblystoma*. *J. Exptl. Zool.* **93**, 403–414.

Iyer, P. A. R. (1943). On the structure of the lungs of a few examples of Apoda. *Half-Yearly J. Mysore Univ.* [*NS*] **B3**, 139–151.

Jacobson, M. (1953). Budding of erythrocytes in the South African clawed toad (*Xenopus laevis*) after splenectomy. *Nature* **172**, 1107–1108.

Johansen, K. (1962). Double circulation in the amphibian *Amphiuma tridactylum*. *Nature* **194**, 991–992.

Jordan, H. E. (1925). A study of the blood of the leopard frog, by the method of supra vital staining combined with the injection of india ink into the dorsal lymph sac, with special reference to the genetic relationships among leucocytes. *Am. J. Anat.* **35**, 105–134.

Jordan, H. E. (1932). The histology of the blood and the blood-forming tissues of the urodele *Proteus anguineus*. *Am. J. Anat.* **51**, 215–252.

Jordan, H. E. (1933). The evolution of the blood-forming tissues. *Quart. Rev. Biol.* **8**, 58–76.

Jordan, H. E. (1938). Comparative hematology. *In* "Handbook of Hematology" (H. Downey ed.), Vol. II, Sect. XII, pp. 704–862. Harper (Hoeber), New York.

Jordan, H. E., and Speidel, C. C. (1923). Studies on lymphocytes 1. Effect of splenectomy, experimental hemorrhage and a hemolytic toxin in the frog. *Am. J. Anat.* **32**, 155–188.

Jordan, H. E., and Speidel, C. C. (1929). The origin and proliferation of thrombocytes in splenectomized salamanders. *Proc. Soc. Exptl. Biol. Med.* **27**, 67–68.

Jordan, H. E., and Speidel, C. C. (1930). The hemocytopoietic effect of splenectomy in the salamander, *Triturus viridescens*. *Am. J. Anat.* **46**, 55–90.

Jordan, H. J. (1929). La régularisation de la consommation d'oxygène chez les animaux à tension gazeuse alvéolaire variable. *Arch. Neerl. Sci. IIIC* **14**, 305–314.

Jullien, A., Ripplinger, J., Cardot, J., Bagle, J. and Tisserand, M. (1958). Influence de la ligature des troncs pulmo-cutanés et de leurs branches sur la survie de la Grenouille et possibilité de rétablissement de la circulation apres arrêt. *Compt. Rend. Soc. Biol.* **152**, 1161–1163.

Kaplan, H. M. (1952a). A study of frog blood in red leg disease. *Trans. Illinois State Acad. Sci.* **44**, 209–215.

Kaplan, H. M. (1952b). Variations in white blood cells between normal and red leg frogs. *Trans. Illinois State Acad. Sci.* **45**, 170–176.

Kirkberger, C. (1953). Temperaturadaptation der Sauerstoffbindung des Blutes von *Rana esculenta* L. *Z. Vergleich Physiol.* **35**, 153–158.

Knisely, M. H., Bloch, E. H., and Warner, L. (1948). Selective phagocytosis I. Microscopic observations concerning the regulation of the blood-flow through the liver and other organs and the mechanism and rate of phagocytic removal of particles from the blood. *Kgl. Danske Videnskab. Selskab Biol. Skrifter* **4**(7), 1–93.

Krogh, A. (1904). On the cutaneous and pulmonary respiration of the frog. *Skand. Arch. Physiol.* **15**, 328–419.

Lawson, R. (1959). The anatomy of *Hypogeophis rostratus* (Cuvier) Amphibia: Apoda or Gymnophiona. Ph.D. thesis, Univ. Durham, King's College, England.

Lehman, H. E. (1953). Observations on macrophage behaviour in the fin of *Xenopus* larvae. *Biol. Bull.* **105**, 490–495.

Liebman, E. (1945). The function of leucocytes in the growth and regression of the egg of *Triturus viridescens*. *Am. J. Anat.* **77**, 273–292.

Lison, L. (1948). Phénomenes d'athrocytose discriminante dans les cellules de Kupffer des Amphibiens. *Compt. Rend. Assoc. Anat.* **52**, 329–334.

Lison, L., and Smulders, J. (1949a). Les éléments discriminants du système reticuloendothélial chez la Grenouille. *Compt. Rend. Soc. Biol.* **143**, 573–575.

Lison, L., and Smulders, J. (1949b). Action de l'histamine sur le système reticuloendothélial chez la Grenouille. *Compt. Rend. Soc. Biol.* **143**, 575–577.

Lowenthal, N. (1929). Des variétés de globules blanc du sang chez *Bombinator pachypus* et *Salmandra atra*. *Arch. Anat. Strasbourg* **9**, 467–502.

Lüdike, R. (1955). Über den Respirationsapparat verschiedener Urodelen und seine Beziehungen zum Herzen. *Z. Morphol. Oekol. Tiere* **43**, 578–615.

Macela, I., and Seliškar, A. (1925). The influence of temperature on the equilibrium between oxygen and haemoglobin of various forms of life. *J. Physiol. (London)* **60**, 428–442.

McCutcheon, F. H. (1936). Hemoglobin function during the life history of the bullfrog. *J. Cellular Comp. Physiol.* **8**, 63–81.

McCutcheon, F. H., and Hall, F. G. (1937). Hemoglobin in the Amphibia. *J. Cellular Comp. Physiol.* **9**, 191–197.

Marcus, H. (1935). Zur Stammesgeschichte des Herzens. *Morphol. Jahr.* **76**, 92–103.

Maximow, A. (1910). Über embryonale Entwicklung der Blutzellen bei Selachiern und Amphibien. *Anat. Anz. Suppl.* **37**, 64–70.

Mendes, E. G. (1941). Sobre a respiração (esofágica, traquéal e cuténea) do *Siphonops annulatus* (Amphibia-Gynmophiona). *Bol. Fac. Filosof. Cienc. Letras Uni;. Sao Paulo Zool.* **5**, 283–304.

Mendes, E. G. (1945). Contribuição para a fisiologica dos sistemas respiratório e circulatório de *Siphonops annulatus* (Amphibia-Gymnophiona). *Bol. Fac. Filosof. Cienc. Letras Univ. Sao Paulo Zool.* **9**, 25–64.

Millard, N. (1941). The vascular anatomy of *Xenopus laevis*. *Trans. Roy. Soc. S. Africa* **28**, 387–439.

Myers, R. B., and Alexander, G. (1945). Erythrocyte counts in Colorado *Amblystoma*. *Copeia* p. 46.

Mylius, I. (1952). Über die Blutbildung in der Urniere des Frosches. *Z. Mikroskop. Anat. Forsch.* **58**, 429–448.

Neil, E., and Zotterman, Y. (1950). Cardiac vagal afferent fibres in the cat and frog. *Acta Physiol. Scand.* **20**, 160–165.

Neil, E., Ström, L., and Zotterman, Y. (1950). Action potential studies of afferent fibres in the IXth and Xth cranial nerves of the frog. *Acta Physiol. Scand.* **20**, 338–350.

Nigrelli, R. F. (1929). Atypical erythrocytes and erythroplastids in the blood of *Triturus viridescens*. *Anat. Record.* **43**, 257–270.

Noble, G. K. (1925). The integumentary, pulmonary and cardiac modifications correlated with increased cutaneous respiration in the Amphibia: a solution of the 'hairy-frog' problem. *J. Morphol. Physiol.* **40**, 341–416.

Noble, G. K. (1931). "The Biology of the Amphibia," 577 pp. McGraw-Hill, New York, reprinted 1954, Dover Publ., New York.

Ouji, M. (1950). The hemopoiesis in the salamander *Hynobius retardatus*. *J. Fac. Sci. Hokkaido Univ. Ser. VI* **10**, 55–59.

Parker, H. W. (1936). The amphibians of the Mamfe Division, Cameroons, I. Zoo-geography and Systematics. *Proc. Zool. Soc. (London)* pp. 135–163.

Pinner, G. (1950). Über die Entwicklung der Spindelzellen sowie über die embryonale Blutbildung und die damit zusammenhängenden Organe bei *Rana esculenta*. *Oesterr. Zool. Z.* **2**, 639–646.

Poczopko, P. (1957). Further investigations on the cutaneous vasomotor reflexes in the edible frog in connection with the problem of regulation of the cutaneous respiration in frogs. *Zool. Polon.* **8**, 161–175.

Prosser, C. L. (ed.) (1950). "Comparative Physiology," 888 pp. Saunders, Philadelphia, Pennsylvania.

Ramaswami, L. S. (1944). An account of the heart and associated vessels in some genera of Apoda (Amphibia). *Proc. Zool. Soc. (London)* **114**, 107–138.

Redfield, A. C. (1933). The evolution of the respiratory function of the blood. *Quart. Rev. Biol.* **8**, 31–59.

Romer, A. S. (1945). "Vertebrate Palaeontology," 2nd ed., 687 pp. Chicago Univ. Press, Chicago, Illinois.

Savage, R. M. (1935). The ecology of young tadpoles, with special reference to some adaptations to the habit of mass spawning in *Rana temporaria temporaria* Linn. *Proc. Zool. Soc. (London)* pp. 605–610.

Savage, R. M. (1939). The distribution of the spawn-ponds of the common frog, *Rana temporaria temporaria* Linn. over a portion of the London clay and associated drift. *Proc. Zool. Soc. (London)* **A109**, 1–19.

Savage, R. M. (1952). Ecological, physiological and anatomical observations on some species of anuran tadpoles. *Proc. Zool. Soc. (London)* **122**, 467–514.

Sawaya, P. (1941). Contribuiçao para o estudo da fisiologia do sistema circulatorio do anfibio *Siphonops annulatus* (Mikan). *Bol. Fac. Filosof. Cienc. Letras Univ. Sao Paulo Zool.* **5**, 209–233.

Schaefer, K. (1935). Blutbildendes Knochenmark bei Urodelen. *Z. Mikroskop. Anat. Forsch.* **38**, 294–317.

Schafer, E. A. (1912). "Text-Book of Microscopic Anatomy," 738 pp. (Quain's Elements of Anatomy, 11th ed., Vol. II, Pt. 1). Longmans, Green, New York.

Schilling, C. (1935). Das Herzen von *Hypogeophis* und seine Entwicklung. *Morphol. Jahrb.* **76**, 52–91.

Schmalhausen, I. I. (1957). Biological basis of the origin of the terrestrial vertebrata (in Russian). *Izv. Akad. Nauk SSSR Ser. Biol.* **22**, 3–31.

Scholton, J. M. (1942). A few remarks on the respiratory movements of the frog. *Arch. Neerl. Sci. IIIC* **26**, 250–268.

Scott, W. J. (1931). Oxygen and carbon-dioxide transport by the blood of the urodele, *Amphiuma tridactyla*. *Biol. Bull.* **61**, 211–222.

Serfaty, A., and Gueutal, J. (1943). La résistance de la Grenouille a l'asphyxie lors d'une immersion prolongée. *Compt. Rend. Soc. Biol.* **137**, 154–156.

Sharma, H. L. (1957). The anatomy and mode of action of the heart of the frog, *Rana tigrina* Daud. *J. Morphol.* **100**, 313–343.

Sharma, H. L. (1961). The circulatory mechanism and anatomy of the heart of the frog, *Rana pipiens*. *J. Morphol.* **109**, 323–349.

Simons, J. R. (1957). The blood pressure and the pressure pulses in the arterial arches of the frog *(Rana temporaria)* and the toad *(Bufo bufo)*. *J. Physiol. (London)* **137**, 12–21.

Simons, J. R. (1959). The distribution of the blood from the heart in some amphibia. *Proc. Zool. Soc. (London)* **132**, 51–64.

Slonimski, P. (1935). Sur la classification des leucoplastids chez les amphibiens. *Compt. Rend. Soc. Biol.* **120**, 375–377.

Smith, H. M. (1925). Cell size and metabolic activity in Amphibia. *Biol. Bull.* **48**, 347–378.

Smyth, D. H. (1939). The central and reflex control of respiration in the frog. *J. Physiol. (London)* **95**, 305–327.

Spitzer, J. J., and Spitzer, J. A. (1952). The blood coagulation mechanism in frogs, with respect to the species specificity of thromboplastin, to intracardial thrombin injection, and to the effect of seasonal changes. *Can. J. Med. Sci.* **30**, 420–424.

Spurway, H., and Haldane, J. B. S. (1953). The comparative ethology of vertebrate breathing: I. Breathing in newts, with a general survey. *Behaviour* **6**, 8–34.

Stephan, F. (1954). Morphologie générale du système circulatoire. *In* "Traité de Zoologie" (P.-P. Grasse, ed.), Vol. XII: Vertébrés, pp. 854–973. Masson, Paris.

Strawinski, S. (1956). Vascularization of respiratory surfaces in ontogeny of the edible frog, *Rana esculenta* L. *Zool. Polon.* **7**, 327–365.

Stuart, L. C. (1951). The distributional implications of temperature tolerances and hemoglobin values in the toads *Bufo marinus* (Linnaeus) and *Bufo bocourti* Brocchi. *Copeia* pp. 220–229.

Szarski, H. (1955). La vascularisation des surfaces respiratoires chez les amphibiens. *Compt. Rend. Assoc. Anat.* **42**, 1267–1273.

Szarski, H. (1959). Some reactions of the skin capillaries of the frog. *Proc. 15th Intern. Congr. Zool. London, 1958* pp. 531–533.

Trotter, W. D. (1956). Banding in salamander erythrocytes. A shape change corresponding to disc-sphere transformation in mammalian red cells. *Exptl. Cell Res.* **11**, 587–603.

Vandervael, F. (1933). Recherches sur le méchanisme de la circulation du sang dans le coeur des Amphibiens anoures. *Arch. Biol. (Paris)* **44**, 571–606.

Varela, M. E., and Sellarés, M. E. (1938). Variations annuelles du sang du crepaud *Bufo arenarum* Hensel. *Compt. Rend. Soc. Biol.* **129**, 1248–1249.

Vos, H. J. (1936). Über die Atembewegungen und den Schnuffelmechanismus (Kehloszillationen) bei Reptilien und Amphibien. *Zool. Anz.* **115**, 142–144.

Wastl, H., and Seliškar, A. (1925). Observations on the combination of CO_2 in the blood of the Bullfrog (*Rana catesbiana*). *J. Physiol. (London)* **60**, 264–268.

Watson, D. M. S. (1925). The evolution and origin of the Amphibia. *Phil. Trans. Roy. Soc. London* **B214**, 189–257.

Willem, V. (1931). Les manoeuvres respiratoires chez les poissons et les amphibiens. *Acad. Roy. Belg. Classe Sci. Mem. Ser.* 2 **10**, 139–192.

Wills, I. A. (1936). The respiratory rate of developing amphibia with special reference to sex differentiation. *J. Exptl. Zool.* **73**, 481–510.

Wolvekamp, H. P. (1932). Untersuchungen über den Sauerstofftransport durch Blutpigmente bei *Helix*, *Rana* und *Planorbis*. *Z. Vergleich. Physiol.* **16**, 1–38.

Wolvekamp, H. P., and Lodewijks, J. M. (1934). Über die Sauerstoffbindung durch Hämoglobin vom Frosch (*Rana esculenta* und *Rana temporaria*). *Z. Vergleich. Physiol.* **20**, 382–387.

Zylbersac, S. (1946). Sur la nature et l'origine des leucocytes pigmentaires dans le sang des Amphibiens. *Arch. Biol. (Paris)* **57**, 307–325.

4

PHYSIOLOGY OF THE AMPHIBIAN HEART

Allan J. Brady[*]

I. Introduction

The Amphibia have played a major role in the development of many fields of vertebrate physiology. One of the most characteristic of these fields is that of cardiac physiology. Ringer's (1880–1882) early work, for example, determined the inorganic ions essential to contraction of the frog's heart. Thus, he pioneered the field of the excised preparations from which has come a wealth of data. The most basic and perhaps the most complete study of cardiac metabolism is found in the amphibian heart. Similarly, the development of cardiac electrophysiology, especially the relatively recent studies of transmembrane potentials, intimately

* This work was performed during the tenure of an Established Investigatorship of the American Heart Association.

involves the amphibian heart. Some notion of the link between excitation and contraction has recently developed based on data from the frog's heart. This data coupled with new data from skeletal muscle injects new life into a long dormant subject. On the other hand, because of the unfavorable geometry of amphibian heart fibers, the mechanics of cardiac muscle contraction has developed more extensively in hearts of other species. However, the entire field of cardiac muscle mechanics has lagged far behind that of skeletal muscle.

The hemodynamics of amphibian circulatory systems, including the heart, are discussed in another chapter (Chapter 3). Also, since the field of cardiac metabolism immediately relevant to excitability and to the generation of tension has advanced little since the extensive studies reported in "Metabolism of the Frog's Heart" (Clark *et al.*, 1938) this field will not be discussed here. Emphasis will be given to recent developments in electrophysiology and excitation-contraction coupling.

II. Structure

A. GROSS FEATURES

One of the most striking features of the beating amphibian heart is its segmental contraction. The beat normally originates in the large thin-walled sinus venosus. Atrial contraction follows after an obvious delay. Following a similar delay, the ventricle contracts, and finally, after a further delay, the bulbus cordis. Functionally, each section appears to contract as a whole. The summed delays often are sufficiently long as to make contraction of the bulbus cordis one whole cycle or more behind the pacemaker. Another fascinating observation in the amphibian heart is the cyclic blushing and bleaching of the ventricle as the blood pervades the highly porous ventricular wall during diastole and then disappears during systole. Both the sinus venosus and the atria play a major role in the propulsion of the blood through the heart and relative to their analogue in the mammalian heart make up considerably larger portions of the total cardiac mass. The data of Clark and White (1930) give the proportions by weight of the frog heart (*Rana temporaria*) as shown in Table I.

The sinus venosus has a large surface area when distended but contains only a few layers of muscle cells. Clark and White (1930) estimate its total thickness when empty to be 250μ in a 140-mg heart. Similarly, the distended auricles also contain only a few layers of cells having a total thickness of 110μ and an endocardial surface area of 176 cm^2 per gram. The ventricle possesses only a small open cavity (less than half the radius of the ventricle) but this chamber communicates with a multi-

TABLE I

PROPORTIONS BY WEIGHT OF COMPONENTS OF FROG HEART

Component	Proportion by weight (%)
Ventricle	70
Auricles and sinus venosus	20
Bulbus arteriosus (cordis)	10

plicity of small fissures between trabecular strands which extend to the epicardial surface (Fig. 1). This structure gives the ventricle a sponge-like characteristic whose volume can change by as much as 300%. The distended ventricle has a wall thickness of 2 mm in *Rana pipiens* or *Rana temporaria* and an endocardial surface area between 500 and 1000 cm² per gram, estimated from sections of the ventricle perfused with a fine suspension of charcoal. On the assumption that the cells are spindle shaped, Clark and associates (1938) estimate a total cellular surface area of 6600 cm² per gram for the distended ventricle. The charcoal perfusion technique also reveals a mean trabecular diameter of only 40μ indicating a diffusion distance for metabolites of only 20μ. Krogh (1929) estimates the average separation of capillaries of the frog's sartorius to be 56μ giving a diffusion distance of 28μ. Thus the frog heart, even in the absence of a coronary circulation, possesses a perfusion system comparable to skeletal muscle.

The muscular wall of the bulbus cordis is relatively thick and possesses a small coronary artery originating from the right carotid canal in the right truncus arteriosus (Gaupp, 1896). This small artery courses over the ventral surface of the bulbus cordis and becomes lost in capillary nets on the border between the bulbus and the ventricle. According to Gaupp there is no extension of these nets into the ventricular wall.

B. MICROSCOPIC FEATURES

Fibers of the frog's heart are generally long branching spindles with frequent cross-links. Table II (Skramlik, 1921) gives the average cell diameter and length found in *Rana temporaria*. Ultramicroscopically, the cells, at least in the frog ventricle, appear as distinct units separated by the intercalated discs. Electronmicrographs of the intercalated disc regions (Sjöstrand *et al.*, 1958) give no indication that myofibrils traverse the discs. Hence, tension must be transferred from cell to cell via the discs.

Figure 2 shows the sarcomere structure in relation to the basement membrane and interposed mitochondria. Of particular interest are the invaginations of the basement membrane and the vesicles in the vicinity

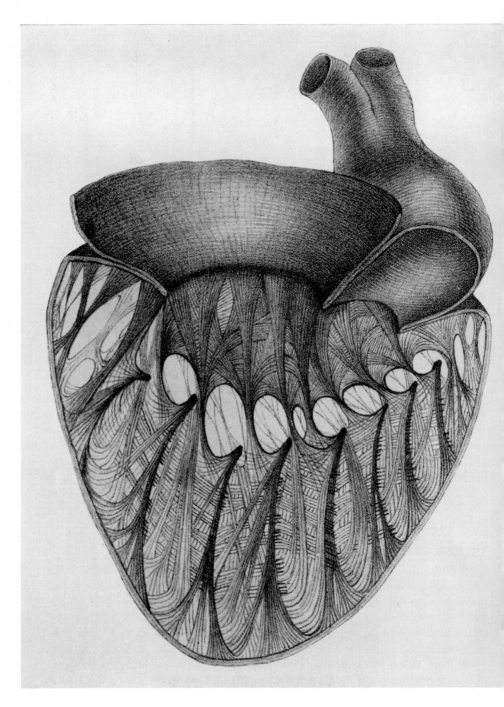

Fig. 1. Sketch of frog ventricle illustrating trabecular structure and porosity of walls. (From Gompertz, 1884.)

TABLE II

FIBER DIAMETER OF COMPONENTS OF FROG HEART

Component	Fiber diameter × length (μ)
Sinus venosus	5.4 × 73
Auricle	5.7 × 193
A-V ring	9.1 × 116
Ventricle	9.2 × 131
Bulbus cordis	6.0 × 130

of the Z-bands. The significance of these relationships with respect to excitation-contraction coupling is discussed in later sections. Other than the Z-bands, the cross-striations are less prominent than in skeletal muscle. Fibrillar structures are distinct, although cross-links, if they exist, are not resolved in this photograph. Particularly prominent, on the other hand, are the cristae within the mitochondria.

III. Innervation

Innervation of the frog heart is entirely by way of the vagus nerve (Bidder, 1852, 1866). Fibers of the IV sympathetic ganglion along with other sympathetic fibers join the vagus in its course to the heart. Many ganglion cells are found attached to the medial border of the vagus.

The course of the right cardiac nerve of the vagus proceeds as follows, the left taking a symmetrical pathway. After the right cardiac nerve, which is thinner than the left, leaves the right intestinal branch of the vagus it perforates the aponeurose of the transversus muscle medial to the pulmonary artery and passes between the lateral pericardium and the lamina media spinalis of the pleuroperitoneum, medio-caudally to the heart. It arrives at the dorsal side of the anterior vena cava (extrapericardially) and follows it to the dorsal wall of the sinus venosus. Near the rostral border of the sinus venosus, the right and left branches of the cardiac nerve converge and enter the rostral wall of the sinus venosus in the neighborhood of the pulmonary vein. Here in the rostral wall of the sinus venosus, dorsal to the end of the pulmonary vein they form an interwoven plexus. This plexus contains the embedded Remak's ganglion and a short anastomosis (cardiac nerve chasma) between the right and left nerve branches. The two nerves form additional ganglion cells to the left of the ostium of the pulmonary vein before they enter the arterial septum. The nerves then pass to the septal wall, one dorsal and one ventral. The dorsal nerve is mainly a continuation of the left branch and the ventral of the right branch. Ganglion cells are found within the atria near the ostium of the pulmonary vein and the insertion of the septum,

Fig. 2. A longitudinal section of frog ventricular myocardium. The sarcolemmas of opposing cells are seen separating the individual fibers. A double basement membrane is occasionally present in the extracellular space and runs parallel to the sarcolemma. Numerous mitochondria are present in the sarcoplasmic matrix between the sarcolemma and the individual myofibrils. The myofibrils run parallel to the longitudinal fiber direction and demonstrate the characteristic striated A, I, Z, and N banding pattern. Numerous intracytoplasmic vesicular components of the sarcoplasmic reticulum are present at the sarcolemmal surface with occasional more dilated components near the myofibrils. No well developed interfibrillar sarcotubular networks are seen.

KEY TO LABELS: M, mitochondria; MF, myofibril; Z, Z-band; I, I-band; A, A-band; N, N-band; SL, sarcolemma; BM, basement membrane; SR, sarcotubular system; V, vesicles.

Fixed in 2.5% osmic acid with collidine buffer. Stained with lead acetate and ammonium hydroxide. (Courtesy of Dr. Stanley Scheyer.)

as part of the ventral branch. The dorsal branch runs directly to the ostium of the atrioventricular aperture. The two nerves go immediately to the large Bidder's ganglion, easily visible to the naked eye, and lying against the atrioventricular valve. From these two ganglia, nerves run between the base of the valve and the muscle wall, subendocardially, through the upper portions of the ventricle, communicating with Dogiel's ganglion cells. The extent of penetration of these nerves into the apex is unknown; however, some authors feel that the apex is nerve-free.

Remak's, Bidder's, and Dogiel's ganglia are not the only ganglion cells in the heart. Many other nerve nets and scattered ganglia occur throughout the sinus venosus, atria, and atrial septum. No nerve cells and only a few nerve fibers are found in the bulbus cordis.

IV. Excitation

The electrical manifestation of excitation can be detected with recording electrodes placed either extracellularly or intracellularly. Either type of recording involves the summed activity of all the tissue with each cell contributing a portion of the signal relative to its distance from the recording electrode. Since extracellular electrodes are remote to the potential source, they record only changes in electrical activity, i.e., only when unbalanced currents are generated by the heart. Intracellular electrodes, on the other hand, can be connected "across" the cell potential and thereby continuously record both resting and active cellular potentials. Insertion of an intracellular electrode reveals a resting potential of the order of -80 mv with respect to the interstitial fluid. Excitation results in a rapid reversal of this potential (depolarization) to about $+20$ mv with a subsequent slow recovery to the resting potential (repolarization). During the major part of the recovery potential, the fibers are absolutely refractory. Excitability returns to normal only during the final phase of repolarization.

Our knowledge of the basic mechanism of excitation is most advanced in certain invertebrate axons, e.g., the squid giant axon, largely due to their size (200–1000 μ) and relative ease of isolation. However, the recording of transmembrane potentials with the recently developed microelectrode technique has given rise to a host of data with which these mechanisms are being delineated in muscle. Our knowledge of impulse conduction in nerve is far from complete; nevertheless, detailed formulations interrelating the electrical parameters of nerve recently have been elucidated, based on ingenious techniques and extensive data. The most detailed of these is the ionic hypothesis proposed by Hodgkin and Huxley (1952). Since this proposed scheme explains so many of the known basic electrical properties of resting and active nerve, it is logical to attempt to interpret muscle data in terms of this theory.

The most fundamental assumption of the hypothesis is that ions move through the cell membrane in accordance with the electrochemical gradients pertinent to each ion species so that the ionic currents obey Ohm's Law. The formulation of this hypothesis is simplified by the experimental observation that excitable cells possess the properties of coaxial transmission cables. For example, in single cell preparations, where the fiber diameter is small compared to its length, these cable properties are readily measurable (Hodgkin and Rushton, 1946). In these fibers the endoplasm can be described as a good conductor surrounded by a high resistance membrane analogous to the insulating layer of the transmission cable. Outside the membrane the low resistance of the extracellular or the interstitial fluid behaves like the shield on the transmission cable. The large resistance and relatively high dielectric constant of the membrane situated between the two good conductors endows the membrane with the ability to store charge; hence the membrane possesses the property of electrical capacitance. The spread of a subthreshold disturbance or the propagation of an impulse necessarily involves the flow of current through these electrical constituents. A knowledge of these properties thus is essential to the interpretation of such physiological processes as electrotonus, threshold, and the propagation of excitation. The rise or fall of subthreshold membrane potential changes in a fiber which is long compared to its diameter has an exponential portion which is described by the product of the membrane resistance and capacitance, i.e., the membrane time constant. The spatial spread of activity is also exponential. It can be shown from the cable properties of cells, for example, that an applied voltage falls to 37% of its initial value at a distance of one space constant from the source. The space constant is defined as

$$\sqrt{\frac{\text{membrane resistivity} \times \text{cell radius}}{\text{resistivity of (external} + \text{internal) fluid}}}$$

Measurements of membrane time constants and space constants help define cellular electrophysiological properties and greatly facilitate comparative studies of excitable cells. In cardiac tissue these constants become more complex to evaluate due to the frequent branching of the cells. Nevertheless, a measurement of these properties is essential to a basic study of cardiac cellular electrical activity.

Since propagation of excitation involves the additional phenomenon of depolarization of the fiber membrane, the parameters of the membrane resting and action potential form an intimate phase of the excitatory process. The Hodgkin-Huxley hypothesis proposes that the rapid depolarization of the membrane is brought about by an increase in sodium (Na) conductance and thus an inward Na current. Repolarization then

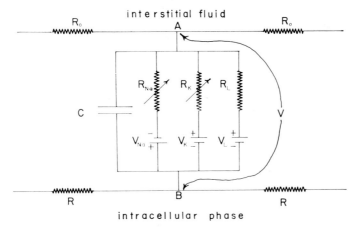

Fig. 3. Equivalent electrical circuit of excitable membrane. Intracellular and extracellular resistivities denoted by R_i and R_o, respectively. V_{Na}, V_K, R_{Na}, R_K denote sodium and potassium concentration potentials and sodium and potassium membrane resistances. V_L and R_L denote the electrical driving force collectively, on ions other than Na and K and R_L the membrane resistance to these ions. V denotes the membrane potential at any time or position as measured with a suitable voltage recorder. C represents the membrane capacitance.

occurs as the Na conductance falls and the potassium (K) conductance increases, i.e., the inward Na current diminishes and the outward K current increases until the resting potential is restored. The frog's heart has played a prominent role in the elucidation of these factors in cardiac tissue, and, therefore, in the general development of our knowledge of cardiac excitability. Considerable information is available on many of these properties; hence they will be discussed as separate topics in the succeeding pages.

A. ELECTRICAL MODEL OF MEMBRANE

The following electrical analogue is helpful in describing many of the passive and active properties of cellular electrical behavior (Fig. 3). In this figure the external and internal phases of the cell are shown as continuous resistances with a representative section of membrane interposed. The membrane capacity C is shown shunting the resistive portion of the membrane which is broken up into three parallel channels representing the respective ionic currents moving through the membrane. The Na and K resistances, R_{Na} and R_K, are made variable to explain the change in membrane potential (V) during excitation (see Section IV,D). The third resistive channel represents the current of ions whose membrane permeability does not change. In the case of nerve, this channel carries only a very small current relative to Na and K. In cardiac muscle during times when the membrane potential changes are relatively slow and the membrane impedance is high, this channel may indeed carry appreciable current attributable to (chloride) Cl (Section IV,D).

Although the barrier to the movement of the ions is represented schematically as a resistance, it is more convenient to discuss ion movements through membranes in terms of conductances, i.e., the reciprocal of the resistance, since ionic conductances are directly related to ionic permeabilities. The values of the respective ionic conductances in amphibian cardiac tissue have not been determined, but some generalizations can be made from existing data. As is the case in many other excitable cells, the myoplasm is high in K and low in Na and Cl with just the reverse distribution outside the cells. The resting membrane potential is negative inside the cell with respect to the outside. The magnitude of this potential is near the concentration potential of the K and Cl distributions but far from and, in fact, reversed from that of the Na concentration potential. In addition, the resting potential is acutely sensitive to the external K concentration but nearly independent of the Na or Cl concentration. These observations lead to the conclusion that the resting membrane conductance is determined largely by K. The relative conductances of Na, K, and Cl, however, have not been established in heart tissue.

B. PASSIVE ELECTRICAL PROPERTIES

Systematic measurements of the cable properties of amphibian heart cells have not been reported, but some data are available. Trautwein, et al. (1956) found a membrane capacitance in frog atrium of 30 μf per cm^2 (probably high) and a membrane resistance of 280 ohm-cm^2 (comparatively low) based on an assumed intracellular resistivity of 100 ohm-cm (Weidmann, 1956a). This capacitance is large relative to Purkinje tissue (12 μf per cm^2, Weidmann, 1952); however, the lower value in Purkinje fibers may reflect the large amount of collagen surrounding the cells. The membrane time constant of the frog atrium averaged about 6 msec and the space constant 320μ. Kahn (1941) reported catelectrotonic and anelectrotonic potentials in the ventricle of Rana temporaria to have a double exponential time course with time constants of 3.5 and 5.5 msec. The membrane resistance and space constant are only one-tenth those of skeletal muscle but the space constant is consistent with that in rat atrium (100–150μ; Woodbury and Crill, 1961). Tanaka (1959) on the other hand, found a membrane resistance of 2000 ohm-cm^2 in toad atrium. The resting membrane is presumably permeable largely to K; hence the membrane resistance and space constant in these tissues would be expected to be strongly dependent on factors affecting K permeability. Acetylcholine (5.5 μmoles per liter) plus prostigmin (30 μmoles per liter) reduces the space constant in frog auricle (probably *Rana pipiens*) by 29% and the time constant by 44–59% (Trautwein *et al.*, 1956). Thus the passive electrical properties would be expected to vary with the extent of cholinergic activity.

C. MEMBRANE RESTING POTENTIAL

The extracellular-intracellular K ratio has long been known to be related to the resting potential of nerve and skeletal muscle cells of many species. In recent years a similar relation has become apparent in the frog ventricle as well. Hajdu (1953) gives a K content of 90 mmoles per liter of fiber water in the ventricle of *Rana pipiens*. The K concentration potential, as defined by the Nernst equation

$$V_K = \frac{RT}{F} \ln \frac{[K]_0}{[K]_i}$$

corresponding to an extracellular K concentration of 2.5 mmoles is 90 mv at 20°C. Intracellularly recorded membrane potentials with microelectrodes give values of 60–80 mv, the higher values being more likely associated with a normal permeability and an intracellular K concentration of 90 mmoles. The resting potential varies little with changes in extracellular Cl so that the 10 mv discrepancy may, perhaps, be attributed to a small but significant resting Na conductance (see Chapter 6 on skeletal muscle). The resting potential tends to follow the K concentration potential in high external K concentrations but falls short of it at lower concentrations. Unlike skeletal muscle or mammalian heart muscle, however, the resting potential does not fall in K-free solutions but is higher (more negative) than in normal Ringer's solution (Lüttgau and Niedergerke, 1958; Brady and Woodbury, 1960). The slope of the curve relating membrane resting potential and log external K is nearly linear (40 mv per decade) in *Rana temporaria* (Lüttgau and Niedergerke, 1958), but is sigmoid in *Rana pipiens* (Brady and Woodbury, 1960). The slope of some phases of the sigmoid curve is greater than 58 mv per decade, indicating a more complex relation than simple dependence on external [K]. Chloride conductance may well be a factor in the determination of the membrane potential when external KCl is changed, as it is in skeletal muscle, but its influence remains to be established.

Antoni and Kotowski (1959) have made an interesting observation regarding the temperature dependence of changes in resting potential of frog ventricle with changes in external KCl. The resting potential in isotonic KCl at both 20°C and 4°C was 15 mv. Upon returning the tissues

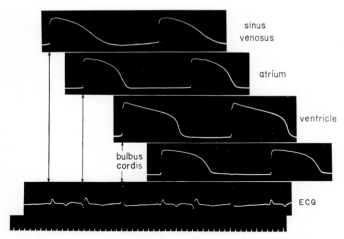

Fig. 4. Transmembrane potentials from frog heart showing their time relation to an electrocardiogram recorded simultaneously (*Rana catesbeiana*). Vertical arrows show correlation between ECG and depolarization of sinus venosus, atrium, and ventricle. Ventricular T wave can be seen as a downward deflection between bulbus cordis depolarization and atrial P waves. Repolarization of the bulbus cordis can be seen as a slow downward deflection between the P and QRS waves. Time marks are 100 msec. Temperature, 22°C.

to normal Ringer's solution without a change in temperature the resting potential of the fibers at 20°C was restored to 59 mv in 3 min and to their normal level of 67 mv within 5–6 min. The fibers at 4°C repolarized to 31 mv in the first 3 min but did not attain the original resting potential of 64 mv until 15 min. Both tissues would be expected to take up considerable KCl because the external KCl product had been greatly increased. The asymmetrical return of the membrane potential is suggestive of the observations in frog skeletal muscle where after soaking in 100 mM KCl the membrane potential becomes a Cl electrode (Hodgkin and Horowicz, 1959b; Adrian, 1960). This effect in skeletal muscle is ascribed to a marked decrease in K efflux such that the membrane becomes a Cl electrode. Not until the excess KCl diffuses out does the membrane return to a K electrode. The observations of Antoni and Kotowski suggest that such may be the case in frog ventricle at 4°C but at 20°C the reduction in K efflux does not occur under the experimental conditions. An immediate test of this interpretation would be to reduce the external [Cl] in the tissue equilibrated to isotonic KCl at 4°C. If it behaves like skeletal muscle the membrane potential should follow external [Cl] rather than $[K]_0$.

D. MEMBRANE ACTION POTENTIAL

Typical membrane action potentials of *Rana catesbeiana* heart along with an electrocardiograph (ECG) are shown in Fig. 4. The transmembrane potentials were recorded with an intracellular microelectrode whose tip diameter was less than 0.5μ (Ling and Gerard, 1949). The correspondence between the electrocardiograph and the various intracellular events is readily apparent. The rapid depolarization potential of each section of the heart with the exception of the sinus venosus, gives rise to large extracellular currents which are easily detected by the ECG electrode. In addition, the rapid phase of repolarization of the more massive ventricle and bulbus cordis contribute visibly to the ECG. The ECG electrode was sufficiently remote to the thin-walled sinus venosus that its action currents are not easily seen. Notable in the sinus venosus record, however, is the slow loss of membrane potential (prepotential) during diastole leading up to the rapid phase of depolarization. The significance of this prepotential is discussed in Section IV,E.

1. Depolarization

Detailed impedance measurements of amphibian heart muscle are lacking but from the gross similarity between the active electrical events of cardiac tissue of frog and mammals, it seems reasonable to assume that following a threshold stimulus the membrane undergoes an increase in ionic conductivity. If this increase in permeability involves Na as in other excitable tissues, the height of the membrane action potential and the rate of depolarization should be related to external Na. Brady and Woodbury (1957, 1960) found that the overshoot diminished with reduction of external [Na], from a normal range of 15–20 mv to a nearly constant level of a few millivolts below zero in solutions below 50% normal [Na]. The maximum rate of depolarization fell to half its peak value of 30 volts per sec in 40% normal [Na] and, conduction was blocked in Na-free media. Thus convincing evidence exists that, depolarization is, indeed, brought about by an increase in Na conductance as in squid nerve and probably also in skeletal muscle.

Elevation of external K reduces the depolarization rate and overshoot probably as a result of its reduction of membrane potential. Weidmann (1955) has shown that prior depolarization of Purkinje tissue with an applied subthreshold current reduces the maximum depolarization rate similar to the K effect. In fact, a short interval of repolarization of a K depolarized fiber restores the overshoot. According to the Hodgkin-Huxley theory the K effect is accounted for by an increase in inactivation of the Na conductance system resulting from the depolarization.

The effect of Ca on depolarization has not been ascertained in Amphibia but in mammalian cardiac muscle Ca has the effect of reducing the amount of depolarization necessary to obtain a given rate of depolarization. Other interactions between Na and Ca will be discussed with relation to excitation-contraction coupling.

Specific measurements of the temperature dependence of the rate of depolarization are lacking in Amphibia; however, in mammalians it has a Q_{10} of about 1.7 (Coraboeuf and Weidmann, 1954). The temperature dependence of conduction velocity, however, further reflects the nature of chemical processes in the excitation mechanism. Thus, depolarization is propagated at relatively slow conduction velocities in Amphibia mostly due to their lower body temperature. For example, the conduction velocity in mammalian ventricle is about 30 cm per sec at 37°C (Scher *et al.*, 1953). In strips of frog ventricle, propagation is conducted at 16 cm per sec at 27°C and 10 cm per sec at 18°C (Bammer and Rothschuh, 1952a,b; Bammer, 1953; Heintzen, 1954). Assuming a Q_{10} of 1.8 for this temperature range, the conduction velocity extrapolates to 29 cm per sec at 37°C. At 3°C the conduction velocity drops to 0.48 cm per sec.

2. Repolarization

Characteristic for cardiac tissue is the slow repolarization of the membrane back to its resting level (Fig. 4). In the frog heart, repolarization normally lasts 500–1000 times as long as in nerve or skeletal muscle. Repolarization is conveniently divided into phases bounded by the points of maximum curvature and with their peak slopes marked by the inflections of the repolarization potential. Phase 1 (not always present in frog heart) occurs just beyond the peak of the action potential. Phase 2 is denoted by the relatively flat region or plateau of repolarization and phase 3 by the final rapid phase of repolarization. In some tissues none of these phases are easily distinguishable; for example, note the repolarization of the sinus venosus in Fig. 4.

The significance of these phases is indicated by their marked difference in sensitivity to environmental factors. Phase 1 is keenly sensitive to external Na. Phase 2 is by far the most labile, being greatly influenced by temperature and stimulus frequency as well as by ionic changes and humoral agents. Phase 3 is most sensitive to external K (Brady and Woodbury, 1957, 1960).

a. *Temperature.* Figure 5 illustrates the temperature dependence of repolarization. The action potential duration (T_{ap}) is here defined as the interval between the time the membrane is depolarized 10% from its resting value and the time at which it is 90% repolarized. *Rana pipiens* T_{ap} has a Q_{10} of 2.3 and *Rana temporaria*, 2.2–2.3 (Heintzen *et al.*, 1956).

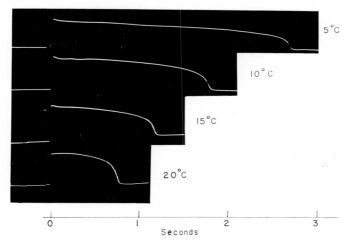

Fig. 5. Temperature dependence of transmembrane potentials from frog ventricle.

Woodbury and associates (1951) found the following slopes in millivolts per second of phases 1, 2, and 3 of *Rana pipiens* ventricle between 0.6° and 23.8°C, respectively: phase 1, 12–135; phase 2, 19–61; phase 3, 230–1100. Although the slope of phases 1 and 3 is the most temperature dependent, the duration of phase 2 is primarily responsible for the large influence of temperature on the total action potential duration. It must be kept in mind, however, that the above data were obtained from a spontaneously beating *in situ* heart so that the action potential duration is elongated both by decreased temperature and a concomitant reduced rate of beating (see next section); hence, all the slopes at the lower temperature are reduced from those obtainable at a constant rate of beating. Ono *et al.* (1960) have measured the Q_{10} of depolarization and the 3 phases of repolarization of a Japanese toad with the following values obtaining for the range 15–20°C: depolarization, 3.20; phase 1, 8.35; phase 2, 4.84; phase 3, 1.74. These values are a more direct measure of the temperature dependence of the action potential since they do not reflect a change in excitation rate.

   b. Stimulus Rate. The lability of T_{ap} relative to the excitation rate or stimulus cycle interval (T_c) in the ventricle of *Rana pipiens* is shown in Figs. 6 and 10, and in *Rana temporaria* in Carmeliet and Lacquet (1958). At stimulus intervals longer that 3.0 sec, T_{ap} is constant at 18°C. With decreasing stimulus intervals the action potential duration shortens until only a small local (nonpropagated) response is elicited by the stimulus. Such short intervals, i.e., such high rates of excitation are difficult to attain in normal Ringer's solution but by reducing the external Na, high

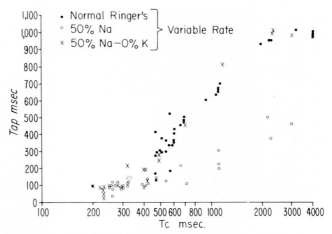

Fig. 6. Action potential duration (T_{ap}) as a function of stimulus interval (T_c) in frog ventricle (*Rana pipiens*). Temperature, 18°C.

rates of excitation are readily attainable. Although the plateau phase is strongly stimulus rate dependent, Brady and Woodbury (1960) showed that over a broad range of stimulus frequencies, phase 3 of the action potentials is surprisingly superimposable. The shorter duration action potentials at high stimulus rates are lower in overshoot but little changed in resting potential giving the appearance of a simple omission of the first region of the plateau phase.

It is evident from the marked shortening of the action potential duration with increased stimulus frequency or reduced $[Na]_o$, that the refractory period must also be labile. Indeed, the absolutely refractory period follows action potential duration even down to the shortest recorded duration action potentials. Thus the refractory state in heart appears to be associated with the extent of membrane repolarization as in other excitable tissues.

c. Ions. Figures 6 and 11 illustrate the influence of external Na and K on repolarization. The effect of reducing external Na is to shorten T_{ap} with phase 1 becoming more prominent and with an increase in slope of phase 2 (Brady and Woodbury, 1957, 1960). Lowering external [K] as well as [Na] has the effect of restoring T_{ap} to normal except that the cell retains its ability to conduct action potentials at very high frequencies. Potassium changes the contour of repolarization mostly by increasing the slope of phase 3. This effect is contrary to that in mammalian cardiac muscle where elevated K slows the rapid phase of repolarization. The shortening of T_{ap} in high [K] is likely due, at least in part, to the initial reduction in resting potential. Weidmann (1955) has shown in Purkinje tissue that subthreshold depolarization of the membrane either with an applied current or high [K] reduces the membrane potential overshoot so that less outward current would be required to repolarize the membrane. The increase in slope of phase 3, however, suggests an increase in K permeability as well. The latter suggestion is supported by the observation that K increases the efflux of K^{42} in the ventricle of *Rana temporaria* (Brady, unpublished).

Calcium has an action on repolarization resembling reduced [Na] in that phase 1 may become more predominant and phase 2 may increase in slope. Phase 3 tends to become less steep with the result that the action potential duration may be lengthened relative to normal. Reduction of external [Ca] decreases the slope of phase 2 and increases the slope of phase 3 such that after prolonged soaking in a Ca-free medium the action potentials are greatly elongated and tend toward a rectangular pattern.

d. Membrane Impedance and Ion Exchange. Tanaka's (1959) measurement of tissue impedance in toad atria shows that the membrane conducance during the plateau is less than or at least no greater than during diastole. A similar relation has been reported in ungulate Purkinje tissue by Weidmann (1951). These findings are in direct contrast to nerve and skeletal muscle where the membrane conductance is elevated throughout repolarization. The question then arises whether an efflux of K is responsible for repolarization as in nerve and most probably in skeletal muscle. Some data do exist (Walker *et al.*, 1962; Wilde *et al.*, 1956) showing that a periodic pulse of K^{42} efflux occurs in beating turtle ventricle and strips of frog ventricle. However, the K^{42} efflux from whole frog ventricle and dog papillary muscle (Brady, unpublished) and rat heart (Taylor, 1962) is independent of the rate of beating. In fact, no change in K^{42} efflux could be detected between quiescence and any rate of beating. These data become consistent, however, if it is assumed that K efflux is lower than the diastolic level during the plateau phase and then increases during phase 3 in such a way that the next K efflux during the action potential is zero.

e. Mechanisms of Repolarization. Membrane repolarization in squid giant axon has been shown to result from an inactivation of the sodium conductance and a delayed increase in K conductance such that the membrane is recharged by an efflux of K ions flowing down their electrochemical gradient (Hodgkin and Huxley, 1952). In frog skeletal muscle enough K leaves a stimulated fiber to account for repolarization, and the rapidity of repolarization implies an increase in K conductance (Hodgkin and Horowicz, 1959a). Whatever the mechanism, any theory of repolarization in heart muscle must explain the dependence of T_{ap} on stimulus rate, the independence of phase 3 on stimulus rate, the independence of K^{42} exchange on stimulus rate, and the high impedance of the membrane during phase 2.

Several theories have been proposed, the simplest of which is that K flowing down its electrochemical gradient repolarizes the cell without an increase in K conductance, i.e., the outward driving force on K is large during the depolarized state, and since the increase in Na conductance is presumably transient, an outward repolarizing current could result with no increase in K conductance. Indeed, the membrane repolarizes sufficiently slowly that such could be the case. However, the shape of the repolarization potential should then be exponential and concave upward. This is obviously not the case in most heart tissues, e.g., Figs. 4, 5, 9, 10, 11.

Another mechanism might be that the plateau results from a sustained increase in inward Na current which nearly balances the outward K current. If this were true the total conductance during the plateau phase should be large. But, the conductance is of the order of its resting value and the balance of currents occurs when the driving voltages on the ions are reversed from those during rest. This means that Na conductance has fallen considerably from its large value during depolarization (it increases by a factor of 100 during depolarization in Purkinje tissue) and K conductance must also have fallen because the driving force on K is now large, but the K current is small. The final rapid phase of repolarization could be the fall in a small residual Na conductance or a rise in K conductance or, more likely, both.

A more detailed mechanism has been proposed by Brady and Woodbury (1960). Sodium conductance is assumed to contain a slowly activating and inactivating component (order of seconds) in addition to the rapid component (order of milliseconds) in the Hodgkin-Huxley formulation. The addition of this factor leads to the following alterations in the Hodgkin-Huxley hypothesis. (1) A sizable Na current persists during the plateau, which is turned off finally by the final rapid phase of repolarization. (2) The ability of the membrane to undergo an increase in Na conductance is not completely recovered for several seconds after repolarization. A second stimulus occurring during the relatively refractory period and for several seconds thereafter cannot produce a full Na conductance increase; hence the overshoot and duration of the succeeding action potential will be short. (3) Potassium conductance falls during the first 100 msec after depolarization and then returns to normal along a time-dependent course rather than a voltage-dependent course as in the case of the squid giant axon. The time-dependent return of K conductance was chosen to explain the superimposability of the later regions of repolarization. Johnson and Tille (1961) recently reported data from rabbit atria showing a membrane conductance equal to its diastolic value during the later phase of depolarization and during the plateau. Their data also suggest a time-dependent return of K conductance to its resting level as repolarization progresses. In addition it is necessary to postulate that K conductance is dependent on external K, in order to explain the dependence of repolarization on K concentration (Weidmann, 1956b). This postulate is supported in part by measurements of K^{42} exchange rates (Brady, unpublished) showing that K^{42} loss is markedly dependent upon external K (the portion of K^{42} loss attributable to exchange diffusion has not been established).

A point of concern, however, in the hypothesis of Brady and Woodbury (1957), as well as in a similar calculation for Purkinje tissue (Noble, 1960) is that these theories of repolarization are based on regenerative conductance changes which require a negative total slope conductance for a short period in phase 3 (Woodbury, 1961, 1962). A negative slope conductance during repolarization means that the membrane response to a pulse of anodal current is an increase rather than a decrease in outward membrane current. Or, on the other hand, a depolarizing applied current results in an increase in membrane conductance similar to the increase in Na conductance following a normal threshold stimulus. It remains to be shown conclusively that such a negative slope conductance during repolarization does exist. Cranefield and Hoffman have proposed that repolarization is brought about by an accumulation of K outside the membrane which regeneratively increases K conductance. Since this hypothesis also requires a negative slope conductance during repolarization it too suffers a major defect.

In order to circumvent the problem of negative slope conductance, Woodbury (1961, 1962) has proposed a system analogous to that of Shanes (1958) in which the membrane conductance is largely independent of membrane potential (contrary to squid axon). This mechanism is time-dependent with a behavior like a chemical transmitter. The essence of this idea is as follows. Depolarization results from a regenerative increase in sodium conductance following a threshold stimulus. Depolarization itself liberates a substance in a quantity depending on the previous history of membrane activity. This substance converts Na channels in the membrane to K channels independently of the membrane potential. As the substance is destroyed or inactivated, sodium conductance falls and potassium conductance increases, giving rise to the plateau and phase 3 of repolarization. Although this hypothesis explains most of the observed behavior of cardiac muscle it remains in the speculative realm.

E. ORIGIN AND SPREAD OF EXCITATION

1. Pacemaker Activity

The technique of local cooling and warming can easily be applied to the sinus venosus and other structures of the hearts of lower vertebrates. This procedure along with the removal of ganglion cells from the heart

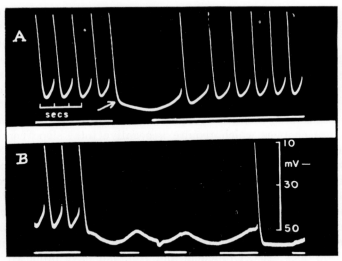

Fig. 7. Transmembrane potentials from frog sinus venosus. Break in reference line denotes intervals of vagal stimulation. A. Vagal stimulation at 20 per second. B. Same as A except intermittent vagal stimulation. Temperature, 22–25°C. (After Hutter and Trautwein, 1956.)

tissue and the local application of inhibitors led to the early knowledge that spontaneity of beating was myogenic in origin and that the more rapid inherent rhythm of the sinus venosus established it as the pacemaker (Gaskell, 1882; Engelmann, 1902). Since the introduction of the micro-electrode technique the basic mechanism of spontaneity on a cellular level has become more clearly defined. Several features characterize the sinus venosus, the most striking of which is a slow fall in diastolic mem-brane potential (Figs. 4 and 7). At threshold, regenerative depolarization occurs, resulting in an action potential. This diastolic fall of potential or pacemaker potential is of the order of 13–15 mv with a maximal diastolic resting potential of 55 mv (Hutter and Trautwein, 1956). Some fibers have an abrupt transition from the pacemaker potential to the rapid phase of depolarization. Others have a more gradual transition with the diastolic fall becoming steeper as threshold is reached. Since the pacemaker po-tential is greatest in the latter type of cell, these are believed to be the pacemaker fibers. Relative to mammalian SA (sinoatrial) nodal tissue this conclusion is supported by the observation that the cells first to undergo rapid depolarization are those with the steepest prepotential. With regard to the mechanism of pacemaker potentials, Trautwein and Kassebaum (1961), postulate the following sequence based on data from sheep Purkinje fibers and fibers of the rabbit sinus node. Following the rise in

K conductance in the final phase of repolarization, K conductance begins to fall, decreasing the membrane potential. Diastolic sodium conductance is high relative to nonpacemaker tissue so that an unstable state is soon reached at which the Na conductance increases regeneratively and a new action potential develops.

A mechanism of controlling the rate of beating is immediately suggested by the strongly temperature-dependent slope of the diastolic prepotential ($Q_{10} = 6.2$ in Purkinje tissue; Coraboeuf and Weidmann, 1954). An additional method of heart rate control is indicated by the reduction in the slope of the pacemaker potential and a hyperpolarization of the membrane resting potential following vagal stimulation (Fig. 7). Sympathetic stimulation increases the slope leading to a more rapid spontaneous rate of beating (Hutter and Trautwein, 1956). The mechanism of hyperpolarization might be sought most immediately from an increase in K conductance such that the membrane potential tends more toward the K concentration potential. Indeed, an increase in K loss has been noted by several investigators following vagal stimulation (Howell and Duke, 1908; Holland et al., 1952). More recent data (Harris and Hutter, 1956) show that K^{42} exchange increases 2- to 3-fold by addition of (acetylcholine) ACh (10^{-7} to 2×10^{-6}). Uptake of K^{42} is also increased in ACh indicating an actual increase in K permeability. Vagal stimulation produces an effect similar to ACh, the latter being blocked with atropine.

2. Conduction

Specialized conduction tissue has not been identified in Amphibia, leading to the assertion that conduction takes place via the syncytial organization of the entire myocardium. However, some specialized regions are apparent from the fact that large delays in conduction occur between the beat of the SV (sinus venosus) and the atria, the atria and the ventricle, and between the ventricle and the bulbus cordis (Fig. 4). The nature of the A-V (atrioventricular) delay in the ring muscle of *Rana temporaria* and *R. nigromaculata* have recently been studied by Inoue (1959) utilizing the microelectrode technique. His findings show that ring muscle action potentials are somewhat end-plate-like, having a step in the rising phase lasting 60–140 msec. Histological evidence shows that the frog A-V fibers are continuous, unlike mammalian A-V fibers (Evans, 1952). Inoue advances the hypothesis that conduction delay in the frog heart is synaptic-like, probably occurring at an intercalated disc.

Syncytial Properties. The issue of syncytial versus nonsyncytial conduction of excitation has recently stirred new interest in the all-or-none contraction mechanism in heart tissue. Sperelakis et al. (1960) have presented evidence that no highly conductive pathway exists between cells in the ventricle of *Rana pipiens*; hence they postulate that conduction must be via a chemical transmitter. However, their data are explicable in terms of cable properties of the cells. Woodbury and Crill (1961) on the other hand, measured the spread of electrotonic potentials both parallel to and perpendicular to the direction of the fibers in rat atria, finding space constants of 160μ and 100μ respectively. Since the space constant at right angles to the fibers is of the order of that parallel to the fibers, there is little reason to believe that excitation cannot spread electrically in the same manner. Similar measurements of space constants in frog heart have not been reported but it seems highly unlikely that the mechanism should differ appreciably from that in rat. Thus either the intercalated discs do not present a barrier to current flow or else external currents in the densely packed heart cells are sufficient to excite adjacent cells in an ephaptic manner. Woodbury (1961) calculated a specific resistance for the intercalated disc in rat atria to be only about 0.1% that of the fiber membrane indicating that the disc is indeed a good conductor. Thus, even though the cells appear as separate well defined units, electrically, the mass of fibers behaves as a single unit.

V. Contraction

A. PRESSURE-VOLUME CHARACTERISTICS AND THEIR RELATION TO O_2 CONSUMPTION

Structurally, the amphibian heart presents a host of problems to the study of its mechanical properties. The organ as a whole is too complex in shape to allow complete control of either tension or length of its component fibers. The trabeculae of which its parts are composed are too short between branches for excision and convenient attachment to measuring instruments. Isolation of the cells themselves present even greater problems of dissection and preservation of functional integrity. Even myocardial strip preparations present perfusion problems since normal diffusion distances *in situ* are only of the order of 20 μ and are greatly increased even in a thin strip. A small amount of information does exist, however, from experiments using myocardial strips and from whole hearts using auxobaric techniques in which the contracting, perfused heart does work by lifting a column of fluid.

Figure 8 illustrates the pressure-volume relations in the auricle of *Rana temporaria* (Clark and White, 1930; see also Reichel, 1956) during contraction at constant volume (isochoric contraction), during auxobaric contraction, and with passive stretch. It is interesting to note that the auxobaric curve is a graphic expression of Starling's Law of the heart, i.e., that systolic pressure increases with increased diastolic filling. The line

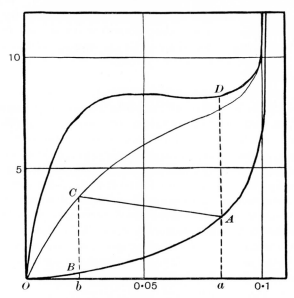

Fig. 8. Pressure-volume relations in frog atria (*Rana temporaria*). Abscissa, atrial volume in cc. Ordinate atrial pressure in cm of H₂O. Lower curve, quiescent heart; upper curve, isochoric contraction (constant volume); middle curve, auxobaric contraction. The line A-C shows the approximate pressure-volume pathway during auxobaric contraction beginning with an atrial filling pressure of 2.7 cm of H₂O and a diastolic volume of 0.085 ml. Temperature, 18°C. (From Clark and White, 1930.)

AC represents the auxobaric response at a filling pressure of 2.6 cm of water and a diastolic volume of 0.083 ml. Under these conditions the auricle expels a volume of 0.06 ml at 3.7 cm of water pressure. The work done is given by the area aACb, of which the area aABb is due to the elasticity of the wall. The area ACB corresponds to 0.12 gm-cm work. Clark and White estimated the energy loss in frictional resistance to be 0.06 gm-cm giving a total work of 0.18 gm-cm. Relating the work done to O_2 consumption, this value gives a mechanical efficiency of 11% where the total O_2 consumption was 19 mm³ per hour at a frequency of 35 per minute and with a resting O_2 consumption of 3 mm³ per hour. Computing the total potential energy released, i.e., the area ADO, gives a mechanical efficiency of 33%. In frog ventricle this efficiency is 56% (Clark and White, 1928). These values are comparable to those of skeletal muscle (40%).

Resting O_2 consumption in frog auricle and ventricle ranges from 0.4 to 1.0 ml per gram per hour which is considerably greater than resting skeletal muscle (0.014 ml per gram per hour; Meyerhof, 1919). Consumption of O_2 increases rapidly, 1–2 ml per gram per cm² increase in surface area, as the diastolic volume is increased. Consumption of O_2 is related to diastolic size rather than pressure, since O_2 consumption in isochoric contraction is equal to or less than under auxobaric conditions.

B. CONTRACTILE COMPONENTS

The only attempts to define the contractile properties of amphibian cardiac muscle have been those of Trendelenburg and Lüllmann (1958) and Reichel and co-workers. Interpretations of these data may become problematical, however, because the fundamental assumptions by which Reichel and co-workers define active tension are considerably different from those defined in the quick stretch and release techniques of Hill and Ritchie (see Chapter 6 on skeletal muscle). Reichel et al. (1956) define active tension during a contraction (*Aktivierung*) as the fall in tension upon an arbitrarily small release, minus the difference occurring between the unreleased tension and the maximum reformed tension following the release. This active tension is then referred to the time of release on the assumption that little change in length of the series elastic element has occurred between the time of release and the time at which peak recovery (reformed) tension occurs. This method gives a continuous decline of *Aktivierung* in skeletal muscle, but a prolonged plateau in heart muscle. Bleichert and Reichel (1957) and Reichel and Bleichert (1958) calculate a plateau phase of *Aktivierung* in the ventricle of *Rana temporaria* lasting through the entire period of increasing tension following the stimulus. Following the plateau, *Aktivierung* falls somewhat faster than the natural course of relaxation.

The method of Ritchie (1954) defines the active tension as the maximum reformed tension following a release to zero tension, but refers this quantity to the time at which the maximum recovery tension occurs rather than to the time of release. Utilizing the Ritchie technique Trendelenburg and Lüllmann (1958) obtained a qualitatively similar form of activation. In addition they conclude that the intensity of the active state in strips of frog ventricle increases with increased muscle length. Under the same conditions neither the duration of the plateau nor the time for complete decay of the active state is changed. Hence, the passive properties appear to be unchanged with stretch. With increased stimulus frequency peak tension and the duration of the active state plateau decreased, but the slope of active state decay remained the same. This behavior suggests that the fall in peak tension at increased stimulus frequencies may result from the shortening of the active state plateau in the absence of an increase in the rate of rise of tension, i.e., in the absence of a change in the force-velocity relation (see Chapter 6 on skeletal muscle).

The question of the duration of the active tension plateau obtained by the two methods is unsettled, however, because: (1) Reichel's methods of referring the reformed tension back to the time of release rather than to the time at which peak recovery occurs tends to give a shorter plateau than the Ritchie method, while (2) allowing only a small change of length during the release rather than a fall to zero tension tends to give an elongated plateau of active tension. Hence, the significance of the close relation between the duration of the *Aktivierung* plateau and the action potential duration (see Section VI on Excitation-Contraction Coupling) must be accepted with reservation until active tension is better defined. The excellent correlation between the plateau of *Aktivierung* and the rise time of tension in the Reichel method leads to an interesting speculation: namely, that a single twitch contraction in frog ventricle is tetanic. Indeed, many environmental factors will augment ventricular tension, but in a single twitch this tissue appears to give its all. If this observation is correct, it forms the basis for the absence of summation in heart muscle.

A mechanical model for cardiac muscle has not been elaborated; but, it is possible to make some generalizations relative to the known properties of skeletal muscle. For example, the maximum tetanic tension in skeletal muscle is of the order of 2 kg per cm². In the cat papillary peak tensions are about 200 gm per cm². On the assumption that the latter value is representative of amphibian cardiac muscle it can be stated that the intensity of the active state is only one-tenth that in skeletal muscle. A further difference is apparent from the rise time of tension in cardiac and skeletal muscles. If these muscles both had the same parallel and series elastic elements (see Chapter 6 on skeletal muscle) and differed only in the intensity of the active state they would still reach their peak tensions in the same times. Abbott and Mommaerts (1959) showed that the extensibility of the series elastic element in cat papillary is about three times that of skeletal muscle. If this difference in extensibility is interpreted as a 3-fold increase in the time constant of the combined series elastic element and viscous property of the contractile element, then the decreased active state intensity and the longer time constants are adequate to account for the difference in the rate of rise of tension.

C. TEMPERATURE, STIMULUS RATE, AND ION EFFECTS

The effects on tension of temperature, excitation rate, and ion concentration in the perfusate so intimately involve the action potential that a detailed discussion of them will be deferred to the next section on excitation-contraction coupling. However, a few general notes are pertinent at this point. Many investigators (e.g., Bernstein, 1908; Clark, 1920) noticed an increase in peak tension with reduced temperatures even though the rate of rise of tension was slowed (Fig. 9). Heintzen and associates (1956)

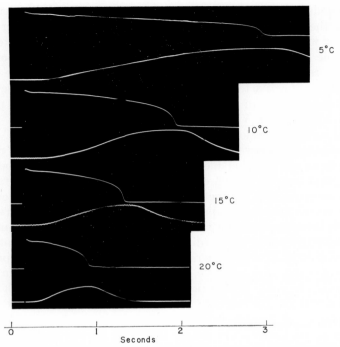

Fig. 9. Temperature dependence of membrane potential and contraction in ventricle of *Rana pipiens*.

found a temperature constant of 30° for the peak tension, i.e., between 0° and 30°C the peak tension falls exponentially to 37% of its value at 0°C. With respect to stimulus rate, contraction amplitude first increases to a maximum and then falls with progressively increased excitation rates. Figure 10 shows the decrease at higher rates. The increase at lower rates is shown with respect to the staircase phenomenon in Figs. 13 and 14. At 22°C the maximum tension occurs at about 30 per minute and falls off toward a partial contracture by 120 per minute. These observations are not to be confused with the staircase phenomenon which relates to transitions between stimulus rates. The effects referred to here are steady state tensions relative to each stimulus rate.

Classically, a great deal of interest centered around the observation that Ca enhances and K depresses contraction in heart muscle (see Fig. 12). In 1921 Daly and Clark observed a considerable augmentation of contraction in reduced Na solutions. The Na effect seemed to stir little interest until recently when its antagonism with Ca was elaborated. The interactions of all three ions, Na, K, and Ca, now find a common mechanism

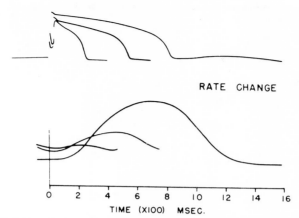

RATE CHANGE

TIME (X100) MSEC.

Fig. 10. Relation between membrane potential and contractile tension with changes in stimulus rate (ventricle of *Rana pipiens*). Stimulus frequencies are 30, 60, and 120 per minute from top to bottom, respectively. Temperature, 20°C.

which is amenable to experimental testing. This mechanism will be discussed in the next section.

VI. Excitation-Contraction Coupling

There is probably little doubt among physiologists that membrane depolarization is the normal initiating process of contraction. On the other hand, the same question arises in heart muscle as in skeletal muscle. "How could a membrane process establish a maximum active state more rapidly than the diffusion time from the cell surface to its interior?" Since cardiac cells are only one-tenth the diameter of skeletal muscle fibers the diffusion problem is greatly lessened, but nevertheless, it still exists. There is some evidence that a sarcotubular system of the type found in skeletal muscle is present in heart muscle, but its function in both types of muscle still remains to be established. In any case, several lines of data from amphibian heart have recently contributed considerably to our knowledge of the coupling between the membrane potential and the contractile mechanism.

A. TEMPERATURE AND STIMULUS RATE RELATIONS

One of the most suggestive lines of coupling evidence is the close relation between action potential duration and the interval between the stimulus and the peak tension, i.e., the rise time of contraction. Under conditions of variable temperature and excitation rate this relation holds to a surprising degree (Figs. 9 and 10). The Q_{10} of both action potential duration and rise time of the tension in *Rana temporaria* is 2.2–2.3 (Heintzen *et al.*, 1956). In *Rana pipiens* the Q_{10} may be significantly different but only by about

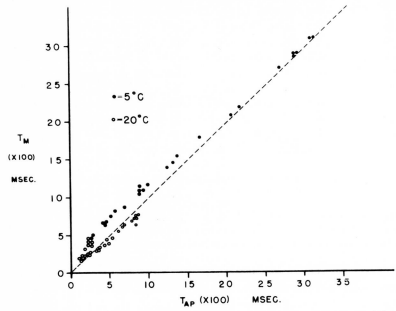

Fig. 11. Relation between the rise time of tension (T_m) and action potential duration (T_{ap}). Dotted line is at 45 degrees to axes. Ventricle of *Rana pipiens*.

10% (Brady, unpublished). Figure 11 illustrates this correspondence at two temperatures and over the range of stimulus rates 10–120 per minute. This close relation between the action potential and the onset of tension, over such a broad range of naturally occurring environmental parameters implies a rather direct coupling between the two events. It is of interest, teleologically, that as heart rate increases the durations of the action potential and the rise time of tension decrease such as to maintain about a 50% duty cycle. In other words, the active phase of contraction is adjusted so as to occupy only half the cycle regardless of the rate of beating. Such a mechanism insures a period of recovery which, undoubtedly, is necessary for survival.

B. TENSION AND MEMBRANE DEPOLARIZATION

Using Reichel's method of defining active tension (*Aktivierung*) the *Aktivierung* plateau and the action potential duration correspond well in the ventricle of *Rana temporaria*. Indeed, the entire action potential (repolarization) superimposes on the *Aktivierung* curve with multiplication of the action potential time axis by a constant somewhat greater than one (Reichel and Bleichert, 1959). In atria of *Rana temporaria Aktivie-*

rung declines continuously rather than displaying a plateau. The plateau phase of the atrial action potential, Fig. 4, is less predominant than that in the ventricle; hence the more rapid fall in membrane potential during repolarization may be related to the continuous decline of *Aktivierung*.

Further support of the relation between the depolarized state of the membrane and the generation of tension is given by Kavaler's (1960) observation that in frog ventricle, maintenance of the action potential plateau by an applied current maintains the tension until the membrane potential is released. The strength of this concept as a general rule, however, is weak because maintenance of the plateau in frog auricle by an applied current does not prolong the tension (Kavaler, 1960).

At this point it still remains to be shown that it is membrane depolarization per se which is responsible for the initiation of tension. Niedergerke (1956b) has elaborated this point by showing that the level of contracture tension in a strip of ventricle (*Rana temporaria* and *R. esculenta*) is proportional to the external K concentration and, thereby, the membrane potential. The contracture is not maintained, however, but falls off slowly in the course of a few minutes even though the membrane potential is constant. Thus, the correlations between the depolarized state of the membrane and the development of tension seem far too great to be completely fortuitous but, nevertheless, the coupling is not direct.

C. CALCIUM-SODIUM RELATIONS

The facilitation of cardiac tension by Ca (Fig. 12) has been known for many decades. Hypodynamic hearts can often be revived and even normal contraction augmented with Ca. Also, Niedergerke (1956b) showed that

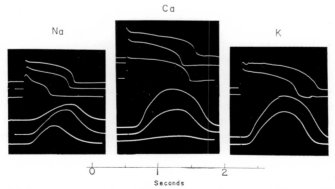

Fig. 12. Ionic dependence of membrane potentials and contraction. Ventricle of *Rana pipiens*. Na: top to bottom, 100, 60, 40% normal Na. Sucrose replacing deficient NaCl. Ca: top to bottom 200, 100, 20% normal Ca. K: top to bottom, K-free and 100% normal K. Temperature, 20°C. Stimulus rate 20 per minute.

tension produced by K contracture is strongly Ca-dependent. In an attempt to locate the site of action of Ca, Niedergerke (1957) followed the time relations of Ca^{45} exchange in ventricular strips of *Rana temporaria* and *R. esculenta* relative to the onset and decay of tension variations produced by altering external Ca. These results showed that changes in tension are faster than the net movements of Ca between the tissue and the perfusate but more than 50% of the Ca exchange is concurrent with the tension changes. In fact, the time course of tension changes could be described by a diffusion equation with a diffusion constant for Ca equal to four times that in the interstitial fluid. These results lead to the conclusion that a mobile quantity of Ca is present in a superficial layer of tissue. This, by the way, is not a new idea (e.g., Boehm, 1914; McLean and Hastings, 1934; Loewi, 1955), but now is supported by more direct evidence.

The question then arises "What is the relation between membrane potential, membrane Ca, and tension?" As a first step to the answer to this question, Niedergerke (1959) showed that Ca^{45} uptake is increased with stimulation. Weidmann (1959) perfused a slug of high Ca through the coronary arteries of turtle which increased the rate of rise and peak tension in the contraction during which the slug was perfused. Hence, the action of Ca is immediate but acutely effective only during the depolarized state of the membrane. The next step was to show that Ca uptake varies with tension changes produced by environmental factors.

One of the most dramatic relations between external ions and tension has been shown for Na and Ca (Lüttgau and Niedergerke, 1958). In ventricular strips of *Rana temporaria* contractile tension varies as $[Ca]/[Na]^2$ indicating a stoichiometric relation between Na and Ca, i.e.,

$$2Na + CaR \rightleftharpoons Na_2R + Ca$$

Niedergerke and Lüttgau postulate that Na and Ca compete for anionic groups (R) on the cell surface. The complex CaR is presumed to be an active coupling agent whereas Na$_2$R is not. Measurements of Sr^{89} uptake in various concentrations of external Na indicate a marked increase in Ca uptake in low Na solutions (Niedergerke and Harris, 1957). On the other hand, the classic antagonism between Ca and K appears to be mediated by changes in Ca uptake. This in indicated by an increase in Ca uptake in K-free solutions (Niedergerke and Harris, 1957; Thomas, 1960). The mechanism of the K antagonism is not so clear-cut, however. One might argue that the fall in tension in high K can be accounted for by the shorter duration action potential which does not allow the active state to be fully transmitted to the external muscle. This may be true in part; however, K also reduces the force-velocity relation, i.e., tension rises less rapidly. This effect suggests a change in active state intensity or the plateau level of *Aktivierung*. A possible mechanism for the change in active state intensity is suggested by the hyperpolarization of the membrane in K-free solutions. If the amount of available CaR, for example, is influenced by the membrane potential, hyperpolarization could increase and depolarization decrease the available CaR. Depolarization by K would then reduce CaR which could be restored either by increasing Ca or decreasing Na.

In summary, at this stage of development excitation-contraction would appear as follows. Following a threshold stimulus membrane depolarization results from an influx of Na ions. The depolarized state of the membrane allows an influx of CaR which initiates tension by an as yet unspecified reaction with the contractile mechanism. CaR continues to enter, or at least is still active, until repolarization progresses into phase 3. With the rapid phase of repolarization active tension or *Aktivierung* dies away leading to relaxation. Whether Na entry during depolarization or K efflux during repolarization is concerned with the onset and decay of tension has yet to be determined. This issue will be discussed to some extent with respect to the staircase phenomenon in the next section.

D. INOTROPIC EFFECTS

1. Staircase (Treppe)

This classic cardiac phenomenon described by Bowditch (1871) consists of a step-like increase (positive staircase) in successive contractions following a rest period. Figure 13 illustrates this effect in the ventricle of *Rana pipiens* for different stimulus frequencies following a short (30-sec) rest period. Figure 14 shows the final steady state tension acquired at each stimulus frequency (solid line). The horizontal line represents the mean amplitude of the first contraction following the brief rest period and the arrows indicate a positive (upward) or negative (downward) staircase at each stimulus frequency. Also, a negative staircase may occur following a period of beating at a constant rate if the stimulus interval is lengthened.

The amplitude of the action potential of the cells is not related to the changes in tension during the staircase. In fact, large changes in the rate of rise of the staircase can be produced by increasing external Ca or diminishing K without concomitant changes in the action potential amplitude. Niedergerke (1956a) has shown that as the positive staircase develops in normal Ca solution the action potential duration shortens, as does the time to the peak of contractile tension, but the rate of tension development increases (*Rana temporaria*). In cat papillary, Abbott and Mommaerts (1959) found either no change or a shortening of the active state plateau

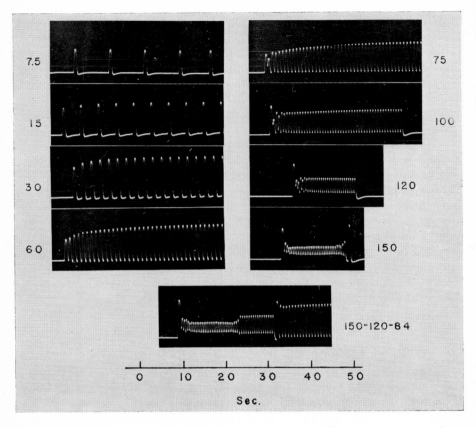

Fig. 13. Tension responses at different stimulus rates following a 30-sec rest interval. Numbers indicate the frequency of contraction in beats per minute. Ventricle of *Rana pipiens*; temperature 22°C.

during a positive staircase. Hence the data indicate either an increase in active state intensity or an alteration in the force-velocity relation or both as the basis for the positive staircase. On the other hand, at high stimulus frequencies the action potential duration shortens (Fig. 10) and a negative staircase develops (Fig. 13), with a shorter rise time to the peak of tension. A negative staircase also occurs in high Ca solutions when the first contraction is large in amplitude and has a relatively long rise time (Niedergerke, 1956a). With successive contractions, peak tension falls, the time to the peak tension shortens, and the action potential duration shortens. The initial rate of rise of tension in elevated Ca is constant indicating no change in either the force-velocity relation or the active state intensity as the negative staircase develops. The negative staircase

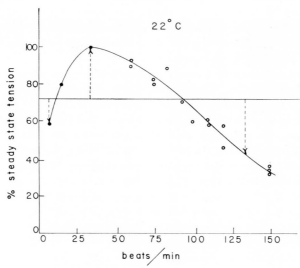

Fig. 14. Steady tension level of ventricular contractions as a function of stimulus frequency. Horizontal line represents mean amplitude of first contraction following a 30-sec rest period. Arrows indicate the general course of positive or negative staircase following first contraction. Temperature, 22°C.

mechanism for high stimulus rate thus appears to be more directly related to the shortening of the action potential and thereby the active state plateau (Trendelenburg and Lüllmann, 1958).

With respect to the more detailed mechanism, K and Ca effects are too slow to be accounted for by diffusion through the extracellular spaces, having half-times of 1.5 and 3.0 minutes respectively. On the other hand, these times are too short for equilibration with the intracellular space. The Ca effects are thus ascribed to a superficial membrane layer with an intermediate exchange rate. A tentative mechanism for the positive staircase phenomenon would be that a quiescent, excised tissue loses Ca from a superficial site which is replenished from an outside or inside store by repeated excitation of the cell (Niedergerke, 1956a). Similarly, as the stimulus interval is increased, Ca tends to be lost from the site giving rise to a negative staircase. This interpretation is supported by the observation that the staircase is short or absent in solutions containing 3–7 moles Ca (Krogh *et al.*, 1944). The negative staircase at high stimulus frequencies in normal Ca, Fig. 12 could be due to (a) a deficiency in O_2 supply which rapidly develops at high stimulus frequencies, (b) the depletion of metabolic substrate necessary to develop tension, or (c) an inadequate duration of active tension development limited by a short duration action potential. At present there is no way of evaluating the first two possibilities, but Figs. 6 and 10 show how short the action potential duration can become at high stimulus rates. The K effects remain unexplained although the effect is likely mediated via the membrane potential, possibly by the mechanism described in Section VI,C.

Wiegmann *et al.* (1957) have made an interesting study of the staircase at various temperatures. The extent of the staircase is least and almost absent at 3°C and increases exponentially to 30°C. Hajdu (1953) explains the staircase in the ventricle of *Rana pipiens* as follows. Potassium enters the cell during the quiescent state thus rendering the contractile mechanism hypodynamic. With the onset of stimulation, the cell progressively loses K which reinstates the contractile mechanism. If too much K is lost, the cell goes into contracture. This theory is difficult to reconcile with the measurement of K^{42} exchange in the ventricle of *Rana temporaria* in which no change in K^{42} efflux occurred in a well perfused heart between the quiescent state and excitation at any frequency (Brady, unpublished). It is unlikely that the discrepancy is merely a species difference; hence more detailed experiments are necessary.

2. Post-extrasystolic Potentiation

If a second stimulus is given a heart muscle during its relatively refractory period the electrical and mechanical responses may be greatly altered. In general, the earlier the second stimulus arrives, the shorter the action potential duration and the smaller the mechanical response. Recovery of the action potential duration, however, is more rapid than the tension amplitude. The third stimulus, on the other hand, occurring at a normal interval from the first, elicits a normal action potential, but the contraction may be greatly augmented. The increased tension (extrasystolic potentiation) does not persist in succeeding responses but dies away to normal somewhat exponentially.

A possible explanation for this response is apparent from the observations of Niedergerke and of Kavaler that during membrane depolarization Ca exchange is increased. Suppose that normally the entry of Ca·is the limiting factor in the generation of tension. Assume also that the rate of recovery of the contractile mechanism is slower than that of the processes governing the duration of membrane depolarization. Then an extrasystole occurring during the relatively refractory period finds the mechanical response less completely recovered than the action potential duration; hence the tension response is now limited, not by the entry of Ca, say, but by the prime factors directly responsible for the generation of tension. It is assumed that the uncombined Ca remains available for the third response, suggested by the fact that the potentiated state can persist for several minutes provided no contraction occurs. A stimulus occurring after the tension generation system has completely recovered adds a normal amount of Ca to that persisting from the limited extrasystolic response. The third response now is potentiated because the Ca entry is not the limiting factor, or at least is less limiting than normally. The earlier the extrasystole is elicited, the smaller is the mechanical response and in general the larger is the potentiated contraction. Where the potentiated state requires several contractions to subside it is postulated that Ca entry does not become limiting until the normal level of tension is reached.

3. Train and High Voltage Stimulus Effects

Contraction of myocardial tissue has long been known to be all-or-none with respect to stimulus amplitude. However, some responses have been described that might appear superficially to disobey this rule. For example, if the stimulus amplitude is elevated 10-fold, tension may increase 2- or even 3-fold over a period of 6–10 beats (in *Rana pipiens*, Brady *et al.*, 1960; in cat papillary, Whalen, 1958). After return to threshold stimuli the inotropy may persist for several minutes. Further, if a brief train of ten times threshold stimuli is applied to the muscle during the absolutely refractory period the succeeding response may be greatly enhanced and require several minutes to subside even though the stimulus remains at the previous threshold level. One might suspect immediately that the high voltage stimuli excite some adrenergic elements which release adrenaline to the tissues. This suspicion has been confirmed by showing that the response is absent in animals previously treated with reserpine, and that DCI (dichlorophenyl-isopropyl aminoethanol) blocks the response when applied directly to perfusion media.

4. Depression by Applied Currents

A more immediate effect of applying currents during the absolutely refractory period is the depression of tension of the response during which the current is applied. A rectangular pulse of current applied to a ventricular strip, e.g., immediately after depolarization depresses the rate of rise of tension for as long as it is applied. Upon the cessation of the pulse the rate of rise of tension sharply increases after a short delay. If the pulse lasts into the relatively refractory period an extrasystole is elicited at the termination of the pulse. The depression of tension observed in both the ventricle of *Rana pipiens* and the cat papillary (Brady *et al.*, 1960) is tentatively ascribed to an early repolarization in some of the tissue due to the applied current similar to the repolarization reported by Cranefield and Hoffman (1958) in cat papillary under the same conditions. At the end of the current pulse, tension rises again as a result of anodal break stimulation of the cells which were repolarized early. Simultaneous recording of intracellular action potential and tension will be necessary, however, in order to establish this point.

VII. Conclusions

It is apparent that the development of amphibian cardiac physiology has centered almost exclusively around the frog, and more specifically around only a few species of frogs. However, in view of the gross similarity of cardiac electrical and mechanical properties in vertebrates as a whole, it seems unlikely that these properties would differ markedly in other amphibia.

Our knowledge of the basis of electrical and mechanical events in frog heart has tended to follow that in other tissues although limited by the peculiar geometry of the amphibian heart. On the other hand, studies of excitation-contraction coupling and general problems of cardiac metabolism in the frog are among the foremost in relation to other cardiac tissue.

Areas of amphibian cardiology particularly in need of development with available techniques are those of ultramicroscopic structure, mechanical properties during rest and activity and heat production and metabolism related to contractility and external work. Undoubtedly, the next decade will bring an enormous volume of data with which to evaluate cardiac function.

References

Abbott, B. C., and Mommaerts, W. F. H. M. (1959). A study of inotropic mechanisms in the papillary muscle preparation. *J. Gen. Physiol.* **42**, 533–551.

Adrian, R. H. (1960). Potassium chloride movement and the membrane potential of frog muscle. *J. Physiol. (London)* **151**, 154–185.

Antoni, H., and Kotowski, H. (1959). Über den Einfluss der Temperatur auf die Repolarisation des Frosch-Myokards nach Kalium-Depolarisation. *Arch. Ges. Physiol. Pflüger's* **270**, 24.

Bammer, H. (1953). Die Beziehungen zwischen der Reizfrequenz und der Geschwindigkeit der Erregungsleitung im Herzmuskel. *Z. Ges. Exptl. Med.* **121**, 488–496.

Bammer, H., and Rothschuh, K. E. (1952a). Über eine Methode zur Messung der Leitungsgeschwindigkeit der Erregung im Froschherzstreifen zur Prüfung pharmakologischer Substanzen. *Arch. Exptl. Pathol. Pharmakol. Naunyn–Schmiedeberg's* **214**, 367–373.

Bammer, H., and Rothschuh, K. E. (1952b). Über die Erregungsleitung im Froschherzstreifen unter der Wirkung von Kalium-ionen und anderen herzmuskeleigenen Substanzen. *Z. Ges. Exptl. Med.* **119**, 402–414.

Bernstein, J. (1908). Zur Thermodynamik der Muskelkontraktion. I. Über die Temperaturkoeffizienten der Muskelenergie. *Arch. Ges. Physiol. Pflüger's* **122**, 129–195.

Bidder, F. (1852). Ueber functionell verschiedene und räumlich getrennte Nervencentra im Froschherzen. *Arch. Anat. Physiol. Wiss. Med.* pp. 163–177.

Bidder, F. (1866). Zur näheren Kenntniss des Froschherzens und seiner Nerven. *Arch. Anat. Physiol. Wiss. Med.* pp. 1–26.

Bleichert, A., and Reichel, H. (1957). B. Normale und pathologische Physiologie. 39. Über den zeitlichen Ablauf der Aktivierung im Herzmuskel. *Verhandl. Deut. Ges. Kreislaufforsch.* **23**, 356–359.

Boehm, R. (1914). Über das Verhalten des isolierten Froschherzens bei reiner Salzdiät. *Arch. Exptl. Pathol. Pharmakol. Naunyn–Schmiedeberg's* **75**, 230–316.

Bowditch, H. P. (1871). Über die Eigenthümlichkeiten der Reizbarkeit, welche die Muskelfasern des Herzens zeigen. *Ber. Sächs. Ges. (Akad) Wiss.* **23**, 652–689.

Brady, A. J., and Woodbury, J. W. (1957). Effects of sodium and potassium on repolarization in frog ventricular fibers. *Ann. N. Y. Acad. Sci.* **65**, 687–692.

Brady, A. J., and Woodbury, J. W. (1960). The sodium-potassium hypothesis as the basis of electrical activity in frog ventricle. *J. Physiol. (London)* **154**, 385–407.

Brady, A. J., Abbott, B. C., and Mommaerts, W. F. H. M. (1960). Inotropic effects of trains of impulses applied during the contraction of cardiac muscle. *J. Gen. Physiol.* **44**, 415–432.

Carmeliet, E., and Lacquet, L. (1958). Durée du potentiel d'action ventriculaire de grenouille en fonction de la fréquence. Influence des variations ioniques de potassium et sodium. *Arch. Intern. Physiol. Biochim.* **66**, 1–21.

Clark, A. J. (1920). The effect of alterations of temperature upon the functions of the isolated heart. *J. Physiol. (London)* **54**, 275–286.

Clark, A. J., and White, A. C. (1928). The oxygen consumption of the frog's heart. I. *J. Physiol. (London)* **66**, 185–202.

Clark, A. J., and White, A. C. (1930). The oxygen consumption of the auricles of the frog and of the tortoise. *J. Physiol. (London)* **68**, 406–432.

Clark, A. J., Eggleton, M. G., Eggleton, P., Gaddie, R., and Stewart, C. P. (1938). "The Metabolism of the Frog's Heart," 308 pp. Oliver & Boyd, London.

Coraboeuf, E., and Weidmann, S. (1954). Temperature effects on the electrical activity of Purkinje fibers. *Helv. Physiol. Pharmacol. Acta* **12**, 32–41.

Cranefield, P. F., and Hoffman, B. F. (1958). Propagated repolarization in heart muscle. *J. Gen. Physiol.* **41**, 633–649.

Daly, I. de Burgh, and Clark, A. J. (1921). The action of ions upon the frog's heart. *J. Physiol. (London)* **54**, 367–383.

Engelmann, T. W. (1902). Die Unabhängigkeit des ionotropen Nervenwirkungen von der Leitungsfähigkeit des Herzens für motorische Reize. *Arch. Anat. Physiol. Abt. Physiol.* pp. 103–134.

Evans, C. L. (1952). "Principles of Human Physiology," 11th ed., p. 548, Churchill, London.

Gaskell, W. H. (1882). On the rhythm of the heart of the frog, and on the nature of the action of the vagus nerve. *Phil. Trans. Roy. Soc. London* **173**, 993–1033.

Gaupp, E. (1896). "A. Ecker's und R. Wiedersheim's Anatomie des Frosches," Part 1, 548 pp. Vieweg, Braunschweig.

Gompertz, C. (1884). Ueber Herz und Blutkreislauf bei nackten Amphibien. *Arch. Anat. Physiol. Abt. Physiol.* pp. 242–260.

Hajdu, S. (1953). Mechanism of staircase and contracture in ventricular muscle. *Am. J. Physiol.* **174**, 371–380.

Harris, E. J., and Hutter, O. F. (1956). The action of acetylcholine on the movements of potassium ions in the sinus venosus of the heart. *J. Physiol. (London)* **133**, 58P–59P.

Heintzen, P. (1954). Untersuchungen über die Temperaturabhängigkeit der elektrischen Erregungsvorgänge am Froschherzen. *Arch. Ges. Physiol. Pflüger's* **259**, 381–399.

Heintzen, P., Kraft, H. G., and Wiegmann, O. (1956). Über die elektrische und mechanische Tätigkeit des Herzstreifenpräparates vom Frosch in Abhängigkeit von der Temperatur. *Z. Biol.* **108**, 401–411.

Hodgkin, A. L., and Horowicz, P. (1959a). Movements of Na and K in single muscle fibers. *J. Physiol. (London)* **145**, 405–432.

Hodgkin, A. L., and Horowicz, P. (1959b). The influence of potassium and chloride ions on the membrane potential of single muscle fibers. *J. Physiol. (London)* **148**, 127–160.

Hodgkin, A. L., and Huxley, A. F. (1952). A quantitative description of membrane current and its application to conduction and excitation in nerve. *J. Physiol. (London)* **117**, 500–544.

Hodgkin, A. L., and Rushton, W. A. H. (1946). The electrical constants of a crustacean nerve fiber. *Proc. Roy. Soc.* **B133**, 444–479.

Holland, W. C., Dunn, C. E., and Greig, M. E. (1952). Studies on permeability. VIII. Role of acetylcholine metabolism in the genesis of the electrocardiogram. *Am. J. Physiol.* **170**, 339–345.

Howell, W. H., and Duke, W. W. (1908). The effect of vagus inhibition on the output of potassium from the heart. *Am. J. Physiol.* **21**, 51–63.

Hutter, O. F., and Trautwein, W. (1956). Vagal and sympathetic effects on the pacemaker fibers in the sinus venosus of the heart. *J. Gen. Physiol.* **39**, 715–733.

Inoue, F. (1959). Slow potential and conduction delay at the atrio-ventricular region in frog's heart. *J. Cellular Comp. Physiol.* **54**, 231–235.

Johnson, E. A., and Tille, J. (1961). Investigations of the electrical properties of cardiac muscle fibers with the aid of intracellular double-barrelled electrodes. *J. Gen. Physiol.* **44**, 443–467.

Kahn, M. (1941). Der physikalische Elektrotonus des Herzmuskels. *Arch. Ges. Physiol. Pflüger's* **245**, 235–264.

Kavaler, F. (1960). Membrane depolarization and contraction in auricle. *Federation Proc.* **19**, 109.

Krogh, A. (1929). "The Anatomy and Physiology of Capillaries," p. 30. Yale Univ. Press, New Haven, Connecticut.

Krogh, A., Lindberg, A.-L., and Schmidt-Nielsen, B. (1944). The exchange of ions between cells and extracellular fluid. II. The exchange of potassium and calcium between the frog heart muscle and the bathing fluid. *Acta Physiol. Scand.* **7**, 221–237.

Ling, G., and Gerard, R. W. (1949). The normal membrane potential of frog sartorius fibers. *J. Cellular Comp. Physiol.* **34**, 383–396.

Loewi, O. (1955). On the mechanism of the positive inotropic action of fluoride, oleate, and calcium on the frog's heart. *J. Pharmacol. Exptl. Therap.* **114**, 90–99.

Lüttgau, H. C., and Niedergerke, R. (1958). The antagonism between Ca and Na ions on the frog's heart. *J. Physiol. (London)* **143**, 486–505.

McLean, F. C., and Hastings, A. B. (1934). A biological method for the estimation of calcium ion concentration. *J. Biol. Chem.* **107**, 337–350.

Meyerhof, O. (1919). Über die Atmung der Froschmuskulatur. *Arch. Ges. Physiol. Pflüger's* **175**, 20–87.

Niedergerke, R. (1956a). The 'staircase' phenomenon and the action of calcium on the heart. *J. Physiol. (London)* **134**, 569–583.

Niedergerke, R. (1956b). The potassium chloride contracture of the heart and its modification by calcium. *J. Physiol. (London)* **134**, 584–599.

Niedergerke, R. (1957). The rate of action of calcium ions on the contraction of the heart. *J. Physiol. (London)* **138**, 506–515.

Niedergerke, R. (1959). Calcium and the activation of contraction. *Experientia* **15**, 128–130.

Niedergerke, R., and Harris, E. J. (1957). Accumulation of calcium (or strontium) under conditions of increasing contractility. *Nature* **179**, 1068–1069.

Noble, D. (1960). Cardiac action and pacemaker potentials based on the Hodgkin-Huxley equations. *Nature* **188**, 495–497.

Noble, G. K. (1931). "The Biology of the Amphibia," 1st ed., 577 pp. McGraw-Hill, New York.

Ono, B., Suekane, K., and Maekawa, F. (1960). Effects of temperature on the action potential of toad ventricular muscle fiber and on its recovery process. *Japan. Circulation J. Engl. Ed.* **24**, 1–10.

Reichel, H. (1956). A. Physiologische Referate. 1. Die Herzdynamik unter dem Einfluss des peripheren Kreislaufs. *Verhandl. Deut. Ges. Kreislaufforsch.* **22**, 3–25.

Reichel, H., and Bleichert, A. (1958). Die Zeitkurve der Aktivierung beim Vorhof des Kaltblüters. *Z. Biol.* **110**, 436–440.

Reichel, H., and Bleichert, A. (1959). Excitation-contraction coupling in heart muscle. *Nature* **183**, 826–827.

Reichel, H., Zimmer, F., and Bleichert, A. (1956). Die elastischen Eigenschaften des Skelett- und Herzmuskels in verschiedenen Phasen der Einzelzuckung. *Z. Biol.* **108**, 188–195.

Ringer, S. (1880–1882). Concerning the influence exerted by each of the constituents of the blood on the contraction of the ventricle. *J. Physiol. (London)* **3**, 380–393.

Ritchie, J. M. (1954). The effect of nitrate on the active state of muscle. *J. Physiol. (London)* **126**, 155–168.

Scher, A. M., Young, A. C., Malmgren, A. L., and Paton, R. R. (1953). Spread of electrical activity through the wall of the ventricle. *Circulation Res.* **1**, 539–547.

Shanes, A. M. (1958). Electrochemical aspects of physiological and pharmacological action in excitable cells. Part II. *Pharmacol. Rev.* **10**, 165–273.

Sjöstrand, F. S., Andersson-Cedergren, E., and Dewey, M. M. (1958). The ultrastructure of the intercalated discs of frog, mouse and guinea pig cardiac muscle. *J. Ultrastruct. Res.* **1**, 271–287.

Skramlik, E. von (1921). Über die anatomische Beschaffenheit der Überleitungsgebilde des Kaltblüterherzens. *Z. Ges. Exptl. Med.* **14**, 246–281.

Sperelakis, N., Hoshiko, T., and Berne, R. M. (1960). Nonsyncytial nature of cardiac muscle: membrane resistance of single cells. *Am. J. Physiol.* **198**, 531–536.

Tanaka, I. (1959). Apparent membrane resistance changes during repolarization of the toad atrium. *Federation Proc.* **18**, 156.

Taylor, I. M. (1962). Potassium exchange in isolated perfused rat hearts: effect of temperature and heart rate. *Federation Proc.* **21**, 144.

Thomas, L. J. (1960). Increase of labeled calcium uptake in heart muscle during potassium lack contracture. *J. Gen. Physiol.* **43**, 1193–1206.

Trautwein, W., and Kassebaum, D. G. (1961). On the mechanism of spontaneous impulse generation in the pacemaker of the heart. *J. Gen. Physiol.* **45**, 317–330.

Trautwein, W., Kuffler, S. W., and Edwards, C. (1956). Changes in membrane characteristics of heart muscle during inhibition. *J. Gen. Physiol.* **40**, 135–145.

Trendelenburg, U., and Lüllmann, H. (1958). Über die Messung des "active state" am Herzmuskel des Frosches. *Biochim. Biophys. Acta* **29**, 13–20.

Walker, J., Lorber, V., Greene, E., and Minarik, M. (1962) Relationship between electrical activity and K^{42} efflux in cardiac muscle. *Federation Proc.* **21**, 129.

Weidmann, S. (1951). Effect of current flow on the membrane potential of cardiac muscle. *J. Physiol. (London)* **115**, 227–236.

Weidmann, S. (1952). The electrical constants of Purkinje fibers. *J. Physiol. (London)* **118**, 348–360.

Weidmann, S. (1955). The effect of the cardiac membrane potential on the rapid availability of the sodium-carrying system. *J. Physiol. (London)* **127**, 213–224.

Weidmann, S. (1956a). "Elektrophysiologie der Herzmuskelfaser," 100 pp. Med. Verlag Hans Huber, Bern and Stuttgart.

Weidmann, S. (1956b). Shortening of the cardiac action potential due to a brief injection of KCl following the onset of activity. *J. Physiol. (London)* **132**, 157–163.

Weidmann, S. (1959). Effect of increasing the calcium concentration during a single heart-beat. *Experientia* **15**, 128.

Whalen, W. J. (1958). Apparent exception to the "all or none" law in cardiac muscle. *Science* **127**, 468–469.

Wiegmann, O., Kraft, H. G., and Küper, J. (1957). Der Einfluss der Schlagfrequenz auf Aktionspotentiale (AP) und Mechanogramme (MG) des Herzstreifens in verschiedenen Temperaturbereichen. *Z. Biol.* **109**, 270–280.

Wilde, W. S., O'Brien, J. M., and Bay, I. (1956). Time relation between potassium K^{42} outflux, action potential, and contraction phase of heart muscle as revealed by the effluogram. *Proc. 1st U. N. Intern. Conf. Peaceful Uses At. Energy Geneva, 1955* **12**, 318–323.

Woodbury, J. W. (1961). Voltage and time dependent membrane conductance changes in cardiac cells. *In* "Biophysics of Physiological and Pharmacological Actions," Publ. No. 69 (A. M. Shanes, ed.), pp. 501–527. Am. Assoc. Advance Sci., Washington, D. C.

Woodbury, J. W. (1962). *In* "Handbook of Physiology" (Am. Physiol. Soc.), Sect. 2: Circulation (W. F. Hamilton, ed.), Vol. I, Chapt. 11. Williams & Wilkins, Baltimore, Maryland.

Woodbury, J. W., and Crill, W. E. (1961). On the problem of impulse conduction in the atrium. *In* "Nervous Inhibition" (E. Florey, ed.), pp. 124–135. Pergamon, New York.

Woodbury, L. A., Hecht, H. H., and Christopherson, A. R. (1951). Membrane resting and action potentials of single cardiac muscle fibers of the frog ventricle. *Am. J. Physiol.* **164**, 307–318.

5

WATER BALANCE AND KIDNEY

Ingrith J. Deyrup

I. Introduction

In amphibians, as in other vertebrates, the fluids of the body can be described in terms of two major populations—the intracellular and extracellular fluids—existing in continuous diffusional and actively mediated exchange with one another. The intracellular fluid is discontinuous and, to a certain extent, fictional, for it represents a conceptual summary of all the water and solutes existing within the physiologically defined boundaries of cells. The extracellular fluid compartment is the sum of a group of continuous fluid masses located outside the cellular boundaries; the blood plasma and lymph circulating in the closed vascular system, in lymphatic capillaries and small vessels, and in the great lymph sacs and sinuses; the peritoneal fluid, and lesser fluid accumulations within the joint spaces, eyes, etc. Water and solutes traverse the boundaries between extracellular and intracellular compartments at rates which are not yet known in detail in Amphibia. Within the extracellular compartment, relatively rapid circulation of fluid is effected primarily by contractions of the heart and the lymph hearts, and by the beating of the nephrostomic cilia driving currents of peritoneal fluid into the mesonephric tubules or the renal venous drainage.

Exchanges of water and solutes between the body fluids and the external environment occur at four major sites: the skin; respiratory epithelium; kidneys; and the gastrointestinal tract and related structures including, in Amphibia, the cloaca and urinary bladder. More strictly, according to the classic concept of Claude Bernard, a relatively small number of epithelial cells and the extracellular fluids are in direct exchange with the external environment, participating in the provision and regulation of the "internal environment" of the great majority of the body cells.

In considering the fluid exchanges between most amphibians and their environments, it is apparent that the major threats to over-all water balance result from excessive gains or loss of water. The buccal and pharyngeal mucosa, gills and lungs (where present), and skin serve as channels for exchange of respiratory gases, but at the same time provide ready routes for both ingress and egress of water. Amphibians have remarkably competent excretory devices and so succeed in avoiding hydration in excess in spite of the fully aquatic life which many of these animals lead. On the other hand, physiological devices to provide against excessive loss of water are not very effective in amphibians, even in those, like toads and tree frogs, which have adapted successfully to life in relatively arid environments.

Excessive gain or loss of osmolytes is not a major problem for most amphibians. With the exception of a limited group of species adapted to life in brackish water, amphibians in general inhabit environments of low solute concentration. Electrolytes are supplied by the diet, and amphibians have effective mechanisms for conserving osmolytes in gastrointestinal, cloacal, mesonephric, and bladder absorption of sodium, potassium, and other ions. Moreover, the body can accumulate sodium and chloride ions against large activity gradients through specific transport processes of the skin. It is not surprising that regulation against excessive accumulation of osmolytes is relatively poor, and essentially cannot operate at all unless the animal has access to water.

Among amphibians, then, success in water balance regulation depends in part on a favorable environment, typically relatively rich in water and poor in osmolytes. Because of the range of habitats occupied by different members of the class, it might be expected that striking differences would exist among different amphibians in ways of regulation and capacity to tolerate stressful conditions. There is some evidence that this is so, but the data are far from complete. Anyone reviewing the literature on amphibian water balance must be struck by the extreme concentration of research efforts in a few narrow areas, with complete neglect of others of potentially great interest. Indeed, a systematic comparative approach to the physiology of water balance in Amphibia is impossible at the present time, for the number of species which have been studied is neither large nor really representative. For instance, investigators of ion and water movement across the skin and the intestinal and bladder walls of amphibians have concentrated on a limited group of species—mainly anurans of the genera *Rana* and *Bufo*. Kidney function has been studied most intensively in these same anurans, and in a very few urodele genera (especially *Necturus* and *Ambystoma*). Virtually nothing is known about problems of water balance in other amphibians, notably, those of most urodeles and all of the members of the order Apoda. This situation is not surprising, for many of the studies relating to amphibian water balance have been carried out without special interest in the problems of Amphibia as such. Rather, these docile, sturdy, and easily available animals have been used extensively as "representative" vertebrates for the study of a wide variety of aspects of physiology. If a review of the special physiology of amphibian water balance is to be of use at the present time, it must serve to a large extent as a summary of unsolved problems and lacunae in knowledge in this field.

II. Water and Osmolytes in the Physiological Organization of Amphibians

A. THE BODY FLUIDS

Water constitutes some 70 to 80% of the total body weight of a variety of amphibians. Some representative data on body water content, summarized in Table I, were obtained by measuring the animals' weights before and after thorough desiccation. In separate series of experiments, relative volumes of extracellular fluid in the body as a whole or in muscle tissue of a few anuran species have been measured by estimating the distribution volumes of solutes conventionally considered to be more or less limited to the extracellular spaces (sucrose, inulin, labeled albumin—in muscle *in vitro*; thiocyanate ions injected *in vivo*). The results for extracellular fluid volume of the muscle or whole body range from about 20 to 48% of the tissue or body weight (Table I). Thus, intracellular fluids might be estimated as about 40 to 80% of the body water mass. Obviously, these latter figures range widely, and in any case they are highly tentative since so few measurements are available, and there are no simultaneous measure-

TABLE I
Body Fluid Volumes in Amphibians
A. Total Body Water (% of Body Weight)

Species	Water content	Reference
Rana pipiens	82.1 (80.2–84.3)[a]	Smith and Jackson (1931)
Rana pipiens	78.9	Thorson and Svihla (1943)
Rana grylio	77.5	Thorson and Svihla (1943)
Rana aurora	79.7	Thorson and Svihla (1943)
Hyla cinerea	80.1	Thorson and Svihla (1943)
Hyla regilla	79.4	Thorson and Svihla (1943)
Bufo terrestris	78.8	Thorson and Svihla (1943)
Bufo boreas	79.8	Thorson and Svihla (1943)
Scaphiopus hammondii	80.0	Thorson and Svihla (1943)
Scaphiopus holbrookii	79.5	Thorson and Svihla (1943)
Batrachoseps attenuatus	73 (72–75)	Ray (1958)
Aneides flavipunctatus	76 (71–78)	Ray (1958)
Aneides lugubris	78 (76–78)	Ray (1958)
Aneides ferreus	78 (77–79)	Ray (1958)
Ensatina eschscholtzi	78 (75–81)	Ray (1958)
Plethodon elongatus	76 (74–78)	Ray (1958)
Rhyacotriton olympicus	78 (77–79)	Ray (1958)
Eurycea bislineata bislineata	80.1	Littleford *et al.* (1947)
Desmognathus fuscus	79.3	Littleford *et al.* (1947)
Plethodon cinereus cinereus	78.6	Littleford *et al.* (1947)

B. Extracellular Fluid Volume (% of body or tissue weight)

Species (Method)	Volume	Reference
Rana pipiens (Thiocyanate volume)	27.3 (23.6–29.8)	Prosser and Weinstein (1950)
Rana catesbeiana (Thiocyanate volume)	29.8–47.9	Prosser and Weinstein (1950)
Rana pipiens—Muscle (Inulin space)	20 ± 1–31 ± 1	Steinbach (1961)
Bufo marinus—Muscle		
(Inulin space)	20.7–31.1	Tasker *et al.* (1959)
(Sucrose space)	22.7–35.8	Tasker *et al.* (1959)
(Albumin space)	17.4–29.5	Tasker *et al.* (1959)

C. Plasma Volume (% of body weight)

Species (Method)	Volume	Reference
Rana pipiens		
(T-1824 space)	7.0 (5.6–9.3)	Prosser and Weinstein (1950)
(Vital red HR space)	6.0 (5.0–6.0)	Conklin (1930b)
Rana catesbeiana		
(T-1824 space)	7.2–8.8	Prosser and Weinstein (1950)

[a] Numbers represent means; ranges given in parentheses.

ments in any species of total body water content and relative distribution of water in the fluid compartments. If any conclusion can be drawn from them, it might be that water—and extracellular water in particular—represents a relatively large fraction of the body mass in amphibians as compared with other vertebrates. More data, covering a much wider range of species, are needed before conclusions may be drawn about the mass and distribution of fluids in amphibians. There is also need to survey the effects of different environmental conditions (note, for instance, increase of body water and interstitial fluid in frogs subjected to chilling, and in frogs and toads in winter as compared with summer—Schmidt-Nielsen and Forster, 1954; Maurer, 1938) ; and varied physiological states (e.g., the occurrence of edema in male *Rana esculenta* and *R. temporaria* during the breeding season—Churchill *et al.*, 1927).

Some measurements have been made of the composition of blood plasma (or serum) in a few anuran species. Representative results are summarized in Table II. Interstitial fluid was collected from frog gastrocnemius muscles by Maurer (1938; Fenn and Maurer, 1935), who inserted capillary tubes between the muscle fibers of frogs after pithing, and later analyzed the fluid which had collected within the tubes (Table II). Although the procedure was ingenious, it is uncertain whether the fluid in the capillary tubes represented normal interstitial fluid, or was distorted in composition because of the method used for the collection. The general pattern of extracellular fluid composition seen in anurans—as, indeed, in most other vertebrates—appears to agree with the few measurements made on plasma from the urodele *Necturus maculosus*. The data for urodeles are scanty and incomplete, however.

Considerably more uncertainty exists about the composition of intracellular fluids. These fluids must be studied indirectly, either from generalization of analyses of free cells like erythrocytes, or by comparing with extracellular (plasma, serum) composition the chemically determined composition of whole tissues. By correcting for the estimated volumes within the tissue of extracellular and intracellular fluids, and with correction for fat content, Donnan distribution of ions, etc., figures may be derived for the composition of intracellular fluids. Conway (1957) has given a careful and extensive listing of such calculations, based on his own work and the data of other investigators. Some of Conway's values for intracellular fluid of muscle are listed in Table II.

B. EXCHANGE BETWEEN THE FLUID COMPARTMENTS

1. Intracellular-Extracellular Exchanges

Apparently water penetrates rapidly throughout the extracellular fluids and through cell membranes, although Hevesy and co-workers (1935)

TABLE II
COMPOSITION OF BODY FLUIDS IN AMPHIBIANS
A. SOME SOLUTES IN EXTRACELLULAR FLUIDS (Concentrations in mmoles/liter unless otherwise specified)

	Plasma (serum) of frogs[a]	Plasma of *Necturus maculosus*	Interstitial fluid (muscle) of frogs[a]	Lymph (leg lymphatics) of frogs[a]
Sodium	—	84.8 ± 2.0 97.47 ± 4.7	—	—
Potassium	—	3.2 ± 0.5 3.6 ± 0.2	—	—
Chloride	81 (64–95)	66.6 ± 5.3	83 (73–95)	—
Inorganic phosphate (mg/100 ml)	1.8–3.3	1.7–4.4 1.8 ± 0.4	—	—
Urea	2.9–4.3	2.3–4.3	—	—
Protein (gm/100 ml)	2.23 4.23 (2.40–5.28)	—	1.53 (0.44–3.54)	0.66–2.47 1.0 (0.29–2.17)
pH	—	7.29 ± 0.14 7.57 ± 0.20	7.2–7.5	—

B. COMPARISON OF INTRACELLULAR AND EXTRACELLULAR FLUID COMPOSITIONS (All concentrations in mmoles/liter, except water in gm/kg)[b]

	Frog plasma	Frog muscle water
Sodium	103.8	3.6
Potassium	2.15	124
Calcium	2.0	4.9
Magnesium	1.2	14.0
Chloride	74.3	1.5
Bicarbonate	25.4	12.4
Inorganic phosphate	3.1	7.3
Sulfate	1.9	0.4
Urea	2.0	2.0
Amino acids	6.9	8.8
Protein	(0.6)	(2.1)
Water (gm/kg)	954	261

[a] Estimates from species in the genus *Rana*. Data from Walker and Hudson (1937b, c); Maurer (1938); Fenn and Maurer (1935); Churchill *et al.* (1927); Conklin (1930c); Shipp *et al.* (1958).

[b] Data from Conway (1957).

did not find uniform distribution of deuterium-labeled water throughout the body water of frogs. Adequate data on intracellular-extracellular water exchange in amphibians are not available. Water exchanges between the animal as a whole and the external environment will be considered in Section V.

It seems quite clear that in amphibians, as in other vertebrates, the distinctive compositions of both cells and the extracellular fluids are the resultant of a series of processes including diffusional and actively mediated exchange of inorganic electrolytes and organic compounds, and synthesis and metabolism of organic osmolytes including proteins, amino acids, urea, glucose, etc. Recently, work in this field has been reviewed extensively, with occasional special reference to amphibians (Shanes, 1955; Murphy, 1957; Conway, 1957; Harris, 1960; Ussing, 1960b). The most fully studied of the exchanges involved in maintenance of cellular osmolyte composition in amphibians are concerned with muscle content of potassium and sodium. As has long been known, potassium is the major intracellular cation, with only a small concentration in extracellular fluids. Sodium (Na) is the major extracellular cation. Besides, sodium is represented within cells, as evidenced by the existence of distinctive fractions of tissue sodium which exchange at relatively slow rates with isotope labeled Na^+ (Levi and Ussing, 1948, among others). There is not yet agreement as to the nature or extent of sodium representation in the intracellular organization—a larger or smaller fraction of this sodium has been described as more available for exchange than the rest, and may possibly be associated with the sarcolemma or other special cellular regions (Levi and Ussing, 1948; Edwards and Harris, 1957; Conway, 1957; among others). The problem of describing the intracellular distribution of sodium is complicated by its small absolute amount and by exchange diffusion between internal and external sodium (Levi and Ussing, 1948; Keynes and Swan, 1959).

Rather rapid penetration of K^+ and Na^+ can occur from the extracellular into the intracellular compartment. Mullins (1959) estimated, for instance, that the rate of influx of K^+ and of Na^+ into isolated frog sartorius muscles at about 20°C averaged 1.82 and 0.08 mmole per kilogram fiber water × hour × millimole external ion concentration, respectively. Thus, the ratio of influx rate constants for K^+ as compared with Na^+ was about 24. Similarly, Conway (1957) gave figures for this ratio, measured by different workers under a variety of conditions, ranging from 24 to 98. In spite of the fact that these cations can enter muscle cells, cellular levels of K and Na are fairly independent, over a wide range, of the absolute ion concentrations in the fluids surrounding the cells (Shaw et al., 1956, among others). Thus, the characteristic cation patterns of cells and extracellular fluids are thought to be dependent on cellular activity.

Further, it has been shown repeatedly that K^+ may be lost and Na^+

taken up by muscles *in vitro* during prolonged soaking in Na^+-rich, K^+-poor Ringer's solution, especially in the cold (Steinbach, 1940). Subsequently, Na^+ may be extruded and K^+ reaccumulated from Ringer's solutions containing these ions at temperatures of about 20°C, but the details of this process are controversial. Carey *et al.* (1959) stated that Na^+ extrusion from frog muscle was dependent on critical Na^+ concentration in the external medium. Yet this was not confirmed by Steinbach (1961) who found that the presence of K^+ levels of about 10 mM in the medium was the only critical requirement for K^+ reaccumulation and Na^+ extrusion from isolated sartorius muscles of *Rana pipiens*.

Presumably, energy is required for restoration of normal K^+-Na^+ balance in isolated skeletal muscles of frogs (Levi and Ussing, 1948; Keynes and Maizel, 1954; Carey *et al.*, 1959), although the results of experiments designed to block readjustments of ion contents by use of various metabolic inhibitors (cold, anoxia, cyanide, iodoacetate, etc.) have given somewhat conflicting results (Keynes and Maizel, 1954; Carey *et al.*, 1959). Apparently, anaerobic metabolic pathways are capable of yielding all the energy needed for such ion transports in frog muscle cells (R. B. Dean, 1941, and others, cited by Ussing, 1960b). G-Strophanthin (Ouabain) and strophanthidin specifically block Na extrusion from, and K reaccumulation into frog muscles—a finding of great interest since these compounds interfere with Na^+ transport in other systems as well (Johnson, 1956; Carey *et al.*, 1959). It is still uncertain whether the processes of K^+ uptake and net Na^+ extrusion are independent, or whether these cations are exchanged for one another by a single energy-requiring mechanism (Keynes, 1954; Steinbach, 1961; among others).

Calcium, too, can exchange across cell membranes of muscle, both *in vivo* and *in vitro* at a rate estimated at about 6% of the rate of sodium penetration (see, for instance, Cosmos, 1958; Gilbert and Fenn, 1957; Mullins, 1959). The mechanisms involved in calcium entrance are complex. Gilbert and Fenn (1957) found evidence that an active transport is involved, while Cosmos and Harris (1961) have shown that concomitant sodium and potassium exchange may be of great importance in affecting the movement of calcium. Both calcium and magnesium probably form undissociated complexes with components (proteins, organic phosphates, etc.) of the cell membrane or intracellular system, and this complicates greatly the study of exchange of these cation species.

Among anions, chloride appears to be able to penetrate readily into muscle cells (Levi and Ussing, 1948; Conway and P. Moore, cited by Conway, 1957; Simon *et al.*, 1959; among others). Bromide also enters muscle cells with ease, whereas the penetrations of bicarbonate and sulfate are very slow. As yet, little is known of the processes determining anion exchange (Conway, 1957).

Because of the difficulties of experimental work in this field, most of the careful studies of ion movements between cells and extracellular fluids have been carried out *in vitro*. As yet, almost no information is available about intracellular-extracellular ionic composition and regulation in amphibian tissues other than muscle or nerve, or in any non-anuran tissues.

2. Fluid Circulation in the Extracellular Compartment

Within the extracellular compartment, the flows of blood and lymph represent, as it were, rapid transit systems for exchange of respiratory gases, water, and electrolytes, and nutrients, hormones, waste products, blood cells, etc. Water and solutes passing through the walls of the blood capillaries enter the tissue spaces and drain into the lymphatic channels. Thence, they may return to the blood stream by way of the great lymph trunks and sinuses and via the lymph hearts. Alternatively, water and solutes may return directly to the blood stream from interstitial fluids and peritoneal fluid by entering the blood capillaries, or the renal nephrostomes (in anurans). The relative roles of these routes of exchange between the divisions of the extracellular fluid have not been assessed. It is clear, however, that the lymphatic route is of great importance, since its blockage soon causes circulatory failure. For instance, in *Bufo arenarum* and *Leptodactylus ocellatus*, death occurred about 4 days after destruction of the lymph hearts, even when hyperhydration of the body was prevented (see Zwemer and Foglia, 1943). The physiology of blood circulation has been discussed in Chapters 3 and 4. The lymphatic system will be considered in this section, while the functioning of the nephrostomes will be treated briefly in the discussion of the kidneys (Section III, D).

Detailed descriptions of the anatomy of the lymphatic channels in frogs and in the salamander, *Salamandra salamandra*, have been given by Gaupp (1899) and Francis (1934). In both anurans and urodeles small lymphatic vessels, or capillaries, lead into meshworks of larger lymph vessels or into the great lymphatic sacs and sinuses. Flow of lymph centrally, from the smaller vessels and lymph spaces, is effected by the contractions of lymph hearts. These are endothelial lined chambers invested with skeletal muscle fibers and connective tissue, and generally opening into veins through apertures guarded by valves. Most lymph hearts have only a single pair of valves, lying just before the entrance into the venous system. In the salamander, the central lymph heart has a second set of valves at the junction between the base of the afferent lymph trunk and the lymph heart.

The number of lymph hearts varies in different amphibians. In certain Apoda, as many as 200 lymph hearts were described by H. Marcus (1908, cited by Noble, 1931). In urodeles there are fewer, yet still numerous, paired lymph hearts. For instance, in *Salamandra salamandra*, 15 pairs of lymph hearts, segmentally arranged, discharge into the lateral veins of the trunk. In addition, there is a central lymph heart lying just within the wall of the truncus arteriosus (Francis, 1934). In adult anurans, Gaupp and others have described two pairs of lymph hearts, an anterior pair opening into the vertebral veins, and a posterior pair emptying into ischiadic veins. Normally the contractions of the lymph hearts are controlled and coordinated by nerve impulses originating in localized centers in the spinal cord (Okada, 1956) and medulla oblongata, yet lymph hearts are also capable of showing autonomous, often rhythmic contractions (e.g., Pratt and Reid, 1939). This has been demonstrated, for instance, in the case of lymph hearts of *Bufo marinus, Rana catesbeiana*, and *R. pipiens* when the lymph hearts continued to show contraction after transplantation to the lymphatic sinus basohyoideous of the tongue (Reid, 1937). Earlier workers had shown essentially the same thing, although less conclusively, by surgical denervation of the lymph hearts (literature summarized by Reid, 1937).

Only a few studies have been made in an attempt to assess the rate of turnover of protein and fluid between circulating plasma and lymph. According to Conklin (1930c), the blood capillaries of *Rana pipiens* are fairly permeable to injected proteins and other large molecules. These large molecules normally return to the blood stream via the lymph. Thus, it is not surprising that measurements of protein concentration in plasma (e.g., averaging 2.23 gm per 100 ml in a small series of *Rana pipiens*; Conklin, 1930c) are not much higher than those recorded for lymph (e.g., averaging 1.0 to 2.5 gm per 100 ml in *Rana pipiens, R. temporaria, R. esculenta*; Conklin, 1930c; Churchill *et al.*, 1927). It would be of interest to estimate plasma protein turnover in amphibians using labeled plasma proteins.

Isayama (1924a) calculated the total volume of lymph production in 24 hours in frogs and toads (species unnamed) as of the order of twice the total body weight. Comparing his estimate of blood and lymph volume, he calculated that the turnover rate of the blood plasma from the capillaries, into the tissues, thence to the lymphatics, and back to the blood stream was of the order of 50 times per day (Isayama, 1924b). These results were derived from the sharp rise in red cell concentration immediately following stoppage of lymph return by blocking the lymph hearts by cauterization or administration of curare. The conclusion may be questioned, since it took no account of possible changes in absolute numbers of circulating red cells or of changed rate of plasma to lymph turnover consequent to the drastic experimental procedure, and other sources of error. Still, these results were generally consistent with estimates for lymph turnover based simply on the rate of contraction and changes in lymph heart size during contraction (E. Th. Brücke, cited by Isayama,

1924a), and with later figures derived by Conklin (1930a) who drained lymph from the crural sacs of *Rana pipiens* after cauterization of the posterior lymph hearts. Thus, it appears that there is a very high rate of turnover of fluid between the plasma and the lymphatic channels. Since the lymph spaces seem to communicate readily with other divisions of the extracellular compartment, it may be justifiable to conclude tentatively that the rate of circulation of extracellular fluids as a whole is quite rapid in amphibians.

III. Sites of Water and Electrolyte Exchange

A. THE SKIN

The skin is an important site of evaporative loss of water and of penetration of water into the body from free fluid bathing the animal. Besides, there are specific transporting systems in the skin which can move ions against significant activity gradients. These have been described in a variety of anurans (e.g., *Rana esculenta, R. temporaria, R. pipiens, Xenopus laevis, Bufo bufo,* and others) and in the urodele *Ambystoma mexicanum* (see, for instance, Krogh, 1937; Jørgensen *et al.,* 1946, 1954). Of these mechanisms, a powerful Na transferring system, in particular, has been studied extensively because it illustrates well certain general problems of active ion transport. In this chapter, ion transport will be discussed only in relation to the role of the skin in the physiology of the animal as a whole. No attempt will be made to summarize the extensive literature concerned with cellular mechanisms of active ion transport by the frog skin, but there are comprehensive reviews of this material by Linderholm (1952), Huf (1955), and Ussing (1960b).

Amphibian skin is relatively thin. In *Rana esculenta* and *R. temporaria,* for instance, 3 to 6 layers of cells make up the epidermis. These range from the outer flattened and cornified cells to the more regular, cylindrical cells of the stratum germinativum. Ottoson *et al.* (1953) have described a distinctive basement membrane, 200 to 300 Å thick, below the epithelium. Beneath this layer is the connective tissue of the corium, containing glands, chromatophores, and muscle fibers. Still deeper lies the narrow, compact cellular layer of the tela subcutanea, blending with connective tissue which attaches the skin as a whole to underlying structures like the septa bounding lymph channels where these lie right below the skin (Engbaek and Hoshiko, 1957; Scheer and Mumbach, 1960; among others). In general, the skin is loosely attached to the body, and fluids may accumulate in considerable amounts subcutaneously. Further, the skin may be removed readily for study *in vitro*. This accounts in part for the wide use of the isolated frog skin in experiments on biological transport systems.

Even in toads and other amphibians with apparently rough, dry skins, there is fairly rapid flux of water across the skin. For instance, Koefoed-Johnsen and Ussing (1953) measured the influx of water into the toad, *Bufo bufo*, with deuterium-labeled water, and found it to average 356 μl per cm^2 $\times$ hour under the conditions used. The inner surface of the epithelium is more permeable to water than the surface oriented toward the outside environment, according to MacRobbie and Ussing (1961), who studied the isolated skin of *Rana temporaria*. Ordinarily, there tends to be a *net* inward flux of water from the relatively dilute fluids bathing the outside of the skin to the inside. Some representative figures for this net flux across resting frog or toad skin at temperatures around 20°C (the optimal temperature, according to Huf and Doss, 1958) range from about 4.7 to 9.2 μl per cm^2 $\times$ hour (Hevesy *et al.*, 1935; Sawyer, 1951a; Koefoed-Johnsen and Ussing, 1953). Species differences in skin permeability have been described. Koefoed-Johnsen and Ussing (1953) found that the net flux of water inward across the isolated skin of the toad *Bufo bufo* was somewhat greater than the net inward flux through the skin of the frog *Rana temporaria* under constant conditions. Some of the hypotheses which have been advanced to explain net water uptake through amphibian skin will be discussed after consideration of net ion exchange. It may be noted that, within a given species, the skin permeability to water is not constant. The skin of the abdomen and thighs is more permeable than the skin covering the webs of the feet (Hevesy *et al.*, 1935). Further variations are seen with sex, fluctuations in blood level of neurohypophyseal hormones, molting, temperature and season (summer *versus* winter), etc. (Hevesy *et al.*, 1935; Boyd and Whyte, 1938; Koefoed-Johnsen and Ussing, 1953; among others).

Sodium and chloride ions penetrate far less readily through the skin than water does, and urea apparently penetrates still less easily. Permeability coefficients for sodium and chloride have been estimated as about 0.02 the permeability coefficient of heavy water, and urea was found to have a permeability coefficient of about 0.01 as compared with heavy water (Garby and Linderholm, 1953, 1954).

Characteristically, both *in vivo* and *in vitro*, the amphibian skin shows a marked electrical gradient, oriented so that the inner surface of the skin is positive with respect to the outside. The potential difference varies somewhat for a given species, depending on conditions; and also from species to species. Values as high as 73 to 145 mv have been reported by different workers for various anurans (e.g., *Rana esculenta*, *R. pipiens*, *R. temporaria*, etc.). This potential, early described by DuBois Reymond in 1848 has been proved to be a direct result of asymmetrical flux of sodium ions through the skin, as demonstrable with doubly labeled sodium ions (Na^{22}, Na^{24}; Ussing, 1949; Ussing and Zerahn, 1951). Thus, Na$^+$

ions pass inward at rates 20 to 100 times the rate of movement in the outward direction through the skin. In these circumstances, there is constant accumulation of sodium ions (and accompanying anions—typically Cl^- ions) from the ambient medium, as long as the medium concentration is above a low minimal level (e.g., about 1×10^{-5} M for salt depleted *Rana esculenta* individuals) (Krogh, 1937, 1938). In animals adapted to life in a highly hypotonic medium, like the aquatic and semiaquatic amphibians, this is undoubtedly a valuable mechanism for supplementing gastrointestinal intake of electrolytes.

The occurrence of net sodium transport inward through the skin is dependent on energy supplied by continuous cellular metabolism. It can be blocked by agents such as some metabolic inhibitors, and Huf and co-workers (1957) were able to differentiate processes related to maintenance of skin cell electrolyte content and active sodium transport by the use of fluoroacetate, azide, etc. G-Strophanthin, a cardiac glycoside known to interfere with sodium transport in many systems, blocks this process in the frog skin (Koefoed-Johnsen, 1957). The transport is specific for Na^+; K^+ is not transferred inward through the skin, nor are other cations, with the exception of Li^+ (Huf and Wills, 1953; Zerahn, 1955). Even Li^+ is clearly distinguished from Na^+ in this system, for when Li^+ ions are present in the ambient medium, they not only compete with Na^+ ions but also tend to accumulate within the skin, rather than continuing to traverse it as do Na^+ ions (Zerahn, 1955). Small anions, like Cl^- (but not the larger $SO_4^=$ ions) accompany Na^+ passively across the isolated skin *in vitro* (Koefoed-Johnsen *et al.*, 1952), and the absolute level of electrical potential developed by the skin depends in part on chloride permeability of the skin (Linderholm, 1953).

The outer surface of the skin is extremely impermeable to K^+ ions, as shown, for instance, by studies with isotopic K^+ and in experiments on osmotic behavior of the skin (Koefoed-Johnsen and Ussing, 1958; MacRobbie and Ussing, 1961). Although K^+ ions thus do not penetrate from the outside, and are not subject to net transport as are Na^+ ions, the isolated skin cannot transport Na^+ unless K^+ (or rubidium or cesium) ions are present in adequate concentrations in fluids bathing the inner surface of the skin (Huf and Wills, 1951; Huf and Arrighi, 1955). Further, when electrical shunting of the skin by movement of Cl^- is prevented, the potential across the skin can be predicted to a good approximation as the sum of the diffusion potentials of Na^+, from the outside to inside the cells, and of K^+, from fluid bathing the inside of the skin to the inside of the cells, as predicted by the Nernst equation (Koefoed-Johnsen and Ussing, 1956, 1958).

Several hypotheses have been advanced to account for active Na transport. Thus, for instance, the observations summarized in the present paragraph have been explained by an ingenious and consistent theory formulated by Koefoed-Johnsen and Ussing (1958; Ussing, 1960a). According to this theory, the operative system of the skin may be thought of as a layer of epithelial cells (stratum germinativum?) with intracellular fluids of relatively high potassium and low sodium activity. The cell membranes facing the outside of the skin are highly permeable to sodium ions, while nearly impermeable to potassium ions. At the surface of the cells oriented toward the inside of the skin, the ionic permeability relationships are opposite, for low sodium and high potassium permeability exist here. At this inner surface the actual mechanism for sodium transport is located, forcing exchange of sodium ions, entering the skin from the outside environment, for potassium ions (and possibly hydrogen ions as well) withdrawn from the body fluids. The operation of such an oriented, energy-dependent sodium-for-potassium exchange would drive sodium ions into the body from the outside; maintain the relatively high potassium level of the cells; and account for the correlation of skin potential with external sodium and internal potassium concentrations. The kinetics of isotope-labeled sodium exchange across the skin of several anurans gave support to this hypothesis (Hoshiko and Ussing, 1959), while studies of osmotic behavior of the *Rana temporaria* skin *in vitro* confirmed the postulates about differential ionic permeability of the inner and outer skin surfaces (MacRobbie and Ussing, 1961).

According to other workers, additional processes and regions of the skin other than the epithelium may be involved in sodium transport. Thus, attempts have been made to localize the site of potential change from the outside to the inside of the skin. Progressive removal of layers of skin eventually alters critically the skin potential. Also, microelectrodes can be inserted progressively deeper and deeper into the skin to determine the level at which sharp changes in potential occur. Ottoson *et al.* (1953) described a single region of sharp potential change, located at the dermal-epidermal boundary, i.e., at the level of the basement membrane which these workers observed in electronmicrographs at the junction between the basal epidermal cells and the corium. This basement membrane, therefore, was considered by Ottoson and co-workers to be the main diffusion barrier of the skin so that here, rather than across the epidermal cell membranes, the skin potential would be developed. In contrast, Engbaek and Hoshiko (1957) found two "potential jumps" in the skin: one close to the surface and probably involving the epidermal cells; the second deeper, possibly at the deepest layer of the epithelial cells, or the most superficial layer of the corium. Using closely similar methods, Fleming (1958) and Scheer and Mumbach (1960) concluded that the site of electrical asymmetry was partly in the stratum germinativum of the epithelium, but partly deeper—in the deepest layer of the corium, or the junction between the corium and the subcutaneous tissue (tela subcutanea). As yet, it is not clear why these results should differ so widely from one group of workers to another. To the usual problems of bioelectric measurements may be added differences in skin condition; effects of compressing, distorting, or tearing the skin; and the difficulty of localizing the exact position within the skin of measurements made with microelectrodes.

The results of treating the skin with a wide variety of chemical agents have been studied with respect to active sodium transport (see review by Ussing, 1960b). Many of the substances tested have been selected for their importance in theoretical analysis of sodium ion and ionic transport in general, rather than because of direct bearing on the physiology of the intact amphibian. One group of compounds of prime interest in this respect, however, are amphibian and mammalian neurohypophyseal and adrenal cortical hormones. In the intact animal, injections of these hormones increase the rate of passage of water and salts through the skin. Besides, these hormones act even on the isolated skin of frogs and toads (A. Novelli, 1936, cited by Ussing, 1960b; Fuhrman and Ussing, 1951; Taylor and Weinstein, 1952; among others), increasing the potential difference and inward sodium movement across the skin. Such hormonal actions will be discussed further in Section IV.

There are a few suggestions that the nervous system participates in the regulation of sodium transport by the skin. For instance, Steggerda and Ponder (1940) observed abrupt depression of the resting potential of the skin of frogs following destruction of the brain or the entire central nervous system. Adolph's (1934) observation of sudden increase in net water intake through the skin of *Rana pipiens* following destruction of the mesencephalon or medulla has not been analyzed further in terms of current knowledge of skin transport systems.

In contrast to cation transport, little is known of mechanisms involved in anion movement across the amphibian skin. Chloride and bromide (but not iodide) ions were taken up rapidly through the skin of *Rana esculenta*, but only after the animals had suffered electrolyte depletion (Krogh, 1937, 1938). Anion (and cation) uptake took place even from solutions with less than 1% of the chloride concentration of the animal's plasma or Ringer's solution. Jørgensen *et al.* (1954) studied sodium and chloride uptake, and flux ratios, after differential depletion of one or the other of these ion species from the body (*Rana temporaria; R. esculenta; R. arvalis; Bufo bufo*). These authors concluded that transfer of these ions could occur independently through the skin. They suggested that active uptake of chloride, as well as of sodium ions can occur. Another situation

involving chloride ion transport has been described by Koefoed-Johnsen
et al. (1952). To explain the breakdown of the usual relationship between
skin potential and net sodium flux in isolated frog skins treated with adrenaline, Koefoed-Johnsen and co-workers suggested that adrenaline stimulates an active secretion of chloride ions from the inside to the outside
of the skin. It is possible that the mucous glands are involved in this
process.

Water tends to pass continuously into amphibians exposed to water or
dilute solutions. Under resting conditions, this may be explained largely
by passive movement of water along the osmotic gradient existing between the external medium and the body fluids. Thus, frogs and toads
immersed in sucrose or glucose solutions isosmotic with their own body
fluids (e.g., 0.23 to 0.24 M sucrose) show no net uptake of water through
the skin (see, for instance, Stewart, 1949; Fuhrman and Ussing, 1951;
Kalman and Ussing, 1955; Kirschner et al., 1960). On the other hand, water is taken up from isosmotic solutions of sodium chloride (Huf, 1936,
cited by Koefoed-Johnsen and Ussing, 1953). This water uptake may be
attributed to osmosis, water accompanying sodium ions (entering the skin
by active transport) and chloride ions (entering by passive diffusion)
(Huf et al., 1957; Koefoed-Johnsen and Ussing, 1953). Further, the maintenance of the skin potential per se has been thought to explain water
uptake by electroosmosis (Adolph, 1925; Capraro and Garampi, 1956;
among others). A specific, nonosmotic, sodium-independent transport of
water was postulated by Kirschner et al. (1960), who found that water
uptake can occur dissociated from sodium transport when active sodium
uptake is blocked by choline esterase inhibitors, or by exposure of animals to modified Ringer's solutions with sodium ions replaced by non-
transportable choline or magnesium ions. Some further evidence that all
water movement may not be explicable in terms of simple osmotic pressure differentials across the skin has been adduced by some workers studying the effects of injections of neurohypophyseal hormones. This point will
be discussed further in Section IV.

While the physiology of the skin of anurans has been studied extensively,
far less is known about urodele skin. Like anurans, Ambystoma mexicanum
showed a net uptake of sodium and chloride ions against a concentration
gradient between the ambient medium and the body fluids (Jørgensen et
al., 1946). However, this ion accumulation was found to be balanced, with
fluctuating precision, by diffusional loss through the skin and respiratory
surfaces and by renal excretion. For instance, starving axolotls took up
sodium at an average rate of 68.7 μEq per day, but lost an average of 94.6
μEq per day (Jørgensen et al., 1946). A mammalian neurohypophyseal
preparation rich in vasopressin enhanced active uptake of sodium and

chloride, while an oxytocin-rich fraction tended rather to enhance loss. It would be interesting to extend these observations, particularly with the use of amphibian neurohypophyseal hormones. *Ambystoma* proved to be highly sensitive to manipulation, so that even pricking of the skin caused fluctuations in net sodium uptake (Jørgensen *et al.*, 1946).

Net uptake of water into the body, as judged by increase in body weight, followed injection of mammalian neurohypophyseal hormones into *Necturus* and *Ambystoma* (Bělehrádek and Huxley, 1927; Steggerda, 1937; Dow and Zuckerman, 1938; Jørgensen *et al.*, 1946). The effects seen were much less than those described in anurans, and it is still unclear to what extent the changes were due to renal as compared with epidermal actions of the hormones.

B. GILLS AND LUNGS

Although it is clear that some water exchange must occur at the gills and lungs, no explicit studies have been found which attempted to assess the part played by respiratory structures in over-all water balance. Probably they are not especially important, at least in comparison with the skin and kidneys. Thus, the relatively low metabolic rates of amphibians limit their obligatory ventilation rates. Mellanby (1941) observed no change in the rate of water loss in air after cessation of respiration in *Rana temporaria*.

Cells capable of active transport of ions exist in the gills of fish, and Krogh (1939) suggested that extrarenal ion transport might occur in amphibians as well. No reference has been found to any consistent search for such mechanisms in the gills of larval or adult amphibians.

C. GASTROINTESTINAL TRACT AND URINARY BLADDER

The role of the gastrointestinal tract in the amphibian's water balance has yet to be clarified. Adult amphibians do not ingest free water (see Section V), nor, in general, do they eat food materials with water contents very different from those of the animal's own body. Uranga (1958b) found no evidence of increased rate of intestinal water absorption in toads (*Bufo arenarum*) subjected to dehydration or injection of posterior pituitary extracts. Intestinal absorption may be much more critical in determining body fluid volume and composition in frog larvae than in adults (Krogh, 1937, 1939). P. Rey (1937, cited by Thorson, 1955) estimated that 50% of the water intake of tadpoles was through the gastrointestinal tract.

Of course both larval and adult amphibians feed on materials containing significant amounts of various osmolytes. Intestinal absorption of these materials, and net transfer across the mucosa of water and ions including H^+, Na^+, K^+, Cl^-, and HCO_3^- in digestive secretions must be considered in studies of water balance. In *in vitro* studies, both the stomach and large intestine of frogs show significant electrical potential differences (30 to 45 mv) across their walls, oriented so that the mucosal surface is negative to the serosal surface (Crane *et al.*, 1948; Hogben, 1955; Cooperstein and Hogben, 1958; and others). Much lower potential differences (about 2 mv) oriented in the same sense have been recorded across the isolated esophagus, ileum, and duodenum of the frog (*Rana temporaria*), while the rectal mucosa showed potential differences of -8 to -27 mv (mucosa negative to serosa) (Crane *et al.*, 1948). In the case of the stomach and intestine, the electrical potentials have been correlated with active ion transports. Thus, the frog stomach appears to transport H^+ and Cl^- actively into the lumen, forming HCl continuously (though at varying rates) both *in vivo* and *in vitro* (Delrue, 1930, 1933; Gray *et al.*, 1940; Crane *et al.*, 1948; Edwards and Edwards, 1951; Theorell, 1951; Hogben, 1955 among others). Acid is not secreted by the stomachs of frogs in winter, and it would be interesting to know what cellular or hormonal or other changes account for this failure of H^+ or Cl^- transport (Gray *et al.*, 1940; M. F. H. Friedman, 1934, cited by Gray *et al.*).

Evidence has been found for active Na^+ transport in the large intestine (Cooperstein and Hogben, 1958), while Cl^- seems to move passively here. Potassium ion transport may occur in both the stomach and large intestine (Cooperstein and Hogben, 1958; Harris and Edelman, 1960).

Net water movement across the mucosa occurs, perhaps osmotically, in connection with the net movement of ions. As yet, however, it is not possible to generalize from these cellular processes to the role of the gastrointestinal tract in the water and electrolyte balance of the animal as a whole.

The urinary bladder may be considered at this point, because of its close relationship, both anatomically and physiologically, with the lower intestine and cloaca. In amphibians the urinary bladder is not merely a provisional storage place for urine before evacuation from the body. It plays a far more significant part in water balance, for water, sodium, and other ions can be absorbed from the bladder. In some cases, these processes are important for the animal's survival. For instance, in Australian desert frogs (e.g., *Chiroleptes platycephalus*, now *Cyclorana platycephalus*, described by G. Sweet, 1909, cited by Marshall and Smith, 1930; see also Buxton, 1923) water is stored in the bladder during the rainy season for use throughout the dry months of the year. Steen (1929) carried out experiments in which he ligated the cloacal orifice in frogs and subsequently dehydrated some of the animals by immersion in 1% NaCl, and others by 20 to 50 hr exposure to dry air. The bladders of control frogs contained amounts of urine significantly larger than those present in the bladders of dehydrated animals. Similar results were described by Ewer (1952a) in

Bufo regularis. Sawyer and Schisgall (1956) measured the rate of water re-absorption from the bladders of normal and dehydrated *Rana catesbeiana* individuals. These rates averaged 11.7 ± 12.6 μl per cm² hour in control animals, and 75.8 ± 12.8 μl per cm² hour in animals subjected to dehydration. In one further anuran species, *Bufo arenarum*, Uranga and Quintana (1958) observed that these toads survived dehydration by immersion in 40% sucrose longer if fluid was present in the bladder at the start of dehydration than if the bladder was empty initially. The fluid was absorbed during the course of dehydration.

The toad bladder is a bilobed sac of varying size. The wall has a relatively simple structure. A single (rarely double) layer of epithelial cells is invested by a connective tissue layer on the serosal side. The latter contains scattered bundles of smooth muscle cells and small blood vessels and is partly bounded on the serosal surface by squamous epithelium (Leaf *et al.*, 1958; Peachey and Rasmussen, 1961). Detailed descriptions of the bladder wall of *Bufo marinus* on the basis of electron micrography have been given by Pak Poy and Bentley (1960) and Peachey and Rasmussen (1961). No characteristic structural changes within the cells were seen during water absorption, either in the resting bladder or after stimulation by treatment with posterior pituitary extracts. Some swelling of the cells occurred in *in vitro* preparations in the course of fluid transfer. A few vesicles were present in the cells, but these did not increase in number as the rate of water movement increased. Nor was there evidence of massive fluid passage through intercellular channels at the mucosal surface, although some intercellular accumulation of fluid was described. Thus it appears that fluid passes directly through the epithelial cells and without special localization in vesicles.

In 1955, Leaf described a marked electrical potential gradient across the wall of the isolated urinary bladder of the toad, *Bufo bufo* (Leaf, 1956). The gradient was oriented in such a manner that the lumen side was negative to the serosal side even when, for instance, both sides of the wall were bathed with identical Ringer's solutions. Potential differences measured across the toad bladder wall may be as high as 120 mv (Leaf *et al.*, 1958), although the range is usually less (*Bufo bufo:* 5 to 20 mv; *Bufo marinus:* 20 to 50 mv). In analogy with the amphibian skin and large intestine, the toad bladder shows an asymmetrical flux of sodium ions. Furthermore, the net sodium transport accounts quantitatively for the current generated by the bladder wall under conditions when it is short-circuited. Thus, it has been established definitely that the bladder wall has the capacity to transport sodium by an active process. With sodium ions, anions (especially chloride ions) and water move from the bladder lumen into the fluid bathing the serosal side. Under specific experimental conditions, changes in the rate of water movement across the bladder wall of *Bufo marinus* may be independent of changes in net sodium transport (Bentley, 1960).

As might, indeed, be expected, this transport of sodium by the bladder wall is energy dependent. The toad (*Bufo marinus*) bladder, like the intestinal mucosa, has an exceptionally high rate of oxygen consumption (Leaf *et al.*, 1959). Leaf and co-workers (1959) estimated that 20 to 50% of the oxygen consumption of the bladder is related directly to sodium transport. At the same time, it appears that net sodium transfer can be supported partially by glycolytic metabolism (Leaf *et al.*, 1958, 1959; Bentley, 1960). Posterior pituitary and interrenal steroids affect net sodium and water movement across the toad bladder wall (see, e.g., Leaf *et al.*, 1958; Leaf and Dempsey, 1960; Crabbé, 1961a,b), and the participation of these hormones in regulating bladder function will be discussed in more detail in Section IV. At this point, it may be noted that the bladder wall is asymmetrical with respect to the action of neurohypophyseal hormones, for these are effective only when applied to the serosal side of the wall (Leaf *et al.*, 1958, 1960). A similar asymmetry of the toad bladder has been demonstrated for a number of other substances as well. For instance, the pH of the bladder urine may differ by as much as 3 pH units from that of plasma. Lactate ions show a striking differential distribution because they penetrate more readily through the serosal side than through the mucosal side of the epithelial cells which form lactate ions in their metabolism (Leaf, 1959; Leaf *et al.*, 1959). Water moves faster along a given osmotic gradient from the epithetial to the serosal side than in the opposite direction (Bentley, 1961). Peachey and Rasmussen (1961) described two distinctive layers (filamentous, granular) adjacent to the plasma membrane of the mucosal surface of epithelial cells, and suggested that one of these layers may represent the structural basis for the polarity in permeability of these cells.

All of the evidence cited so far has come from experiments on a few species of toads. Water movement and active sodium transport across the wall of the urinary bladder have been described also in *Rana catesbeiana* (Sawyer, 1960b). In this species, injection of a variety of neurohypophyseal substances was not followed by demonstrable change in active sodium transport, though movement of water in either direction (mucosal to serosal, or serosal to mucosal) was accelerated (Sawyer, 1960b). Beyond these observations, it is not possible to draw conclusions about the generality, variability, or control of bladder reabsorption processes among various amphibians, for the data are too scanty. It would be of interest to study the bladders of urodeles, both those that are adapted to aquatic or semiaquatic life, and those with more terrestrial habits. Clues offered by structural differences may not be valid, for the aquatic urodele *Amphiuma* has an exceptionally large bladder, as do the terrestrially adapted toads (Noble, 1931).

D. THE KIDNEYS

Understanding of the mechanisms of renal function in vertebrates in general was established in large part through the study of amphibian kidneys. The classic work has been reviewed extensively (e.g., Marshall, 1926, 1934; Smith, 1951) and no attempt will be made here to recapitulate the history of controversy and final clarification of renal function through the work of Bowman, Heidenhain, Ludwig, Nussbaum, Cushny, Richards, Marshall, Smith, and others. As in other vertebrates, the basic unit of the amphibian kidney is the nephron, and the raw material of urine is blood. Fluid is filtered from the plasma at the glomerular capillary membranes to enter the glomerular portion of the mesonephric tubule under a low head of pressure, representing the differential between intracapillary pressure on the one hand and the sum of plasma oncotic pressure and tubular back pressure on the other. Thence, the fluid flows along the tubule, driven, as it were, by the residual filtration pressure and drawn by the currents set up by beating of the cilia at various loci along the tubule. As it passes the cells lining the lumen, the composition of the intratubular fluid is modified. Water, sodium and chloride ions, glucose, and some other solutes pass from the tubular lumen into the blood vessels surrounding them (reabsorption). Other solutes (urea, some inorganic ions and dyes) show a net movement from blood to tubular lumen (secretion). Such processes of change in composition of the potential urine continue throughout the entire course traversed by the fluid from the glomerulus through the cloaca and urinary bladder.

The urine of amphibians is typically dilute as compared with the body fluids, and thus the mesonephros is particularly effective in ridding the body of excess water. Nitrogen-containing products of metabolism represent a special problem in excretion. From data so far available, it appears that ammonia and urea are the major end products formed from nitrogen compounds in amphibian metabolism, although some additional nitrogen-containing substances are found in the urine. Ammonia synthesis is metabolically "inexpensive" as compared with urea or uric acid synthesis, but ammonia is highly toxic to cells and must be excreted at low concentrations, i.e., in the presence of a relatively large supply of water. Urea is less toxic, although still less conservative of water than, for instance, the uric acid characteristically excreted by birds and reptiles. Needham (1931) and others have stressed the importance of the shift from ammonia excretion to the use of urea or uric acid as an excretory nitrogen-vehicle in animals adapting to a nonaquatic habitat. Amphibian larvae generally utilize ammonia in nitrogen excretion. Among adult amphibians, those which are adapted to life in water may excrete ammonia in predominance over other nitrogen waste vehicles, while terrestrially adapted forms excrete relatively large amounts of urea and only small to trace amounts of ammonia, uric acid, creatinine, etc. (Needham, 1931; Underhay and Baldwin, 1955; Cragg *et al.*, 1961). Although relatively few species have been studied as yet, it is striking that this generalization holds for both urodeles and anurans. For instance, ammonia represented $92.53 \pm 2.78\%$ of the total (ammonia + urea nitrogen) excreted by *Pipa pipa* (aquatic anuran) and only $4.77 \pm 1.25\%$ of this total in *Bufo bufo* (terrestrial anuran) (Cragg *et al.*, 1961). Adult *Xenopus laevis* individuals show an interesting transitional pattern, for they excrete ammonia as the major nitrogen metabolite under ordinary conditions, but form and later excrete urea in large amounts if the water supply is restricted (Munro, 1953; Balinsky *et al.*, 1961).

While discussion of metabolism of nitrogen compounds does not fall strictly within the limits of renal physiology as such, the patterns of kidney function are intimately involved. The mesonephric tubules of frogs (*Rana pipiens, R. catesbeiana, R. clamitans*) secrete urea actively into the urine, whereas such urea secretion does not take place in the mesonephros of *Necturus*. Forster (1954) suggested that the difference between these species may be correlated with their habitats, for renal tubular urea secretion must function as a water-conserving mechanism which might be of advantage in survival to the partially terrestrial frogs, but not to the fully aquatic *Necturus*. It will be interesting to compare the manner of excretion of ammonia and urea in a much wider range of anurans and urodeles with varying habitats, when the requisite data have been collected.

In mesonephric function as a whole, the rate of glomerular filtration and the processes involved in tubular reabsorption and secretion of discrete substances are subject to change under varying conditions. Only a few of the neural, hormonal, and other mechanisms involved in these changes have as yet been established.

The number of nephrons in each kidney differs from species to species. For instance, representative figures for the number of tubules (counted from glomeruli) in the two kidneys include: *Salamandra maculosa*—800 (Steinbach, 1927); *Rana esculenta, R. pipiens*—2000 to 2500 (Steinbach, 1927; Hayman, 1929); *Rana catesbeiana*—6400 to 8150 (Marshall, 1934); *Bufo vulgaris*—2500 to 2800 (Vogel, 1949).

The structure of the mesonephric tubule will be reviewed only briefly here, but fuller accounts of nephron anatomy, dimensions, and pertinent literature have been given, among others, by Gaupp (1899), Stewart (1927), Edwards and Schnitter (1933), and Vogel (1949) for ranids; Bargmann *et al.* (1955) for *Xenopus laevis*; and Chase (1923), Dawson

(1924–1925), Curry (1929), Kempton (1937), and Windhager *et al.* (1959) for *Necturus maculosus*. Bowman's capsule, a structure of squamous cells investing the capillaries of the glomerulus, leads into a short neck segment, lined with flattened or cuboidal cells, usually invested with long cilia (Fawcett and Porter, 1954). In urodeles, some of the tubules are joined at the neck segment by a ciliated channel, the outer tubule leading from a peritoneal nephrostome on the ventral surface of the kidney. This is not true in most adult anurans, for in these animals the nephrostomes connect with the renal veins, rather than with the nephric tubules. Beyond the neck segment is the proximal convoluted tubule composed of cells of columnar or cuboidal form. Toward the lumen, the surfaces of these cells are extended in a thick pile of microvilli (brush border). Next comes an intermediate segment, formed of cuboidal, usually ciliated cells, connecting with a distal tubule which varies in length in different species and is formed by low columnar epithelium without cilia or a typical brush border. Dawson (1951) commented on the lack of ciliation of neck and intermediate segments in Australian desert frogs (*Cyclorana* sp.). Beyond the nephrons proper lies the system of collecting ducts with drainage into the Wolffian ducts and thence to the cloaca and urinary bladder. The latter, lying ventral to the rectum, opens from the cloaca and is without direct connection to the Wolffian ducts.

The kidneys function in many male amphibians as part of the pathway for sperm transfer, but it is not known whether this modifies renal function.

Blood flows into the glomerular capillaries from arterioles derived ultimately from the renal arteries, branches of the multiple pairs (e.g., 4 to 7) of urogenital arteries arising from the aorta. From the glomeruli, blood remaining after filtration flows on through efferent arterioles which lead again to capillaries meshing about the tubular walls. Exchange between fluid in these capillaries and the tubular contents takes place across the tubular walls. The latter are supplied also by a relatively few arterial branches arising directly from the renal arteries without passing through glomeruli (arteriae rectae). Further, the proximal tubules in particular are supplied with blood from the renal portal veins, draining the extremities, distal portion of the trunk, and the reproductive organs. About half of the tubular flow of the bullfrog, *Rana catesbeiana*, originates in the portal supply, according to Forster (1943) who based this conclusion on comparison of iodopyracet (Diodrast) clearances (identified with effective flow of plasma to the kidneys) before and after tying off the renal portal veins. Anastomoses apparently exist between the arterial and renal portal supply in *Rana catesbeiana* (Richards and Walker, 1927; Beiter and Hirschfelder, 1929; among others), but it is still not clear how much interchange occurs between the two supplies under normal conditions. At least in the perfused kidney, this interchange varies with the relative pressure of the arterial and renal portal inputs (Oliver and Shevsky, 1929; among others). Blood drains from the kidneys through the renal veins. Detailed descriptions of the renal circulation may be found in papers by Chase (1923) and Hayman (1929). The total flow of plasma to the kidneys has been estimated as about 70 to 80 ml per 100 gm body weight × hour in *Rana catesbeiana* and *R. clamitans* (Forster, 1943; Schmidt-Nielsen and Forster, 1954).

1. Glomerular Filtration

The circulation through the glomerular capillaries in Amphibia appears rather rapid. Here filtration occurs at rates assessed with creatinine or inulin clearance as ranging from about 2 to 13 ml per 100 gm body weight × hour under basal conditions (i.e., neither dehydration nor excessive hydration) in several anurans (Table III). The rate of filtration changes strikingly with state of hydration, temperature, and other conditions.

The glomerular circulation appears to be intermittent, that is, the flow through individual capillaries within a glomerulus, or through whole glomeruli, may be slowed or stopped, or accelerated from time to time. Glomerular intermittency was described by Richards and Schmidt (1924–1925), who observed directly the kidneys of *Rana pipiens* and *R. catesbeiana* exposed in acute experiments. Although the exposed kidney is unlikely to be normal in function, the observations have been confirmed repeatedly by other workers, including Forster (1942) who used an entirely different method of study. This was comparison of glomerular filtration rate (inulin or creatinine clearance) and tubular function (maximal tubular transfer of glucose) in unanesthetized bullfrogs, *Rana catesbeiana*. Maximal rates of tubular reabsorption of glucose varied directly with filtration rate, a finding most easily explained by limitation of tubular function by the occurrence of variation in glomerular filtration.

Alterations in glomerular blood flow and vascular resistance—hence, of filtration rate—are believed to be of major importance in controlling the rate of urine formation. Richards and Schmidt (1924–1925), for instance, described an increase in the number of active glomeruli in frogs receiving intravenous injections of blood or salt solutions, and, further, fluctuations in glomerular blood flow could be induced with electrical stimulation of the sciatic or renal sympathetic nerves, and by injections of various hormones and pharmacological agents including adrenaline and mammalian posterior pituitary extracts (Adolph, 1936a). Adolph (1936b) compared the rate of urine flow and the number of active glomeruli, and found that vigorous glomerular circulation was a necessary but not sufficient condition for urine formation. Again, these results have been confirmed in general by workers

TABLE III

SOME MEASUREMENTS OF URINE FLOW, GLOMERULAR FILTRATION RATE,
AND RENAL PLASMA FLOW IN AMPHIBIANS

A. URINE FLOW (ml/hr $\times$ 100 gm body weight)[a]

Species	Rate	Reference
Rana pipiens (20°C)	2.0 ± 0.5	Hong (1957)
Rana pipiens (1°C)	0.2 ± 0.01	Hong (1957)
Rana pipiens (20°C)	1.3	Adolph (1927b)
Rana pipiens	2.6 ± 0.45	Sawyer (1951b)
Rana catesbeiana	0.15–2.07	Marshall (1932)
Rana clamitans	1.32	Schmidt-Nielsen and Forster (1954)

B. GLOMERULAR FILTRATION RATE (ml/hr $\times$ 100 gm body weight)

Species	Rate	Reference
Rana clamitans (20–25°C)	3.4 (0.3–5.7)[b]	Schmidt-Nielsen and Forster (1954)
Rana clamitans (5°C)	0.45[b]	Schmidt-Nielsen and Forster (1954)
Rana catesbeiana	0.84–3.36[c]	Forster (1938)
Bufo arenarum (summer)	13.5 ± 1.4[c]	Uranga (1958a)
Bufo arenarum (winter)	2.4 ± 0.27[c]	Uranga (1958a)

C. RENAL PLASMA FLOW (ml/hr $\times$ 100 gm body weight)

Species	Rate	Reference
Rana clamitans	Variable—77.5[d] when GFR = 3.0	Schmidt-Nielsen and Forster (1954)
Rana catesbeiana	70.0[e]	Forster (1943)
Rana catesbeiana—renal portal veins tied off	35.0[e]	Forster (1943)

[a] Urine flow usually measured with the animal partly immersed in water, but not during diuresis.

[b] Measured as creatinine clearance. It is not fully settled whether there is some secretion of creatinine, partially balanced by back diffusion in the anuran kidney (Swanson, 1956). Bott (1952) found no evidence of creatinine secretion in the tubules of *Necturus maculosus*.

[c] Measured as inulin clearance.

[d] Measured as para-aminohippurate clearance.

[e] Measured as Diodrast clearance.

using more recently developed and less drastically nonphysiological methods. Sawyer (1951b) made approximate estimates of glomerular filtration rates in *Rana pipiens* with a modified creatinine clearance technique, and found that urine flow paralleled changes in glomerular filtration in various conditions including experiments with injection of posterior pituitary extracts. Similarly, Forster (1938) showed that urine flow in *Rana catesbeiana* was directly proportional to glomerular filtration rate at low and intermediate urine flows. Filtration could be increased to a maximum of about 10 ml per kilogram body weight × hour. Only when these high rates were attained was it clear that variations in tubular reabsorption, rather than in glomerular filtration, limited further changes in urine flow.

Although it would be of interest to compare glomerular filtration rates in various amphibians adapted to a wide range of environments, from fully aquatic to nearly fully terrestrial, this is not possible because so few data are as yet available. On morphological grounds alone, striking variations would be expected. In general, the glomeruli of urodeles are much larger than those of anurans. At the opposite extreme of this range, at least some of the glomeruli are small in size and poorly vascularized in the kidneys of the Australian desert frogs, *Cyclorana* (*Chiroleptes*) *platycephalus* and *C. alboguttatus* (G. Sweet, cited by Marshall and Smith, 1930; Dawson, 1951).

2. Tubular Function

Once having entered the glomerular portion of the tubule, the plasma ultrafiltrate starts to move distally from this region, undergoing marked modification and reduction in volume as it passes the cells lining the tubular lumen. In contrast to the situation in mammals, in which about 1% of the glomerular filtrate is finally lost from the body, 14 to 90% of the filtrate may escape reabsorption and issue from the bodies of even normally hydrated anurans (Forster, 1938; Schmidt-Nielsen and Forster, 1954; Uranga, 1958d).

In addition to the net filtration pressure, ciliary activity probably facilitates the movement of fluid along the tubule (White, 1929a). As noted above, in general the neck and intermediate segments are ciliated. With the glomerulus torn open, and the proximal tubule occluded near its junction with the neck segment, pressures of 4.0 to 5.7 cm H_2O were built up by cilia beating in the neck segments of *Necturus* kidneys (White, 1929b). Further, the pressures caused by ciliary beating in outer segments leading to nephrostomes could prevent back flow through the nephrostomes when intraglomerular pressure was raised as high as 8 to 11 cm H_2O (White, 1929b). Beyond these observations made on pithed or anesthetized (urethane) *Necturus*, virtually nothing is known of the role of cilia in over-all renal function in amphibians. It has been suggested by Singer (1933) and Lucas and White (1933) that contractions of cells of the neck and intermediate segments in *Necturus maculosus* and in frogs may play a part in regulating distribution and flow of fluid from the glomerulus to the distal tubule.

Knowledge of details and localization of tubular function in modifying the glomerular filtrate has come primarily from the admirable experiments, involving tubular puncture, fluid sampling, and tubular perfusion of A. N. Richards and his co-workers (Wearn *et al.*, 1923–1924; Wearn and Richards, 1924; Richards and Walker, 1937; and others), recently continued and extended by Bott, Giebisch, Solomon, Windhager, and others. Only a few amphibian species have been studied in this way—*Necturus maculosus* and a few ranids. This is partly because the studies have been designed from the point of view of renal physiology in general, rather than with special interest in amphibians as such. Besides, there are experimental problems related to the size and placement of glomeruli and characteristic tubular loci, and *Necturus* and members of a few other species have proved to be relatively susceptible to study.

In general, these experiments have defined sites of absorption of substances into the peritubular fluid from the tubular lumen, or secretion in the opposite direction. A powerful ion transporting system, apparently related to active sodium ion transport, maintains an electrical potential gradient across the tubular wall. Somewhat variable in magnitude in *Necturus maculosus*, this potential averages about 20 mv (Giebisch, 1958) with the luminal surface negative to the peritubular surface of the kidney tubule. Evidence has been presented by Whittembury and co-workers (1961) for an active sodium-for-potassium exchanging "pump" in the perfused proximal tubule of *Necturus*, a mechanism closely similar to the system proposed by Ussing and co-workers to explain active sodium transport by the amphibian skin. Earlier, Wilbrandt (1938) had described an electrical potential difference across the *Necturus* renal tubular wall, although technical difficulties led to great variability in the results. In the proximal tubule, the lumen side was negative, while the lumen was positive to the peritubular surface in the intermediate segment (Wilbrandt, 1938).

Water reabsorption occurs to a considerable extent in the proximal convoluted tubule. For instance, Walker and Hudson (1937a) concluded from comparisons of concentrations of glucose in the proximal tubules of normal and phlorizinized *Rana pipiens* and *Necturus maculosus* individuals that an average of 20% (*Necturus*) to 29% (*Rana*) of the water filtered at the glomeruli was reabsorbed in the proximal tubules. Most of the early workers in this field agreed that this water reabsorption was a passive process, secondary to absorption of osmolytes (e.g., sodium, chloride, glucose, etc.). The evidence for this was chiefly the isotonicity of intraluminal fluid throughout the length of the tubule, despite significant and varied osmolyte reabsorption (Walker et al., 1937; Walker and Hudson, 1937a). Recently, studies of Whittembury, Windhager, Solomon, and co-workers on the isolated, perfused Necturus proximal tubule in situ have demonstrated clearly that this hypothesis is tenable. Active sodium transport has been shown to occur, water absorption is proportional to net sodium efflux from the tubule, and pharmacological agents which depress this sodium transport (ouabain, dinitrophenol) also decrease, without abolishing altogether, net water transport (Schatzmann et al., 1958; Oken et al., 1959; Windhager et al., 1959). Neither intratubular hydrostatic pressure, nor transtubular colloidal osmotic pressure could account for the water reabsorption seen (Windhager et al., 1959; Whittembury et al., 1959; see also Whittembury, 1960).

In its course from the proximal tubule, the intratubular urine is modified by further reabsorption of solutes without osmotically equivalent amounts of water. Thus, in the distal tubules of Necturus and Rana the fluid is definitely (though variably) hypotonic (Walker et al., 1937). In contrast to the situation in other amphibians so far studied, Xenopus laevis tubules may not reabsorb water, according to Balinsky and Baldwin (1961) who found that plasma and urine urea concentrations were identical over a wide range of plasma urea concentrations. The alternative explanation of this finding, i.e., identity of reabsorption of water and urea throughout the spectrum of conditions tested, seems somewhat less likely on a priori grounds than the absence of water reabsorption.

Sodium and potassium ions are not only reabsorbed actively from the tubular lumen into the peritubular fluid, but also appear to move passively in the opposite direction in the perfused kidney (Necturus, Rana catesbeiana; Hoshiko et al., 1956; Shipp et al., 1958; Schatzmann et al., 1958). Active sodium ion transport can lower the sodium content of the intratubular fluid to the point where concentrations as low as 2.8 ± 1.7 mEq/liter have been measured in ureteral urine of Necturus, contrasting with plasma concentrations in the range 85 to 97 mEq/liter (Shipp et al., 1958). Chloride ions may be absorbed passively, accompanying sodium ions (Walker et al., 1937), with a marked fall in concentration occurring first in the distal tubule. Phospate is reabsorbed in the proximal tubules of frogs and Necturus (Walker and Hudson, 1937c; Hogben and Bollman, 1951).

Amphibians have a limited capacity for adjusting urinary pH in regulation of the acid-base balance of the body fluids. Responses to lowered pH in Rana catesbeiana and R. limnocharis have been described by Yoshimura and co-workers (1961). In these circumstances, urinary ammonia excretion was increased, and circumstantial evidence suggested the existence of tubular exchange of sodium for hydrogen ions—a mechanism well established as participating in renal pH regulation in mammals. Adjustment of intratubular pH occurs only in the distal tubules of *Necturus* (Montgomery and Pierce, 1937; Giebisch, 1956), while Ellinger (1940) claimed that, when urinary pH was much lower than plasma pH, urinary acidification took place in the proximal tubules as well as the distal tubules of *Rana temporaria* and *R. esculenta*. Ellinger based this conclusion on a somewhat different method of investigation—microscopic study of the kidneys after administration of a fluorescent dye (fluorescein).

Glucose and xylose are reabsorbed actively, primarily in the proximal tubules in *Rana* and *Necturus* (Walker and Hudson, 1937a). Glucose showed a maximal rate of reabsorption which varied somewhat with the rate of urine flow in *Rana catesbiana* (Forster, 1938, 1942). As in other systems where glucose movement is dependent on cellular active transport, renal reabsorption of glucose was blocked by phlorizin in the frog kidney (Marshall, 1932—*Rana catesbeiana*).

For years, physiologists argued about the possibility of secretion of urea by the renal tubules of frogs. Marshall (1932) gave convincing evidence that much of the excreted urea had originally entered the urine by tubular secretion, rather than by glomerular filtration. Urea secretion has been described further by Forster (1954; Schmidt-Nielsen and Forster, 1954). Maximal urea concentrations were achieved in distal tubules of *Rana pipiens* (Walker and Hudson, 1937b). Perhaps related to this mechanism is the energy-dependent capacity of renal tissue of *Rana pipiens* to maintain urea concentrations above that of the medium under *in vitro* conditions (O'Dell and Schmidt-Nielsen, 1961). In the intact animal, some of the filtered and secreted urea seems to return to the blood stream, probably by passive diffusion (Love and Lifson, 1958). In contrast to the situation in frogs, there was no evidence of urea secretion in *Necturus maculosus* (Walker and Hudson, 1937b), nor in *Xenopus laevis* (Balinsky and Baldwin, 1961).

Amphibian kidneys, like those of other vertebrates, show active secretion by the proximal tubules of a now well known group of organic anions, including the dye phenol red, para-aminohippurate, and the organic iodine compound iodopyracet (Diodrast). In experiments with doubly labeled para-aminohippurate and iodopyracet, both of these compounds have proved to have divergent patterns of excretion as if they were actively secreted and, in addition, actively reabsorbed by the kidneys of *Necturus maculosus* (Kinter, 1959; Kinter and Tanner, 1961).

Little is known about the role of the nephrostomes in mesonephric function of urodeles. Colloidal particles (dyes, iron salts, proteins, etc.) apparently can pass rapidly from the peritoneal fluid via the nephrostomes to the renal tubules (Dawson, 1924–1925; Lambert, 1933; Rugh, 1938). The nephrostomes also serve as a secondary route for fluid transport from the extracellular fluid into the nephric tubules, bypassing the blood stream in urodeles. In pithed or anesthetized (urethane) *Necturus*, White (1929a) estimated that the rate of fluid entrance into the tubules through the nephrostomes was about 11% of the glomerular filtration rate of the corresponding nephron. Beyond this, no measurements have been found of the amounts of fluid coming directly from the peritoneum in this way, nor is it known to what extent the nephrostomes participate in regulation of the extracellular fluid.

3. Adjustment of Renal Function

Probably the single most critical function of the kidneys in aquatic amphibians is to rid the body of excess water. In these animals, but also in terrestrially adapted forms, urine is never hypertonic to plasma, and frequently is much more dilute (see, for instance, Crane, 1927; Adolph, 1927b). Even in strongly dehydrated toads, urine hypertonic to plasma was not formed (Leaf *et al.*, 1958). Marked variations in urine volume and tonicity take place, however, under varying conditions of relative hydration or dehydration. When frogs are hyperhydrated experimentally by injection of water or relatively dilute solutions subcutaneously or into the lymph sacs, diuresis ensues and the body water content returns to the normal level (Adolph, 1927b; Sawyer, 1951b; Buchborn, 1956; among others). Correlated with this is increased glomerular filtration and decreased tubular water reabsorption (Schmidt-Nielsen and Forster, 1954; Sawyer, 1957). In these circumstances, the increased filtration is not fully explained—it may result, at least in part, from circulatory changes secondary to the increased extracellular volume. The depressed tubular reabsorption has been attributed to lowered tubular endothelial permeability to water consequent to decreased secretion rate of neurohypophyseal hormones (Sawyer, 1957; Buchborn, 1956).

On the other hand, amphibians immersed in, or injected with strongly hypertonic solutions, or dehydrated by water deprivation, show a striking reduction in urine formation (Eliassen and Jørgensen, 1951). *Bufo marinus*, *Rana clamitans* and *R. catesbeiana* have definite reduction in glomerular filtration rate and increased tubular reabsorption during water deprivation (Schmidt-Nielsen and Forster, 1954; Sawyer, 1957). Even removal of frogs from water results in fall in urine flow (Adolph, 1927b) and initiates the changes in glomerular filtration and tubular reabsorption characteristic of dehydration (Schmidt-Nielsen and Forster, 1954). In this case, too, the neurohypophysis may be implicated (Eliassen and Jørgensen, 1951), althrough Jørgensen *et al.* (1956) found no difference in antidiuretic response to water deprivation between control toads (*Bufo bufo*) and toads in which the preoptic-neurohypopyseal tract had been sectioned. Administration of relatively large doses of mammalian neurohypophyseal hormones (oxytocin, vasopressin), related in physiological effects to the endogenous secretion of the amphibian neurohypophysis, is followed by shut-down of the glomerular circulation and increased tubular reabsorption of water. Details of the effects of posterior pituitary hormones on amphibian water balance will be discussed in Section IV.

Urine formation in the frog is sensitive to other changes in conditions as well—e.g., oxygen supply and body temperature (see, e.g., Adolph, 1927b, 1935; Krause, 1928; Hong, 1957; Uranga, 1961). Thus, urine flow in *Rana pipiens* decreased by 2- or 3-fold with each 10°C fall in temperature (Adolph, 1927b). This change may be dependent primarily on reduction of entrance of water into the body through the skin (Krause, 1928). Yet kidney function itself is clearly affected by temperature. Schmidt-Nielsen and Forster (1954) showed that the fall in urine flow in *Rana clamitans* subjected to cooling from room temperature to 2 to 5°C was the result of a sharp reduction in glomerular filtration rate, while renal water reabsorption also was depressed. Paralleling these changes under acute conditions are seasonal differences in kidney function. For instance, Uranga (1958d) found a much higher rate of water reabsorption (glomerular filtration less urine flow) in the toad *Bufo arenarum* in summer than in the winter. The basic mechanisms involved in these renal temperature responses are still unclear—possibly circulatory, neural, and endocrine changes combine in their development. The over-all response of Amphibia to lowered body temperature will be considered further in Section V.

IV. Control of Water Balance

A. MECHANISMS OF CONTROL

Over-all water and electrolyte balances in amphibians are regulated with precision. Even on *a priori* grounds, this would lead to speculation as to possible neural and endocrine mechanisms participating in the integration of the various processes involved.

Little is known in detail about nervous controls. There are scattered observations in the literature on formation of edema and other indications of disturbed fluid exchange in amphibians following damage to the central nervous system (e.g., Pohle, 1920; Adolph, 1934). Yet so intimately is water-electrolyte balance dependent on blood circulation, lymph heart contractions and lymph flow, endocrine control, etc., that any neural effect on one of these systems may readily affect the over-all water balance. This was recognized by early workers (for instance, Pohle, 1920). Amphibians do not tolerate easily operations as extensive as those involving the central nervous system, and results of operations are difficult to interpret in the acute stage. In chronic preparations, starvation, depressed motor activity, and disturbances of endocrine balance are major sources of error which have not, as yet, been controlled adequately. Nevertheless, there is some evidence for participation of nerves in regulation of body water content. Pohle (1920) found no clear-cut effects in *Rana esculenta* following destruction of the cerebral hemispheres, the medulla oblongata, the thoracic spinal cord, nor following denervation of the skin. Water exchange (uptake through the skin and loss via the kidneys) was increased after destruction of the optic lobes or dorsal root section. All other types of nerve damage tested (sympathectomy, destruction of the entire spinal cord, and section of all spinal roots or motor roots alone) resulted in depressed exchange. Generally, animals subjected to any of the above operations showed a net increase in water content. Adolph (1934) also described net increase of body water in *Rana pipiens* following destruction of specific parts of the brain. Lesions of the mesencephalon or medulla, but not of the optic lobes alone, resulted in a sharp increase of rate of entry of water through the skin. Kidney function was often depressed, especially when respiration was impaired, and the net effects of these operations depended in part on ambient temperatures. Pora and Stoicovici (1955) observed that destruction of various regions of the brain and spinal cord interfered with adaptations of *Bufo viridis* to media of varying tonicity. The skin and kidneys are presumptive sites for the exertion of such neural control, as suggested in Section III. All of these observations on neural participation in water balance should be reassessed in the light of the more extensive knowledge of endocrine control outlined below.

In contrast to the meager knowledge of neural regulation, a significant amount of information has been obtained about endocrine control of water balance. As pointed out previously, the neurohypophysis participates in this control, and in addition there is less detailed information about anterior pituitary, interrenal, and adrenal medullary effects on both water and electrolyte exchange. There are tenuous suggestions of effects of other hormones as well, yet clearly the field must be investigated more intensively before a satisfactory account can be given of the regulation of amphibian water balance as a whole.

Various problems arise in the study of hormonal control of water balance in Amphibia, and in the interpretation of the results. The experiments themselves are beset with sources of error, like the significant loss of sodium and chloride ions through the skin of amphibians subjected merely to rinsing or gentle handling (Jørgensen *et al.*, 1946; Krogh, 1937; Jørgensen,

1954; Bentley, 1958a). Water balance in frogs and toads is affected markedly by temperature, season (summer versus winter) (Heller, 1930; Jørgensen, 1950c; Uranga, 1958c; among others), and physiological conditions such as molting (Jørgensen, 1950c). Concomitant circulatory disturbances, accidental urine loss and other factors complicating experimental procedures may not always have been recognized, especially by early workers in the field.

Further, in many studies with amphibians, use has been made of more or less carefully purified hormones or glandular extracts from mammalian sources. Heller (1941a), Jørgensen (1950c), and others have stressed the hazards of this procedure, and it is apparent that the effects of the specific anuran water balance hormone(s) differ both qualitatively and quantitatively from those of mammalian vasopressin or neurohypophyseal extracts. Thus, for all their theoretical interest, experiments on the action of mammalian neurohypophyseal hormones on amphibian membranes and transport systems cannot be applied directly to amphibian physiology. Finally, as in so many other areas in this field, comparative data are deficient, for generally the urodeles have been neglected in studies of endocrine control of water balance.

B. THE NEUROHYPOPHYSIS

The effects of neurohypophyseal hormones on the skin, kidney, and urinary bladder have been cited previously. At all the sites listed, injected neurohypophyseal extracts may enhance membrane permeability to water and other small molecules and thus accelerate net movement of water, along osmotic gradients, into the body from hypotonic fluids and from hypotonic urine in the renal tubule and urinary bladder. Thus, body weight gains of 20 to 50%, lasting from a few hours to several days (e.g., 3) have been reported in the case of various anurans immersed in water after injection of neurohypophyseal extracts (Brunn reaction—named for Brunn's description in 1921). Ewer (1952a,b) noted that injection of posterior pituitary extracts into the toad *Bufo regularis* appeared to increase body fluid content without significant increase in the water content of muscles, liver, or skin, and concluded that the increased water load was held in lymphatic channels. Indeed, Ewer was able to demonstrate directly changes in the amount of fluid which could be collected from the femoral lymph sacs and body cavity following injections of neurohypophyseal extracts. Heller (1945) also stressed accumulation of fluid in the lymphatics in amphibians under these conditions.

There is a good deal of controversy as to the mechanism of action of injected posterior pituitary hormones in increasing body water content. The action on the skin of frogs and toads has been thought to include not only the generally accepted increase in permeability to water and other small molecules (Novelli, 1933; Sawyer, 1951a; Koefoed-Johnsen and Ussing, 1953; Andersen and Ussing, 1957; MacRobbie and Ussing, 1961; among others), but also enhancement of active sodium transport (Fuhrman and Ussing, 1951; Kalman and Ussing, 1955; Bourguet and Maetz, 1961) and a postulated specific water transport (see, for instance, Capraro and Bernini, 1952; Capraro and Garampi, 1956; Buchborn, 1956; Hong, 1957; Kirschner *et al.*, 1960). When relatively large doses of amphibian or mammalian neurohypophyseal hormones are administered to intact amphibians, or to amphibian skin *in vitro*, water moves much more rapidly through the skin. For instance, Sawyer (1951a) treated *Rana pipiens* individuals with the mammalian neurohypophyseal preparation, Pituitrin, and found that the rate of net inward movement of water increased, under otherwise constant conditions, from the control level of 4.54 ± 0.51 μl per cm^2 × hours to 26.7 ± 1.88 μl per cm^2 × hours. As total influx of water (measured with deuterium-labeled water) was not increased greatly, Koefoed-Johnsen and Ussing (1953) concluded that skin pore size was increased without increase in the area available for diffusion of water. In corroboration of this idea, it will be recalled that increase in net water uptake is paralleled by lowered skin resistance to the penetration of sodium and chloride ions, and to certain small molecules (thiourea, glucose, etc.— Andersen and Ussing, 1957). MacRobbie and Ussing (1961) found that the increase in permeability to water was localized at the relatively impermeable outward-facing permeability barrier of the frog skin. Capraro and Bernini (1952) and Capraro and Garampi (1956) postulated an "active" electroosmotic water transfer under the influence of neurohypophyseal hormones. Buchborn (1956), too, observed that water movement after posterior pituitary injections was disproportionate to osmotic differentials. Hong (1957) found that injected hormones did not accelerate net water movement into the body of frogs (*Rana pipiens*) subjected to cold (1°C), anoxia, or poisoning with several metabolic inhibitors (iodoacetate, cyanide), and so inferred that the incremental water influx through the skin after injection of these hormones must be mediated actively by cells. More recently, Bourguet and Maetz (1961) have stressed the lack of parallel changes in active sodium transport and water movement across the skin of *Rana esculenta* under the influence of neurohypophyseal peptides. From this, they have argued that these hormones have independent actions on the epithelial cell sites for active transport and water permeability. As yet, these observations and hypotheses have not been reconciled in the development of a single, consistent explanation of neurohypophyseal control of the skin.

Like the skin, the urinary bladder of the toad is highly sensitive to neurohypophyseal hormones. Leaf and co-workers (1958, 1960) presented data showing that oxytocin and vasopressin increased net sodium transport if they were placed on the serosal side of the *Bufo marinus* bladder *in vitro*. On the mucosal side, they were without effect. Loss of water from the body from the urinary bladder of anurans is minimized by enhanced reabsorption into the body following administration of neurohypophyseal hormones (Ewer, 1952a,b; Sawyer and Schisgall, 1956; Uranga and Quintana, 1958). Leaf and co-workers have suggested that a primary effect of these hormones is to decrease the relative impermeability of the mucosal surface of the bladder epithelial cells to water and other substances (Hays *et al.*, 1959; Leaf, 1960). By permitting freer access to the intracellular site where the active sodium transporting system may operate, neurohypophyseal hormones could thus increase the rate of operation of this transporting system. Sawyer (1960b), too, stated that the primary effect of neurohypophyseal hormones on the frog bladder was to increase the cellular permeability to water. Yet Bentley (1961) found that there was a differential effect on water permeability in the two directions, serosal to mucosal versus mucosal to serosal, since the movement in the latter direction was increased to a far greater degree by vasopressin. This led to the suggestion that neurohypophyseal hormones could not simply operate to increase membrane "pore size" indiscriminately. As in the case of the skin, the bladder of *Rana esculenta* showed some independence of effects of neurohypophyseal hormones on water permeability and on active transport of sodium, according to the observations of Bourguet and Maetz (1961).

Finally, it is definite that renal function is changed by increased concentration of neurohypophyseal hormones circulating in the body fluids. Decreased urine flow is attributed to decreased glomerular filtration and also to increased tubular reabsorption of water. At least with large doses of neurohypophyseal hormones, reduced blood flow and filtration occur in the glomeruli (Richards and Schmidt, 1924–1925; Sawyer, 1951b; Sawyer and Sawyer, 1952). Uranga (1958a), however, found no change in glomerular filtration (inulin clearance) in response to injection of neurohypophyseal extracts or vasopressin in the toad *Bufo arenarum*. Beyond this, water reabsorption in the renal tubules may increase in frogs and toads (Pasqualini, 1938, cited by Sawyer, 1957; Sawyer, 1957; Uranga, 1958a), although here, as in the case of studies of glomerular filtration rate, the results reported by various workers are not consistent. When large doses of neurohypophyseal hormones are given, or if urine is collected from the bladder, effects on the tubules may be masked (Sawyer, 1957). Sawyer and Sawyer (1952), for instance, did not note change in tubular reabsorption in *Bufo marinus* after injection of a mammalian pituitary extract

(Pituitrin). Later studies by Sawyer (1957) and others have given clear evidence of increased tubular reabsorption after injections of neurohypophyseal hormones. In these circumstances, the osmotic pressure of the urine may rise toward that of plasma. Since "free water clearance" was decreased by injection of these hormones, without concomitant speeding of osmolyte reabsorption, Sawyer suggested that the primary effect of neurohypophyseal hormones on renal tubules might be similar to their effect on the skin and bladder—increase in water permeability. This suggestion has received support from recent studies of Whittembury and co-workers (1960) on mesonephric (largely proximal tubular) slices from *Necturus maculosus*. The average equivalent pore radius for the tissue cells was estimated at 5.6 Å before treatment with a mammalian antidiuretic extract (the commercial preparation Pitressin), while after the treatment the equivalent pore radius had risen to 6.5 Å.

In general, in both frogs and toads the renal response (antidiuresis) to neurohypophyseal hormones is seen at far smaller dose levels than are the skin and bladder responses (Jørgensen, 1950c; Buchborn, 1956; Uranga, 1958d). For instance, Jørgensen (1950c) could detect an effect on urine flow in the toad, *Bufo bufo*, on injection of toad neurohypophyseal substances (extracted in 0.25% acetic acid) corresponding to 1/2,000 to 1/20,000 of the initial mass of the gland. An effect on cutaneous water uptake was noted only when 1/200 to 1/2,000 of the initial gland material had been injected. These observations have led to queries as to the physiological relevance of the increased water uptake of the skin seen in Brunn reactions following injection of large doses of exogenous pituitary extracts (Buchborn, 1956). It may be noted that *Xenopus laevis* differs from other anurans so far studied, since in this animal injections of posterior pituitary hormones affect the skin water uptake without, apparently, any significant suppression of urine formation (Ewer, 1952b).

Amphibian species vary in their sensitivity to neurohypophyseal hormones. Thus, among anurans, the skin of the frog *Rana temporaria* was far less sensitive to amphibian neurohypophyseal extracts, as judged by net water uptake, than was the skin of the toad *Bufo bufo* (Jørgensen, 1950c). The two species were more nearly comparable in sensitivity of the kidneys to these extracts, although the frogs were definitely less sensitive than the toads. The latter finding was confirmed in comparisons of *Rana catesbeiana*, *R. pipiens*, and *Bufo marinus* by Sawyer and Sawyer (1952). There is extensive literature on the differential responses of amphibians to mammalian neurohypophyseal hormones. The skin and kidneys of toads (*Bufo bufo, B. marinus, B. arenarum, B. regularis, B. carens*) are much more sensitive to vasopressin than to oxytocin (Jørgensen, 1950c; Sawyer and Sawyer, 1952; Uranga, 1958c,d; Ewer, 1952a,b; among others) whereas in frogs (*Rana temporaria, R. catesbeiana, R. pipiens*) the sensitivity is greater to oxytocin (Oldham, 1936; Boyd and Whyte, 1939; Sawyer and Sawyer, 1952). *Xenopus laevis* shows relatively low and equal sensitivity to both hormones (Ewer, 1952b). As compared with anurans, urodeles have shown lesser increases in net body water content after injections of neurohypophyseal hormones. The largest gains in body weight recorded after injection of neurohypophyseal preparations have been of the order of 10% or less in *Necturus* and *Ambystoma* (Bĕlehrádek and Huxley, 1927; Steggerda, 1937; Dow and Zuckerman, 1938; Jørgensen *et al.*, 1946). Since urodele hormones have never been tested on the homologous species, positive conclusions cannot be drawn from these observations. It is quite possible, however, that aquatic forms, as compared with terrestrially adapted amphibians, may give less response to the water balance hormones (Heller, 1945). In this connection, Ewer (1952b) stressed the weak response of *Xenopus laevis*, an aquatic species, as compared with any of the other anurans that have been tested. It has been suggested that increasing sensitivity of target sites (kidneys, skin) may have played a part in amphibian adaptation to life on land (e.g., Jørgensen, 1950c; Ewer, 1952a,b).

Despite the large mass of data on water balance effects of injected neurohypophyseal hormones, it is still not fully established how, and to what extent, the neurohypophysis participates in water balance in the intact amphibian under ordinary and stress conditions. Thus, it has been shown convincingly that the neurohypophyseal content of substances implicated in water and electrolyte regulation is reduced during dehydration of frogs and toads (Levinsky and Sawyer, 1953; Jørgensen *et al.*, 1956; Uranga, 1957). Hormones thus mobilized from the neurohypophysis would certainly be expected to affect water absorption and excretion, at least in the highly sensitive toad. In line with this hypothesis, Adolph (1927a), Eliassen and Jørgensen (1951), and others found that frogs (*Rana pipiens, R. temporaria*) and toads (*Bufo bufo*) showed a depressed rate of urine formation when the osmotic pressure of their body fluids was raised by injection of, or body immersion in hypertonic solutions. This observation, and the increased rate of water uptake through the skin in toads, suggested that the animals might have increased levels of circulating water balance principles (Eliassen and Jørgensen, 1951; Buchborn, 1956). Besides, experimental injections of mammalian posterior pituitary hormones slow dehydration and increase survival time of anurans (e.g., Boyd and Whyte, 1938, 1939; Sawyer, 1951b), perhaps chiefly by facilitating water conservation by the kidneys and urinary bladder.

It is well known that, in mammals, removal of the neurohypophysis results in chronic increase in urine formation, and a similar result has been noted in anurans following neurohypophysectomy or hypothalamic lesions (Pohle, 1920, and others cited by Heller, 1945), with or without parenteral administration of saline or immersion in water (Pasqualini, 1936). In the toad, *Bufo arenarum*, urine flow was enhanced by hypophysectomy only in summer animals (Uranga, 1958c,d). In spite of the changed rate of urine flow, body weight and over-all water balance are not conspicuously changed by neurohypophysectomy in anurans. Further, removal or denervation of the neurohypophysis apparently does not impair greatly the anuran's response to dehydration. Levinsky and Sawyer (1953) found that total hypophysectomy did not accelerate dehydration of *Rana pipiens*, although the condition was accompanied by a somewhat slower than normal rehydration rate after reexposure to water. Heller (1945) stated, too, that hypophysectomy did not affect dehydration in frogs, and Jørgensen and co-workers (1956) were unable to observe any differences in response to dehydration or rehydration between control toads (*Bufo bufo*) and toads after transection of the supraopticohypophyseal tract and degeneration of the posterior pituitary. Uranga (1958d) found that the sharp fall in urine flow of toads (*Bufo arenarum*) exposed to hypertonic sucrose was unchanged by hypophysectomy, removal of the pars distalis, or transection of the preoptic-hypophyseal tract.

Although the mechanisms involved in posterior pituitary release of hormones controlling water balance have not been worked out as yet, it has been assumed tentatively that blood tonicity may be a major controlling factor in amphibians, as in mammals (Jørgensen, 1950c). There is seasonal variation in the amount of active neurohypophyseal substance that can be detected in the hypophysis and brain. Uranga (1957) found that antidiuretic activity was much higher in summer than in winter in the parts of the *Bufo arenarum* brain which gave this reaction (choroid plexus of the third ventricle; preoptic nucleus; infundibulum; neurohypophysis). Finally, there appear to be significant differences among anurans in the amounts of neurohypophyseal hormones present in the posterior pituitary. Thus, Jørgensen (1950c) found that the toad (*Bufo bufo*) neurohypophysis contained far more water balance principle than did that of the frog, *Rana temporaria*.

Amphibian neurohypophyses contain more than one active substance, probably including oxytocin, an octapeptide widely distributed in the vertebrate series (Sawyer *et al.*, 1959). Recently Acher *et al.* (1960), Sawyer and co-workers (1959; Sawyer 1960a,b), and Heller and Pickering (1961) have presented evidence, from amino acid identification and assays of antidiuresis in the toad, water permeability of the frog bladder, and other biological test systems, for the identification of a characteristic water balance principle of anuran (*Rana catesbeiana, R. temporaria, Bufo americanus, B. bufo*) neurohypophyses as arginine vasotocin (8-arginine oxytocin). Arginine vasotocin is a cyclic octapeptide distinct from both oxytocin and vasopressin, the mammalian antidiuretic hormone of the neurohypophysis, in chemical structure and physiological properties (Katsoyannis and du Vigneaud, 1958; Acher *et al.*, 1960; Uranga and Sawyer, 1960; see also Chapter 7). Maetz and co-workers (1959) and Morel *et al.* (1961) distinguish another active substance in extracts of *Rana esculenta* neurohypophysis, separable from arginine vasotocin and having a primary effect of enhancing sodium transport by the isolated frog skin. Beyond these recent observations, little is known of the identity of amphibian water balance hormones in general. Information bearing on the urodeles is particularly meager.

C. ADRENAL AND ADENOHYPOPHYSEAL HORMONES

It has been noted previously that adrenaline stimulated active chloride transport from the inside to the outside of the isolated frog skin (Koefoed-Johnsen *et al.*, 1952). Possibly related to this phenomenon is adrenaline stimulation of secretion of an unidentified protein-containing material from the skin glands of *Xenopus laevis* (Bastian and Zarrow, 1954). Apparently, adrenaline is without effect on sodium transport by the toad bladder (Leaf *et al.*, 1958). The only other known water balance effect of adrenaline is on the kidneys. Here, as noted previously, injected adrenaline (and noradrenaline?) may affect markedly the glomerular circulation and filtration. Both increase and decrease in glomerular perfusion have been observed in anesthetized amphibians, the varied results correlated, apparently, with dose and differential sensitivity of renal and systemic vessels (Richards and Schmidt, 1924–1925; Adolph, 1936a; Forster, 1943). Adolph (1936a), however, found no consistent effect on urine flow of large doses of adrenaline injected into intact *Rana pipiens*.

Amphibian interrenal tissue appears to play an important part in water balance, as does the physiologically related mammalian adrenal cortex. Fowler and Chester Jones (1955; Chester Jones, 1957a,b) described the effects of interrenalectomy in *Rana temporaria*. These were strikingly dependent on the season. In the active "summer" frog, progressive hyperhydration followed interrenalectomy and death ensued within 24 to 48 hr. On the other hand, "winter" frogs tolerated the operation fairly well, disturbances in water balance were relatively slight, and the animals survived up to several months. Interrenalectomy enhanced the rate of sodium loss from the body, particularly in summer frogs. Absolute levels of sodium in the tissues fell, potassium was unchanged, and water content increased. The importance of the electrolyte disturbances in the over-all effects of interrenalectomy was stressed by the observation that even summer frogs could survive for long periods after the operation if immersed in salt solutions (e.g., 0.73% NaCl) rather than in water. When animals were kept in frog Ringer's solution, sodium and potassium contents were similar to those in control frogs.

Interrenal participation in water balance regulation has been attributed in part to primary effects of the hormones on the skin and urinary bladder. In addition, on the basis of fragmentary evidence, both the kidneys and tissue cells in general have been implicated in these effects. Total interrenalectomy was followed by death of *Rana pipiens* individuals in about 10 days in experiments of Bishop *et al.* (1961), but prior to this there were definite changes in the skin. These included an increase in electrical resistance and a decrease in the current generated by the short-circuited skin, attributed to decreased active transport of sodium (Bishop *et al.*, 1961). These effects were reversed only partially by adrenal cortical hormones (aldosterone, hydrocortisone). Williams and Angerer (1959) studied the electrical potential difference across the skin of frogs subjected to adrenalectomy, "control renal damage," and injection of a commercial mammalian cortical extract. Adrenalectomy lowered, and cortical extract injection increased, the skin potential difference. In general confirmation of these findings are reports of increase in rate and duration of active transport of sodium ions from the epithelium toward the corium across the isolated skin treated with various adrenal steroids (Taylor and Weinstein, 1952; Taubenhaus, *et al.*, 1956; McAfee and Locke, 1961). The hormones act on both sides of the membrane, though more effectively when placed on the outside (epithelial side), according to Taylor and Weinstein (1952). Taubenhaus and Morton (1958) found than not only sodium and potassium ions move across the skin under the influence of adrenal hormones, but also unidentified substances of marked osmotic activity. Sodium ion transport by the isolated bladder of *Bufo marinus* was enhanced by aldosterone administration, or by conditions stimulating *in vivo* production of aldosterone by the interrenal glands (Crabbé 1961a,b).

Angerer (1942) found that tissues of adrenalectomized frogs (*Rana pipiens*) had a higher water content than control tissues, and later Angerer and Angerer (1949) described decrease in rate of net water loss of adrenalectomized frogs as compared with controls, although the adrenalectomized animals were more sensitive to water loss than were sham-operated or renal-damaged controls. These findings are not inconsistent with those of Westphal (1957) who described decrease in sodium and potassium reabsorption, with unimpaired rates of water and glucose reabsorption in perfused kidneys of *R. esculenta* following interrenalectomy. Fowler (cited by Chester Jones, 1957a) observed faster renal excretion of sodium ions in interrenalectomized *Rana temporaria*, irrespective of season.

Additional experiments have been carried out to assess the effects of treatment of amphibians with mammalian adrenal cortical extracts, hormones, and related compounds (aldosterone, deoxycorticosterone glucoside, hydrocortisone, 2-methyl-9-fluorohydrocortisone). Early observations included those of Dow and Zuckerman (1938), who injected mammalian adrenal cortical extracts into axolotls and found that the animals showed significant, though not consistent weight loss. Pasqualini and Riseau (1951) reported that toads injected with deoxycorticosterone glucoside gain weight in sodium chloride solutions but not in water, indicating, perhaps, a specific effect of the steroid on skin transport of sodium. More recent studies have demonstrated an increase in current generated by the isolated, short-circuited frog skin following injections into the whole animal of aldosterone. Crabbé (1961a) described the effects of injection of aldosterone into intact *Bufo marinus* individuals maintained for several days in distilled water or saline solution (125 mEq Na per liter). Although plasma electrolytes were not affected greatly, the excretion of sodium and chloride ions was increased, and potassium loss in the urine decreased. Aldosterone injections increased the sodium uptake of intact frogs maintained in an isotonic (0.7%) sodium chloride medium (Maetz *et al.*, 1958). It should be noted that aldosterone is one of the cortical steroids which has been established as occurring in amphibian (*Rana catesbeiana*, *Bufo marinus*) interrenal tissues and blood (Carstensen *et al.*, 1961; Crabbé, 1961b).

Interrenal function is dependent on adenohypophyseal control in amphibians, as in mammals. Adenohypophysectomy is followed by tissue electrolyte changes reminiscent of those seen after interrenalectomy (Chester Jones, 1957a,b), and these changes can be reversed by injection of ACTH (adrenocorticotropic hormone). ACTH stimulates aldosterone release by adrenal tissues (*Rana catesbeiana*) *in vitro* (Carstensen *et al.*, 1961). Further, ACTH has definite effects on amphibian water balance. Generally, these are implied to be secondary to ACTH stimulation of the interrenal tissue. For instance, ACTH injections in axolotls increased the rate of sodium and chloride uptake through the skin (Koefoed-Johnsen and Ussing, 1949), an effect which is consistent with the known action of adrenal cortical hormones on sodium ion transport. Removal of the entire hypophysis abolishes or reduces greatly the water balance response of anurans (Jones and Steggerda, 1935; Chen *et al.*, 1943), and this effect may be reversed partially by injection of mammalian ACTH (Levinsky and Sawyer, 1952). Skin taken from adenohypophysectomized frogs showed a marked increase in outward flux of sodium (passive permeability to sodium ions) through the skin, reversible by treatment with aldosterone or ACTH (Meyers *et al.*, 1956, 1961). Bishop *et al.* (1961) noted that hypophysectomy decreased, while interrenalectomy did not change passive permeability of the skin to sodium. These authors suggested that the different effects of adenohypophysectomy and interrenalectomy might be caused by the great differential in survival time of animals subjected to the two operations, for destruction of the interrenal tissue is compatible with only brief survival. Previously, Fowler and Chester Jones (1955) had reported that interrenalectomy *per se* increased skin permeability to sodium. Huf and Wills (1953) described decreased trans-skin sodium transport in experiments with isolated skins of frogs pretreated with ACTH. This finding was not consistent with most of the results of other workers on skin effects of ACTH, but the authors themselves questioned the purity of the hormone preparation which they used. The skins tested did not respond directly to adrenal cortical steroids. It is possible, too, that the apparently anomalous effects of ACTH in this instance resulted from pretreatment of the animals with excessive doses of the hormone, for this may result in overstimulation and subsequent depression of adrenal function (data cited by Chester Jones, 1957a; Jørgensen, 1962).

One additional way in which the hypophysis participates in water economy may be mentioned at this point. The terrestrial eft stage of newts and other urodeles migrate to ponds in response to what is interpreted as a powerful "water drive." This behavior is absent in hypophysectomized efts, and the pattern can be restored specifically by injection of anterior pituitary extracts from mammals, as well as from teleost sources (Chadwick, 1941; Grant and Grant, 1958; Grant and Pickford, 1959). The mammalian hormone which is capable of restoring the water drive is prolactin (Chadwick, 1940).

D. OTHER HORMONES

The thyroid gland has been implicated as a possible participant in the water balance response to neurohypophyseal hormones. Heller (1930) found that thyroxine enhanced the reaction of winter frogs to mammalian neurohypophyseal extracts, while Levinsky and Sawyer (1952) showed that thyroxine was necessary, as a supplement to ACTH, for restoration of the water balance response to pitocin (mammalian posterior pituitary preparation), in hypophysectomized *Rana pipiens*. Moreover, in a few experiments in axolotls, Koefoed-Johnsen and Ussing (1949) observed enhanced uptake of sodium and chloride through the skin following thyroxine injections. As yet, these results do not cast much light on the physiological role of the thyroid in over-all water balance.

Dow and Zuckerman (1938) injected a variety of mammalian hormones into axolotls, and followed weight changes over the course of the next few hours. Injections of testosterone, estrone, and progesterone were followed by slight and transient increase in body weight, considered significant by the experimenters. Taubenhaus and co-workers (1956) could demonstrate slight increases in osmotic pressure of fluids held in sacs of isolated frog skins treated with high concentrations of estriol while testosterone was without effect. Unfortunately, such fragmentary observations leave unanswered the question whether sex hormones normally participate in water balance regulation in amphibians.

V. Exchange between the Amphibian and the Environment

A. OVER-ALL EXCHANGE

Most amphibians live in environments which are either characterized by the presence of fresh water, containing little solute as compared with the body fluids of the animal, or else in terrestrial habitats where water as such may be scarce yet the environment is not hypertonic with respect to solutes. Consequently, the major problems in general amphibian water balance are regulation against excessive gain or loss of water. Members of the other vertebrate classes frequently show adaptation to marine and other environments where absolute gain or loss of osmolytes represent the major threat to body water balance. Such situations are rare in amphibians and, with a few notable exceptions, have been studied only under artificial experimental conditions.

This section will present a brief discussion of responses of amphibians to each of four major stresses affecting water balance, namely: (1) excess water intake; (2) excess water loss; (3) exposure to media of high osmotic pressure—absolute increase in body content of osmolytes; (4) absolute decrease in body content of osmolytes. Amphibians exposed to such stresses show characteristic responses involving all the routes of exchange, although the skin and kidneys are of prime importance quantitatively.

1. Excess Water Intake

In general, except when subjected to severe experimental manipulation, normal adult amphibians rarely show acute increase in body water, even though they may spend much of their lives immersed in water. This is as true of the terrestrially adapted forms like *Bufo bufo* as it is of fully aquatic amphibians like *Necturus* and some ranids. Yet water moves continuously and fairly rapidly through the skin into the body, e.g., at rates of about 30% (5 to 93%) of the body weight per 24 hr in *Rana pipiens* at room temperature (about 24°C) (Adolph, 1927b; Sawyer, 1951a; among others). This inward movement of water appears to result primarily from osmotic gradients between body fluids and the ambient medium, as noted in Section III,A. The kidneys play a major role in stabilizing body water load, for urine formation parallels closely the net skin uptake of water (see, for instance, Adolph, 1927a—*Rana* sp.; Ewer, 1952a—*Bufo regularis*). Thus, if the cloacal orifice is obstructed so that urine is retained in the bladder and lower gastrointestinal tract, amphibians show a progressive increase in weight. If the cloacal orifice is then opened and the collected urine expelled, the volume of accumulated urine can be shown to equal almost exactly the net increase in body weight (Adolph, 1927a). Over-all water turnover has been estimated in a variety of amphibians as ranging from 22 to 117% of the body weight per day at 20°C in *Rana pipiens, R. temporaria, Bufo vulgaris, Triton marmoratus*, etc. (Spector, 1956).

There are two frequently studied situations in which marked deviations may be observed from balance between skin uptake of water and urinary excretion rate. Frogs which are exposed to cold (8°C and below) while immersed in water show gains in body weight up to 20% of the control level (Adolph, 1927b; P. Rey, 1937, cited by Jørgensen, 1950c; Jørgensen, 1950a; Schmidt-Nielsen and Forster, 1954; Hong, 1957). Such increases are observed, for instance, in frogs hibernating in ponds in winter in the temperate zones (de Haan, cited by Jørgensen, 1950a). The second set of conditions in which frank hyperhydration of the body has been studied intensively involves increase in circulating blood levels of vertebrate posterior pituitary hormones (Brunn reaction—see Section IV).

The hyperhydration seen in chilled frogs cannot be attributed to increased skin permeability to water, for water moves somewhat faster into frogs at 30°C than at 0°C (Krause, 1928; Hevesy *et al.*, 1935). Water uptake may accompany excessive accumulation of electrolytes—particularly sodium and chloride ions—according to Jørgensen (1950a), but in both *Rana esculenta* and *R. pipiens* net water load is increased even if the animals are immersed in water (Jørgensen, 1950a; Hong, 1957). Thus, while water uptake persists, change of kidney function is implicated as a major cause for the onset of hyperhydration in the cold. Indeed, Adolph (1927b) showed that urine flow changed markedly with temperature, decreasing 2- or 3-fold for each 10°C drop in temperature between 24 and 1°C. Krause (1928) explained his comparable results on the basis of decreased skin uptake of water, however, rather than by depressed kidney function. Jørgensen (1950a) stated that a differential effect of cold on renal function could be demonstrated, with water excretory mechanisms less severely depressed than renal processes involved in salt elimination. Thus, water injected into chilled frogs was eliminated more rapidly than injected hypertonic solutions.

Schmidt-Nielsen and Forster (1954) found that frogs (*Rana clamitans*) cooled from room temperature to 2 to 5°C failed to form urine for 12 to 18 hr while the body increased in weight progressively by about 5 to 6%. Later, urine formation began again, but remained at a relatively low level—about 25% of the rate at 20 to 25°C. Since glomerular filtration rate was depressed even more than urine flow, Schmidt-Nielsen and Forster concluded that tubular reabsorption of water and solutes was depressed disproportionately as compared with glomerular filtration. Throughout the period of chilling, the body fluids remained dilute in comparison with control values. For instance, plasma chloride concentration averaged 90 mM in chilled animals and 111 mM in controls. Only when the animals were warmed was the excess water load removed. J. de Haan (1927, cited by Jørgensen, 1950a) had shown previously that resolution of the excess fluid load of chilled green frogs involved a copious flow of chloride-rich urine when the animals were placed in a warm environment. In general agreement with these findings, Parsons and van Rossum (1961) described increased liver cell hydration and serum dilution in frogs (*Rana temporaria*) exposed to temperatures of 4°C. The authors suggested that intracellular accumulation of organic anions might account for the swelling of the liver tissue.

Scattered observations have been reported indicating that the changes in body water mass and urine function in the experimental animal are paralleled by changes in amphibians under normal conditions. As noted above, hibernating frogs are hyperhydrated as compared with their condition when normally active during the warm months of the year. Ott (1924) showed that hyperhydrated hibernating frogs (*Rana pipiens*) had normal or even lowered water content in most of the tissues. Thus, it seems likely that the major part of the excess fluid is located extracellularly (in lymphatic channels). According to Uranga (1958a), the rate of glomerular filtration was nearly six times as high in the summer as in the winter in *Bufo arenarum*.

2. Excess Water Loss

Numerous studies have been made to assess the rate and intensity of dehydration occurring in amphibians as a result of water deprivation. For the most part, this work has been carried out by ecologists. Frequently, their studies have been motivated by interest in the general problems involved in vertebrate adaptation to terrestrial life (Thorson and Svihla, 1943; Thorson, 1955). Beyond this, such studies may aid in explaining the existence of amphibian "preferences" for habitats ranging from completely aquatic to nearly completely terrestrial (Thorson and Svihla, 1943; Littleford et al., 1947). The work bears directly on amphibian physiology in that it provides some quantitative evidence about rates of water exchange, and some clues to modes of adjustment and regulation of exchange.

Generally in these studies, individuals of varying species have been exposed to a moving stream of dry air while body weight changes have been followed in order to assess the rate of water loss. In these extreme experimental conditions, many sources of error are inherent, as Ray (1958) and others have emphasized. These sources of error include local variations and irregularities in air temperature and relative humidity, and the possible recirculation of air. Results may vary depending on the absolute rate at which drying takes place. Individuals and species vary, too, in behavioral responses (struggling, changes in body position, etc.) and in volume to surface area ratios. These complicate comparisons between measurements of individuals of a given species, and are still more troublesome in interspecific or intergeneric comparisons. It has been stressed repeatedly that survival of a given species may be determined critically by the events of, and capacity to tolerate, milder degrees of dehydration, rather than the extreme degrees produced under the laboratory conditions typically used (see, e.g., Jørgensen, 1950c; Ray, 1958). Similarly, detailed analyses of physiological adjustments to dehydration could be carried out in a more meaningful way if less rigorous conditions were used. Nevertheless, some consistent conclusions may be drawn. As compared with reptiles, birds, and mammals, amphibians show extremely rapid rates of dehydration in dry air. For instance, *Rana pipiens* individuals allowed to dry in air at 23 to 26°C (relative humidity 20 to 29%) lost an average of 52% of their body weight in 29 hr (Smith and Jackson, 1931). A striking example was given by Thorson (1955) who compared the water loss of a reptile, *Thamnophis sirtalis*, and an amphibian, *Rana pipiens*, of comparable body weight. Frogs lost about 13% of the body weight as water in 2 to 4 hr. The snake lost an equivalent fraction of its water mass in 7 days.

Amphibians can tolerate significant losses of water (7 to 60% of the body weight). Maximal tolerance figures were obtained in studies with anurans, although some terrestrial urodeles can survive up to 30 to 40% loss of body water. Severe desiccation results in death in a relatively brief period. In a group of salamanders of varying species studied by Ray (1958), even the most resistant of the animals exposed to a stream of dry air (temperature about 22°C; humidity about 2%) died within 1 to 5 hours. The more rapid the dehydration, the less is tolerable (Kunde, 1857; Durig, 1901; and others, cited by Ozorio de Almeida, 1926). The differential effects of fast as compared with slow drying have been attributed to greater damage to the rapidly dehydrated skin, as evidenced by striking changes in contour, strength, color, etc., with drying (Ozorio de Almeida, 1926).

Most of the recent studies in this field agree in the conclusion that amphibians which live normally in fully terrestrial or semiaquatic conditions (e.g., *Scaphiopus hammondii, Bufo boreas*) survive dehydration longer, and can endure larger losses of water than can fully aquatic or semiaquatic forms (*Rana pipiens, R. grylio, Rhyacotriton olympicus*, and others) (Thorson and Svihla, 1943; Ray, 1958).

The major route of water loss in a dry environment is the skin. Water evaporates rapidly from the skin surface, at a rate comparable with the evaporation from a free water surface (Overton, 1904, and Rey, 1937, cited by Jørgensen, 1950c). In contrast, renal water excretion slows and stops early in the dehydration process. Thus, Schmidt-Nielsen and Forster (1954) subjected *Rana clamitans* individuals to relatively mild dehydration by removing them from water and allowing them to remain in the laboratory air at ordinary room temperature. Within the first hour, the rate of glomerular filtration (estimated from creatinine clearance) fell by a few per cent, but in the next hour it had fallen to half the control level. Meanwhile, conservation of water by reabsorption in the tubules was increased by 4-fold, and correspondingly the urine flow showed a reduction to a fraction of its initial level. Comparable results with other anurans have been described by Sawyer (1957). Water reabsorption in the urinary bladder is faster in dehydrated frogs and toads than under normal conditions (see Section III, C). It may be noted at this point that water synthesis in oxidative processes is negligible compared with skin and urinary exchanges. For instance, Adolph (1932) estimated metabolic water production as 1.6 mg per hour in a 30-gm *Rana pipiens* individual, whereas water uptake across the skin of such an animal after 15 to 35% body weight loss by desiccation averaged 800 mg per hour.

The relatively greater tolerance of dehydration shown by terrestrial amphibians has led to speculation as to possible physiological and behavioral adjustments which may aid the individual in survival. There has been considerable controversy as to whether the skins of terrestrial amphibians are or are not less permeable to water than those of aquatic species. F. Scala (1936, cited by Thorson, 1955) and Cohen (1952) among others found lower water permeability in skins of terrestrial amphibians. Skin structure and thickness vary among amphibian species, and also change during dehydration (Steinbach, 1927). Possibly the mucous secretion observed, for instance, by Ray (1958) in dehydrated salamanders of the genera *Batrachoceps* and *Aneides* may reduce skin water loss. On the other hand, Thorson (1955), who discussed the problem in detail from the point of view of sources of error, was unable in his own work to demonstrate correlation between rate of water loss and adaptation to terrestrial versus aquatic habitat in 5 species of anurans. Essentially similar results had been obtained by Littleford *et al.* (1947), working with a group of several species of plethodont salamanders. In any case, the rate of water loss is rapid in all amphibians, and apparently differences between species in this respect do not account for critical differences in over-all capacity of the animal to endure intense, rapid dehydration.

Although the neurohypophysis has been considered a probable participant in adjustment against dehydration (Section IV), its importance in survival has not been established. Of other factors which play a part in species toleration of dehydration, virtually nothing is known. Circulatory, neural, and extraneurohypophyseal endocrine factors may be guessed at as participants in the reaction to severe dehydration. Metabolic adjustments may take place as well. Thus, nitrogenous wastes can be stored in the body in the relatively nontoxic form of urea (e.g., in *Bufo calamita*; Balinsky *et al.*, 1961). Further, as mentioned in Section III,D, nitrogen metabolism may be responsive to change in body hydration, for urea, rather than ammonia, is synthesized by *Xenopus laevis* individuals subjected to dehydration by water deprivation or exposure to hypertonic salt solutions (Balinsky *et al.*, 1961). Body contour, and other variables including, perhaps, sex, may play a part in the over-all response (Thorson, 1955; Ray, 1958). Littleford *et al.* (1947) found in a variety of salamanders no evidence of progressive slowing of dehydration with time, and the authors concluded from this observation that these animals lack physiological mechanisms for water conservation. Thorson (1956), too, found no deceleration—rather a late increase in rate—of body weight loss with progressive dehydration of *Rana pipiens*, *R. clamitans*, and *Scaphiopus hammondii*. On the other hand, when survivors of severe desiccation were subjected to a second dehydration procedure, many of the animals showed a slight but consistent decrease in water loss, possibly suggesting that rudimentary water conservation mechanisms had been activated by the initial dehydration. The nature of such mechanisms is, of course, entirely unknown.

Desiccated amphibians placed in direct contact with water rehydrate rapidly. Individuals of some species may survive at least 40 to 60% loss of body water (Thorson and Svihla, 1943). Usually rehydration to the initial level is completed within 12 to 26 hr (Smith and Jackson, 1931; Thorson and Svihla, 1943, and others). Water is taken in only through the skin, when there is direct contact with liquid water, for, as noted in Section III,C, drinking of water does not occur, and water cannot be absorbed even from saturated air (Adolph, 1932; Thorson, 1955). Several workers have found that the rate of water penetration through the skin, both in normally hydrated and dehydrated animals, is correlated with habitat, so that the fastest uptake occurs in terrestrial forms and the slowest in aquatic amphibians (Jørgensen, 1950c; Bentley *et al.*, 1958). A striking comparison of this sort was described by Ewer (1952b) between

Bufo regularis and *Xenopus laevis*. Normally, *Bufo* took up water far faster than did *Xenopus*, and this difference was magnified by dehydration. Control rates for animals of comparable size (about 30 to 40 gm) under comparable conditions (temperature, etc.) were about 2 gm per 100 gm body weight per hour for *Xenopus*, and about 5.5 to 7 gm per 100 gm body weight per hour for *Bufo*. After desiccation with loss of 10 to 19% of the body weight, the animals were rehydrated by immersion in water. In *Bufo*, the rate of water uptake had increased several fold, to range from 3 to 7 times the control rate. In contrast, in *Xenopus* it was slightly decreased, unchanged, or increased by a maximum of 27%. It would not be fair to generalize, however, about responses of terrestrial and aquatic forms from comparisons between *Bufo regularis* and *Xenopus laevis*, for although *Xenopus* normally lives in water, it may survive by estivation severe drying under natural conditions (Alexander and Bellerby, 1938). Beyond this, there is not yet full agreement that habitat and maximal rate of rehydration are correlated (Thorson, 1955).

3. Exposure to Media of High Osmotic Pressure—Absolute Increase in Body Osmolytes

Most amphibians are not able to survive more than brief exposure to media of high electrolyte content (e.g., about 0.22 M sodium chloride; Przylecki, 1922, among others). Water balance is conspicuously distorted, but the causes of death under these circumstances are still unclear. In a few cases, adult and larval amphibians have been described in environments where the available water had relatively high salt contents (Pearse, 1911, cited by Pearse, 1950; bibliographies in Schmidt, 1957; Ruibal, 1959, among others). In a nearly unique physiological study of such animals, Gordon *et al.* (1961) worked with *Rana cancrivora*, a euryhaline frog living in mangrove swamps on the Gulf of Thailand. These frogs can tolerate media of unusually high salinity (up to about 28 parts per thousand, or about 0.48 M sodium chloride). Net water uptake through the relatively water-permeable skin occurs continuously, for the osmotic pressure of the plasma remains above that of the environment. This is caused in part by elevated levels of plasma electrolytes, and in part by exceptionally high concentrations of urea in the blood (up to 480 mM urea). It is interesting that the net inward transport of sodium by the skin continues even when the animals are adapted to media of high salinity. The green toad, *Bufo viridis*, also tolerates media of high salt concentration and maintains plasma osmotic pressure somewhat above that of the medium. In this case, electrolytes, rather than urea, account for the major part of the plasma osmotic pressure (Gordon, 1961).

Some effects of experimental manipulations causing transient, absolute excess of electrolytes are known in the case of a few anuran species. After injection of hypertonic (e.g., 1 to 5%) sodium chloride subcutaneously or into the dorsal lymph sac, or immersion in isosmotic or hypertonic (up to 8%) sodium chloride solutions and subsequent transfer to water or dilute salt solutions, frogs and toads show a sharp increase in body water content. This is attributable in part to osmotic factors, for the plasma sodium and chloride levels are elevated. In addition, skin and bladder permeability is enhanced, under the influence of neurohypophyseal hormones (Jørgensen, 1948; Eliassen and Jørgensen, 1951; Bentley, 1958b). The rate of urine formation is low, and the urinary osmotic pressure high, although urine hypertonic to plasma is not formed (Przylecki, 1922; Adolph, 1927a; Jørgensen, 1950a). As water continues to enter the body through the skin, the tissue fluids become progressively more dilute, urine flow increases, and gradually the excess salt load is dissipated through the kidneys (Jørgensen, 1954). Jørgensen (1954) was unable to find evidence for any important site of extrarenal sodium or chloride ion excretion in the frog *Rana temporaria* or the toad *Bufo bufo*. Large loads of sodium chloride were administered by injection or body immersion in concentrated sodium chloride solutions. Although a small fraction (up to 12%) of the salt load was lost through the skin, this could be attributed to skin salt leakage typically seen during experimental manipulation.

During prolonged exposure of frogs (*Rana esculenta*) and other ranids to media of high sodium chloride content (e.g., 0.15 M), plasma and urine electrolyte concentrations increase (e.g., plasma sodium—from control levels of 120 to 140 mM to values as high as 160 to 180 mM; Scheer, 1961). The body weight falls at first, and later rises (Przylecki, 1922; Adolph, 1927a). Maetz and co-workers (1958) described a reduction in skin short circuit current (indicative of active sodium transport) in frogs immersed in saline solutions. Treatment of the animals with aldosterone prevented the fall in short circuit current, although the skin *in vitro* did not respond to the hormone. Scheer found no effect of aldosterone on the elevated plasma and urine sodium concentrations of frogs immersed in 0.15 M sodium chloride, and suggested that the kidneys are not responsive to interrenal hormones. In the euryhaline frog *Rana cancrivora*, Gordon *et al.* (1961) observed vigorous sodium transport inward across the skin despite high salinity of the media in which the frogs were immersed. It is not known whether the difference in response to external medium hypertonicity between *Rana cancrivora* and *R. esculenta*, for instance, results from differences in hormonal control or in the skin ion transports.

4. Absolute Decrease in Body Osmolytes

Frogs and toads have been depleted of extracellular electrolytes by prolonged immersion or rinsing in distilled water (Krogh, 1937; Jørgensen,

1950b). They adjust to this situation by reduction of skin and urinary salt loss, and increased skin sodium transport so that, when replaced in tap water, *Rana esculenta*, *R. temporaria*, and *Bufo bufo* rapidly reaccumulated electrolytes, even if these were present in the medium at concentrations as low as 5×10^{-5} M with respect to sodium ions (Krogh, 1937; Jørgensen, 1950b). Increased flux of sodium and chloride ions inward through the skin occurred. Jørgensen (1950b) noted values as high as 7 μEq sodium per hour per 100 cm^2 body surface for sodium uptake by salt-depleted *Bufo bufo* individuals immersed in 3 to 4 mM sodium chloride solutions. The normal controls showed rates of about 1 to 3 μEq sodium per hour per 100 cm^2 body surface from the same solution. In general confirmation of these observations, Crabbé (1961b) showed that active sodium transport by the isolated urinary bladder of the toad *Bufo marinus* was increased following a few days of immersion in distilled water. This increase was correlated with an elevated level of aldosterone in the blood. Active reaccumulation of chloride ions independently of sodium ions in chloride-depleted toads (*Bufo bufo*) has been described (Jørgensen *et al.*, 1954).

B. REGULATION OF EXCHANGE

The participation of hormones in regulation of water and electrolyte exchange has been touched on in this discussion, and is summarized well in a brief review by Sawyer (1956). A few behavioral responses concerned with water balance should be noted as well. These include the search for sheltered places (burrows, crevices, etc.) and postural and activity patterns. Among the latter are initial rapid movements, then depressed activity, lowering of the head, and placement of the limbs next to the body (Shelford, 1913; Ozorio de Almeida, 1926; Thorson and Svihla, 1943; among others). A characteristic body stance, "hugging" the substratum (Cohen, 1952), and tail coiling (Cohen, 1952; Ray, 1958) have been described. All of these would tend to reduce skin evaporative loss. When animals are allowed access to a moist surface or free water, the "hugging" posture and immersion of the body facilitate restoration of body water content, whereas water uptake may be slower in forms that stand erect, with only the feet in contact with water (Cohen, 1952). Adolph's (1932) results suggest however, that rehydration rates are not correlated directly with the area of the body exposed to water.

There is general agreement that dehydrated amphibians do not drink when given access to water (Durig, 1901, and others, cited by Adolph, 1927a). Drinking (intake of water by mouth) has been observed repeatedly, however, in frogs and toads immersed in hypertonic solutions (Overton, 1904, cited by Jørgensen, 1954; Krogh, 1939; Uranga, 1958b; among others). Jørgensen (1954) questioned whether this apparent drinking could be accounted for by struggling movements in which the mouth, stimulated by the hypertonic solution, is moved and rubbed by the forelimbs. In any case, fluid is taken into the body as a result of this process, as indicated by weight changes and effects on the animals of solutes in the ambient medium (Krogh, 1939). Gordon and co-workers (1961) did not observe drinking in adult *Rana cancrivora* individuals immersed in solutions of high tonicity, and it will be recalled that, in these amphibians, fluid balance is maintained by continued net water uptake through the skin.

The existence of physiological and behavioral adjustments to dehydration implies, of course, capacity on the part of the animal to sense variation in its state of hydration. Shelford (1913) observed that the salamanders, *Plethodon cinereus, P. glutinosus,* but not the frog *Rana sylvatica,* oriented along a humidity gradient. Ray (1958) has commented on the sensitivity of some salamanders to dry air, with "irritation" or excited behavior correlated with the presence of dry air. Further, Stebbins (1945) inferred from the behavior of California salamanders that they can recognize changes in air humidity. When the fall rains come on, these animals emerge from the niches in the earth where they survive the summer drought. In these movements, the animals may anticipate the actual penetration of rain water to moisten the soil about them.

Virtually nothing is known of the receptor side of this mechanism, although Andersson and Zotterman (1950) reported that specific nerve endings located in the tongues of frogs (*Rana temporaria, R. esculenta*) respond to water or highly dilute solutions (NaCl solutions to 0.05%) with increase of action potentials in the glossopharyngeal nerves. Osmoreceptors, which are believed to participate in the regulation of formation and release of antidiuretic hormones in birds and mammals, may play a part in amphibian water balance control, but no conclusions can be drawn about this question at the present time. Indeed, there is a research area virtually untouched, relating the physiological and behavioral responses of amphibians to their water requirements. One observation in this field is the initiation by injected prolactin (anterior pituitary hormone) of migration toward water of hypophysectomized urodeles (*Triturus viridescens, Diemyctylus viridescens*—Chadwick, 1941; Grant and Grant, 1958; Section IV).

VI. Water Balance Problems in Amphibian Development

Amphibian eggs and larvae exist, typically, in liquid environments. Even where development of amphibian eggs occurs outside of free water, the environment is moist and exchange may occur between the organism and this environment. Apparently the jelly coats about some amphibian eggs afford protection from abrupt or extreme changes in the external medium. Further, some species have developed special devices whereby the embryos are retained in parental skin or mucosal pouches. Yet, by and large, ingress and egress of water and solutes must represent an important phenomenon in amphibian development.

Water uptake and fluid shifts within the body are part of the over-all developmental process, both normal and pathological. Thus, incorporation of water without significant increase in dry weight may be a factor in rapid increase in size (C. B. Davenport, 1897, cited by Adolph, 1927d) and changes of form of embryos before feeding starts (see, e.g.,Rappaport, 1954; Tuft, 1957). In general, development in amphibians is accompanied by rapid water absorption, after a brief loss from the egg during the formation of the perivitelline space. The early work in this field has been fully summarized by Needham (1931), who also stressed the importance of ambient conditions (e.g., temperature) for the rate of water uptake (data of Davenport, Bialascewicz, Galloway, and others). Naturally, changes in over-all body water content must involve many discrete processes, and early workers attributed such changes to alterations in cell membrane permeability or the concentration of intracellular osmolytes (see, for instance, Krogh et al., 1938; Holtfreter, 1943; Briggs, 1939). Within the organism itself, massive movements of water and solutes may take place at critical times in development, e.g., at gastrulation and at the time of collapse of the archenteron (Briggs, 1939; Brown, 1941; Tuft, 1957). The mechanisms by which such fluid translocations take place are still to be clarified. These mechanisms may involve changes in cell form, elasticity, and permeability of cell membranes, aggregation and movement of cells, as well as intracellular metabolism and specific cellular processes resulting in net water transfer.

A. OVER-ALL WATER BALANCE

Although many studies have been carried out in attempts to assess water exchanges and osmotic behavior of amphibian eggs and embryos in early developmental stages, the results are limited and often contradictory. Cellular osmotic pressure is hard to measure accurately, especially since physiologists are still unable to define intracellular solute activites. Besides, membrane permeability to various solutes and to water has been measured in only a few cases, and under restricted conditions. Further, the necessary experimental datum of surface area across which exchanges take place is difficult to assess. Shrinkage or swelling of embryos may cause changes in shape and exposed surface, as well as collapse or distension of fluid-filled cavities like the blastocoele. Moreover, in early studies there was often a tacit assumption that water movement alone accounted for the major fluid exchanges, and that the cell membranes were essentially impermeable to solutes such as sodium, potassium, and chloride ions. This is an erroneous assumption, however. There are special experimental problems in working with embryos. For instance, larval amphibians are highly sensitive to mechanical manipulation, and even slight surface damage may cause gross disturbances in fluid regulation (Adolph, 1927d; Holtfreter, 1943).

Despite the many discrepancies in the experimental results, there are some areas of agreement among the various workers in the field. Immature (ovarian) eggs are approximately isotonic with the maternal extracellular fluids, and the cell membrane is fairly permeable, at least to water (Holtfreter, 1943). Characteristic differences have been described in diffusion and filtration permeability (indicative of membrane structure) between ovarian eggs and eggs taken from the body cavity of *Rana temporaria* (Prescott and Zeuthen, 1953). At some time between shedding and fertilization, but probably not as a direct result of fertilization, amphibian eggs become hypotonic to adult plasma—very hypotonic, according to early workers; more moderately hypotonic, according to Krogh *et al.* (1938) and Holtfreter (1943). For a brief period timed approximately with the first cleavage, anuran eggs appear to become relatively impermeable to water (e.g., Krogh *et al.*, 1937). Later, the rate of penetration of water into the embryo increases. Løvtrup (1960) studied the rate of diffusion of heavy water through the surface of the developing axolotl. In confirmation of the general conclusions outlined above, Løvtrup described increased water permeability during segmentation, followed by reduced rate and then a second peak in gastrulation. During neurulation, the rate rose again and steadied at this higher level. These changes may have resulted from altered cell surface area, rather than from changing membrane characteristics.

Throughout these early stages of development, the embryo is extremely sensitive to external medium tonicity, for it is only partially protected by the osmotic barrier of the highly sensitive surface coat (Holtfreter, 1943), and, to a much more limited extent, by the extraneous egg membranes. Needham's (1931) summary of experiments related to over-all tonicity changes during amphibian development may be consulted for details of early studies, and these will be only abstracted briefly here. L. Backmann and J. Runnström (1909, cited by Needham, 1931) noted a sharp decrease in freezing point depression of breis of frog eggs just after fertilization. The finding was especially striking because freezing point depressions of breis of ripe ovarian eggs were close to those of samples of adult serum. During later development, the estimated osmotic pressure of embryo breis rose gradually toward the level of adult serum. Other workers confirmed these findings, at least in general outline. Attempts to discover the mechanisms involved in these changes were only partially successful. In most experiments, it appeared that simple water intake by the egg could not account for the fall in estimated osmotic pressure following fertilization, for this fall was accompanied by only a slight increase in egg volume. Consequently, it was attributed by various workers either to aggregation of intracellular osmolytes, or to loss of solutes into the perivitelline space or external medium by secretion or diffusion through egg cell membranes rendered abruptly more permeable at the time of fertilization. The subsequent rise in measured osmotic pressure was explained in terms of metabolic production of osmolytes within the cells of the embryo. In contrast, Krogh and co-workers (1938) saw greater volume changes in *Rana temporaria* larvae, and suggested that these changes followed fairly closely cell osmotic pressure (measured with a micro vapor pressure method).

The results outlined above are of great interest, particularly when considered in light of the fact that most amphibian eggs will not develop normally in salt solutions or other fluids isosmotic with adult plasma (Backmann and Runnström, and others, cited by Needham, 1931; Holtfreter, 1943). Yet the early results do not contain information on which to base satisfactory hypotheses to explain the results observed. Systematic accounting was not made of actual exchange of water and osmolytes. Today, it is not clear what, if any, relation exists between the osmotic pressure of a given tissue brei and activity of osmolytes present in the living cells which originally made up the tissue before homogenization (see, e.g., Conway *et al.*, 1955), for cellular disorganization and rapid autolysis may affect greatly the concentration of osmolytes released into the disintegration mixture. Besides, Holtfreter (1943) has pointed out the errors inherent in these studies because of contamination of eggs and embryos with extraneous membrane material.

Studies of volume changes of eggs and embryos in various stages add to the sum of the evidence on over-all water and electrolyte exchange. In such studies, swelling or shrinkage may result from net ingress or egress of water, or of osmolytes accompanied by water, so that the interpretation of results is never easy.

Adolph (1927d) found that unfertilized eggs of *Rana pipiens* behaved unpredictably when immersed in a variety of solutions, showing both swelling and shrinkage in a given solution (e.g., 0.1 M sodium chloride). He concluded that the eggs are somewhat permeable to sodium chloride, and that the permeability may change with changing ambient salt concentration. At later stages of development, before hatching, the osmotic behavior and apparent salt permeability of the amphibian embryo varied with species and age (Backmann, 1912, cited by Adolph, 1927d), while the data were further confused by the presence of extraneous membranes surrounding the embryo. Thus, the extraneous coats about the egg may affect the rate of penetration of solutes across the cell-medium interspace. Evidence for this comes, for instance, from the studies of Krogh *et al.* (1938) and Richards (1940) on capsular fluids in *Rana temporaria* and *Ambystoma punctatum* (now *Ambystoma maculatum*). These fluids may differ consistently from the ambient medium in electrolyte composition and osmotic pressure. The presence of such special periembryonic fluid is not necessary for development, and various chemical agents in the medium act similarly on the developing embryo whether or not the jelly coats have been stripped from the eggs (Holtfreter, 1943; O. Mangold, 1920, and G. Ruud, 1925, cited by Holtfreter, 1943).

Some of the results outlined above have been questioned by Holtfreter (1943) who described the surface coat of the egg, both in the mature, unfertilized egg and also after fertilization, as a significant and variable osmotic barrier rendering unreliable much of the early experimental work done to characterize the osmotic behavior of these cells. The normal functioning of the surface coat of the egg, which remains as an external protective layer surrounding the embryo as development proceeds, could be inferred from the observation that eggs and embryos develop normally in tap water, but fragments of the embryo, no longer protected by the membrane, swell up and die in tap water. Such fragments can survive only in a medium of relatively high salt concentration (about half the total osmotic pressure of adult plasma). Also, gastrulae with the surface membrane intact can survive 10 to 60 min exposure to 0.0125 M potassium cyanide, while fragments of gastrulae, of the same age but no longer protected by the surface membrane, begin to show breakdown in 0.0125 M potassium cyanide in 3 to 5 min. Løvtrup (1960) pointed out that the role of the surface coat may be primarily mechanical, its elasticity opposing distension by osmotic swelling of the egg. According to Løvtrup, the main diffusion barrier of the embryo is probably located at the cell membrane, rather than in the elastic coat.

The surface membrane described by Holtfreter is sensitive to hypertonic solutions and to alkaline media (including potassium cyanide solutions), and many of the irregularities in osmotic behavior of eggs and embryos described by early workers may be attributed to damage or increased permeability of the surface layer incidental to the use of solutions of varying tonicity. Thus, according to Holtfreter, amphibian eggs (anuran, urodele) from the time of oviposition until the neurula stage has been reached continue to have a relatively high tonicity (about 0.38% sodium chloride). The marked changes in apparent tonicity with development reflect changes in the external surface, rather than in physicochemical organization of the intracellular fluids.

Rappaport (1954) showed that explanted tail and gill tissue from *Ambystoma punctatum* (now *Ambystoma maculatum*) and *Rana pipiens* took up water at rates which could not be accounted for simply in terms of osmotic differentials between the cells and the external medium. Osmotic and volume regulation in early embryonic life were very inadequate (Adolph, 1927d), but even before hatching, the larva of *Rana pipiens* showed a definite capacity to regulate its concentration and absorb solutes from the ambient medium. According to Adolph (1927d), acquisition by the larva of capacity to regulate fluid concentration coincided with ectodermal differentiation.

Recently Tuft (1957, 1961a,b,c) has described studies on the dynamics of water content in *Xenopus laevis* embryos. The densities and reduced weights (indicative of relative water content) of embryos and the freezing point depressions (indicative of osmotic pressure) of blastocoele and archenteron fluids were followed through early development stages. In agreement with Rappaport (1954), Tuft found that simple changes in osmotic pressure or cell membrane permeability could not account for the transfers of fluid occurring from the external medium into the cells and fluid spaces, or between the blastocoele and archenteron. Therefore, energy-dependent processes must be postulated to account for these fluid movements, and Tuft developed an argument by which the orientation of corresponding "active" processes of ectoderm versus endoderm could explain the direction and pattern of water shifts. According to this hypothesis, the net flux of water is inward through the animal pole and ectodermal cells in general, and outward (originally in the direction from the cell mass toward the external environment) through the endodermal cells and vegetal pole. The formation of the blastocoele, the transfer of fluid from the blastocoele to the archenteron, and the increase in cellular hydration following emptying of the archenteron could be accounted for by such oriented net water fluxes and the known changes in relative position of ectodermal and endodermal cells. Treatment of *Xenopus laevis* embryos with β-mercaptoethanol caused characteristic disturbances of water distribution. Tuft (1961a) suggested that these might be explained by differential suppression of net movement of water through the endodermal cells.

After hatching, larvae of *Rana pipiens*, *R. catesbeiana*, and *Ambystoma punctatum* (*Ambystoma maculatum*) showed definite though varying ability to regulate body fluid volume against hyperhydration in very dilute solutions (e.g., tap water) (Adolph, 1927c). Regulation against loss of fluid was less successful than regulation against hyperhydration, for Adolph (1927c) found that larval *Rana pipiens* and *R. catesbeiana* transferred from tap water to a variety of solutions lost weight in even relatively dilute solutions (e.g., 0.025 to 0.04 M sodium chloride) of a variety of salts and nonelectrolytes. Larval age before metamorphosis did not appear to be correlated with this loss, whereas, as might indeed be expected, body mass affected markedly the rate of fluid exchange. Somewhat similar results were obtained with larval *Ambystoma*, although weight loss was not significant unless the tonicity of the medium was raised to that corresponding with 0.1 M sodium chloride. Two or more days after fore limbs were acquired during metamorphosis, young *Rana pipiens* individuals showed a rather abrupt change in their pattern of response to immersion in dilute solutions (Adolph, 1927d). At this time, body weight increased slightly when animals were immersed in dilute (e.g., 0.08 M sodium chloride) solutions, rather than showing a decrease as in the earlier stages of development. Thus, the frog at this later stage resembled adults of the species (Adolph, 1927a). Adolph (1927d) noted abrupt morphological changes in the skin toward the adult condition at this stage, and stressed its coincidence with alteration in the skin regulation of fluid exchange.

B. THE ROLES OF SKIN, CIRCULATION, GILLS, DIGESTIVE TRACT AND NEPHRONS
    IN WATER BALANCE IN AMPHIBIAN EMBRYOS

At later stages in development, as body size and complexity increase, fluid exchange through the epidermis and gills, circulation of blood and lymph, and the onset of pronephric (later, mesonephric) function become conspicuous as factors in larval water balance.

Apparently the epidermis of young anuran larvae is quite permeable to water, for the body becomes greatly hyperhydrated following pronephrectomy (Swingle, 1919; Howland, 1921; Rappaport, 1955). It is not known whether mechanisms for active ion transport exist in the larval skin, although Adolph's (1927d) results on fluid exchange suggest that the powerful sodium transporting system of the adult anuran skin does not appear until after metamorphosis. Krogh (1937, 1939), too, found that tadpoles of *Rana temporaria* (with covered gills, no legs) did not accumulate sodium and chloride ions from the external medium in the manner characteristic of adults of the species. Thus, these tadpoles were markedly depleted of water and chloride ions when kept in dilute solutions and deprived of food.

Scattered attempts have been made to test whether the skin and other potential target organs are sensitive to posterior pituitary hormones in amphibian larvae. As yet, the results are not conclusive. Thus Bělehrádek and Huxley (1927) described transient and slight (about 4 to 7%) increase of body weight of axolotls following injections of mammalian posterior pituitary extracts (Pituitrin). The authors attributed the changes to increased net water uptake by the body, but the results are questionable because only a few animals were studied, the changes were small, and the larvae did not survive the experimental treatment. In young tadpoles of the toad *Bufo bufo*, commercial extracts of mammalian posterior pituitary were without effect on body water content (Howes, 1940). A slight and variable response of increased body weight was seen first at about the tail resorption stage, but a pronounced effect occurred only when adult skin color was attained. It would be interesting to reinvestigate this problem using a wider range of species and developmental stages, and with administration of amphibian, rather than mammalian neurohypophyseal hormones. As yet, it is not known at what stage in development hormones affecting water balance appear in the neurohypophysis, or whether amphibian larvae have hormone spectra identical with those of adults of the same species.

The part played by the circulation of blood and lymph in fluid distribution in amphibian embryos has received relatively little attention. Removal of the heart in *Rana pipiens* larvae is followed by gross disturbance in fluid balance (edema, lymphatic engorgement; Kemp, 1953), as well as other changes—as might be expected, indeed, from the severity of the procedure. Rappaport (1955) noted a sharp localization of edema in larvae following pronephrectomy, and, on this basis, queried the effectiveness of the circulation in distribution of fluid and rapid regulation of the internal environment as a whole. Other possibilities could explain the finding, however, such as fluid accumulation in lymphatic channels, differential sites of excess filtration, and varying tissue resistance to fluid infiltration. Frieden *et al.* (1957) described distinctive changes in plasma protein patterns, possibly correlated with plasma oncotic pressure changes, in ranids during development and metamorphosis.

The lymphatic system can be recognized early in embryos of anurans and urodeles (for instance, at about 6.5-mm body length in *Rana palustris*, according to Knower, 1908). The paired anterior lymph hearts of anurans arise in conjunction with one of the paired intersegmental veins, generally the fourth pair. According to Knower (1908) and Kampmeier (1925), the posterior pairs of lymph hearts in *Rana* and *Bufo* appear sometime later than the anterior pairs. First formed from a simple layer of endothelial cells, the lymph hearts later become invested with skeletal muscle fibers. About the 7.5- to 8-mm stage in *Rana palustris* embryos, two pairs of major lymphatic trunks are observed leading into the anterior lymph hearts from the head and from the trunk. Later, these give rise to branches which coalesce to form lymph sacs (Knower, 1908). Thus, extensive lymphatic development early in embryonic life appears characteristic of anurans (see the detailed accounts of Kampmeier, 1920, 1922, 1925; Knower, 1939). In the West Indian tree frog, *Hyloides martinicensis*, the lymphatic development extends so remarkably that the embryo has been described in later stages as completely encased in great lymphatic sacs (Sampson,

1904). In conjunction with detailed anatomical descriptions, scattered observations have been made of the functioning of the lymphatic system, even in very young amphibian larvae. For instance, Knower (1908) observed contractions of the lymph hearts in edematous embryos after removal or inactivation of the systemic heart. McClure (1919) found evidence in some edematous frog larvae that the anterior lymph hearts had failed to develop. It is apparent, then, that the physiology of the lymphatics in amphibian embryos is a field requiring much more extensive study.

Similarly, far too little is known about the participation of the gills and digestive tract in over-all water and electrolyte balance of amphibian larvae. Krogh (1939) argued that the intestinal tract must be an important site for salt uptake in young amphibians before the skin mechanism for ion accumulation becomes effective. The gill region is a typical site of edema fluid accumulation. Rappaport (1955) suggested that the decreased water uptake of *Rana pipiens* larvae after removal of the heart might be related to restriction of the gill circulation. Krogh *et al.* (1938) noted a sharp increase in chloride uptake by larvae of *Rana temporaria* coincidental with budding of the gills.

The amphibian pronephros develops early and is a conspicuous anterior structure on each side of the young larva's body. Characteristically, median dorsal glomeruli, knots of capillaries rising from branches of the aorta, extend freely into the coelomic cavity. Jaffee (1954a) has described these in *Rana pipiens* larvae, just at the stage of hatching, as rich tufts of capillaries with walls made up of sparse endothelial cells and epithelial cells interconnected by protoplasmic processes. Within the capillaries at this stage, primitive blood cells are seen. Lateral to the glomeruli lie the 2 or 3 pairs of ciliated nephrostomal funnels leading into coiled tubes of the pronephros. Only among embryonic Apoda have more than 3 pairs of pronephric tubules been described (literature cited by Jaffee, 1954a). The pronephric duct connects with the cloaca at an early stage of development (about the 5-mm stage in *Rana pipiens*; H. H. Field, 1891, cited by Rappaport, 1954) when the heart is just beginning to beat (Jaffee, 1954a). Fraser (1950) has reviewed the course of morphological change in the amphibian pronephros.

The pronephrons begin to function about the time when the pronephric ducts come into association with the cloaca. Shortly after the heart had begun to beat, but before circulation in the gills was visible, Rappaport (1955) observed that bilaterally pronephrectomized *Rana pipens* embryos retained fluid in excess of normal controls, as evidenced by decreased specific gravity. A little later, frank edema appeared, especially in the region of the pronephros and gills. Working with 5- to 7-mm *Rana sylvatica* larvae, Swingle (1919) had shown that bilateral pronephrectomy was followed by conspicuous edema within 24 hr or more. Swelling of the body was so severe that the larve frequently burst. After healing, fluid accumulation started again and eventually all of the pronephrectomized animals died.

Relatively few experiments have been carried out to establish the mechanism of pronephric function. The structure itself, and analogy with the mesonephros of the adult, suggest that fluid is filtered from the blood stream through the glomeruli into the coelom, and is thence collected by the nephrostomes to pass into the tubules. Rappaport (1955) questioned the importance of glomerular filtration in regulating body fluid content, for removal of the heart (and subsequent presumed suppression of glomerular filtration) did not lead to severe edema in embryos of *Rana pipens* which survived for as long as 7 days after the operation. In contrast, removal of the pronephrons caused extreme edema, and resulted finally in death. In any case, the nephrostomes doubtless collect some fluid from the coelom and pass it into the tubules. Jaffee (1954a) noted the passage of India ink particles from the coelom into the pronephric tubules as late as the second month of development in *Rana pipiens* larvae.

The pronephric tubules receive a rich blood supply from the postcardinal veins, for as development proceeds the tubules come to lie adjacent to large venous sinuses developed in connection with pronephrons (Field, 1891, cited by Howland, 1921). At later stages in development, much of the blood flow is diverted away from the pronephros (Jaffee, 1954a).

Jaffee (1954b) attempted to assess the time at which tubular secretory function first appeared in the pronephric tubules of *Rana pipiens*. The method of *in vitro* accumulation of dyes, introduced by Chambers and co-workers (e.g., Chambers and Kempton, 1933) and Forster (1948) was used to study phenol red transfer from the ambient medium to the tubular lumina. Jaffee found that no phenol red was transported at the 6-mm stage, when the pronephros had been fully formed although the cells were still not completely differentiated cytologically. Between the ninth and eleventh days of development, the cells became characteristically differentiated in structure, and now phenol red was taken up vigorously. This phenol red transport resembled the transport found in adult *Rana pipiens* and other vertebrates, e.g., it was inhibited by substances known to inhibit oxidative phosphorylation and oxidative processes in general; and by para-aminohippurate and other specific competitors of the phenol red transport system.

The pronephrons, which communicate freely with the coelom in early stages of development, gradually become separated from it by enclosure within the pronephric chambers. Late in larval life, the pronephric tubules and glomeruli undergo extensive degenerative changes, described in detail

by Jaffee (1954a). Meantime, the mesonephros has progressed in development, with formation of both Malpighian tubules and peritoneal funnels.
An anatomical description of this development in *Rana temporaria* was
given by Gray (1930). Jaffee (1954a) found that mesonephric structure
was complete in the 1-month-old *Rana pipiens* tadpole. Swingle (1919) inferred that the mesonephros began to function very early in development
in *R. sylvatica*, accounting perhaps, for the freedom from edema seen in
some embryos subjected to pronephrectomy. Further, Jaffee (1954b)
demonstrated that the mesonephric cells began to show capacity to secrete
phenol red relatively early, so that, during the last 2 to 3 months needed
for larval development of *Rana pipiens* under the conditions of the experiment, both pronephric and mesonephric tubules showed evidence *in vitro*
of the presence of specific transports for phenol red (and hence, perhaps,
for the organic ion series so commonly transported by vertebrate kidneys).
Except for this study of phenol red secretion, there is no information as
to changes in excretion patterns which may occur as pronephric function
is progressively replaced by functioning of the developing mesonephros.

Although the pronephric tubules of *Ambystoma punctatum* (*Ambystoma
maculatum*) larvae did not regenerate after removal, hypertrophy of the
remaining pronephros occurred when the opposite organ was removed
(Howland, 1921). Swingle (1919), too, noted hypertrophy and distension
of the pronephros remaining after unilateral pronephrectomy in *Rana
sylvatica* larvae. This sort of "compensatory" change is characteristically
seen in the case of adult kidneys, and is consistent with the apparent importance of pronephric function. Howland (1921) used anatomical measurements to estimate size change in the pronephric tubules following
removal of the pronephros on the opposite side. She noted lengthening
and widening of the tubules, some increase in number of tubular cells, and
estimated the increase of tubular surface to be as great as 100%.

C. ABNORMALITIES OF WATER BALANCE IN AMPHIBIAN EMBRYOS

Many workers have noted aberrations in development involving obvious
disturbances of fluid balance. These include accumulation of fluid in the
coelom and lymphatic channels and formation of blisters under the epidermis and elsewhere. The conditions in which such disturbances occur
are bewilderingly various, including, for instance, treatment with anesthetics and various toxic agents (e.g., Harrison, 1904); exposure to excessive light, or to X-rays or other high-energy radiation (R. Hertwig,
1911, cited by McClure, 1919; Rugh, 1950); haploidy and other abnormal
chromosomal patterns (see Fankhauser and Humphrey, 1950). Such disturbances are poorly understood. In general, they are attributed to failure
of normal blood and lymph circulation, to impaired pronephric function

(McClure, 1919, 1928; Kemp, 1953; among others), or, more vaguely, to abnormalities of membrane permeability of the skin, gills, and pronephrons. In haploid embryos, edema formation is seen as a typical disturbance. As noted above, this has been attributed to circulatory and pronephric failure, and it was reversed in a single successful experiment with *Triturus pyrrhogaster* larvae by parabiosis of haploid and diploid embryos (Kaylor, 1940). However, the extent and manner of disturbed circulatory and pronephric functions in this situation in haploids is still unclear.

A striking upset of fluid balance has been described by Humphrey (1948) in larvae of *Ambystoma mexicanum*, with swelling and disturbed fluid exchange recognizable even during cleavage stages. This condition is heritable, with transmission through a Mendelian recessive gene. The effects of the gene in homozygous condition were exacerbated when the mother, as well as the offspring, was homozygous (Humphrey, 1960). The condition was relieved by parabiotic union of the affected embryo with a normal embryo, but as yet nothing is known of its genesis beyond Humphrey's suggestion that the fluid accumulated results from some abnormality of the endoderm. Clearly, it cannot be attributed to failures of circulation or pronephric excretion, since the condition may be fully expressed long before the heart and pronephrons become functional. Rafftery (1961) transplanted diploid pronephric anlagen into haploid *Rana pipiens* embryos without significant effect on the edema or other features of the haploid syndrome. The initial size of the haploid embryo affects the results, since, within a given species (*R. pipiens*) haploid embryos formed from large eggs showed an earlier onset and more severe form of edema and related fluid disturbance than did haploid individuals arising from eggs of small initial size (Briggs, 1949).

Not only do various disturbances in development lead to conspicuous abnormalities in fluid balance, but, in addition, primary changes in fluid balance are typically accompanied by upsets in developmental patterns. Thus, ambient medium tonicity has long been recognized as a critical factor in development of amphibian embryos (Bachmann and Runnström, 1912, cited by Needham, 1931; Holtfreter, 1943; among others). Urodele and anuran eggs develop normally in pond water or very dilute salt solutions, but in salt solutions isosmotic with the adult body fluids the embryos shrink, development is delayed, and many structural abnormalities occur, including impaired cleavage, obliteration of the blastocoele, and failure of invagination (Holtfreter, 1943). Driscoll and Eakin (1955), following up the studies of earlier workers, have described in detail abnormalities of anuran embryos (*Hyla regilla, Bufo boreas, Rana pipiens, R. boyli*) exposed to strongly hypertonic (10%) solutions of sucrose, an osmolyte commonly considered to be "inert" physiologically. A striking case in which

larvae of an amphibian species develop naturally in media of relatively
high osmotic pressure (up to 39 parts per thousand) is that of the euryhaline frog, *Rana cancrivora*, studied by Gordon *et al.* (1961). It will be of
interest to learn more details of the developmental processes in this species,
and in other species adapted to life in waters of high salinity. Possibly in
some of the species in which the young stay within skin or gular sacs (e.g.,
Gastrotheca marsupiata, *Rhinoderma darwini*), fluid relationships may be
exceptional, but no physiological studies of these forms have been found in
the literature.

Acknowledgments

This chapter has been read, in various stages of development, by Dr. M. S. Gordon,
Dr. C. B. Jørgensen, Dr. J. A. Moore, and Dr. E. E. Windhager; their advice and
criticisms are acknowledged with gratitude.

References

Acher, R., Chauvet, J., Lenci, M. T., Morel, F., and Maetz, J. (1960). Présence d'une
    vasotocine dans la neurohypophyse de la grenouille (*Rana esculenta* L.). *Biochim.
    Biophys. Acta* **42,** 379–380.
Adolph, E. F. (1925). The passage of water through the skin of the frog, and the
    relation between diffusion and permeability. *Am. J. Physiol.* **73,** 85–195.
Adolph, E. F. (1927a). The skin and kidneys as regulators of the body volume of
    frogs. *J. Exptl. Zool.* **47,** 1–30.
Adolph, E. F. (1927b). The excretion of water by the kidneys of frogs. *Am. J. Physiol.*
    81, 315–324.
Adolph, E. F. (1927c). Changes in body volume in several species of larval Amphibia
    in relation to the osmotic pressure of the environment. *J. Exptl. Zool.* **47,** 163–178.
Adolph, E. F. (1927d). Changes in the physiological regulation of body volume in
    Rana pipiens during ontogeny and metamorphosis. *J. Exptl. Zool.* **47,** 179–195.
Adolph, E. F. (1932). The vapour tension relations of frogs. *Biol. Bull.* **62,** 112–125.
Adolph, E. F. (1934). Influence of the nervous system on the intake and excretion of
    water by the frog. *J. Cellular Comp. Physiol.* **5,** 123–139.
Adolph, E. F. (1935). Oxygen tension and urine production in frogs. *Am. J. Physiol.*
    111, 75–82.
Adolph, E. F. (1936a). Epinephrine and urine formation in the frog. *Am. J. Physiol.*
    115, 200–209.
Adolph, E. F. (1936b). Control of urine formation in the frog by the renal circula-
    tion. *Am. J. Physiol.* **117,** 366–379.
Alexander, S. S., and Bellerby, C. W. (1938). Experimental studies on the sexual
    cycle of the South African clawed toad (*Xenopus laevis*). *J. Exptl. Biol.* **15,** 74–81.
Andersen, B., and Ussing, H. H. (1957). Solvent drag on non-electrolytes during
    osmotic flow through isolated toad skin and its response to antidiuretic hormone.
    Acta Physiol. Scand. **39,** 228–239.
Andersson, B., and Zotterman, Y. (1950). The water taste in the frog. *Acta Physiol.
    Scand.* **20,** 95–100.
Angerer, C. A. (1942). Water content of sartorius of adrenalectomized frogs. *Federa-
    tion Proc.* **1,** 3.

Angerer, C. A., and Angerer, H. H. (1949). The rate of total loss of body water on survival time of adrenalectomized frogs. *Proc. Soc. Exptl. Biol. Med.* **71**, 661–665.

Balinsky, J. B., and Baldwin, E. (1961). The mode of excretion of ammonia and urea in *Xenopus laevis. J. Exptl. Biol.* **38**, 695–706.

Balinsky, J. B., Cragg, M. M., and Baldwin, E. (1961). The adaptation of amphibian waste nitrogen excretion to dehydration. *Comp. Biochem. Physiol.* **3**, 236–244.

Bargmann, W., Knoop, A., and Schiebler, T. H. (1955). Histologische, cytochemische und elektronmikroskopische Untersuchungen am Nephron (mit Berücksichtigung der Mitochondrien). *Z. Zellforsch. Mikroskop. Anat.* **42**, 386–422.

Bastian, J. W., and Zarrow, M. X. (1954). Stimulation of the secretory glands of the skin of the South African frog (*Xenopus laevis*). *Endocrinology* **54**, 116–117.

Beiter, R. N., and Hirschfelder, A. D. (1929). The role of the glomeruli as a preferential route for excretion of phenolsulfonphthalein in the frog's kidney. *Am. J. Physiol.* **91**, 178–200.

Bělehrádek, J., and Huxley, J. S. (1927). The effects of pituitrin and narcosis on water-regulation in larval and metamorphosed *Amblystoma. Brit. J. Exptl. Biol.* **5**, 89–96.

Bentley, P. J. (1958a). The effects of vasopressin on water uptake of the toad, *Bufo marinus*, while bathed in different hypertonic solutions. *J. Endocrinol.* **16**, 126–134.

Bentley, P. J. (1958b). The effects of neurohypophyseal extracts on water transfer across the wall of the isolated bladder of the toad, *Bufo marinus. J. Endocrinol.* **17**, 201–209.

Bentley, P. J. (1960). The effects of vasopressin on the short-circuit current across the wall of the isolated bladder of the toad, *Bufo marinus. J. Endocrinol.* **21**, 161–170.

Bentley, P. J. (1961). Directional differences in the permeability to water of the isolated urinary bladder of the toad, *Bufo marinus. J. Endocrinol.* **22**, 95–100.

Bentley, P. J., Lee, A. K., and Main, A. R. (1958). Comparison of dehydration and rehydration of two genera of frogs (*Heleioporus* and *Neobatrachus*) that live in areas of varying aridity. *J. Exptl. Biol.* **35**, 677–684.

Bishop, W. R., Mumbach, M. M., and Scheer, B. T. (1961). Interrenal control of active sodium transport across frog skin. *Am. J. Physiol.* **200**, 451–453.

Bott, P. A. (1952). Renal excretion of creatinine in *Necturus. Am. J. Physiol.* **168**, 107–113.

Bourguet, J., and Maetz, J. (1961). Arguments en faveur de l'indépendance des méchanismes d'action de divers peptides neurohypophysaires sur le flux osmotique de l'eau et sur le transport actif de sodium au sein d'un même recepteur; études sur la vessie et la peau de *Rana esculenta* L. *Biochim. Biophys. Acta* **52**, 552–564.

Boyd, E. M., and Whyte, D. W. (1938). The effect of extract of the posterior hypophysis on the loss of water by frogs in a dry environment. *Am. J. Physiol.* **124**, 759–766.

Boyd, E. M., and Whyte, D. W. (1939). The effect of posterior hypophyseal extract on the retention of water and salt injected into frogs. *Am. J. Physiol.* **125**, 415–422.

Briggs, R. W. (1939). Changes in density of the frog embryo (*Rana pipiens*) during development. *J. Cellular Comp. Physiol.* **13**, 77–89.

Briggs, R. W. (1949). The influence of egg volume on the development of haploid and diploid embryos of the frog, *Rana pipiens. J. Exptl. Zool.* **111**, 255–293.

Brown, M. G. (1941). Collapse of the archenteron of embryos of *Amblystoma* and *Rana. J. Exptl. Zool.* **88**, 95–105.

Buchborn, E. (1956). Zur Kinetiks des Wasserhaushaltes bei der Kröte. *Arch. Ges. Physiol. Pflüger's* **262**, 377–394.

Buxton, P. A. (1923). "Animal Life in Deserts," 176 pp. Arnold, London.

Capraro, V., and Bernini, G. (1952). Mechanism of action of extracts of posthypophysis on water transport through the skin of the frog. *Nature* **169**, 454.

Capraro, V., and Garampi, M. L. (1956). Studies on the frog skin. *Mem. Soc. Endocrinol.* **5**, 61–66.

Carey, M. J., Conway, E. J., and Kernan, R. P. (1959). Secretion of sodium ions by frog's sartorius muscle. *J. Physiol. (London)* **148**, 51–82.

Carstensen, H., Burgers, A. C. J., and Li, C. H. (1961). Demonstration of aldosterone and corticosterone as the principal steroids formed in incubates of adrenals of the American bullfrog (*Rana catesbeiana*) and stimulation of their production by mammalian adrenocorticotrophin. *Gen. Comp. Endocrinol.* **1**, 37–50.

Chadwick, C. S. (1940). Identity of prolactin with water drive factor in *Triturus viridescens. Proc. Soc. Exptl. Biol. Med.* **45**, 335–337.

Chadwick, C. S. (1941). Further observations on the water drive in *Triturus viridescens. J. Exptl. Zool.* **86**, 175–187.

Chambers, R., and Kempton, R. T. (1933). Indications of function of the chick mesonephros in tissue culture with phenol red. *J. Cellular Comp. Physiol.* **3**, 131–168.

Chase, S. W. (1923). The mesonephros and urogenital ducts of *Necturus maculosus* Rafinesque. *J. Morphol.* **37**, 457–532.

Chen, G., Oldham, F. K., and Geiling, E. M. K. (1943). Effect of posterior pituitary extract on water uptake in frogs after hypophysectomy and infundibular lesions. *Proc. Soc. Exptl. Biol. Med.* **52**, 108–111.

Chester Jones, I. (1957a). Comparative aspects of adrenocortical neurohypophysial relationships. *In* "The Neurohypophysis" (H. Heller, ed.) pp. 253–275. Academic Press, New York.

Chester Jones, I. (1957b). "The Adrenal Cortex," 316 pp. Cambridge Univ. Press, London and New York.

Churchill, E. D., Nakazawa, F., and Drinker, C. K. (1927). The circulation of body fluids in the frog. *J. Physiol. (London)* **63**, 304–308.

Cohen, N. W. (1952). Comparative rates of dehydration and hydration in some California salamanders. *Ecology* **33**, 462–479.

Conklin, R. E. (1930a). The formation and circulation of lymph in the frog. I. The rate of lymph production. *Am. J. Physiol.* **95**, 79–90.

Conklin, R. E. (1930b). The formation and circulation of lymph in the frog. II. Volume and blood pressure. *Am. J. Physiol.* **95**, 91–97.

Conklin, R. E. (1930c). The formation and circulation of lymph in the frog. III. The permeability of the capillaries to protein. *Am. J. Physiol.* **95**, 98–100.

Conway, E. J. (1957). The nature and significance of concentration relations of potassium and sodium in skeletal muscle. *Physiol. Rev.* **37**, 84–132.

Conway, E. J., Geoghegan, H., and McCormack, J. I. (1955). Autolytic changes at zero degrees Centigrade in ground mammalian tissues. *J. Physiol. (London)* **130**, 427–437.

Cooperstein, I. L., and Hogben, C. A. M. (1958). Ionic transfers across the isolated frog large intestine. *J. Gen. Physiol.* **42**, 461–474.

Cosmos, E. (1958). Factors influencing movement of calcium in vertebrate striated muscle. *Am. J. Physiol.* **195**, 705–711.

Cosmos, E., and Harris, E. J. (1961). *In vitro* studies of gain and exchange of calcium in frog skeletal muscle. *J. Gen. Physiol.* **44**, 1121–1130.

Crabbé, J. (1961a). Stimulation of active sodium transport by the isolated toad bladder with aldosterone *in vitro*. *J. Clin. Invest.* **40**, 2103–2110.

Crabbé, J. (1961b). Stimulation of active transport across the isolated toad bladder after injection of aldosterone to the animal. *Endocrinology* **69**, 673–682.

Cragg, M. M., Balinsky, J. B., and Baldwin, E. (1961). A comparative study of nitrogen excretion in some Amphibia and reptiles. *Comp. Biochem. Physiol.* **3**, 227–235.

Crane, M. M. (1927). Observations on the function of the frog's kidney. *Am. J. Physiol.* **81**, 232–243.

Crane, E. E., Davies, R. E., and Longmuir, N. M. (1948). Relations between hydrochloric acid secretion and electrical phenomena in frog gastric mucosa. *Biochem. J.* **43**, 321–336.

Curry, L. F. (1929). A cytological study of the proximal and distal tubules of *Necturus maculosus*. *J. Morphol. Physiol.* **48**, 173–252.

Dawson, A. B. (1951). Functional, and degenerate or rudimentary glomeruli in the kidney of two species of Australian frog, *Cyclorana* (*Chiroleptes*) *platycephalus* and *alboguttatus* (Günther). *Anat. Record* **109**, 417–430.

Dawson, A. B. (1924–1925). Glomerular versus tubular activity in the mesonephros of *Necturus*: elimination of iron salts. *Am. J. Physiol.* **71**, 679–687.

Delrue, G. (1930). Étude de la sécrétion acide de l'estomac. I. *Arch. Intern. Physiol.* **33**, 196–216.

Delrue, G. (1933). Étude de la sécrétion de l'estomac. II. *Arch. Intern. Physiol.* **36**, 129–136.

Dow, D., and Zuckerman, S. (1938). The effect of vasopressin, sex hormones and adrenal cortical hormones on body water in axolotls. *J. Endocrinol.* **1**, 387–398.

Driscoll, W. T., and Eakin, R. M. (1955). The effects of sucrose on amphibian development with special reference to the pituitary body. *J. Exptl. Zool.* **129**, 149–176.

Edwards, C., and Harris, E. J. (1957). Factors influencing the sodium movement in frog muscle, with a discussion of the mechanics of Na movement. *J. Physiol. (London)* **135**, 567–580.

Edwards, J. G., and Schnitter, G. (1933). The renal unit in the kidney of vertebrates. *Am. J. Anat.* **53**, 55–70.

Edwards, L. E., and Edwards, C. T. (1951). A method for the *in vitro* collection of pure gastric juice from the isolated mucosa. *J. Cellular Comp. Physiol.* **38**, 183–197.

Eliassen, E., and Jørgensen, C. B. (1951). The effect of increase in osmotic pressure of the body fluid on the water balance of anurans. *Acta Physiol. Scand.* **23**, 143–151.

Ellinger, P. (1940). The site of acidification of the urine in the frog's and rat's kidney. *Quart. J. Exptl. Physiol.* **30**, 205–218.

Engbaek, L., and Hoshiko, T. (1957). Electrical gradients through frog skin. *Acta Physiol. Scand.* **39**, 348–355.

Ewer, R. F. (1952a). The effect of pituitrin on fluid distribution in *Bufo regularis* Reuss. *J. Exptl. Biol.* **29**, 173–177.

Ewer, R. F. (1952b). The effects of posterior pituitary extracts on water balance in *Bufo carens* and *Xenopus laevis*, together with some general considerations of anuran water economy. *J. Exptl. Biol.* **29**, 429–439.

Fankhauser, G., and Humphrey, R. R. (1950). Chromosome number and development of progeny of triploid axolotl females mated with diploid males. *J. Exptl. Zool.* **115**, 207–250.

Fawcett, D. W., and Porter, K. R. (1954). A study of the fine structure of ciliated epithelium. *J. Morphol.* **94**, 221–264.

Fenn, W. O., and Maurer, F. W. (1935). The pH of muscle. *Protoplasma* **24**, 337–345.

Flemming, W. R. (1958). The role of the corium in ion transport across the isolated frog skin. *J. Cellular Comp. Physiol.* **51**, 189–198.

Forster, R. P. (1938). The use of inulin and creatinine as glomerular filtrate measuring substances in the frog. *J. Cellular Comp. Physiol.* **12**, 213–222.

Forster, R. P. (1942). The nature of the glucose reabsorptive process in the frog renal tubule. Evidence for intermittency of glomerular function in the intact animal. *J. Cellular Comp. Physiol.* **20**, 55–69.

Forster, R. P. (1943). The effect of epinephrine upon frog renal hemodynamics in the intact animal. *Am. J. Physiol.* **140**, 221–225.

Forster, R. P. (1948). Use of thin slices of isolated renal tubules for direct study of cellular transport kinetics. *Science* **108**, 65–67.

Forster, R. P. (1954). Active cellular transport of urea by frog renal tubules. *Am. J. Physiol.* **179**, 372–377.

Fowler, M. A., and Chester Jones, I. (1955). The adrenal cortex in *Rana temporaria* and its relationship to water and salt-electrolyte metabolism. *J. Endocrinol.* **13**, 6P–7P.

Francis, E. T. B. (1934). "The Anatomy of the Salamander," 381 pp. Oxford Univ. Press (Clarendon), London and New York.

Fraser, E. A. (1950). The development of the vertebrate excretory system. *Biol. Rev. Cambridge Phil. Soc.* **25**, 159–187.

Frieden, E., Herner, A. E., Fish, L., and Lewis, E. J. C. (1957). Changes in serum proteins in amphibian metamorphosis. *Science* **126**, 559–560.

Fuheman, F. A., and Ussing, H. H. (1951). A characteristic response of the isolated frog skin potential to neurohypophysial principles and its relation to the transport of sodium and water. *J. Cellular Comp. Physiol.* **38**, 109–130.

Garby, L., and Linderholm, H. (1953). The permeability of frog skin to heavy water and to ions, with special reference to the effects of some diuretics. *Acta Physiol. Scand.* **28**, 336–346.

Garby, L., and Linderholm, H. (1954). The permeability of the frog skin to urea with special reference to the effect of aminophylline. *Acta Physiol. Scand.* **32**, 264–265.

Gaupp, E. (1899). "A. Ecker's und R. Wiedersheim's *Anatomie des Frosches,* auf Grund eigener Untersuchungen durchaus neu bearbeitet." 548 pp. Friedrich Vieweg, Braunschweig.

Giebisch, G. (1956). Measurements of pH, chloride and inulin concentrations in proximal tubule fluid of *Necturus*. *Am. J. Physiol.* **185**, 171–174.

Giebisch, G. (1958). Electrical potential measurements on single nephrons of *Necturus*. *J. Cellular Comp. Physiol.* **51**, 221–239.

Gilbert, D. L., and Fenn, W. O. (1957). Calcium equilibrium in muscle. *J. Gen. Physiol.* **40**, 393–408.

Gordon, M. S., (1961). Personal communication.

Gordon, M. S., Schmidt-Nielsen, K., and Kelly, H. M. (1961). Osmotic regulation in the crab-eating frog (*Rana cancrivora*). *J. Exptl. Biol.* **38**, 659–678.

Grant, W. C., and Grant, J. A. (1958). Water drive studies in hypophysectomized efts of *Diemyctylus viridescens*. *Biol. Bull.* **114**, 1–9.

Grant, W. C., and Pickford, G. E. (1959). Presence of the red eft water-drive factor Prolactin in the pituitaries of teleosts. *Biol. Bull.* **116**, 429–435.

Gray, A. S., Adkinson, J. L., and Zelle, K. (1940). The *in vitro* secretion of acid by the gastric mucosa of the frog. *Am. J. Physiol.* **130**, 327–331.

Gray, P. (1930). The development of the amphibian kidney. Part I. The development of the mesonephros of *Rana temporaria*. *Quart. J. Microscop. Sci.* **73**, 507–546.

Harris, E. J. (1960). "Transport and Accumulation in Biological Systems," 279 pp. Butterworth, London.

Harris, J. B., and Edelman, I. S. (1960). Transport of potassium by the gastric mucosa of the frog. *Am. J. Physiol.* **198**, 280–284.

Harrison, R. G. (1904). An experimental study of the relation of the nervous system to the developing musculature of the embryo of the frog. *Am. J. Anat.* **3**, 197–220.

Hayman, J. M. (1929). Notes on the arrangement of blood vessels within the frog's kidney together with some measurements of blood pressure in the renal portal vein and renal veins. *Am. J. Physiol.* **86**, 331–339.

Hays, R. M., Lamdin, E., Maffly, R. H., and Leaf, A. (1959). Permeability of the toad bladder to urea and the effect of neurohypophyseal hormone. *Federation Proc.* **18**, 66.

Heller, H. (1930). Über die Einwirkung von Hypophysenhinterlappenextrakten auf den Wasserhaushalt des Frosches. *Arch. Exptl. Pathol. Pharmakol. Naunyn–Schmiedeberg's* **157**, 298–322.

Heller, H. (1941a). The distribution of the pituitary antidiuretic hormone throughout the vertebrate series. *J. Physiol. (London)* **99**, 246–256.

Heller, H. (1941b). Differentiation of an (amphibian) water balance principle from the antidiuretic principle of the posterior pituitary gland. *J. Physiol. (London)* **100**, 125–141.

Heller, H. (1945). The effect of neurohypophysial extracts on the water balance of lower vertebrates. *Biol. Rev. Cambridge Phil. Soc.* **20**, 147–158.

Heller, H., and Pickering, B. T. (1961). Neurohypophysial hormones of non-mammalian vertebrates. *J. Physiol. (London)* **155**, 98–114.

Hevesy, G., Hofer, E., and Krogh, A. (1935). The permeability of the skin of frogs to water as determined by D_2O and H_2O. *Skand. Arch. Physiol.* **72**, 199–214.

Hogben, C. A. M. (1955). Biological aspects of active transport. *In* "Electrolytes in Biological Systems" (A. M. Shanes, ed.), pp. 176–204. Am. Physiol. Soc., Washington, D.C.

Hogben, C. A. M., and Bollman, J. L. (1951). Excretion of phosphate by isolated frog kidney. *Am. J. Physiol.* **164**, 662–669.

Holtfreter, J. (1943). Properties and functions of the surface coat in amphibian embryos. *J. Exptl. Biol.* **93**, 251–323.

Hong, S. K. (1957). Effects of Pituitrin and cold on water exchanges of frogs. *Am. J. Physiol.* **188**, 439–442.

Hoshiko, T., and Ussing, H. H. (1959). The kinetics of Na^{24} flux across amphibian skin and bladder. *Acta Physiol. Scand.* **49**, 74–81.

Hoshiko, T., Swanson, R. E., and Visscher, M. B. (1956). Excretion of Na^{22} and K^{42} by the perfused bullfrog kidney and the effect of some poisons. *Am. J. Physiol.* **184**, 542–547.

Howes, N. H. (1940). The response of the water-regulating mechanism of developmental stages of the common toad, *Bufo bufo bufo*(L), to treatment with extracts of the posterior lobe of the pituitary body. *J. Exptl. Biol.* **17**, 128–138.

Howland, R. B. (1921). Experiments on the effects of removal of the pronephros of *Amblystoma punctatum*. *J. Exptl. Zool.* **32**, 355–396.

Huf, E. G. (1955). Ion transport and ion exchange in frog skin. *In* "Electrolytes in Biological Systems" (A. M. Shanes, ed.), pp. 205–238. Am. Physiol. Soc., Washington, D.C.

Huf, E. G., and Arrighi, M. F. (1955). Electrolyte distribution and active salt uptake in frog skin. *J. Gen. Physiol.* **38**, 867–888.

Huf, E. G., and Doss, N. S. (1958). Effect of temperature on electrolyte metabolism of isolated frog skin. *J. Gen. Physiol.* **42**, 525–532.

Huf, E. G., and Wills, J. (1951). Influence of some inorganic cations on active salt and water uptake by isolated frog skin. *Am. J. Physiol.* **167**, 255–260.

Huf, E. G., and Wills, J. (1953). The relationship of sodium uptake, potassium rejection, and skin potential in isolated frog skin. *J. Gen. Physiol.* **36**, 473–487.

Huf, E. G., Doss, N. S., and Wills, J. (1957). Effect of metabolic inhibitors and drugs on ion transport and oxygen consumption in isolated frog skin. *J. Gen. Physiol.* **41**, 397–417.

Humphrey, R. R. (1948). A lethal fluid imbalance in the Mexican axolotl. *J. Heredity* **39**, 255–261.

Humphrey, R. R. (1960). A maternal effect of a gene (f) for a fluid imbalance in the Mexican axolotl. *Develop. Biol.* **2**, 105–128.

Isayama, S. (1924a). Über die Strömung der Lymphe bei den Amphibien. *Z. Biol.* **82**, 90–100.

Isayama, S. (1924b). Über die Geschwindigkeit des Flüssigkeitsaustausches zwischen Blut und Gewebe. *Z. Biol.* **82**, 101–106.

Jaffee, O. C. (1954a). Morphogenesis of the pronephros of the leopard frog (*Rana pipiens*). *J. Morphol.* **95**, 109–124.

Jaffee, O. C. (1954b). Phenol red transport in the pronephros and mesonephros of the developing frog (*Rana pipiens*). *J. Cellular Comp. Physiol.* **44**, 347–361.

Johnson, J. (1956). Influence of ouabain, strophanthidin and dihydrostrophanthidin on potassium and sodium transport in frog sartorii. *Am. J. Physiol.* **187**, 328–332.

Jones, M. E., and Steggerda, F. R. (1935). Studies on water metabolism in normal and hypophysectomized frogs. *Am. J. Physiol.* **112**, 397–400.

Jørgensen, C. B. (1948). On the osmotic regulation in amphibians. *Acta Physiol. Scand.* Suppl. **78**, 37–38.

Jørgensen, C. B. (1950a). Osmotic regulation in the frog, *Rana esculenta* (L.), at low temperatures. *Acta Physiol. Scand.* **20**, 46–55.

Jørgensen, C. B. (1950b). The influence of salt loss on osmotic regulation in anurans. *Acta Physiol. Scand.* **20**, 56–61.

Jørgensen, C. B. (1950c). The amphibian water economy. *Acta Physiol. Scand.* Suppl. **78**, 1–79.

Jørgensen, C. B. (1954). On excretion of chloride in sodium chloride loaded toads. *Acta Physiol. Scand.* **30**, 171–177.

Jørgensen, C. B. (1962). Personal communication.

Jørgensen, C. B., Levi, H., and Ussing, H. H. (1946). On the influence of the neurohypophyseal principles on the sodium metabolism in the axolotl (*Amblystoma mexicanum*). *Acta Physiol. Scand.* **12**, 350–371.

Jørgensen, C. B., Levi, H., and Zerahn, K. (1954). An active uptake of sodium and chloride ions in anurans. *Acta Physiol. Scand.* **30**, 178–190.

Jørgensen, C. B., Wingstrand, K. G., and Rosenkilde, P. (1956). The neurohypophysis and water metabolism in the toad, *Bufo bufo* L. *Endocrinology* **59**, 601–610.

Kalman, S. M., and Ussing, H. H. (1955). Active sodium uptake by the toad and its response to the antidiuretic hormone. *J. Gen. Physiol.* **38**, 361–370.

Kampmeier, O. F. (1920). The changes in the systemic venous plan during development and the relation of the lymph hearts to them in Anura. *Anat. Record* **19**, 83–96.

Kampmeier, O. F. (1922). The development of the anterior lymphatics and lymph hearts in anuran embryos. *Am. J. Anat.* **30,** 61–132.

Kampmeier, O. F. (1925). The development of the trunk and tail lymphatics and posterior lymph hearts in anuran embryos. *J. Morphol. Physiol.* **41,** 95–157.

Katsoyannis, P. G., and du Vigneaud, V. (1958). Arginine-vasotocin, a synthetic analogue of the posterior pituitary hormones containing the ring of oxytocin and the side chain of vasopressin. *J. Biol. Chem.* **233,** 1352–1354.

Kaylor, C. T. (1940). Experiments on parabiotic union of haploid and diploid larvae of *Triturus pyrrhogaster*. *Anat. Record* **78** (Suppl), 52–53.

Kemp, N. E. (1953). Morphogenesis and metabolism of amphibian larvae after excision on the heart. *Anat. Record* **117,** 405–425.

Kempton, R. T. (1937). The dimensions of the renal tubule of *Necturus maculosus*. *J. Morphol.* **61,** 51–58.

Keynes, R. D. (1954). The ionic fluxes of frog muscle. *Proc. Roy. Soc.* **B142,** 359–382.

Keynes, R. D., and Maizel, C. W. (1954). The energy requirement for sodium extrusion from frog muscle. *Proc. Roy. Soc.* **B142,** 383–392.

Keynes, R. D., and Swan, R. C. (1959). The effect of external sodium concentration on the sodium fluxes in a frog skeletal muscle. *J. Physiol. (London)* **147,** 591–625.

Kinter, W. B. (1959). Renal tubular transport of Diodrast-I^{131} and PAH in *Necturus*: evidence for simultaneous reabsorption and secretion. *Am. J. Physiol.* **196,** 1141–1149.

Kinter, W. B., and Tanner, G. A. (1961). Simultaneous bidirectional transport of Diodrast and PAH in *Necturus* kidney. *Federation Proc.* **20,** 413.

Kirschner, L. B., Maxwell, R., and Flemming, D. (1960). Non-osmotic water movement across the isolated frog skin. *J. Cellular Comp. Physiol.* **55,** 267–273.

Knower, H. McE. (1908). The origin and development of the anterior lymph hearts and subcutaneous lymph sacs in the frog. *Anat. Record* **2,** 59–62.

Knower, H. McE. (1939). "A Resurvey of the Development of Lymphatics and Associated Blood Vessels in Anuran Amphibia by the Method of Injection," 125 pp. Wistar Inst., Philadelphia, Pennsylvania.

Koefoed-Johnsen, V. (1957). The effects of G-strophanthin (Ouabain) on the active transport of sodium through the isolated frog skin. *Acta Physiol. Scand.* Suppl. **145,** 87–88.

Koefoed-Johnsen, V., and Ussing, H. H. (1949). The influence of corticotrophic hormone from ox on the active salt uptake in the axolotl. *Acta Physiol. Scand.* **17,** 38–43.

Koefoed-Johnsen, V., and Ussing, H. H. (1952). The mode of passage of chloride ions through the isolated frog skin. *Acta Physiol. Scand.* **25,** 150–163.

Koefoed-Johnsen, V., and Ussing, H. H. (1953). The contribution of diffusion and flow to the passage of D$_2$O through living membranes. *Acta Physiol. Scand.* **28,** 60–76.

Koefoed-Johnsen, V., and Ussing, H. H. (1958). The nature of the frog skin potential. *Acta Physiol. Scand.* **42,** 298–308.

Koefoed-Johnsen, V., Ussing, H. H., and Zerahn, K. (1952). The origin of the short-circuit current in the adrenaline stimulated frog skin. *Acta Physiol. Scand.* **27,** 38–48.

Krause, F. (1928). Über den Einfluss der Temperatur auf die Geschwindigkeit der Harnabscheidung beim Frosche. *Z. Biol.* **87,** 167–174.

Krogh, A. (1937). Osmotic regulation in the frog (*Rana esculenta*) by active absorption of chloride ions. *Skand. Arch. Physiol.* **76,** 60–74.

Krogh, A. (1938). The active absorption of ions in some fresh water animals. *Z. Vergleich. Physiol.* **25**, 335–350.

Krogh, A. (1939). "Osmotic Regulation in Aquatic Animals," 242 pp. Cambridge Univ. Press, London and New York.

Krogh, A., Schmidt-Nielsen, K., and Zeuthen, E. (1938). The osmotic behavior of frog eggs and young tadpoles. *Z. vergleich. Physiol.* **26**, 230–238.

Lambert, P. (1933). Sur l'exsistence d'un gradient de perméabilité dans les néphrons ouverts des urodèles. *Compt. Rend. Soc. Biol.* **114**, 1370–1372.

Leaf, A. (1956). Ion transport by the isolated bladder of the toad. *Proc. Intern. Congr. Biochem. 3rd Brussels 1955*, p. 107.

Leaf, A. (1959). The mechanism of the asymmetrical distribution of endogenous lactate about the isolated toad bladder. *J. Cellular Comp. Physiol.* **54**, 103–108.

Leaf, A. (1960). Some actions of neurohypophyseal hormones on a living membrane. *J. Gen. Physiol.* **43**, 175–189.

Leaf, A., and Dempsey, E. (1960). Some effects of mammalian neurohypophyseal hormones on metabolism and active transport of sodium by the isolated toad bladder. *J. Biol. Chem.* **235**, 2160–2163.

Leaf, A., Anderson, J., and Page, L. B. (1958). Active sodium transport by the isolated toad bladder. *J. Gen. Physiol.* **41**, 657–668.

Leaf, A., Page, L. B., and Anderson, J. (1959). Respiration and active sodium transport of isolated toad bladder. *J. Biol. Chem.* **234**, 1625–1629.

Levi, H., and Ussing, H. H. (1948). The exchange of sodium and chloride ions across the fibre membrane of the isolated frog sartorius. *Acta Physiol. Scand.* **16**, 232–249.

Levinsky, N. G., and Sawyer, W. H. (1952). Influence of the adenohypophysis on the frog water-balance response. *Endocrinology* **51**, 110–116.

Levinsky, N. G., and Sawyer, W. H. (1953). Significance of neurohypophysis in regulation of fluid balance in the frog. *Proc. Soc. Exptl. Biol. Med.* **82**, 272–274.

Linderholm, H. (1952). Active transport of ions through frog skin with special reference to the action of certain diuretics. *Acta Physiol. Scand.* Suppl. **97**, 1–144.

Linderholm, H. (1953). The electrical potential across isolated frog skin and its dependence on the permeability of the skin to chloride ions. *Acta Physiol. Scand.* **28**, 211–217.

Littleford, R. A., Keller, W. F., and Phillips, N. E. (1947). Studies on the vital limits of water loss in the plethodont salamanders. *Ecology* **28**, 440–447.

Love, J. K., and Lifson, N. (1958). Transtubular movements of urea in the doubly perfused bullfrog kidney. *Am. J. Physiol.* **193**, 662–668.

Løvtrup, S. (1960). Water permeation in the amphibian embryo. *J. Exptl. Zool.* **145**, 139–150.

Lucas, A. M., and White, H. L. (1933). Contractility of the ciliated neck in the *Necturus* kidney. *Anat. Record* **57**, 7–11.

McAfee, R. D., and Locke, W. (1961). Effects of certain steroids on bioelectric current of isolated frog skin. *Am. J. Physiol.* **200**, 797–800.

McClure, C. F. W. (1919). Experimental production of edema in larval and adult Anura. *J. Gen. Physiol.* **1**, 261–268.

McClure, C. F. W. (1928). On the structure of the pronephros in the oedematous larva of Anura. *Anat. Record* **39**, 349–358.

MacRobbie, E. A., and Ussing, H. H. (1961). Osmotic behavior of the epithelial cells of frog skin. *Acta Physiol. Scand.* **53**, 348–365.

Maetz, J., Jard, S., and Morel, F. (1958). Action de l'aldostérone sur le transport actif de sodium de la peau de grenouille. *Compt. Rend.* **247**, 516–518.

Maetz, J., Morel, F., and Race, B. (1959). Mise en évidence dans le neurohypophyse de *Rana esculenta* L. d'un facteur hormonal nouveau stimulant le transport actif de sodium à travers la peau. *Biochim. Biophys. Acta* **36**, 317–326.

Marshall, E. K. (1926). The secretion of urine. *Physiol. Rev.* **6**, 440–484.

Marshall, E. K. (1932). The secretion of urea in the frog. *J. Cellular Comp. Physiol.* **2**, 349–353.

Marshall, E. K. (1934). The comparative physiology of the kidney in relation to theories of renal secretion. *Physiol. Rev.* **14**, 133–159.

Marshall, E. K., and Smith, H. W. (1930). The glomerular development of the vertebrate kidney in relation to habitat. *Biol. Bull.* **59**, 135–153.

Maurer, F. W. (1938). Isolation and analysis of extracellular muscle fluid in the frog. *Am. J. Physiol.* **124**, 546–557.

Mellanby, K. (1941). The body temperature of the frog. *J. Exptl. Biol.* **18**, 55–61.

Montgomery, H., and Pierce, J. A. (1937). The site of acidification of the urine within the renal tubule in Amphibia. *Am. J. Physiol.* **118**, 144–152.

Morel, F., Maetz, J., Acher, R., Chauvet, J., and Lenci, M. T. (1961). A "natriferic" principle other than arginine-vasotocin in the frog neurohypophysis. *Nature* **190**, 828–829.

Mullins, L. J. (1959). The penetration of some cations into muscle. *J. Gen. Physiol.* **42**, 817–829.

Munro, A. F. (1953). The ammonia and urea excretion of different species of Amphibia during their development and metamorphosis. *Biochem. J.* **54**, 29–36.

Murphy, Q. R. (ed.) (1957). "Metabolic Aspects of Transport Across Cell Membranes," 379 pp. Univ. Wisconsin Press, Madison, Wisconsin.

Myers, R. M., Fleming, W. R., and Scheer, B. T. (1956). Pituitary-adrenal control of sodium flux across the frog skin. *Endocrinology* **58**, 674–676.

Myers, R. M., Bishop, W. R., and Scheer, B. T. (1961). Anterior pituitary control of active sodium transport across frog skin. *Am. J. Physiol.* **200**, 444–450.

Needham, J. (1931). "Chemical Embryology," 2021 pp. Cambridge Univ. Press, London and New York.

Noble, G. K. (1931). "The Biology of Amphibia," 577 pp. McGraw-Hill, New York.

Novelli, A. (1933). Extrait postéro-hypophysaire et imbibition des Batraciens. *Compt. Rend. Soc. Biol.* **112**, 506–507.

O'Dell, R. M., and Schmidt-Nielsen, B. (1961). Retention of urea by frog and mammalian kidney slices *in vitro*. *J. Cellular Comp. Physiol.* **57**, 211–219.

Okada, H. (1956). On the action potentials of the lymph-cardiac spinal center. *Japan. J. Physiol.* **6**, 249–258.

Oken, D. E., Whittembury, G. W., Windhager, E. E., Schatzmann, H. J., and Solomon, A. K. (1959). Active transport by the proximal tubule of *Necturus* kidney. *J. Clin. Invest.* **38**, 1029.

Oldham, F. K. (1936). The action of the preparations from the posterior lobe of the pituitary gland upon the imbibition of water by the frog. *Am. J. Physiol.* **115**, 275–280.

Oliver, J., and Shevsky, E. (1929). A comparison of the manner of excretion of neutral red and phenol red by the frog's kidney. *J. Exptl. Med.* **29**, 15–29.

Ott, M. D. (1924). Changes in the weights of the various organs and parts of the leopard frog (*Rana pipiens*) at different stages of inanition. *Am. J. Anat.* **33**, 17–56.

Ottoson, D., Sjöstrand, F., Stenström, S., and Svaetichin, G. (1953). Microelectrode studies on the EMF of the frog skin related to electron microscopy of the dermoepithelial junction. *Acta Physiol. Scand.* Suppl. **106**, 611–624.

Ozorio de Almeida, M. (1926). Sur les effets de la déshydration des Batraciens produits par la ventilation. *J. Physiol. Pathol. Gen.* **24**, 243–249.

Pak Poy, R. F. K., and Bentley, P. J. (1960). Fine structure of the epithelial cells of the toad urinary bladder. *Exptl. Cell Res.* **20**, 235–237.

Parsons, D. S., and van Rossum, G. D. V. (1961). Regulation of fluid and electrolytes in liver of *Rana temporaria*. *Biochim. Biophys. Acta* **54**, 364–366.

Pasqualini, R.-Q. (1936). La diurèse des crapauds hypophysoprives, à sec ou après l'injection d'eau. *Compt. Rend. Soc. Biol.* **123**, 71–73.

Pasqualini, R.-Q., and Riseau, J. C. (1951). Action de la désoxycorticostérone sur l'absorption cutanée chez le crapaud. *Compt. Rend. Soc. Biol.* **146**, 604–606.

Peachey, L. D., and Rasmussen, H. (1961). Structure of the toad's urinary bladder as related to its physiology. *J. Biophys. Biochem. Cytol.* **10**, 529–554.

Pearse, A. S. (1950). "The Emigrations of Animals from the Sea," 210 pp. Dryden, New York.

Pohle, E. (1920). Der Einfluss des Nervensystems auf die Osmoregulation der Amphibien. *Arch. Ges. Physiol. Pflüger's* **182**, 215–231.

Pora, E. A., and Stoicovici, F. (1955). Recherches sur le rôle du système nerveux de *Bufo viridis* dans les phénomènes d'adaptation à la salinité. *Acad. Rep. Populare Romine Bul. Sect. Biol. Stiinte Agr.* **7**, 59–89 (seen in abstract only).

Pratt, F. H., and Reid, M. A. (1939). Synchronization of anuran lymph hearts and the integration of their spinal centers. *J. Physiol. (London)* **95**, 345–355.

Prescott, M., and Zeuthen, E. (1953). Comparison of water diffusion and water filtration across cell surfaces. *Acta Physiol. Scand.* **28**, 77–94.

Prosser, C. L., and Weinstein, S. J. F. (1950). Comparison of blood volumes in animals with open and closed circulatory systems. *Physiol. Zool.* **23**, 113–124.

Przylecki, S. J. (1922). L'échange de l'eau et des sels chez les amphibiens. *Arch. Intern. Physiol.* **19**, 148–159.

Rafftery, N. S. (1961). A study of the relationship between the pronephros and the haploid syndrome in frog larvae. *J. Morphol.* **108**, 203–218.

Rappaport, R. (1954). The uptake of water during development of amphibian tissues. *J. Exptl. Zool.* **127**, 27–52.

Rappaport, R. (1955). The initiation of pronephric function in *Rana pipiens*. *J. Exptl. Zool.* **128**, 481–514.

Ray, C. (1958). Vital limits and rates of desiccation in salamanders. *Ecology* **39**, 75–83.

Reid, M. A. (1937). Automaticity in transplanted anuran lymph hearts. *J. Exptl. Biol.* **76**, 47–63.

Richards, A. N., and Schmidt, C. F. (1924–1925). A description of the glomerular circulation in the frog's kidney and observations concerning the action of adrenaline and various other substances upon it. *Am. J. Physiol.* **71**, 178–208.

Richards, A. N., and Walker, A. M. (1927). The accessibility of the glomerular vessels to fluid perfused through the renal portal system of the frog's kidney. *Am. J. Physiol.* **79**, 419–432.

Richards, A. N., and Walker, A. M. (1937). Methods of collecting fluid from known regions of the renal tubules of Amphibia and of perfusing the lumen of a single tubule. *Am. J. Physiol.* **118**, 111–120.

Richards, O. W. (1940). The capsular fluid of *Amblystoma punctatum* eggs compared with Holtfreter's and Ringer's solutions. *J. Exptl. Zool.* **83**, 401–406.

Rugh, R. (1938). Structure and function of the peritoneal funnels of the frog, *Rana pipiens*. *Proc. Soc. Exptl. Biol. Med.* **37**, 717–721.

Rugh, R. (1950). Inhibition of growth and the production of oedema by X-radiation. *J. Exptl. Zool.* **114**, 137–158.

Ruibal, R. (1959). The ecology of a brackish water population of *Rana pipiens*. *Copeia* **4**, 315–322.

Sampson, L. V. (1904). A contribution to the embryology of *Hyloides Martinicensi* *Am. J. Anat.* **3**, 473–504.

Sawyer, W. H. (1951a). Effect of posterior pituitary extract on permeability of frog skin to water. *Am. J. Physiol.* **164**, 44–48.

Sawyer, W. H. (1951b). Effects of posterior pituitary extracts on urine formation and glomerular circulation in the frog. *Am. J. Physiol.* **164**, 457–466.

Sawyer, W. H. (1956). The hormonal control of water and salt-electrolyte metabolism with special reference to the Amphibia. *Mem. Soc. Endocrinol.* **5**, 44–56.

Sawyer, W. H. (1957). Increased reabsorption of osmotically free water by the toad (*Bufo marinus*) in response to neurohypophysial hormones. *Am. J. Physiol.* **189**, 564–568.

Sawyer, W. H. (1960a). Evidence for the identity of Natriferin, the frog water balance principle, and arginine vasotocin. *Nature* **187**, 1030–1031.

Sawyer, W. H. (1960b). Increased water permeability of the bullfrog (*Rana catesbeiana*) bladder *in vitro* in response to synthetic oxytocin and arginine vasotocin and to neurohypophysial extracts from non-mammalian vertebrates. *Endocrinology* **66**, 112–120.

Sawyer, W. H., and Sawyer, M. K. (1952). Adaptive responses to neurohypophyseal fractions in vertebrates. *Physiol. Zool.* **25**, 84–98.

Sawyer, W. H., and Schisgall, R. M. (1956). Increased permeability of the frog bladder to water in response to dehydration and neurohypophysial extracts. *Am. J. Physiol.* **187**, 312–314.

Sawyer, W. H., Munsick, R. A., and van Dyke, H. B. (1959). Pharmacological evidence for the presence of arginine vasotocin and oxytocin in neurohypophysial extracts from cold-blooded vertebrates. *Nature* **184**, 1464–1465.

Schatzmann, H. J., Windhager, E. E., and Solomon, A. K. (1958). Single proximal tubules of the *Necturus* kidney. II. Effect of 2,4-dinitrophenol and ouabain on water reabsorption. *Am. J. Physiol.* **195**, 570–574.

Scheer, B. T. (1961). Hormonal regulation of salt balance in frogs. *Federation Proc.* **20**, 177.

Scheer, B. T., and Mumbach, M. W. (1960). The locus of the electromotive force in frog skin. *J. Cellular Comp. Physiol.* **55**, 259–266.

Schmidt, K. P. (1957). Amphibians. Mem. Geol. Soc. Amer. **67**, 1211–1212.

Schmidt-Nielsen, B., and Forster, R. P. (1954). The effect of dehydration and low temperature on renal function in the bullfrog. *J. Cellular Comp. Physiol.* **44**, 233–246.

Shanes, A. M. (ed.) (1955). "Electrolytes in Biological Systems," 243 pp. Am. Physiol. Soc., Washington, D.C.

Shaw, F. H., Simon, S. E., Johnstone, B. M., and Holmes, M. E. (1956). The effect of changes of environment on the electrical and ionic pattern of muscle. *J. Gen. Physiol.* **40**, 263–288.

Shelford, V. E. (1913). The reactions of certain animals to gradients of evaporating power of air. A study in experimental ecology. *Biol. Bull.* **25**, 79–120.

Shipp, J. C., Hanenson, I. B., Windhager, E. E., Schatzmann, H. J., Whittembury, G., Yoshimura, H., and Solomon, A. K. (1958). Single proximal tubules of the *Necturus* kidney. Methods for micropuncture and microperfusion. *Am. J. Physiol.* **195**, 563–569.

Simon, E. E., Johnstone, B. M., Shankly, K. H., and Shaw, F. H. (1959). Muscle: a three phase system. *J. Gen. Physiol.* **43**, 55–79.

Singer, E. (1933). A study of the morphological physiology of the frog's kidney with the fluorescence microscope. *Anat. Record* **55** (Suppl.), 37.

Smith, H. W. (1951). "The Kidney. Structure and Function in Health and Disease," 1049 pp. Oxford Univ. Press, London and New York.

Smith, V. D. E., and Jackson, C. M. (1931). The changes during desiccation and rehydration in the body and organs of the leopard frog (*Rana pipiens*). *Biol. Bull.* **60**, 80–93.

Spector, W. S. (ed.) (1956). "Handbook of Biological Data," 584 pp. Saunders, Philadelphia.

Stebbins, R. E. (1945). Water absorption in a terrestrial salamander. *Copeia* **1**, 25–28.

Steen, W. B. (1929). On the permeability of the frog's bladder to water. *Anat. Record* **43**, 215–220.

Steggerda, F. R. (1931). The relation of pitressin to water interchange in frogs. *Am. J. Physiol.* **98**, 255–261.

Steggerda, F. R. (1937). Comparative study of water metabolism in amphibians injected with pituitrin. *Proc. Soc. Exptl. Biol. Med.* **36**, 103–106.

Steggerda, F. R., and Ponder, E. (1940). The relation of the nervous system to skin potentials in the intact frog. *Proc. Soc. Exptl. Biol. Med.* **45**, 617–621.

Steinbach, C. (1927). Über Zusammenhänge zwischen dem Nierenindex und dem histologischen Bau der Haut bei Amphibien. *Z. Zellforsch. Mikroskop. Anat.* **4**, 382–412.

Steinbach, H. B. (1940). Sodium and potassium in frog muscle. *J. Biol. Chem.* **133**, 695–701.

Steinbach, H. B. (1961). Na extrusion by the sartorius of *Rana pipiens*. *J. Gen. Physiol.* **44**, 1131–1142.

Stewart, S. G. (1927). The morphology of the frog's kidney. *Anat. Record* **36**, 259–269.

Stewart, W. C. (1949). The effect of mammalian (posterior lobe) pituitary extract on water balance of frogs when placed in different osmotic environments. *Am. J. Physiol.* **157**, 412–417.

Swanson, R. E. (1956). Creatinine secretion by the frog renal tubule. *Am. J. Physiol.* **184**, 527–534.

Swingle, W. W. (1919). On the experimental production of edema by nephrectomy. *J. Gen. Physiol.* **1**, 504–514.

Tasker, P., Simon, S. E., Johnstone, B. M., Shankly, K. H., and Shaw, F. V. (1959). The dimensions of the extracellular space in sartorius muscle. *J. Gen. Physiol.* **43**, 39–53.

Taubenhaus, M., and Morton, J. M. (1958). Influence of steroids upon osmotic pressure changes in isolated frog skin pouches. *Proc. Soc. Exptl. Biol. Med.* **98**, 162–164.

Taubenhaus, M., Fritz, I. B., and Morton, J. M. (1956). *In vitro* effects of steroids upon electrolyte transfer through frog skin. *Endocrinology* **59**, 458–462.

Taylor, A. B., and Weinstein, I. (1952). The effect of desoxycorticosterone glucoside (DCG) upon the potential of isolated frog skin. *Anat. Record* **113**, 611.

Theorell, T. (1951). The acid-base balance of the secreting isolated gastric mucosa. *J. Physiol. (London)* **114**, 267–276.

Thorson, T. (1955). The relationship of water economy to terrestrialism in amphibians. *Ecology* **36**, 100–116.

Thorson, T. (1956). Adjustment of water loss in response to desiccation. *Copeia* pp. 230–237.

Thorson, T., and Svihla, A. (1943). Correlation of the habitats of amphibians with their ability to survive the loss of body water. *Ecology* **24**, 374–381.

Tuft, P. (1957). Changes in the osmotic activity of the blastocoel and archenteron contents during the early development of *Xenopus laevis. Proc. Roy. Phys. Soc. Edinburgh* **26**, 41–48.

Tuft, P. (1961a). The effect of a morphogenetic inhibitor (β-mercapto-ethanol) on the uptake and distribution of water in the embryo of *Xenopus laevis. Proc. Roy. Phys. Soc. Edinburgh* **28**, 123–130.

Tuft, P. (1961b). A morphogenetic effect of β-mercaptoethanol. *Nature* **191**, 1072–1073.

Tuft, P. (1961c). Role of water-regulating mechanisms in amphibian morphogenesis; a quantitative hypothesis. *Nature* **192**, 1049–1050.

Underhay, E. E., and Baldwin, E. (1955). Nitrogen excretion in the tadpoles of *Xenopus laevis* Daudin. *Biochem. J.* **61**, 544–547.

Uranga, J. (1957). Variacion estacionel de la accion antidiuretica del encefalo y la hipofisis del sapo. *Rev. Soc. Arg. Biol.* **33**, 238–251.

Uranga, J. (1958a). Reabsorcion de agua en el riñon del sapo. *Rev. Soc. Arg. Biol.* **34**, 111–116.

Uranga, J. (1958b). Absorcion de agua en el intestino del sapo. *Rev. Soc. Arg. Biol.* **34**, 161–164.

Uranga, J. (1958c). Absorcion de agua por la piel del sapo. *Rev. Soc. Arg. Biol.* **34**, 233–238.

Uranga, J. (1958d). Influencias de las hormonas neurohipofisarias y de la extirpacion de la hipofisis sobre la diuresis del sapo. *Rev. Soc. Arg. Biol.* **34**, 290–304.

Uranga, J. (1961). Action de l'ocytocine et de la température sur le filtrat glomérulaire du Crapaud. *Compt. Rend. Soc. Biol.* **155**, 173–174.

Uranga, J., and Quintana, G. (1958). Absorcion de agua en la vijiga del sapa. *Rev. Soc. Arg. Biol.* **34**, 75–81.

Uranga, J., and Sawyer, W. H. (1960). Renal responses of the bullfrog to oxytocin, arginine vasotocin, and frog neurohypophysial extract. *Am. J. Physiol.* **198**, 1287–1290.

Ussing, H. H. (1949). The active ion transport through the isolated frog skin. *Acta Physiol. Scand.* **17**, 1–37.

Ussing, H. H. (1960a). The frog skin potential. *J. Gen. Physiol.* **43**, 135–147.

Ussing, H. H. (1960b). The alkali metals in biology. *In* "Handbuch der experimentellen Pharmakologie" (O. Eichler and A. Farah, eds.), 195 pp. Springer, Berlin.

Ussing, H. H., and Zerahn, K. (1951). Active transport of sodium as the source of electric current in the short-circuited isolated frog skin. *Acta Physiol. Scand.* **23**, 110–127.

Vogel, G. (1949). Die Grösse und Leistung der filtrierenden und resorbierenden Flächen in der Amphibienniere. *Arch. Ges. Physiol. Pflüger's* **252**, 40–51.

Walker, A. M., and Hudson, C. L. (1937a). The reabsorption of glucose from the renal tubule in Amphibia and the action of phlorizin upon it. *Am. J. Physiol.* **118**, 140–143.

Walker, A. M., and Hudson, C. L. (1937b). The role of the tubule in the excretion of urea by the amphibian kidney. *Am. J. Physiol.* **118**, 153–166.

Walker, A. M., and Hudson, C. L. (1937c). The role of the tubule in the excretion of inorganic phosphates in the amphibian kidney. *Am. J. Physiol.* **118**, 167–173.

Walker, A. M., Hudson, C. L., Findlay, T., and Richards, A. N. (1937). The total molecular concentration and the chloride concentration of fluid from different segments of the renal tubule of Amphibia. *Am. J. Physiol.* **118**, 121–129.

Wearn, J. T., and Richards, A. N. (1924). Observations on the composition of glomerular urine, with particular reference to the problem of reabsorption in the renal tubules. *Am. J. Physiol.* **71**, 209–227.

Wearn, J. F., Schmidt, C. F., and Richards, A. N. (1923–1924). Observations on the glomerular circulation and on the composition of glomerular urine in the frog's kidney. *Quart. J. Exptl. Physiol.* **13**, 235–236.

Westphal, W. (1957). Der Einfluss der Adrenalektomie auf die tubulare Reabsorption von Natrium und Kalium in der künstlich perfundierten Froschniere. *Arch. Ges. Physiol. Pflüger's* **226**, 61–62.

White, H. L. (1929a). The question of water reabsorption by the renal tubule and its bearing on the problem of renal secretion. *Am. J. Physiol.* **88**, 267–281.

White, H. L. (1929b). Some measurements of ciliary activity. *Am. J. Physiol.* **88**, 282–285.

Whittembury, G. (1960). Ion and water transport in the proximal tubules of the kidney of *Necturus maculosus*. *J. Gen. Physiol.* **43**, 43–56.

Whittembury, G., Oken, D. E., Windhager, E. E., and Solomon, A. K. (1959). Single proximal tubules of *Necturus* kidney. IV. Dependence of H_2O movement on osmotic gradients. *Am. J. Physiol.* **197**, 1121–1127.

Whittembury, G., Sugino, N., and Solomon, A. K. (1960). Effect of anti-diuretic hormone and calcium on the equivalent pore radius of kidney slices from *Necturus*. *Nature* **187**, 699–701.

Whittembury, G., Sugino, N., and Solomon, A. K. (1961). Ionic permeability and electrical potential differences in *Necturus* kidney cells. *J. Gen. Physiol.* **44**, 689–712.

Wilbrandt, W. (1938). Electrical potential differences across the wall of kidney tubules in *Necturus*. *J. Cellular Comp. Physiol.* **11**, 425–431.

Williams, M. W., and Angerer, C. A. (1959). Adrenal cortex and frog skin potentials. *Proc. Soc. Exptl. Biol. Med.* **102**, 112–114.

Windhager, E. E., Whittembury, G., Oken, D. E., Schatzmann, H. J., and Solomon, A. K. (1959). Single proximal tubules of the *Necturus* kidney. *Am. J. Physiol.* **197**, 313–318.

Yoshimura, H., Yata, M., Yuasa, M., and Wolbach, R. (1961). Renal regulation of acid-base balance in the bullfrog. *Am. J. Physiol.* **201**, 980–986.

Zerahn, K. (1955). Studies on the active transport of lithium in the isolated frog skin. *Acta Physiol. Scand.* **33**, 347–358.

Zwemer, R. L., and Foglia, V. G. (1943). Fatal loss of plasma volume after lymph heart destruction in toads. *Proc. Soc. Exptl. Biol. Med.* **53**, 14–17.

6

AMPHIBIAN MUSCLE

B. C. Abbott and A. J. Brady

I. Introduction

The muscular system consists of groups of muscles with contractile cells, tendons, and connective tissues. Three major divisions can be recognized in amphibians: skeletal, smooth, and cardiac muscles. The skeletal muscles have tendinous attachments to skeletal structures and are striated and voluntary. Smooth muscles consist of small spindle shape fibers under the control of the autonomic nervous system and are the muscles of the walls of the digestive, excretory, circulatory, respiratory, and reproductive systems. Cardiac muscle is striated and is discussed in the chapter on the amphibian heart (Chapter 4).

So much of our knowledge of muscle physiology is based on studies of frog skeletal muscle that it is difficult to condense the information adequately and equally difficult to provide a comparative account.

The sartorius muscle of frogs has been widely used for several reasons. It is a sheet of muscle thin enough to be adequately aerated by diffusion when isolated from the body; the muscle is viable down to 0°C where the slow response aids in temporal resolution of the events in contraction; the fibers run the length of the muscle and excitation anywhere on the fiber is propagated to activate all the fiber with a single shock inducing a large mechanical twitch. Analysis of mechanical properties is simplest in a parallel-fibered muscle, and the studies on skeletal muscles in other animals have provided results only quantitatively different. The gastrocnemius muscle, in particular, is less suitable for critical studies than the sartorius because the fibers are short and not orientated along the length of the muscle and the muscle is too thick to obtain adequate oxygen by diffusion alone. On the other hand, certain other muscles must be mentioned. The extensor longus digitorum IV of the frog is long and cylindrical with about 50 parallel fibers. This shape and size makes it ideal for studies on membrane activity and ionic exchange, and facilitates the study of the sensory properties of the extra-fusal fibers. A similarly shaped muscle is available in the cutaneous abdominis muscle which inserts into skin at one end and to the pelvic bone at the other, and can easily be dissected with its motor nerve.

The sternocutaneous muscle provides, on the other hand, a very thin sheet of muscle several millimeters long. It has been used for optical studies on the fibers during activity to demonstrate changes in diffraction during the early events of contraction (D. K. Hill, 1953).

II. Skeletal Muscle

Every muscle can be thought of as a machine which changes its physical properties when activated such that it can develop tension, can shorten, and can perform external work. Its characteristics can be studied, as can those of any machine, in terms of its performance. To this end, certain methods of study have been adopted and a terminology established. The forces which the muscle machine can develop are studied under *isometric* conditions, i.e., at constant length, in which one end of the muscle is fixed and the other end is connected to a tension transducer. The connecting link and the transducer are as noncompliant as possible in order to minimize change in muscle length during contraction.

Muscle movements are usually studied *isotonically*, where length can change but load on the muscle remains constant. The load is applied near to the pivot axis of a simple lever with a ratio of about 20 to 1 so that the load on the muscle is almost inertia-free. Movement of the lever is recorded directly on a smoked drum or by a transducer device. The relationships between load and distance, speed, acceleration, and work done by the muscle during activity can thus be studied.

Isotonic contractions are usually *afterloaded*, which means that the resting muscle is kept at reference length by a stop which supports the applied load and is subjected to the load only when tension develops within the muscle sufficiently to lift the load off a holding stop. In *preloaded* contractions this stop is absent, and the load to be lifted is already carried by the resting muscle. The muscle thus starts at a different length for each load, which complicates the study of the mechanical relations. Such studies are informative but are unlike contractions in the body where even at maximum length the resting muscle is stressed only slightly.

A *twitch* is a transient response of the muscle to a single stimulus, and may be regarded as the basic unit of the response of skeletal muscle; tension or shortening rises to a peak value and returns to its starting level. A series of isotonic twitches under various loads for sartorius muscles from *Rana pipiens* at 0°C are shown in Fig. 1 and a normal isometric twitch is seen in Fig. 9a. The time course of the isotonic twitches differs with load; as the afterload increases the latent period increases, and relaxation occurs earlier. Jewell and Wilkie (1960) have shown that the rise of tension up to the value where the load is lifted and its decay to zero after the load has dropped again follows the same time course as in the isometric twitch.

Repeated stimuli will result in an incomplete tetanus at low frequencies of stimulation. Above a certain frequency the individual responses disappear giving a fused tetanus in which the activity appears to be continuous. This frequency depends on the inertia and resolution of the transducer and the recording systems, but also differs with type of muscle and species of animal. The fusion frequency using direct stimulation is about 40 pulses per second for *Rana temporaria* at 0°C, but is only about 15 pulses per second for *R. pipiens*. The maximum isometric tension developed in a fused tetanus will be referred to as P_0. At the end of activity,

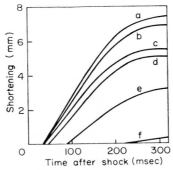

Fig. 1. Afterloaded isotonic twitches of frog sartorius at 0°C., length 27 mm, weight 65 mg. Loads (in gm wt) applied: (a) 0.95, (b) 1.25, (c) 1.9, (d) 2.5, (e) 5.1, (f) 12 gm wt (From Abbott and Ritchie, 1951b.)

the muscle relaxes and completes a physical cycle back to the original resting state, although the chemical events are by no means complete.

Skeletal muscle in general displays marked twitch responses, with high fusion frequency and rapid relaxation as a characteristic. Certain skeletal fibers in Amphibia, however, emphasize *tonic* responses in which relaxation after activity is very slow and the muscles can remain in a state of tonus. These fibers can be identified by their mechanical and electrical responses and appear to function for maintenance of steady tone within the animal's musculature, e.g., in the clasp reflex of mating.

Muscle has a resting metabolism. This is evidenced by the oxygen consumption (30 mm³ per gram per hour in *Rana pipiens* at 20°C) and also by a small steady production of heat (100 to 150 gm cm per gm min). When activity occurs, a larger burst of heat appears. This reflects the chemical events and can be measured as a small temperature rise in the muscle by means of a sensitive thermopile (Hill, 1937). Heat is liberated during the initial process of activity and also later in the recovery period. The heat H is measured in units of calories or gm cm (the same dimensions as energy or work), and in the muscle

$$H = Jms\Delta T \text{ gm cm}$$

where

J = mechanical equivalent of heat = 4.18×10^4 gm cm per calorie

m = mass of muscle in grams

s = specific heat

ΔT = temperature rise in °C

or more simply at 0°C as approximately:

$$H = 4 \times 10^4 \, W\Delta T \text{ gm cm}$$

assuming

s = 0.95 for muscle

W = muscle weight in grams

If the heat dissipated during muscle activity is measured together with work done and fuel used, then total energy liberation can be discussed in terms of the efficiency of the system. The fuel consumption can be registered in a number of ways. Glycogen is the major substrate of muscle, but is not a convenient measure experimentally. Oxygen used by the resting muscle maintains the dynamic state of the cell, and correspondingly carbon dioxide is liberated. Oxygen is also used in the recovery processes following activity and is a measure of the total metabolism as in the accompanying aerobic recovery heat. Activity itself, however, is anaerobic and the immediate fuel costs have to be recorded in more complex biochemical changes. At the end of mechanical activity the physical system has returned to its initial state long before the chemical cycle is completed: full oxidative recovery in *Rana temporaria* takes nearly an hour at 0°C. The chemical changes at the end of activity can be studied by chemical analysis of the muscles which are frozen very rapidly so that the chemical reactions are arrested. Emphasis is placed on the changes in the level of creatine phosphate which appears to be the immediate substance utilized to maintain constant the level of the presumed primary energy source, adenosine triphosphate.

The conventional definition of efficiency is the ratio of external work done to the total energy involved. This has a practical value if calculated over the whole cycle, physical and chemical including recovery (the total energy can be measured in terms of the oxygen consumed or of the total energy, work plus heat, liberated). It has only limited value, however, if referred to the initial phase only, i.e., if applied to the physical cycle as measured by the ratio (external work) : (external work + initial heat) which has a maximum value of about 0.4 in *Rana temporaria*. At this stage of the cycle there is a large undetermined entropy change, which can be thought of as the obligatory change due to the chemical breakdown of substances such as creatine phosphate (Mommaerts, 1959). This obligatory entropy component is reversed during the recovery part of the cycle and the entropy change has a very small value for the whole cycle because the recovery part of the cycle involves the oxidation of glycogen in which the free energy change and the enthalpy change are both large and nearly equal. Thus in the whole cycle the entropy term is negligible as contrasted with the contraction phase only. The relationship of the work done by the muscle to the metabolism (total O_2 used or total energy, heat and work liberated) thus represents an efficiency, whose maximum experimental value is about 20%.

Wilkie (1960) has proposed an alternative definition of efficiency. By this definition, efficiency is the ratio of actual work performed to the free energy change which occurs. It provides a more realistic concept of efficiency but is less immediately applicable since the free energy change cannot be readily determined.

A. MUSCLE STRUCTURE

Skeletal muscles (voluntary or striated muscles) consist of long fibers with diameter between 30μ and 100μ. Each fiber is a multinucleate cylinder enclosed in an elastic sheath, the sarcolemma. The length of the fiber is

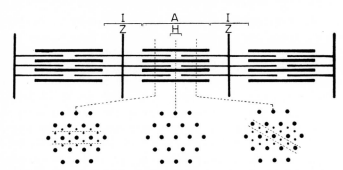

Fig. 2. Diagram illustrating the arrangement of the two kinds of protein filaments in a myofibril. At the top are three sarcomeres drawn as they would appear in longitudinal section. Below are transverse sections taken through the H-zone (center) and through the other parts of the A-band (right and left) where the arrays of thick and thin filaments interdigitate. (From Huxley and Hanson, 1960.)

characterized by transverse striations which show up in a polarizing microscope as isotropic (I) bands and anisotropic (A) bands. These bands can also be visualized in fixed, stained sections of the muscle, and a thin Z-band bisects the I-band (Walls, 1960, p. 23; Fig. 2). The twitch type fibers are composed of fibrils, of the order of 1μ visible through the light microscope, but electron microscope pictures show that the fibrils are themselves composed of protein filaments (Huxley and Hanson, 1960). Thin filaments about 50 Å diameter run lengthwise down the fibril and consist mainly of intertwined chains of fibrous actin. Other filaments in the A-band are considerably thicker, at about 110 Å, and consist mainly of another fibrous protein, myosin. In transverse sections the filaments are in a regular array: the thicker A-filaments are distributed hexagonally, with the thin filaments also arranged hexagonally relative to the major hexagon in a 2:1 ratio. Longitudinally the filaments in each fibril are in register giving A- and I-bands: tthe I-band contains the thin filaments while the thicker myosin filaments run the length of the A-band and taper at the ends. The thin filaments also run into the A-band, interdigitating with the thick filaments up to the limits of the central H-band (Fig. 2). Interdigitation and H-band size vary with muscle length. By suitable treatment the sarcomere can be disintegrated so that the A- and I-filaments are separated and the thin I-filaments remain attached on both sides of the Z-membrane with shapes resembling a shaving brush (Huxley, 1962).

Contraction is believed to have its focus in the region of overlap of the two types of filament. Tension development is generally considered to result from cyclic interactions between active sites on the thick and thin filaments, and shortening to result from the progressive interdigitation of the two sets of filaments: the A-band remains almost constant in length at about 1.5μ, while the I-band decreases. The fundamental contractile unit is the sarcomere bounded by adjacent Z-lines (with resting length about 2.5μ), and the muscle movement is the sum of movements of all the sarcomeres along a fiber. The Z-line is a band of protein fibers whose organization is not obvious in micrographs but which Knappeis and Carlsen (1962) suggest is formed by thin filaments which bend through an angle of 45° as they enter the region and link up in fours within the Z-band.

In the living fiber the optical absorption in A- and I-bands is almost the same, and no striations can be seen when a muscle is viewed through a microscope focused accurately on the fiber. The birefringence differences permit visualization with polarized light, and Inoué has demonstrated a detailed banding pattern using his improved polarizing microscope. A. F. Huxley (1957) explains how the striations become visible when living fibers are viewed through a normal microscope if it is defocused slightly. The bands also appear in fixed stained muscle sections because they react differently to acid and alkaline stains.

The outer sheath, the sarcolemma 1000 Å thick, is very extensible and consists of a network of supporting filaments. Beneath this sarcolemma lies the semipermeable plasma membrane, a lipoprotein structure about 75 Å thick. Across it is maintained the ion distribution described later, and this is the site of membrane and action potentials. It must be noted that Bennett (1960) refers to the plasma membrane as sarcolemma, in conformity to the original description by Schwann, and to the outer covering as a connective tissue coat. Within the muscle cell are the various cytoplasmic inclusions such as the mitochondria and the golgi apparatus. A well developed endoplasmic reticulum (or sarcotubular) system can be seen with the electron microscope. There are, in fact, two systems: a set of small vesicles 30 Å wide transverse to the long axis of the fiber near the Z-line which appear to make contact with the plasma membrane, and a less defined system which runs longitudinally from near the Z-line toward the middle of the sarcomere enveloping each fibril bundle within the fiber and making contact with the first system. It seems likely that the sarcotubular system is responsible for the spread of excitation through the thickness of the fiber and that it is also connected with the control of relaxation: skeletal muscles are remarkable both for the speed of initial activation and for the rapidity of relaxation.

Tension and movement are transmitted to the skeleton of the animal through tendinous insertions. Each fiber merges from contractile tissue through a jelly-like cup insertion into the tendinous material. There exists only a limited functional description of this region.

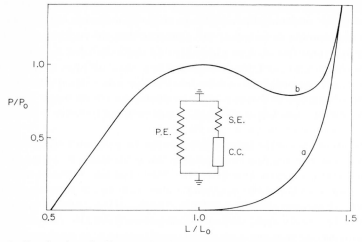

Fig. 3. Tension-length diagram for frog muscle (a) resting, (b) total tension in tetanic activity. Insert shows analogue of muscle with contractile component (C.C.), series elastic element (S.E.), and parallel elastic element (P.E.).

B. RESTING MUSCLE

Skeletal muscles at rest in the body are soft, plastic tissues, under zero tension in the absence of nervous excitation. At about the maximum length in the body, defined as l_0 or reference length, a resting tension appears. If the muscle is isolated and extended further its stiffness increases rapidly. This describes the well known resting tension-length curve (Fig. 3) for a frog sartorius muscle and demonstrates a property of many animal tissues, that when stretched beyond a certain length they resist like elastic bodies, although not like a simple Hooke's Law spring which has a linear force-extension relationship. Two major types of elastic phenomena occur in nature: (1) "normal" elasticity in which tension appears when the internal energy of a material is increased by extension which disturbs the molecules from a stable minimum potential state. Such elasticity displays a Hooke's Law relationship but is reversible for only about 1 or 2% extension, beyond which a yield-point is reached. (2) "Rubber-like" elasticity occurs in materials which consist of randomly orientated linked chains of long molecules. When a piece of such material is extended, tension appears because the random motions of the chains become limited and the entropy of the material is reduced. "Rubber-like" materials may show reversible extensibility for more than a 100% extension.

The range of reversible extensibility of muscles varies widely but is always large compared with that for "normal" elastic materials. The origin of tension and type of elasticity is thus of interest—be it normal, rubber-like, or of some other origin. In the frog sartorius muscle, the main structural elements involved are the contractile protein filaments and the sarcolemma material. The extensibility is larger than for a gastrocnemius muscle where fiber and tendon orientations are oblique and the whole muscle is surrounded by a tough inextensible sac. There has been considerable disagreement over which component is responsible for resting tension, and the answer is probably that each component is involved at different extensions in each muscle type.

Buchthal et al. (1951) believe that the resting tension in parallel-fibered muscles is exerted by the filaments of the contractile material stretched beyond a certain length. One line of evidence brought forward comes from considerations of the stiffness of single muscle fibers. Stiffness is defined as the rate of tension increment with length, $dP:dl$, and was measured statically by equilibrium measurements at each length and dynamically by recording tension changes when small sinusoidal changes in length were imposed on the muscle. Torsional rigidity was measured by Sten-Knudsen (1953) in terms of the resistance of the fiber to oscillatory twisting. The values of stiffness for stretched resting and activated muscle (the measurements on the latter being at much shorter lengths, however) turns out to be about the same at the same tension, suggesting that tension has the same origin at rest and in activity. These arguments are reinforced by direct measurements on the extensibility of the sarcolemma. For such experiments a single muscle fiber is isolated and squeezed between forceps so that the contractile filaments are broken and retract from the damaged area leaving only the supporting material. This material, mainly sarcolemma, is elastic with a coefficient of the same order as the intact fiber (but exerts tension only at a length much longer than would exist in the intact fiber).

In a carefully developed theory, Buchthal et al. (1951) proposed an origin for the tension and elasticity of muscle. He suggests that the contractile protein units can exist in two forms, a short one (α) and a long one (β); and that tension in the muscle depends on the rates of transition between the two forms. Thus, resting tension represents a dynamic equilibrium between units in long and short states, and developed tension appears because during activity the transformation rate to the shorter configuration increases.

On the other hand a majority of physiologists agree with Hill's view that most of the resting tension is due to stretch of connective and supporting tissues, although the resting contractile system may exert some tension. Perhaps the strongest support comes from Hill's (1952) measurements of thermoelasticity, in which the heat changes associated with stretch and release of resting muscle are studied. For about 25% extension beyond reference length the muscle has a positive thermoelastic coefficient like rubber, so that heat is given out when the muscle is stretched and is absorbed when the muscle is released. The thermoelastic properties are described by Hill in terms of the thermoelastic (heat:tension) ratio defined as $\Delta Q/l_0\Delta P$ where ΔQ is the heat change due to a tension change ΔP. The maximum value in this length range at 0°C is between 0.1 and 0.15, which is of the same order as predicted for rubber. Beyond this length the thermoelastic coefficient is reversed, and heat is absorbed during stretch, as in a "normal" type of elasticity. At about the same length, the tension-extension curve of the resting muscle shows a sudden change in character from an exponential relationship to a much steeper function as if a stiff component (the supporting tissues) begin to share the tension. Thus it is probable that the small initial tension is exerted by the contractile component and the rest by the sarcolemma and connective tissue. When the muscle is activated and develops tension, contractile proteins are transformed from an extensible rubber-like system to a material with normal elasticity, with a negative thermoelastic (heat to tension) ratio of 0.14 (Woledge, 1961), about the same as that for ebonite or wood. Thus the resting muscle shows the long range elasticity characteristic of rubber, while the force exerted by active muscle is not of this thermokinetic origin.

The comparison of elastic properties of resting muscle at lengths greater than reference with those of activated muscle at much shorter lengths has been questioned (above). But such a comparison is of historical importance: when studies first were made on the energetics of muscle it was realized that an extended resting muscle, like an extended spring, stores up energy which can later be released. The actively developed tension in an isometric tetanus also shows a variation with length similar to that of a spring in that it decreases with muscle length (Fig. 3). Thus it was believed that when a muscle is stimulated it is suddenly transformed from a spring whose resting length is that of the muscle in the body (reference length l_0) to a spring whose length is much shorter—about 0.7 l_0. Such a spring would liberate energy as it shortens, and the total energy available would be the area under the tension-length curve—about $P_0l_0/6$. This energy could appear as work or heat but the sum would be constant. This is the origin of the elastic theory of muscle which was later modified to include a viscous component. Under this theory the energy available is that of a spring, and it is easy to correlate this idea with the view that whether resting or active, the source of tension is the same.

As a result of the work of Fenn and of Hill, the concept of the muscle as a viscoelastic system has been abandoned. In particular, Fenn (1923, 1924) showed that extra energy is liberated by the muscle whenever work is done by the active muscle, so that the sum of heat and work is not a constant. The current concept of the muscle can be described by an analogue model (Fig. 3).

The contractile proteins are considered a dynamic machine, with viscosity inherent in the "contractile component" (C.C.) all of which is in series with an undamped "series elastic" element (S.E.). At rest the contractile component is plastic and exerts negligible tension, so that any resting tension is due to the supporting tissue and can be represented as a spring in parallel with the other two components ("parallel elastic" element [P.E.], Fig. 3). At lengths below the reference length, the P.E. is unstressed and can exert no tension; so that active contraction can be considered as the interplay of contractile and series elastic components.

III. Electrophysiology of Skeletal Muscle

A. MEMBRANE POTENTIAL AND IONIC DISTRIBUTION

In 1902 Bernstein proposed that the membrane potential of tissue cells was related to the potassium (K) distribution across the membrane. Bernstein's theory was based on the supposition that the cell was permeable only to K^+ so that the K^+ distribution determined the membrane potential. Considerable revision of the membrane potential hypothesis became necessary when it was found that during excitation the membrane potential actually reversed and that a resting muscle cell displayed a moderate permeability to (chloride) Cl^- as well as a slight permeability to (sodium) Na^+. From data collected largely from frog skeletal muscle (*Rana temporaria*) Boyle and Conway (1941) proposed that the cell could be represented by a Donnan equilibrium system of K^+ and Cl^-. In other words, the resting membrane potential should be determined by

$$V = \frac{RT}{F} \ln (K_o^+/K_i^+) \quad \text{or} \quad = \frac{RT}{F} \ln (Cl_i^-/Cl_o^-)$$

in situations in which no net transfer of KCl occurs across the membrane, i.e. [K+] [Cl−] is constant. The subscripts o and i refer to extracellular and intracellular concentrations respectively; R is the gas constant, T the absolute temperature, and F the Faraday.

With the development of the intercellular microelectrode (Ling and Gerard, 1949) it became feasible to check the Boyle-Conway proposal more accurately. Adrian (1956, 1960) and Hodgkin and Horowicz (1959b, 1960a) have shown that in sartorii and in single fiber preparations of the semitendinosus of *Rana temporaria* the membrane potential behaves like a Donnan system for KCl in K^+_o greater than 10 mM, i.e., the relation $V - \ln K^+_o$ is linear with the slope of 58 mv per decade at 20°C. Below

10 mM K^+_o the slope falls progressively to zero at about 0.5 mM K^+_o. In potassium-free solutions the resting potential falls a few millivolts. If allowance is made for a small Na$^+$ permeability the resting potential, in the absence of Cl^-_o, is considerably more accurately defined in lower K^+_o concentrations. Thus, assuming P_{Na^+} to be only 1% of P_{K^+}, i.e.,

$$V = RT/\text{F} \ln \frac{[\text{K}^+]_o + 0.01\,[\text{Na}^+]_o}{[\text{K}^+]_i + 0.01\,[\text{Na}^+]_i}$$

a reasonable description of the membrane potential is obtained down to 1 mM K^+_o (Hodgkin and Horowicz, 1959b).

In the presence of Cl^-_o the resting muscle membrane displays a higher conductance to Cl$^-$ than to K$^+$. Indeed the resting potential of a muscle fiber equilibrated to 100 mM KCl behaves like a Cl$^-$ electrode. Furthermore, in response to changes in the Cl$^-$ gradient the membrane potential shows a large time-dependence suggesting the transfer of Cl$^-$ across the cell membrane. Hodgkin and Horowicz calculated the resting K$^+$ and Cl$^-$ conductances to be 100 and 200 μmho/cm^2, respectively.

B. MEMBRANE ACTION POTENTIAL

In view of the success of the detailed description of membrane potential phenomena of the squid giant axon (Hodgkin and Huxley, 1952) it is of considerable interest to determine to what extent this ionic hypothesis is applicable to muscle. It has been known since the work of Overton (1902) that excitation in muscle fibers is blocked in Na$^+$-free solutions. From measurements of muscle membrane capacitance and the amplitude of the conducted action potential it is possible to compute the minimum entry and exit of charge which must flow across the cell membrane to account for the potential change. Such a calculation gives a value of 9 pmoles* per cm^2 per impulse for a membrane capacitance of 7.5 μ F per cm^2 (Fatt and Katz, 1951) and an action potential of 120 mv. Hodgkin and Horowicz (1959a) obtained a net Na^{24} influx of 15.6 pmoles per cm^2 per impulse, more than adequate to account for depolarization; K$^+$ loss averaged 9.6 pmoles per cm^2 per impulse. They also point out that the rapidity of repolarization and the potassium conductance calculated from the K$^+$ flux indicate that a delayed increase in K$^+$ conductance also occurs as in the case of the squid axon. Alterations of the nerve hypothesis as applied to muscle become apparent, however, (1) with Katz's observation (1949a) that the resistance of the muscle membrane under a cathode is greater than under an anode in potassium sulfate solutions, i.e., the rectification is opposite to that of nerve, (2) with the finding that the increase in K$^+$ flux is not maintained with continued depolarization, i.e., the conductance increase is

---

* The abbreviation pmoles stands for moles $\times$ 10^{-12}.

only transitory, and (3) with Hodgkin and Horowicz's (1959b) data which show an inward P_{K^+} of the order of 8×10^{-6} cm per second while the outward P_{K^+} may be as low as 0.05×10^{-6} cm per second in resting muscle. The outward P_{K^+} is inversely dependent on the inward-outward electrochemical gradient; P_{Cl^-} is equal in each direction and constant at 4×10^{-6} cm per second.

C. EXCITATION-CONTRACTION COUPLING

Over the years adequate excitation-contraction theories have been difficult to formulate because of the rapidity with which contraction follows membrane depolarization. In amphibian muscle, for example, Hill (1948) showed that diffusion of a substance from the exterior of a 100μ-diameter fiber to its center would only be 50% complete in 400 msec at 0°C, yet such a muscle can sustain a tetanic tension within a few milliseconds after depolarization if the muscle is stretched slightly following the stimulus. The possibility of coupling by the spreading local membrane currents is ruled out by the observation that a muscle contracts only along those bands where current is leaving the muscle membrane and not where it only traverses the myoplasm longitudinally, i.e., contraction occurs only where membrane depolarization occurs (Sten-Knudsen, 1960). This concept is further verified by the findings of Huxley and Taylor (1958) on the localization of excitation in a single muscle fiber. A glass capillary microelectrode with a very smooth edge and about 2μ diameter was placed against the fiber surface so that there was very little current leakage and a stimulating current through the capillary passed into the membrane region defined by the capillary. By this means a highly localized stimulation was possible without electrical spread. They found that in frog muscle no propagated action potential occurred but local nonpropagated and graded responses occurred when the electrode was positioned near the Z-line. Moreover responses could be elicited only at certain spots at intervals of about 5μ along the line of contact of each Z-line with the sarcolemma. When a propagated action potential was induced, the whole fiber was activated. This shows that the mechanical response is of an "all-or-none" nature only because it is induced by the "all-or-none" action potential as suggested earlier by Gelfan (1933) and by Sichel and Prosser (1940).

The time element thus seems to demand a rapid transit system for distribution of the excitatory process throughout the interior of the muscle cell in but a few milliseconds. A possible basis for such a system has recently appeared from electron microscopy. Tubular structures located in the region of the Z-bands and extending throughout the internal cell structure (Porter and Palade, 1957), appear to communicate with the external membrane. If the membranes of the tubular structures are in electrical contact with the outside membrane such that their interior is, in effect, electrically outside the cell, such a distribution system might exist.

1. *Membrane Potential*

In support of this possibility, Hodgkin and Horowicz (1960a) have shown the membrane potential of muscle cells to fall more rapidly with the addition of excess K^+ than it rises upon depletion of external K^+. The time course of these events is such as to suggest that 1/500 to 1/200 of the fiber is a special region in which K^+ can be retained for a short period, the inference being that although the tubular structures are in communication with the outside of the cell their small size prevents rapid equilibration with the external environment. Assuming that the distribution system may be something of this type, the problem of coupling the membrane potential to the contractile mechanism still exists. The experiments of Hodkin and Horowicz (1960b) show that this coupling is, indeed, fairly direct. Thus the muscle tension developed by K^+ depolarization is related to the corresponding membrane potential by a steep S-shaped function. In other words, the extent of contracture is directly related to the membrane potential. The threshold for tension development is about -50 mv corresponding to an external K^+ of 20–30 mM. Peak tension occurs in 100 mM K^+_o with a membrane potential of -25 mv. The tension cannot be maintained, however, but shows a plateau for 3–5 sec and then ends in a rapid relaxation, both plateau duration and rate of fall being dependent on external K^+. Excitability, spontaneous activity, and the ability to undergo a contracture all return about the same time following the removal of excess K^+ from muscles in contracture.

2. *Calcium*

Calcium has long been known to be essential to cardiac contractility; however, its immediate role in skeletal muscle has been less specific. In the sartorius of *Rana pipiens* Shanes (1958) attributes this difference in Ca^{++} sensitivity to a difference in binding of Ca^{++} on the muscle membrane. He observed a rapid fall in fiber spike potentials and in contraction in repetitively stimulated skeletal muscle in Ca^{++}-free media. Both spikes and contraction height were restored after a short rest period. With continued stimulation, failure became apparent, but could be temporarily restored with the addition of SCN^- for Cl^-, for example. With continued stimulation tension again slowly declined until failure was complete. Shanes attributes this fatigue to the depletion of Ca^{++} coming from intracellular sites. The postulate is that a membrane protein retains Ca^{++} in the presence of the substituted anions similar to the anion effect on the bonding of divalent cations to serum albumin (Scatchard and Black, 1949; Scatchard et al., 1957).

More direct evidence for the role of Ca^{++} in excitation-contraction coupling in amphibian muscle is given by Bianchi and Shanes (1959) and by Shanes and Bianchi (1960) showing the following. (1) Ca^{45} influx in stimulated muscle is 30 times greater than in nerve. (2) Augmented twitch tensions recorded in NO_3^- solutions are coincident with a 60% increase in Ca^{++} uptake. (3) Ca^{++} uptake is 3–5 times larger during K^+ contracture but declines as the tension falls. (4) The simultaneous addition of Ca^{45} and K^+ produce no measurable increase in Ca^{45} uptake. (5) Ca^{45} loss is equally well correlated with stimulation implying an increase in Ca^{++} permeability during membrane depolarization. (6) Ca^{45} exchange is constant at 0.2–0.3 $\mu\mu$moles per cm^2 per impulse between excitation rates of 0.5 per second and 20 per second.

At this point it appears that in the excitation-contraction mechanism membrane depolarization initiates an influx of Ca^{++} which in some as yet unknown manner is responsible for the onset of the active state in the contractile system.

What controls the duration of the increased Ca^{++} permeability? The interesting correlation between the action potential duration and the rise of tension observed in heart muscle does not appear in skeletal muscle except possibly in considerations of the membrane-afterpotential. Here Hutter and Noble (1960) found that replacement of Cl^- with methylsulfate or pyroglutamate in sartorius muscles of Rana temporaria showed a lengthening of both the magnitude and duration of the afterpotential and of the active state duration. The temperature dependence of the afterpotential and the active state duration is not identical, however, hence their coupling cannot be direct.

The details of the coupling mechanism thus remain obscure. An interesting speculation, however (Hodgkin and Horowicz, 1960a), is that the tubular system contains an activator substance, perhaps a negatively charged Ca^{++} complex, which can permeate the depolarized membrane, thereby activating the contractile mechanism. How such a calcium complex enters into the active state mechanism is, perhaps, second order speculation at this time.

IV. Latent Period

There is always an interval between the stimulus applied to a muscle and the first sign of mechanical response. The action potential at the cathode has very little delay so that the latency is mainly in the coupling to the contractile machine. Considerable effort was exerted at the beginning of the century to prove that the latent period was only an artifact of recording. These efforts showed that the value diminishes as sensitivity and speed of recording improves but never to zero.

The first gross sign of mechanical activity in an isometric contraction is an increase in tension occurring 20 msec after stimulation at 0°C, and 5 msec at 20°C for frog sartorius muscle. If, however, the recorder is very sensitive, very rigid, and has very low inertia, a slight decrease in tension precedes the main rise.

Rauh (1922) first noted the phenomenon and Sandow (1944) studied this "latency relaxation" (L.R.) in detail. The time course of the early changes is seen in Fig. 4, where tension change first occurs at 7 msec at 0°C compared with the action potential peak at about 2 msec. At 20°C the latency drops to about 2 msec. Such a fall in tension can obviously occur only at lengths where the muscle is under resting tension; and at an optimum extension, the tension drops by 1/1000 of the peak twitch tension. At shorter lengths the L.R. decreases until only the tension rise remains and starts at 10 msec at 0°C.

Thus in an isometric muscle twitch there is suggestion of two processes, an early coupling process which induces a slight tension fall or extension of the system followed a few milliseconds later by the onset of mechanical activity.

No equivalent change has been described in the latent period studied isotonically, but shortening begins at about the time of the earliest tension rise. The transition from rest to activity is very abrupt: if a lightly loaded muscle is stimulated with a multielectrode assembly it begins to move at maximum speed soon after the end of the latent period (Fig. 5).

Excitation of muscle with a multielectrode assembly provides excitation

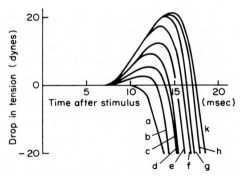

Fig. 4. Early tension changes during isometric twitches of frog sartorius at 0°C at various muscle lengths, in millimeters: (a) 27, (b) 30, (c) 31, (d) 32, (e) 33, (f) 34, (g) 35, (h) 36, (k) 37 mm. Length in body 30.5 mm, weight 75 mg. (From Abbott and Ritchie, 1951a.)

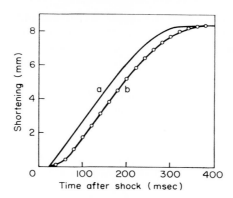

Fig. 5. Isotonic twitches of frog sartorius under small load. Curve (a) simultaneous stimulation along the muscle length; curve (b) stimulation at one end only. (From Abbott and Ritchie, 1951b.)

at many points along the muscle simultaneously through a series of alternate anodal and cathodal electrodes spaced 2 or 3 mm apart along the muscle length and eliminates much of the propagation time of the action potential along the muscle. Stimulation of the muscle by an electrical discharge passed between massive electrodes placed parallel to the muscle length provides even more rapid excitation but has the disadvantage of demanding very heavy currents. The difference when excitation occurs only at one end of the muscle can be seen in Fig. 5 where the slower onset of shortening represents mobilization along the muscle, and the delay between the two curves equals half the propagation time along the muscle.

Although the link between excitation and contraction is elusive, the coupling has many physical indicators. A. V. Hill (1950, 1957) has shown that increased heat production appears before any sign of mechanical activity. D. K. Hill (1949, 1953) studied the optical changes in the sartorius muscle of *Rana temporaria* and found that after a latent period there is a transitory increase in light transmitted through the muscle which may be due to diffraction or to a transparency change and is reminiscent of the Latency Relaxation. This transparency increase is followed by an increase in scattering which accompanies the tension rise of the twitch.

Muscle volume is another parameter which changes during contraction. An early transient increase in volume of about 10^{-6} cc per gram begins at about the same time as the latency relaxation (Abbott and Baskin, 1962) and is reversed rapidly as the twitch develops (Fig. 6).

The onset of activity is also accompanied by an increase in the rigidity of the muscle as shown by experiments where the muscle is slowly stretched at various times after stimulation. Slow stretch of an unstimulated muscle

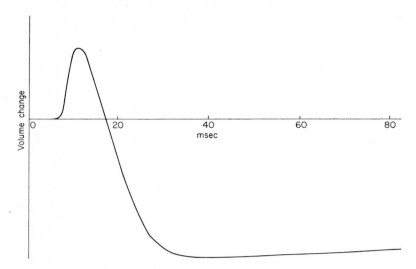

Fig. 6. Volume changes at 0°C during twitch of frog sartorius muscle. Increase upward. Tension peak reached at 120 msec.

below resting length induces very little tension. But when the stimulated muscle is stretched, the tension rises above the normally developing twitch tension very early in the twitch, indicating an increase in the rigidity of the contractile material. Further experiments by A. V. Hill (1949) with more rapid stretches showed that not only is there an early appearance of activity but that the contractile system rapidly reaches its full state of activity long before developed tension reaches its peak.

V. Contractile Component

The study of muscle contraction must be a study of the contractile proteins; and consideration of the analogue muscle model (Fig. 3) suggests that the properties of the combined series elastic element (S.E.) and contractile component (C.C.) can be studied most simply when the parallel elastic element is unstretched, i.e., at or below reference length. The contractile component is plastic at rest, so that the series elastic element is also unstressed. When the system is activated, tension can be developed by the muscle only when the contractile component shortens and extends this series elastic element thus putting it under stress. At the peak of isometric tetanic contractions, where tension is maintained constant, the contractile component and series elastic element must be in equilibrium and the length of the C.C. is not changing. The tension which the C.C. can exert isometrically at any length can thus be obtained from the isometric tetanic tensions at that length. This gives the familiar developed tension-length curve (Fig. 3) which has a maximum at just about the reference length (l_0) and decreases on either side. The value of P_0 at l_0 lies between 2 and 2.5 kg per cm^2 at 0°C and falls to zero at about 0.7 l_0 for sartorius muscles of frog. Sartorius muscles from the toad *Bufo bufo* can shorten down to 0.4 l_0, but gastrocnemius muscles shorten much less, to only about 0.8 l_0. Ramsey and Street (1940) showed that the isolated muscle fiber from a frog sartorius muscle can shorten further than when *in situ* in the muscle, presumably because of the absence of connective constraints. But if the single fiber is shortened maximally to below 0.3 l_0 the shortening is irreversible and the fiber is in the "delta state."

Whenever contraction occurs, heat is liberated in excess of the small resting heat (100 to 150 gm cm per gram minute at 20°C). In a single twitch the C.C. goes through a cycle of activity followed by a return to rest at the end of relaxation. Heat is liberated during the twitch, and a significant part of the heat (that not linked with internal shortening or with relaxation) is called activation heat" which accompanies the transformation of the contractile system from resting into full activity.

When the muscle is stimulated repetitively so as to sustain a fused isometric tetanus, the active state of the muscle is kept at its full value by restoration of any decay of that state at each stimulus. The heat which accompanies the maintenance of this isometric tension is "maintenance heat" and thus represents the energy dissipated in keeping the contractile mechanism activated. The activation heat of a frog sartorius muscle at 0°C lies between 1 and 1.5 mcal per gram muscle; the heat in a twitch with maximal shortening is about 3 mcal per gram muscle, and the maintenance heat begins at about 8 mcal per gram second for a fused response. This maintenance heat rate drops to 25% over the first few seconds of a tetanus, while at the same time the rate of mechanical relaxation also shows up, i.e., the muscle becomes more economical in the maintenance of tension. Aubert (1956) has shown that the rate of the heat production (h cal per gram second) can be described by the equation:

$$h = h_A e^{-\alpha t} + h_B$$

where

h_A, h_B and α are constants

h_A represents the initial rapid burst of heat which decreses with a decay constant α (of between 0.4 and 1.0 sec^{-1} in frog at 0°C)

while

h_B is the final steady level of maintenance heat rate

When the tetanus is studied at different lengths the value of h_B decreases from its maximum value of about 2 mcal per gram second at reference

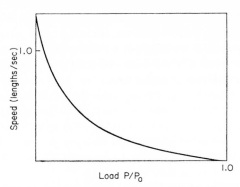

Fig. 7. Force-velocity curve in frog muscle at 0°C. Abscissa, isotonic afterload in units of P_0; ordinate, speed of shortening in units of l_0 per second.

length l_0 but varies linearly with developed tension rather than muscle length. This relation may be of importance in elucidating the character of the contractile machine.

In any study of the dynamic properties of the contractile element the series elastic element is inevitably included (Fig. 3). Fenn and Marsh (1935) however, realized that any undamped S.E. would be effectively eliminated in isotonic contractions because at constant load the length of the S.E. must remain constant, and so the dynamics of the contractile material can be studied. The muscle is attached to an isotonic lever and afterloaded with various loads, i.e., before excitation it is at reference length and cannot shorten until its tension reaches the value of the afterload. Therefore any movement recorded is that of the contractile component, and the muscle shortens with a velocity which is determined by the load lifted. In a tetanic contraction the latent period for any load represents the time needed for the isometric tension to develope to that value, and so a plot of latency against isotonic load gives the profile of the isometric tetanus (cf. Fig. 1 for twitches under various loads). The speed at which the C.C. shortens is expressed by the slope of the shortening-time curve. When speed is plotted against load, the dynamic characteristic of the C.C. is revealed (Fig. 7).

This force-velocity curve can be described numerically and a number of equations have been proposed. Fenn and Marsh (1935) suggested the relation:

$$P = P_0 e^{-\alpha V} - kV$$

where
P and V are force and velocity respectively
α and k are constants

and

P_0 is the isometric tetanic tension

This finally disposed of the simple viscoelastic theories of muscle contraction which demand a linear force-velocity relationship. Aubert (1956) has suggested an alternative equation:

$$P = P_0 e^{-V/B} \pm F$$

where

P, V, and P_0 are as defined above

B and F are constants

and

the $+$ sign applies to extension

$-$ sign to shortening of the muscle

This also fits the experimental values and within limits can be applied both to shortening and to forcible extension of the active muscle.

The most useful formulation, however, is the characteristic relation suggested by Hill (1938). He noted that the curve of Fig. 7 can be adequately expressed as a section of the hyperbola:

$$(P + a)\ (V + b) = \text{constant}$$

where

a and b are constants.

In the case of an isometric tetanus no shortening occurs $(V = 0)$ and the tension is P_0; therefore:

$$(P + a)\ (V + b) = b(P_0 + a)$$

In addition to this derivation from purely mechanical results, Hill also derived the equation from values based on measurement of the energy released during contraction.

According to the viscoelastic theory of muscle a definite amount of energy would be available for contraction, and this would appear as either work or heat, but the sum must remain constant. In 1923 Fenn showed this to be untrue, although his findings were rejected for nearly 15 years. In isotonic contraction he found that when work was done, thermal energy was liberated in excess of the maintenance heat (the Fenn effect) and he believed that the extra heat was proportional to work done. Hill (1937) developed much more rapid recording techniques and designed the "protected" thermopile which permitted reliable heat measurements during isotonic shortening. He reinvestigated the heat relationships and found that the extra heat is accurately proportional to the distance moved in isotonic contraction and independent of the work done. The details of Hill's experiments on afterloaded isotonic contractions have been described in detail several times (Hill, 1938; Davson, 1959). Only the salient points of the experiments are given here. A pair of frog sartorius muscles was mounted on a protected thermopile at 0°C and connected by a light chain to an isotonic lever. The muscles were stimulated maximally at fusion frequency and were allowed to shorten isotonically from the "reference" length. Movement of the muscle was recorded simultaneously with the voltage output from the thermopile which was amplified with a galvanometer and photocell system. After correction for heat loss and delays in the system, the galvanometer deflection at any time represented the heat produced up to that instant.

The heat liberated in isometric contraction represents the maintenance activity, and the larger value when isotonic shortening occurs reflects the extra heat associated with shortening of the muscle. Hill showed that this extra heat is proportional to shortening and is independent of the time at which release occurred. The constant of proportionality is denoted as "a" gram centimeter per centimeter shortened, the value expressed per unit cross section of frog muscle is about 350 gm per cm^2, and the proportionality is valid over the full range of shortening.

The rate of extra heat liberation during the isotonic contraction would thus be $h = a \cdot V$ gm cm per second where V is the speed of shortening. During this shortening under load P, the work rate will be $P \cdot V$ gm cm per second. Therefore, total extra energy rate above the maintenance heat production is equal to:

$$(P + a)V \text{ gm cm per second}$$

Hill found that if he plotted the experimental values of this total energy rate against load P he obtained a straight line with negative slope "b" which crossed the load axis at $P = P_0$. The equation of this line is:

$$(P + a)V = b(P_0 - P)$$

and rewriting, this equation is:

$$(P + a)(V + b) = b(P_0 + a)$$

The values for a and b are exactly the same as from the purely mechanical measurements. The dimension of a is force, and of b speed. The published values show that P_0/A_0, a/P_0 and b/V_{max} are nearly constant over a wide range of muscles where A_0 is the cross-sectional area of the muscle and V_{max} is the speed of shortening of the muscle C.C. under zero load. The ratios have values of about 2500 gm per cm^2, 0.25, and 0.25 respectively. The value of V_{max} differs widely between muscle types and is temperature-dependent: its value at 0°C for the sartorius of *Rana temporaria* is about 4/3 muscle length per second compared with about 2/3 l_0 per second for *Bufo bufo*. The implication of the equation is that the total "extra" energy rate when work is done is proportional to the deficit of the load below the maximum P_0, while the rate of extra heat production is proportional to speed of shortening.

This relationship describes the dynamics of the contractile system but only at the reference length where the maximum isometric tension (P_0) is developed. The tetanic tension varies with length as in Fig. 3, so that at any desired length e the isometric tension can be defined as P_0. The characteristic equation above can be made quite general if it is written:

$$(P + a)(V + b) = b(P_{0,l} + a)$$

where $P_{0,l}$ is the isometric tetanic tension at length e. This generalized equation is reasonably valid over the range of lengths less than e, using the same values for a and b.

Measurements of the total chemical changes in the muscle at the end of a series of contractions have given values at variance with those values obtained from the thermal-mechanical experiments. Carlson and Siger (1958) reported briefly and Mommaerts and co-workers (1963) have shown in more detail that in iodoacetate poisoned muscles there is a breakdown of creatine phosphate corresponding to maintenance activity, an extra breakdown corresponding to the work done, but no breakdown proportional to shortening. Carlson and associates (1962) have further shown that if total heat is measured there is no correlation between heat liberated and distance shortened or work done in a twitch.*

Hill's observations of shortening heat are certainly valid in tetanus and it appears that while the dynamic relationship is valid during the period of shortening, there may be a later compensation made for the extra heat of shortening. Thus, the act of shortening associated with the performance of external work is accompanied by a liberation of heat proportional to the distance shortened and liberated at a rate proportional to the speed of movement, but the total heat liberated during the whole contraction may be a constant.

A. SERIES ELASTICITY

The concept of series elasticity developed from attempts to confirm the viscoelastic theory of muscle activity, according to which a definite maximum amount of work W_0 would be available during contraction. If the muscle shortened with a velocity V, the viscous element would cause an internal dissipation of some energy into heat, so that the external work W would be:

$$W = W_0(1 - k/t)$$

---

* Recent experiments by Hill indicate that in a twitch there is tension-dependent heat in addition to activation and shortening heat, explaining Carlson's results.

where t is the time taken for the contraction. This can be represented by a model of a damped spring (or spring and a damping dashpot) in which external tension P is linearly related to velocity:

$$P = P_0(1 - k'V)$$

where P_0 is the isometric tetanic tension.

Levin and Wyman (1927) investigated the model by measuring the work done during movement of tetanized striated muscle at controlled constant speed. The tension was recorded as length changed in stretch and in release using a Levin-Wyman ergometer, which is a lever moved by a strong spring but with its velocity kept constant by an oil-filled dashpot with pre-set aperture. The muscle was connected by an inextensible thread to a torsion spring tension recorder fixed on one end of the lever. The pointer of the tension recorder was oriented vertically and wrote on a fixed piece of smoked glass. When the lever moved, the pointer recorded movement on an arc vertically, and tension on an arc horizontally so that the area traced out represented work done. The graph of work versus speed was an S-shaped curve and not a straight line as required by the simple model. Levin and Wyman were able to explain these results by supposing that an undamped elastic spring acts in series with the viscoelastic element of contracting muscle.

As described above, the studies of isotonic contractions disproved the viscoelastic theory and replaced the viscous spring with a contractile component having a dynamic force-velocity characteristic. But this component acts in series with the undamped elastic element as in Fig. 3.

Any tension actively developed by a muscle is transmitted through the series elastic element as a result of its extension by the contractile component. A. V. Hill (1953) determined the tension-extension curve of this series elastic element, taking advantage of the fact that even under zero load the speed of shortening of the contractile component is limited to value V_{max} of about 3.5 cm per second for a moderate size of frog sartorius at 0°C. At the height of an isometric tetanus, the arm of a Levin-Wyman ergometer was released so that the muscle shortened about 1.5 mm very rapidly: the undamped series elastic element released its tension but the contractile component shortened very little. Tension in the muscle was recorded, and the tension-time curve of release gave immediately the tension-extension curve of the S.E.: a curve that was nearly exponential. Wilkie (1956) confirmed this relationship by measuring the sudden shortening of a muscle when released from an isometric tetanus to isotonic loading under different weights. He showed that the tension-extension curve (Fig. 8) is independent of time of release and of temperature, but that it appears less compliant when extreme precautions are taken to eliminate compliance in muscle-transducer connections.

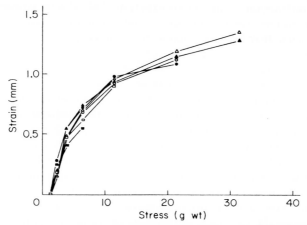

Fig. 8. Stress-strain curves of the series elastic element at the following times (msec) after a single stimulus: □, 100; △, 200; ▲, 280; ●, 480; ■, 640; ○, 200 msec control. Frog's sartorius 0°C; 30 mm long, 80 mg. (From Wilkie, 1956.)

The tension rise during an isometric tetanus follows a course determined by the interplay of the S.E. and C.C. The total muscle length is constant and tension is developed only as the C.C., by shortening, strains the S.E. If the tension-extension curve of the S.E. is denoted by the relation:

$$P = f(y)$$

where P is the developed tension and y is extension of this element, then the contractile component must be exerting a force P and its speed of shortening by dy/dt. Using the characteristic relation for that component:

$$dy/dt = b[P_0 - f(y)] [a + f(y)]$$

which can be solved by numerical integration to predict the rise of tension during a tetanus.

The function of the series elastic component was discussed by Levin and Wyman (1927) in terms of protection of the musculature in the body against sudden stretch which would otherwise damage the tissues. The morphological identity of the S.E. cannot be specified precisely. The tendon connections provide some of the elasticity but much of it is probably with the C.C. itself. The linkage between actin and myosin filaments may display elasticity as also may the micelles into which the muscle proteins are organized.

B. ACTIVE STATE

The description of the contractile component referred to events during a fused maintained tetanus, when maximal activity is maintained. In the

course of contraction a muscle goes from a state of rest to one of activity
and returns to rest after stimulation is ended. The concept of the "active
state" has been introduced to enable the changes in level of activity to be
followed quantitatively, and a value for the active state has been defined
by A. V. Hill (1949) as that tension which the contractile component can
exert when it is neither lengthening or shortening. Whenever during an
isometric contraction the developed tension is not changing with respect
to time (i.e. $dP/dt = 0$) then the tension at that instant must equal the
instantaneous level of the active state. Thus, the value of the full active
state is the isometric tetanic tension P_0.

In the isometric twitch, tension starts to rise along the same curve as
in the tetanus, but later falls off to reach a lower peak value. This initial
rate of rise supports the idea that the muscle is fully activated soon after
stimulation. Further evidence is supplied by A. V. Hill's (1949) experiments based on the fact that at the peak of isometric tetanic tension P_0,
the C.C. must have shortened by an amount which produces a stress in
the S.E. equal to P_0. If the C.C. does become fully active early in the
twitch (i.e. capable of maintaining a tension P_0) then a suitable stretch
applied to the ends of the muscle should eliminate the need for internal
shortening and the tetanic tension P_0 should be immediately exhibited.

A frog muscle at 0°C on a multielectrode assembly was connected to a
tension recorder mounted on the armature of a magnet arranged to stretch
the muscle rapidly at various times relative to stimulation. The amount of
stretch employed was also variable. If the stretch was applied before the
stimulus arrived, then only a transient tension increment occurred. If
the stretch started at the end of the latent period, tension rose very
sharply. For just one value of stretch (Fig. 9) the tension rose rapidly to
the tetanic tension P_0 and stayed on a plateau at that level before dropping

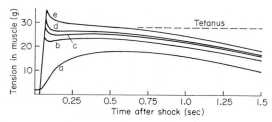

Fig. 9. Effect of stretching a muscle various amounts at the same moment shortly
after a maximal shock. Toad's sartorius 0°C, 62 mg, 36 mm under 1.7 gm; latent period
32 msec; 30 gm tension equivalent to 1.8 kg/cm². Stretch started in (b), (c), (d), and
(e) 34 msec after and in (a), for comparison, 70 msec before, the shock. Stretches as
follows: (a) 4.3 mm, (b) 3.9 mm, (c) 4.3 mm, (d) 4.7 mm, (e) 5.1 mm. Final stretched
length 36 mm throughout. Broken line, final level of tension in isometric tetanus at
length 36 mm. (From A. V. Hill, 1949.)

Fig. 10. Decay of "active state": tension-time curves of frog sartorius at 0°C following quick releases at different times after stimulation. The vertical bars represent peaks of the contraction curves and therefore individual values of the active state. Time unit, 20 msec. (From Ritchie, 1954.)

in relaxation. If the stretch was too small the tension continued to rise after the stretch was ended. Stretches applied later in the rising phase required progressively less stretch in order to reach the plateau level.

Thus, even in a twitch the muscle becomes fully activated, but activity in the twitch begins to decay before full tetanic tension can be reached. The tension at the peak of the twitch must be one point on the curve of decay of the active state since at the peak $dP/dt = 0$, the criterion for an active state value. The rest of the decay curve has been determined by Ritchie (1954) and is shown in Fig. 10. A muscle was stimulated isometrically and at a chosen (variable) time during the twitch a vary rapid release was permitted. The release allowed was about 3 mm, sufficient to release the stress on the series elastic component. The contractile component then began to shorten again and a "secondary" twitch was recorded for each release time. The tension redeveloped depended on the level of the active state, so the peak of each secondary twitch represented another point on the active state decay curve.

Thus, in a twitch the active state rises to its full value, and stays at a plateau before decaying to zero again. The duration of the plateau has been determined for *Rana temporaria* at 0°C from the time at which twitch and tetanic curves separate (Macpherson and Wilkie, 1953), from the interval between stimuli at the fusion frequency, and also from the first sign of tension relaxation after the last stimulus of a tetanus (Ritchie, 1954). At 0°C the plateau lasts 35 msec.

The rapidity of the onset of activity has been emphasized above and it was assumed in discussing the rise of tension in isometric tetanus that the contractile component becomes fully active at the end of the latent period. This is not strictly true, for the tetanic tension rises slower than the calculated value, and slower than the tension redevelopment if a tetanized muscle is suddenly released and held isometric at its new length (Jewell & Wilkie, 1958). The plateau of active state is probably reached within 30 msec in a frog's sartorius at 0°C, compared with about 100 msec for the peak of twitch tension. A further comparison may be made with the volume changes during a twitch (Fig. 6) in which the full volume decrease at 0°C is reached also at about 35 msec, well before the tension peak. Since volume decrease may well result from chemical changes, the peak of active state may correspond to the completion of chemical changes driving the twitch contraction. If a second stimulus is applied before this peak volume decrease no extra volume decrease occurs, and only the transitory volume increase is seen.

C. NEGATIVE WORK

The descriptions of muscular activity in this chapter have been concerned with shortening of the muscle, in which loads less than the isometric tetanic tension of the muscle (P_0) are lifted. In the living animal almost half of the muscular activity must be that of controlled stretch of active muscle. Each time a frog lands after a jump, deceleration must occur by "braking" as a result of stretch of the same muscles which induced the jump: activation of the opponent muscles cannot help in the deceleration. If the gastrocnemius contracts to start the jump, it must resist stretch to slow the animal in landing. Under such conditions work is done on the muscle and it is defined as "negative work" or "eccentric work." This is the reverse of the events of shortening and implies negative velocity as well as negative work.

When an active muscle shortens against a load, work is done and shortening heat is produced in excess of the isometric condition. The energy mobilized by the muscle for work in excess of the maintenance requirements is the sum of the extra heat plus the work. When an active muscle is stretched, the heat liberation associated with the negative work is again measured in excess of that liberated under isometric conditions. The energy mobilized is then the sum of extra heat and negative work. The results show that the sum is negative and that depending on the speed of stretch, some of the work done on the muscle disappears and is not detectable as heat or as potential energy. As the speed of stretch diminishes the extra heat drops until in a slow isotonic stretch under a load of about $1.2 P_0$ the extra heat becomes negative, i.e., the total heat production becomes less than the isometric value (Fig. 11) and all of the work is absorbed by the muscle. The amount of work absorbed is never greater than the maintenance energy required during the period of stretch, and although the fate of the work is still unknown, it may influence the coupling of the maintenance reactions.

The fall of the heat production in slow stretch to a value less than the isometric value, suggests a negative heat of lengthening. The propor-

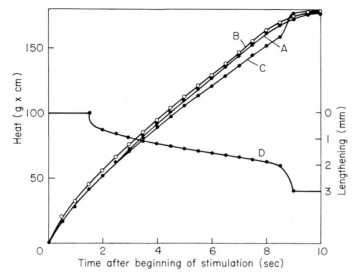

Fig. 11. Negative work. Heat production during lengthening. A and B, heat production in isometric contractions at lengths 25 and 26.5 mm; C, heat production during slow stretch under isotonic load; D, mechanical record of lengthening. Frog sartorius: 0°C, $l_0 = 25.5$ mm, weight 105 mg. Tetanus 8 sec, five shocks per second. (From Abbott and Aubert, 1952.)

tionality constant (heat per unit distance of stretch) increases as speed diminishes unlike the positive shortening heat a which is independent of speed. This negative value for the heat of lengthening of about 2 kg per cm² indicates that shortening heat (ax) is not energy dissipation in an internal resistance (or viscosity), because such a dissipation would not be expected to change sign when direction of movement changes.

Stretch can be forced on an active muscle by applying a constant load greater than the isometric tension or by forcibly pulling its ends apart with a Levin-Wyman ergometer. In the first case the resultant movement can be recorded, as seen in Fig. 11, and in the second case the resultant tension can be registered. It can be seen that at constant load the speed varies throughout the stretch, so that no unique value of speed can be related to a given load. This means that the force-velocity curve of shortening cannot be extrapolated to the case of stretch. When extension is imposed at constant speed, tension rises above the isometric value at a rate which depends on the speed of stretch, but in amphibian muscle this tension never rises to more than double the isometric value. At the end of stretch the tension drops back again toward the isometric level if the stimulus is continued. No damage is incurred by stretch as long as the final length is less than that which would damage the resting muscle if it were extended to that length.

This reaction to stretch contributes to economy in the animal. Tension in limb muscles is controlled partly by variation in the number of fibers active and partly by the rate of the activation of these fibers. Inspection of the force-velocity curve (Fig. 7) will show that the tension developed by an activated muscle fiber decreases rapidly as speed of shortening increases. Thus, for an intact muscle to exert a constant force, more fibers must be mobilized as shortening speed rises, and oxygen consumption must rise steeply. Resistance by the same force in stretch at equivalent speeds will demand far less fibers mobilized, since each fiber activated can exert a force of nearly twice its isometric tension. Thus, controlled stretch is very economical in the animal and cannot be ignored as a fundamental part of muscle physiology.

VI. Relaxation

During relaxation the contractile proteins revert from activity to the resting state. This process is thermoneutral if no work is done on the system during relaxation. If work is done in lowering a load, for example, then the work is dissipated as heat in the muscle. It is probable that relaxation is a process of decay from activity rather than a period of high energy expenditure resetting a system to be ready for another contraction. The thermal measurements in relaxation, however, are normally complicated by the dissipation of energy stored in the series elastic element and by the thermoelastic heat as contractile component and series elastic element lose their tension.

In the isometric twitch, relaxation time is determined by the fall of tension as the S.E. stretches the relaxing C.C. Under isotonic conditions the load is lowered on to the after-stop, and the duration appears shorter (Fig. 12). But Jewell and Wilkie (1960) have shown that the tension drop proceeds from the isotonic value for exactly the same time as for the isometric twitch.

Relaxation in skeletal twitch muscle takes about the same time as the rising phase, so that an isometric twitch is almost symmetrical. This is unlike almost all other muscles, where the relaxation phase is very slow compared to the rising phase. It may be that this high speed of relaxation is a very special property of these muscles.

The rate of relaxation varies during activity much more than does the shortening rate: during the first 4 or 5 sec of a tetanic contraction at 0°C relaxation rate slows to about a quarter coincident with a similar decrease in maintenance heat rate. If repeated twitches are induced, then fatigue develops; but as the mechanical response decreases the relaxation

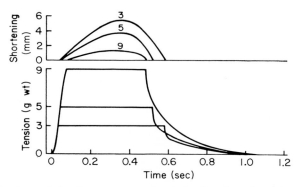

Fig. 12. Tracings of simultaneous records of the length and tension changes in a frog sartorius (30 mm, 5 mg, 0°C) during after-loaded isotonic twitches against loads of 3, 5, and 9 gm wt. (From Jewell and Wilkie, 1960.)

speed drops 12–15 times more than the shortening speed. During such fatigue the twitch height falls but there is little or no change in action potential, in speed of shortening or in ATP level in the muscle, while the creatine phosphate in iodoacetate poisoned muscle may drop to as low as 30% of its initial value. But relaxation becomes slowed to the extent that the twitch approaches the asymmetrical type characteristic of invertebrate smooth muscle.

Relaxation has also been studied on the glycerol-extracted fiber models, and relaxation factors which induce relaxation of the model can be prepared from muscles. Recent work has shown that a soluble factor can be prepared biosynthetically from centrifuged microsomal fragments of the sarcotubular system (Briggs and Fuchs, 1960) or directly from the muscle after oxalate treatment (Fuchs and Briggs, 1961). The microsomal vesicles contain a high level of calcium (Ebashi, 1961a,b) and have been shown to concentrate calcium against a gradient at the expense of ATP. Weber *et al.* (1963) have shown that the vesicles of the relaxing factor can reduce the concentration of ionized calcium in the surrounding medium to less than 0.02 μM. At this concentration the calcium-actomyosin complex is dissociated and the actomyosin is then inhibited by physiological concentrations of ATP.

The events of contraction and relaxation are closely associated with the state of calcium in the sarcoplasm. It is possible that at rest the contractile protein system is plasticized by the presence of ATP with the ATPase kept low by the retention of Ca^{++} in the relaxing system. When activity is begun Ca^{++} may be liberated from the sarcotubular system allowing contraction to occur. Relaxation could be the reverse process, and the measurements of Infante and Davies (1962) show that ATP is hydrolyzed during relaxation as well as during the rising phase of contraction.

VII. Metabolism and Contractile Proteins

Contraction is associated with two proteins which can be extracted from muscle: actin and myosin. Neither substance alone is contractile, but an actomyosin gel undergoes syneresis when ATP is added in the presence of magnesium ions in equimolar concentrations of about 3 mmoles per liter. Myosin is a fibrous protein of molecular weight about 420,000, estimated in size at 1600 Å long and 32 Å diameter (Hodge, 1959), and is an ATPase. The myosin molecule is split by brief treatment with trypsin into two molecules of light meromyosin of molecular weight 94,000 and a molecule of heavy meromyosin which retains the ATPase activity. Actin can exist in two forms: G-actin which is a globular protein, with a molecular weight of 60,000 is a sphere of 55 Å diameter; and F-actin which is formed from G-actin when it polymerizes in the presence of ATP. The thin filament probably consists of two chains of actin each built up of a series of globular actin molecules and coiled with an axial repeat distance of 350 Å (Hanson and Lowy, 1962).

If a mascerated muscle is soaked in 0.6 M KCl for 20 min, myosin is extracted. Electron microscope studies show that the thick filaments of the A-band are removed. Prolonged extraction of the muscle removes actomyosin, and studies of the remainder show that the thin filaments of the I-band, which interdigitate with the myosin filaments within the A-band, have also disappeared. The localization of the proteins is confirmed by fluorescent microscopy, after labeling each protein with a specific fluorescent antibody (Finch et al., 1956).

Contraction within the muscle is generally thought to result from longitudinal forces developed as a result of cyclic interaction between active sites on adjacent myosin and actin molecules. Bridges can be seen linking the filaments, and these bridges are helically distributed along the thick filaments. If a muscle is suitably disintegrated, the rodlets which form the A-band can be isolated and protrusions corresponding to the bridges become more visible with negative staining (Huxley, 1962). The longitudinal forces in each sarcomere provide active tension, while movement results from interdigitation of the sets of filaments as a result of the forces. The main evidence for these concepts comes from the electron microscope pictures and extraction studies of Huxley and Hanson (1960). There is also some evidence that the myosin is laid down in a mirror symmetry on opposite sides of the two bands (Huxley, 1962). Further support is given by the contractility of the glycerol-extracted model. If a bundle of skeletal muscle fibers is soaked in a 50% glycerol-water solution at 20°C for several weeks, the crystalloids and soluble proteins are removed. The contractile proteins remain, however, and the electron microscope pictures of such a muscle show clearly the two sets of filaments. Mechanically the fiber bundle resembles a muscle in rigor. Addition of ATP first plasticizes the bundle and then, in the presence of calcium or magnesium ions, induces contraction while ATP is hydrolyzed. The movements of such a bundle are slow, but maximal tetanic tensions can be developed.

A. F. Huxley (1957) proposed a mechanism for contraction in the inter-digitating model of muscle, with values for the forces and energies involved. According to this model there are sites on the thick and thin filaments which can react chemically, with tension and shortening derived from the random motion of the molecules involved. The direction of motion is determined by spacial asymmetry which interferes with the chemical reaction or by suitably located masking molecules which can reverse the reaction. Interdigitation results from the summated movements of the sites which are distributed along the muscle sarcomeres. Huxley shows that the energy of thermal motion of the molecules is sufficient to be compatible with the experimental values and reasonable values for the mechanics and energetics of muscle can be predicted.

The theory of contraction as a result of interdigitation is not universally accepted because electron microscope pictures from muscle fixed directly do not show the two sets of filaments as clearly separated as in the glycerol-extracted muscle and in vertebrate plain muscle the filaments are of uniform size (and it is not possible to identify two species of filament). It is possible that interdigitation may occur but contraction be derived from molecular folding. Shortening could occur by change in molecular figuration as in rubber-like materials, and Pryor (1950) proposed a contraction cycle by release of a plasticizing agent. However, the thermal changes associated with activity are not those predicted from rubber-like elasticity, for heat is liberated when muscle shortens whereas a rubber would cool (Woledge, 1961).

Shortening can also result from folding of molecules as in the super-contraction of keratin threads (Astbury, 1950). In such material the changes are reflected in changes in the X-ray diffraction patterns of the molecules. No equivalent changes have been reported during muscle activity or contracture. Thus, the carefully developed theories of Buchthal et al. (1951) and Polissar (1952) which are based on cyclic transitions of the contractile molecules between two states, one long and one short, have little direct experimental support.

Podolsky (1960) suggests that the two-filament model of Huxley may shorten as a result of folding in the thin filaments, perhaps with the bridges to the thick filaments acting as anchors for the movement.

The primary source of the energy for contraction is believed to be ATP and in glycerol-extracted fibers this is the only substance hydrolyzed. In normal living muscle, however, efforts to show a decrease in ATP as a result of normal activity have been unsuccessful. The eventual source of skeletal muscle energy is mainly glycogen, but if the glycolytic pathway is blocked by monoiodoacetic acid and the system is kept anaerobic, contraction occurs at the expense of creatine phosphate. In a fresh sartorius muscle there are about 25 μmoles per gram of creatine phosphate and a very low level of inorganic phosphate when extracted in alcohol technique (K. Seraydarian *et al.*, 1961). Carlson and Siger (1959) have shown that an average of 0.3 μmole per gram of creatine phosphate is hydrolyzed per isometric twitch, with no change in ATP level. When the contraction is isotonic, extra creatine phosphate is hydrolyzed in proportion to the physical work performed (Mommaerts *et al.*, 1962). In repeated twitches under these anaerobic and iodoacetate conditions, the height of contraction decreases and relaxation slows markedly. Creatine phosphate decreases steadily, but no decrease in ATP occurs until almost all the creatine phosphate has been hydrolyzed, and the muscle goes into rigor (M. W. Seraydarian *et al.*, 1961).

The level of ATP in the muscle is kept constant at the expense of creatine phosphate by the action of creatine phosphoryltransferase. This enzyme can be blocked by 1-fluoro-2,4-dinitrobenzene (Cain and Davies, 1962) and in a muscle thus poisoned there is a decrease in ATP content during the rising phase of a twitch. The creatine phosphate level remains constant, while the ADP level is kept very low by the action of myokinase which converts each two molecules of ADP into an AMP and an ATP molecule. Thus, ATP can be inferred as the prime activator, and in addition, still more ATP is hydrolyzed during the relaxation phase of sartorius muscle of frog (Infante and Davies, 1962)—perhaps linked to the uptake of calcium ions by the vesicles of the relaxing factor.

The true sequence of events in contraction is still uncertain, but it seems probable that the energy for contraction comes from coupled exothermic reactions during the initial events; that relaxation is a passive event and essentially thermoneutral; and that in recovery the energy stores are replenished.

VIII. Slow Muscle Fibers

Within the group of the twitch-type skeletal muscles in any animal there are considerable differences in contraction times which appear to be correlated with muscle function. A phasic jumping muscle is more rapid than a posture muscle, but in addition certain muscles exhibit "tonic" properties in which a long maintained contraction results from neural stimulation. Kuffler and Vaughan Williams (1953a,b) showed that these slow and fast responses were the result of two fiber systems in the muscle: (a) a small nerve-fiber, slow muscle-fiber system in which small nerves conducted the motor impulses from the central nervous system at from

2 to 8 meters per second and (b) a large nerve-fiber twitch-muscle fiber system with impulse conduction along the nerve between 8 and 40 meters per second. Kruger (1952) produced evidence that the two types of muscle fibers are structurally different and it is now certain that the fibril structure seen in transverse sections of twitch fibers is replaced by a uniform distribution of filaments in the tonic fibers.

Gray (1957, 1958) has shown that the nerve endings to these fibers are different: the large nerve fibers end on twitch-type or *endbuschel* end plates on the "twitch" fibers, and the small nerve fibers terminate as "grape" end plates on the tonic fibers (Fig. 13). Amphibian muscles have

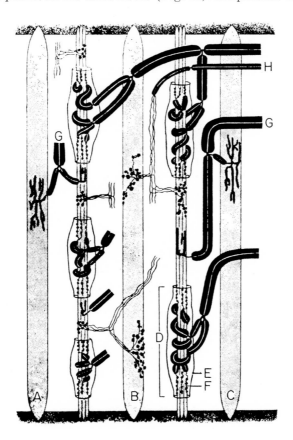

Fig. 13. Schematic presentation of the innervation of the frog muscle, extensor longus digitorum IV. Two spindle systems are shown between three extrafusal fibers, A, B, and C. A and C are "twitch" fibers and B a "tonic" fiber. Each of the two types has its characteristic end plate. Both types of end plate also occur on different fibers of the intrafusal bundle, between the sensory endings. (From Gray, 1957.)

varying proportions of tonic fibers, and the distribution within the frog has been described by Kuffler and Vaughan Williams, while Sommerkamp (1928) has described the isolation of a tonus bundle from the ileofibularis of frog.

The slow muscle fiber membrane has a resting potential across it of about 60 mv, and "grape" endings are distributed along the length of the fiber. A nerve impulse depolarizes the muscle membrane giving a slow junction potential (s.j.p.) of about 15 mv which is not propagated. This contrasts with the twitch fiber where the membrane potential is more than 90 mv and a propagated action potential of 120 mv results from a nerve impulse.

A single nerve impulse induces very little mechanical response in the slow fibers. Repeated stimuli produce mechanical facilitation, and the speed of tension rise increases with stimulus frequency. Full activation needs many stimuli in contrast to the twitch muscle. The most noticeable difference is in relaxation: at 22°C a twitch muscle relaxes within a few tens of milliseconds, but isotonic relaxation of a slow fiber lasts more than 10 min.

Slow fibers respond to acetylcholine or increased KCl concentration with a prolonged contracture, and this characteristic is employed when the rectus abduminus muscle of frogs is used as a bioassay material. The muscle is striated and about a third of the fibers are tonic. When activated by acetylcholine, all the fibers contract. The fast fibers, however, fail to maintain a contracture and relax very rapidly at room temperature. The slow fibers retain their tonus, which is suitable for assay studies since the response is a function of the concentration of applied acetylcholine.

The function of these fibers is obviously in the economic maintenance of tension for long periods of time, as in the mating clasp reflex. Slow fibers can quickly be brought into action to give a tension which is then maintained and acts as a tonic level on which twitch activity can be superimposed.

IX. Intrafusal Muscle Fibers

In addition to the twitch and tonic muscle fibers (so-called extrafusal fibers) amphibian muscles also contain bundles of a third type of fiber, the spindle or intrafusal fiber, with sensory properties over portions of its length. A detailed study of the structure and innervation of spindle systems has been made by Gray (1957) on the extensor longus digit, IV of frog, and a scheme is shown in Fig. 13 taken from his paper. Three extrafusal fibers are included. A and C are twitch fibers with typical "twitch" end plates and innervated by large efferent motor axons, G; B represents a tonic fiber, with the "grape" type end plates and innervated by a small efferent motor axon *H*. The other two fibers illustrate spindle fibers. The muscle contains two or three spindle systems each with bundles of from 3 to 12 fibers of diameter 4 to 12 μ. These fibers run the length of the muscle and have three sensory regions encapsulating the fiber where the muscle striations are absent. The sensory capsules, between 300 and 900 μ long, surround the fiber with a lymph space enclosing the coiled sensory afferents and "flower spray" endings which extend along the muscle fiber.

In between the sensory capsules the intrafusal muscle fibers receive innervation from branches of both large and small motor axons. Both twitch type end plates and grape end plates occur, probably on the same fibers. The intrafusal bundles can thus be expected to have fast and slow properties, and to be activated whenever the *G* (large) or *H* (small) motor axons are excited. Katz (1950) showed that when the muscle is stretched the sensory nerve endings are depolarized, and a local potential change occurs in the sensory axon near the spindle which gives rise to repetitive impulses in the sensory nerve. The variation in discharge frequency during contraction of the muscle varies with the conditions of contraction (isometric or isotonic) and with the muscle (Katz, 1949b; Matthews, 1931). Obviously the discharge will be affected by the activity of the intrafusal fibers and with any muscle movement which occurs.

Koketsu and Nishi (1957) have studied the electrical activity of the spindle fibers. Two types were detectable by motor nerve stimulation, an action potential with transient reversal of membrane potential, and an intrafusal junction potential (i.j.p.). These correspond to the two types of motor end plate described. The time course of the i.j.p. is longer than the twitch end plate (e.p.p.) but shorter than the s.j.p. of the tonic (grape) end plate. This is explained in terms of the relative number of endings in each case, the spindle having less than the tonic fiber.

The function of the intrafusal bundles and the sensory discharge system is certainly related to control of muscle movement. The afferent impulses are dependent on activation and on movement of the muscle, on the duration of these events, and also on the relative activities of twitch and tonic systems. But the interplay of these parameters and the total loop properties, including the feedback to the motor nerves, has not been worked out.

References

Abbott, B. C., and Aubert, X. (1952). Changes of energy in a muscle during very slow stretches. *Proc. Roy. Soc.* **B139**, 104–117.

Abbott, B. C., and Baskin, R. J. (1962). Volume changes in frog muscle during contraction. *J. Physiol. (London)* **161**, 379–391.

Abbott, B. C., and Ritchie, J. M. (1951a). Early tension relaxation during a muscle twitch. *J. Physiol. (London)* **113**, 330–335.

Abbott, B. C., and Ritchie, J. M. (1951b). The onset of shortening in striated muscle. *J. Physiol. (London)* **113**, 336–345.

Adrian, R. H. (1956). The effect of internal and external potassium concentration on the membrane potential of the frog muscle. *J. Physiol. (London)* **133**, 631–658.

Adrian, R. H. (1960). Potassium chloride movement and the membrane potential of frog muscle. *J. Physiol. (London)* **151**, 154–185.

Astbury, W. T. (1950). X-ray studies of muscle. *Proc. Roy. Soc.* **B137**, 58–63.

Aubert, X. (1956). "Le Couplage énergetique de la contraction musculaire. Thèse d'agrégation," 320 pp. Editions Arscia, Brussels.

Bennett, H. S. (1960). The structure of striated muscle as seen by the electron microscope. *In* "Structure and Function of Muscle" (G. H. Bourne, ed.), Vol. I. Academic Press, New York.

Bernstein, J. (1902). Untersuchungen zur Thermodynamik der bioelectrischen Ströme. *Arch. Ges. Physiol. Pflüger's* **92**, 521–562.

Bianchi, C. P., and Shanes, A. M. (1959). Calcium influx in skeletal muscle at rest, during activity, and during potassium contracture. *J. Gen. Physiol.* **42**, 803–815.

Boyle, P., and Conway, E. J. (1941). Potassium accumulation in muscle and associated changes. *J. Physiol. (London)* **100**, 1–63.

Briggs, F. N., and Fuchs, F. (1960). The biosynthesis of a muscle relaxing susbtance. *Biochim. Biophys. Acta* **42**, 519–527.

Buchthal, F., Kaiser, E., and Rosenfalk, P. (1951). The rheology of the cross-striated muscle fiber with particular reference to isotonic conditions. *Biol. Medd. Kjobenhavn* **21**, 1–318.

Cain, D. F., and Davies, R. E. (1962). Breakdown of adenosine triphosphate during a single contraction of working muscle. *Biochem. Biophys. Res. Commun.* **8**, 361–366.

Carlson, F. D., and Siger, A. (1958). Abstract. Biophysical Society.

Carlson, F. D., and Siger, A. (1959). The creatine phosphoryltransfer reaction in iodoacetate-poisoned muscle. *J. Gen. Physiol.* **43**, 301–313.

Carlson, F. D., Hardy, D., and Wilkie, D. R. (1963). Total energy production and phosphocreatine hydrolysis in the isotonic twitch. *J. Gen. Physiol.* **46**, 851–882.

Davson, H. (1959). "A Textbook of General Physiology," 2nd ed., p. 846. Little, Brown, Boston, Massachusetts.

Ebashi, S. (1961a). Calcium binding activity of vesicular relaxing factor. *J. Biochem. (Tokyo)* **50**, 236–244.

Ebashi, S. (1961b). The role of relaxing factor in contraction-relaxation cycle of muscle. *Progr. Theoret. Phys. (Kyoto)* Suppl. **17**, 35–40.

Fatt, P., and Katz, B. (1951). An analysis of the end-plate potential recorded with an intracellular electrode. *J. Physiol. (London)* **115**, 320–370.

Fenn, W. O. (1923). A quantitative comparison between the energy liberated and the work performed by the isolated sartorius muscle of the frog. *J. Physiol. (London)* **58**, 175–203.

Fenn, W. O. (1924). The relation between the work performed and the energy liberated in muscular contraction. *J. Physiol. (London)* **58**, 373–395.

Fenn, W. O., and Marsh, B. S. (1935). Muscular force at different speeds of shortening. *J. Physiol. (London)* **85**, 277–297.

Finch, H., Holtzer, H., and Marshall, H. (1956). An immunochemical study of the distribution of myosin in glycerol extracted muscle. *J. Biophys. Biochem. Cytol.* Suppl. **2**, 175–178.

Fuchs, F., and Briggs, F. N. (1961). Direct isolation of a soluble relaxing system from muscle. *Biochim. Biophys. Acta* **51**, 423–425.

Gelfan, S. (1933). The submaximal responses of the single muscle fiber. *J. Physiol. (London)* **80**, 285–295.

Gray, E. G. (1957). The spindle and extrafusal innervation of a frog muscle. *Proc. Roy. Soc.* **B147**, 416–430.

Gray, E. G. (1958). The structures of fast and slow muscle fibers in the frog. *J. Anat.* **92**, 559–562.

Hanson, J., and Lowy, J. (1962). Actin in contractile systems. *Proc. Intern. Conf. Electron Microscopy 5th Conf.* **2**.

Hill, A. V. (1937). Methods of analyzing the heat production of muscle. *Proc. Roy. Soc.* **B124**, 114–136.

Hill, A. V. (1938). The heat of shortening and the dynamic constants of muscle. *Proc. Roy. Soc.* **B126**, 136–195.

Hill, A. V. (1948). On the time for diffusion and its relation to processes in muscle. *Proc. Roy. Soc.* **B135**, 446–453.

Hill, A. V. (1949). The abrupt transition from rest to activity in muscle. *Proc. Roy. Soc.* **B136**, 399–420.

Hill, A. V. (1950). Does heat production precede mechanical response in muscular contraction? *Proc. Roy. Soc.* **B137**, 268–273.

Hill, A. V. (1952). The thermodynamics of elasticity in resting muscle. *Proc. Roy. Soc.* **B139**, 464–497.

Hill, A. V. (1953). The mechanics of active muscle. *Proc. Roy. Soc.* **B141**, 104–117.

Hill. A. V. (1957). The priority of heat production in a muscle twitch. *Proc. Roy Soc.* **B148**, 397–402.

Hill, D. K. (1949). Changes in transparency of muscle in a twitch. *J. Physiol. (London)* **119**, 501–512.

Hill, D. K. (1953). The effect of stimulation on the diffraction of light by striated muscle. *J. Physiol. (London)* **119**, 501–512.

Hodge, A. J. (1959). Fibrous Protein of Muscle. *Rev. Mod. Phys.* **31**, 409–425.

Hodgkin, A. L., and Horowicz, P. (1959a). Movements of Na and K in single muscle fibers. *J. Physiol. (London)* **145**, 405–432.

Hodgkin, A. L., and Horowicz, P. (1959b). The influence of potassium and chloride ions on the membrane potential of the single muscle fibers. *J. Physiol. (London)* **148**, 127–160.

Hodgkin, A. L., and Horowicz, P. (1960a). The effect of sudden changes in ionic concentrations on the membrane potential of single muscle fibers. *J. Physiol. (London)* **153**, 370–385.

Hodgkin, A. L. and Horowicz, P. (1960b). Potassium contracture in single muscle fibers. *J. Physiol. (London)* **153**, 386–403.

Hodgkin, A. L., and Huxley, A. F. (1952). A quantitative description of membrane current and its application to conduction and excitation in nerve. *J. Physiol. (London)*, **117**, 500–544.

Hutter, O. F., and Noble, D. (1960). The chloride conductance of frog and skeletal muscle. *J. Physiol. (London)* **151**, 89–102.

Huxley, A. F. (1957). Muscle structure and theories of contraction. *Progr. Biophys. Biophys. Chem.* **7**, 255–318.

Huxley, A. F., and Taylor, R. E. (1958). Local activation of striated muscle fibers. *J. Physiol. (London)* **144**, 426–441.

Huxley, H. E. (1962). Studies on the structure of natural and synthetic protein fila-
    ments from muscle. *Proc. 5th Intern. Cong. Electron Microscopy, Philadelphia*, **2**,
    Section 0, p 1.
Huxley, H. E., and Hanson, J. (1960). The molecular basis of contraction in cross-
    striated muscles. *In* "Structure and Function of Muscle" (G. H. Bourne, ed.),
    Vol. I. Academic Press, New York.
Infante, A. A., and Davies, R. E. (1962). Adenosine triphosphate breakdown during
    a single isotonic twitch of frog sartorius muscle. *Biochem. Biophys. Res. Com-
    mun.* **9**, 410–415.
Jewell, B. R., and Wilkie, D. R. (1958). An analysis of the mechanical components in
    frog's striated muscle. *J. Physiol. (London)* **143**, 515–540.
Jewell, B. R., and Wilkie, D. R. (1960). The mechanical properties of relaxing muscle.
    J. Physiol. (London) **152**, 30–47.
Katz, B. (1949a). Les constantes électriques de la membrane du muscle. *Arch. Sci.
    Physiol.* **3**, 285–300.
Katz, B. (1949b). The efferent regulation of the muscle spindle in frog. *J. Exptl.
    Biol.* **26**, 201–217.
Katz, B. (1950). Depolarization of sensory terminals and the initiation of impulses in
    the muscle spindle. *J. Physiol. (London)* **111**, 261–282.
Knappeis, G. G., and Carlsen, F. (1962). The ultrastructure of the Z disc in skeletal
    muscle. *J. Cell Biol.* **13**, 323–335.
Koketsu, K., and Nishi, S. (1957). An analysis of junctional potentials of intrafusal
    muscle fibers in frogs. *J. Physiol. (London)* **139**, 15–26.
Kruger, P. (1952). "Tetanus und Tonus der quergestreiften Skelettmuskeln der
    Wirbeltiere und des Menschen." Akademische Verlag., Leipzig.
Kuffler, S. W., and Vaughan Williams, E. M. (1953a). Small-nerve junctional poten-
    tials. The distribution of small motor nerves to frog skeletal muscle, and the
    membrane characteristics of the fibers they innervate. *J. Physiol. (London)* **121**,
    289–317.
Kuffler, S. W., and Vaughan Williams, E. M. (1953b). Properties of the 'slow' skeletal
    muscle fibers of the frog. *J. Physiol. (London)* **121**, 318–340.
Ling, G., and Gerard, R. W. (1949). The normal membrane potential of frog sartorius
    fibers. *J. Cellular Comp. Physiol.* **34**, 383–396.
Levin, A., and Wyman, J. (1927). The viscous elastic properties of muscle. *Proc. Roy.
    Soc.* **B101**, 218–243.
Macpherson, L., and Wilkie, D. R. (1953). Duration of active state in a muscle twitch.
    J. Physiol. (London) **124**, 292–299.
Matthews, B. H. C. (1931). The response of a single end organ. *J. Physiol. (London)*
    71, 64–110.
Mommaerts, W. F. H. M. (1959). Physiology of muscular contraction. *In* "Cardiology:
    Encyclopedia of the Cardiovascular System" (A. A. Luisada, ed.), Vol. II.
    McGraw-Hill (Blakiston), New York.
Mommaerts, W. F. H. M., Seraydarian, K., and Marechal, G. (1963). Work and
    chemical change in isotonic muscular contractions. *Biochim. Biophys. Acta* **57**,
    1–12.
Overton, E. (1902). Beiträge zur allgemeinen Muskel- und Nervenphysiologie. *Arch.
    Ges. Physiol. Pflüger's* **92**, 346–386.
Podolsky, R. J. (1960). Thermodynamics of muscle. *In* "Structure and Function of
    Muscle" (G. H. Bourne, ed.), Vol. II. Academic Press, New York.
Podolsky, R. J. (1962). Mechano-chemical basis of muscular contraction. *Federation
    Proc.* **21**, 964–974.

Polissar, M. J. (1952). Physical chemistry of contractile processes in muscle. *Am. J. Physiol.* **168**, 763–811.

Porter, K. R., and Palade, G. E. (1957). Studies on the endoplasmic reticulum. III. Its form and distribution in striated muscle fibers. *J. Biophys. Biochem. Cytol.* **3**, 269–300.

Pryor, M. G. M. (1950). Mechanical properties of fibers and muscles. *Progr. Biophys. Biophys. Chem.* **1**, 216–268.

Ramsey, R. W., and Street, S. F. (1940). The isometric length-tension diagram of isolated skeletal muscle fibers of the frog. *J. Cellular Comp. Physiol.* **15**, 11–34.

Rauh, F. (1922). Die Latenzeit des Muskelementes. *Z. Biol.* **76**, 25–28.

Ritchie, J. M. (1954). The effect of nitrate on active muscle. *J. Physiol. (London)* **126**, 155–168.

Sandow, A. (1944). General properties of latency relaxation. *J. Cellular Comp. Physiol.* **24**, 221–256.

Scatchard, G., and Black, E. S. (1949). The effect of salts on the isotonic and isoelectric points of proteins. *J. Phys. Chem.* **53**, 88–89.

Scatchard, G., Coleman, J. S., and Shen, A. L. (1957). Physical chemistry of protein solutions. VII. The binding of some small anions to serum albumin. *J. Am. Chem. Soc.* **79**, 12–79.

Seraydarian, M. W., Abbott, B. C., and Williams, E. B. (1961). Studies on the frog's sartorius at different stages of activity. *Biochim. Biophys. Acta* **46**, 355–363.

Seraydarian, K., Mommaerts, W. F. H. M., Wallner, A., and Guillory, R. J. (1961). True inorganic phosphate estimation in frog sartorius. *J. Biol. Chem.* **236**, 2071–2075.

Shanes, A. M. (1958). Electrochemical aspects of physiological and pharmacological action in excitable cells. II. The action potential and excitation. *Pharmacol. Rev.* **10**, 165–273.

Shanes, A. M., and Bianchi, C. P. (1960). Radiocalcium release by stimulated and potassium-treated sartorius muscles of the frog. *J. Gen. Physiol.* **43**, 481–493.

Sichel, F. J. M., and Prosser, C. L. (1940). Summation and the absence of a refractory period in isolated skeletal muscle fibers. *Am. J. Physiol.* **128**, 203–212.

Sommerkamp, H. (1928). Das Substrat der Dauerverkürzung am Froschmuskel. *Arch. Exptl. Pathol. Pharmakol. Naunyn-Schmiedeberg's* **128**, 99–115.

Sten-Knudsen, O. (1953). Torsional elasticity of the isolated cross-striated muscle fiber. *Acta Physiol. Scand.* **28** (Suppl. 104), 1–240.

Sten-Knudsen, O. (1960). Is muscle contraction initiated by internal current flow? *J. Physiol. (London)* **151**, 363–384.

Walls, E. W. (1960). The microanatomy of muscle. *In* "Structure and Function of Muscle" (G. H. Bourne, ed.), Vol. I. Academic Press, New York.

Weber, A., Herg, R., and Reiss, I. (1963). On the mechanism of the relaxing effect of fragmented sarcoplasmic reticulum. *J. Gen. Physiol.* **46**, 679–702.

Wilkie, D. R. (1956.) Measurement of the series elastic component at various times during a single muscle twitch. *J. Physiol. (London)* **134**, 527–530.

Wilkie, D. R. (1960). Thermodynamics and the interpretation of biological heat measurements. *Progr. Biophys. Biophys. Chem.* **10**, 260–298.

Woledge, R. C. (1961). The thermoelastic effect of change of tension in active muscle. *J. Physiol. (London)* **155**, 187–208.

Note Added in Proof

In a recent article Davies (1963) explains interdigitating contraction in terms of microfolding at the filament level. The protrusions on the thick (myosin) rodlets are described as molecules of heavy meromyosin able to exist in a coiled or in an elongated configuration. The protrusions are pictured as bridges to sites on the thin (actin) fibers which, by a succession of molecular shortening, disengagement, molecular elongation and reattachment to new sites induces shortening. Contraction is produced by calcium activation of myosin ATPase, and relaxation by withdrawal of the calcium ions.

An alternative hypothesis by Szent-Gyorgi and Johnson (1964), suggests a folding mechanism based on observations with fluorescent antibody techniques; that myosin moves away from the center of the A band during contraction. Folding is proposed within a constant length thick filament; interdigitation is explained by supposing that the thin filaments attach to sites on the thick filament such that shortening pulls the filaments in to give interdigitation. Meanwhile Sjöstrand (1964) has produced micrographs not readily compatible with simple interdigitation.

7

ENDOCRINOLOGY OF THE AMPHIBIA

Aubrey Gorbman

I. Historical and General Introduction

It is difficult to recognize any phases of endocrine physiology which are outstandingly "amphibian." All of the endocrine glands that are known in reptiles, birds, and mammals are found also in the amphibians. Although some of the amphibian hormones have not yet been identified with certainty, it appears that amphibian endocrine secretions resemble those known in other vertebrates. Accordingly, many of the statements which will be made in this chapter about amphibian endocrinology may apply as well to other vertebrate groups.

On the other hand, it is in the adaptation of various physiological mechanisms to regulation by certain hormones that certain specific and characteristic features may be seen. Thus, thyroxine is produced by all thyroid glands, but it is linked to metamorphosis only in Amphibia. The androgenic and estrogenic steroids of amphibians are of general occurrence but their action upon the thumb pad, on pigmentation, on behavior, and other aspects of the reproductive process are particular and characteristic of certain families or even certain species. A frequently quoted statement by Hisaw (1959) summarizes this point: "It is not the hormones that have evolved, but the uses to which they are put."

In a historical sense, experimental work with amphibians has contributed in an important way to the development of endocrinology as a whole. The early work of B. M. Allen (1916) and P. E. Smith (1916) with hypophysectomized tadpoles was the first to show conclusively that a regulatory relationship exists between the hypophysis and thyroid, adrenal, and gonadal development. This was made possible by the easy accessibility of the tadpole's adenohypophyseal rudiment to surgical removal (Fig. 1). Since this time the accumulation of information in the field of amphibian endocrinology has been uneven, some areas of research having been pursued intensively and others largely neglected. Thyroid physiology, for example has been well studied, particularly since the discovery by Gudernatsch (1912) that feeding thyroid tissue to tadpoles accelerated their embryonic development. Amphibian reproductive endocrinology also has received much attention, particularly the factors which affect sexual differentiation in the embryo, and seasonal gametogenesis and gamete release in the adult.

The melanophore response in amphibian skin (to intermedin and adrenaline) and the transfer of water through the skin (in response to vasopressin) have benefited from much recent study. The melanophore response in particular, is in a relatively "sophisticated" stage of endocrine analysis, since it is being studied at the level of cellular mechanisms.

Areas of amphibian endocrinology in which relatively little information is available are the following: (a) nature and action of gastrointestinal hormones; (b) control of carbohydrate metabolism; (c) adrenal-cortical physiology; (d) parathyroid function; (e) chemical nature of all but thyroid and adrenal hormones.

II. Pituitary Gland

The pituitary gland of anurans and urodeles is formed in the embryo (Fig. 1) by union of a solid finger-like ectodermal ingrowth (equivalent to the hollow "Rathke's pouch" of other vertebrates) with the distal end of a sac-like diverticulum of the diencephalon, the infundibulum. Much discussion has been expended on the question of whether the differentiation of the buccal ingrowth (adenohypophysis) is dependent upon induction by the neurohypophyseal part of the infundibulum with which it comes in contact (for some of the literature see Thurmond and Eakin, 1959; Etkin, 1958). Although the question is not yet completely settled, there seems to be good evidence that both pars distalis and pars intermedia of the adenohypophysis can differentiate functionally without actual

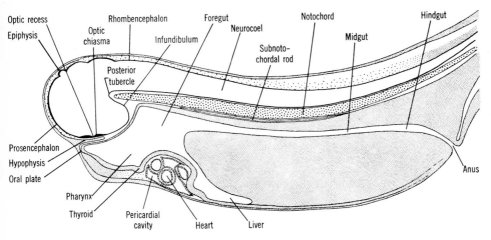

Fig. 1. Median sagittal section of a 5.5-mm frog embryo showing the rudiments of the pituitary and thyroid glands.

contact with the neurohypophysis. However, the regulation of this function may not be normal when the adenohypophysis-neurohypophysis relation is disturbed. For example, Etkin (1940; Etkin and Lehrer, 1961) has found that the pars intermedia becomes hypertrophic when transplanted, and in a location away from the brain it secretes unusually large amounts of intermedin. He interprets this as a response to freedom from a *normally inhibitory* influence by the brain. A similar inhibitory relationship appears to exist between the hypothalamus and growth hormone secretion by the anterior pituitary of frog tadpoles (Etkin and Lehrer, 1960).

A. MORPHOLOGY AND RELATION TO BRAIN

It has been known for a long time that hormonal secretion by the adenohypophysis of most vertebrates, including the Amphibia, is linked to physical changes (e.g., in light or temperature) in the environment. These physical "clues," acting as primary stimuli to nervous receptors, are in some way integrated by the central nervous system, and appropriate impulses are relayed to hypothalamic neurosecretory nervous nuclei. In Amphibia there is a bilateral pair of such neurosecretory cell-body groups, the preoptic nuclei (Fig. 2A). From these nuclei a pair of preoptico-hypophyseal axonal fiber tracts (Figs. 2A and 3) extend into the neuro-hypophyseal part of the pituitary (Scharrer and Scharrer, 1954; Hild, 1951a; Dawson, 1953; Wilson *et al.*, 1957). It may be appreciated from this brief statement that a knowledge of anatomical relationships between the pituitary and the brain is basic for an understanding of the mechanisms

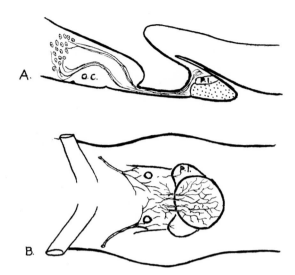

Fig. 2. A. Sagittal section of the floor of the brain of a frog, in the hypophyseal region. O.C., optic chiasma; P.I., pars intermedia. The preoptic nucleus is the group of cells indicated anterior (to the left) to the optic chiasma. Extending from it in two groups are the axons which join as a hypothalamo-hypophyseal tract in the wall of the infundibulum and then extend as far as the pars nervosa of the pituitary (dorsal to the pars intermedia). The pars distalis of the adenohypophysis is stippled.

B. Ventral view of the brain of a frog or toad (after Jorgensen and Rosenkilde, 1956) showing the arrangement of blood vessels near the hypophysis. Just posterior (to the right) of the optic nerves two small branches of the internal carotid arteries may be seen. They break up into capillaries in the median eminence, the part of the infundibular floor near the adenohypophysis. The two round objects shown laterally on the infundibular floor are the partes tuberalis. The blood from the median eminence is gathered into portal vessels (four are shown) which extend to the adenohypophysis where they again break up into capillaries and sinusoids.

by which pituitary function is coordinated with external environmental events. By such mechanisms the timing of discontinuous pituitary-controlled phenomena (e.g., reproduction or skin color adjustment) is achieved.

The adult amphibian pituitary gland (Fig. 3) consists of a pars distalis, pars intermedia, bilobed pars tuberalis (lacking in many urodeles), and a neurohypophysis. The first three, together, comprise the adenohypophysis. The neurohypophysis is actually the floor of the broad infundibular sac, and it is divisible into two regions, the pars nervosa and the median eminence. The hypothalamo-hypophyseal neurosecretory fiber tracts, already mentioned (see Figs. 2 and 3) reach the neurohypophysis along the ventral wall of the infundibulum. Some of these fibers terminate in the

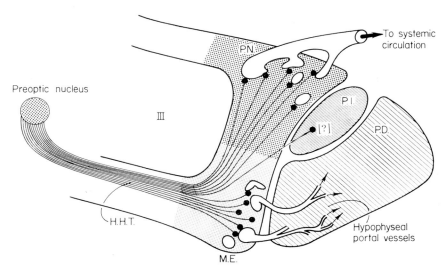

Fig. 3. Diagram of the sagittal section of the hypophyseal region of a frog to show the distribution of neurosecretory fibers from the preoptic nucleus. This figure is adapted from Dierickx and van den Abeele (1959). According to these authors the hypothalamo-hypophyseal axonal tract (HHT) has some endings in the median eminence (M.E.), but most endings are in the pars nervosa (P.N.). There is still question whether some endings may occur in the pars intermedia (P.I.). From the median eminence blood vessels (the hypophyseal portal vessels in Fig. 2) extend into the pars distalis (P.D.). From the pars nervosa blood would take neurosecretory material directly to the systemic circulation; III is the third ventricle.

median eminence (Dawson, 1953; Dierickx and van den Abeele, 1959), but most terminate in the posterodorsal part of the neurohypophysis, the pars nervosa. Dawson (1953) has described in *Rana pipiens* terminations of some of these fibers in the pars intermedia. Mazzi (1947) described a similar situation in *Triturus cristatus*. In all instances these neurosecretory endings are near blood vessels and it is presumed that neurosecretory materials pass into these vessels to produce local or systemic effects.

In hypothalamo-hypophyseal regulation the arrangement of blood vessels in the hypophyseal region is of great importance. The existence of a system of venous portal blood vessels connecting median eminence with pars distalis has been amply demonstrated and reviewed in mammals and birds (see Green, 1951; Green and Maxwell, 1959). Pertinent anatomical evidence for the existence of a hypophyseal portal system in amphibians has been presented by Green (1947). In fishes the vascular arrangement is such that arterial blood which enters the neurohypophysis traverses the adenohypophysis before it leaves the gland. Accordingly, there is opportunity for *local* action in the adenohypophysis by substances ultimately derived from the hypothalamus. In Amphibia this *local* effect upon adenohypophyseal secretion is very likely served through the hypophyseal portal vessels, and possibly through neurosecretory endings in the pars intermedia. In the Amphibia for the first time in the vertebrate series there is found a separate circulatory supply to a specialized part of the neurohypophysis, the pars nervosa. Thus, in the Amphibia there is the first anatomical basis for direct release of hypothalamus-derived materials into the systemic blood. It is frequently pointed out that the neurohypophyseal substances so released are important in physiological water conservation, and the Amphibia, being the first terrestrial vertebrates, are the first animals to encounter the need for water conservation. An interesting corollary is the fact that in dipnoan fish (lungfish), which face this need, there is a partial anatomical organization of this kind (Wingstrand, 1959). Furthermore, the aquatic salamanders with a lesser need, or no need, for water conservation have a less well developed hypophyseal portal system than do the anurans.

Since the anatomical basis for neuroendocrine reflexes exists in the amphibians, there is reason to believe that this system functions as it does in mammals and birds. Unfortunately, there is still little direct experimental evidence from the amphibians which shows that the hypothalamus is the integrating center between environmental changes and hypophyseal secretory responses. Cutting of the hypothalamo-hypophyseal tract (Hild, 1951b; Wilson *et al.*, 1957; Jorgensen *et al.*, 1960) of frogs and toads shows that neurosecretory material is moving in it toward the adenohypophysis. Cycles (usually seasonal) of accumulation and depletion of neurosecretory material have been described in various anuran and urodele species. It is important that Dierickx *et al.* 1960; Dierickx and van den Abeele, (1959) find such a seasonal neurosecretory cycle in the median eminence of *Rana temporaria*, since this part of the neurohypophysis is presumably involved in regulating secretion of the tropic hormones by the pars distalis. In mammals and birds (Harris, 1959; Ganong, 1959) specifically placed surgical lesions in the hypothalamus have been found to interfere with secretion of certain adenohypophyseal hormones. Similar experiments with amphibians remain to be done.

Perhaps the best available evidence of hypothalamic neurosecretory regulation of the amphibian adenohypophysis is included in recent work of Jorgensen *et al.* (1960). In these experiments, with *Bufo*, the median eminence was removed and interruption of thyrotropic secretion was judged by molting. Molting was inhibited only until vascularization was reestablished between the cut hypothalamic neurons and the pars distalis. Thus, the median eminence *per se* is not the important factor in regulating adenohypophyseal thyrotropic secretion, but the development of an adequate means of carrying hypothalamus-produced substances from the nerve tract to the pars distalis is required (see also B. Scharrer, 1959).

The nature of the substances normally carried from the median eminence to pars distalis to influence secretion of tropic hormones is still unknown. In mammals there is evidence that they may be closely related to the hormones of the pars nervosa. This possibility is also suggested in the fact synthetic lysine vasopressin injections into toads stimulate release of thyrotropin, ACTH, and perhaps other hormones of the pars distalis (Jorgensen and Nielsen, 1958; Jorgensen and Larsen, 1960a).

B. ADENOHYPOPHYSEAL HORMONES

1. Pars Distalis

After use of a wide variety of experimental procedures (hypophysectomy, chemical extraction, and injection or implantation into a variety of test animals) a large volume of accumulated research has shown that the amphibian pituitary gland contains all the hormones of the pars distalis known in other vertebrates: gonadotropin (FSH and LH), prolactin, thyrotropin, adrenocorticotropin, and somatotropin (see reviews in Gorbman, 1941; von Buddenbrock, 1950; Herlant, 1954; Pickford and Atz, 1957).

These amphibian hormones have been identified only by their biological activities. None has been available in sufficient amount to permit chemical identification. Further discussion of the biological action of the tropic hormones will be presented in detail in later sections of this chapter in relation to the thyroid gland, adrenal gland, reproductive function, or carbohydrate metabolism.

Since the demonstration by Leblond and Noble (1937) of prolactin in amphibian pituitaries, the question of its function in this class has been a difficult one. Chadwick (1940) discovered that purified mammalian prolactin induces a behavioral response, "water-drive," in *Triturus*. This finding has since been amplified by Grant and Grant (1958) and others. Accordingly, it is most likely that prolactin is involved in reproductive behavior in other Amphibia, particularly in those phases having to do with providing a proper medium for development of the young. It would be of interest to know whether prolactin is concerned in the unusual reproductive patterns of forms like *Alytes* with marsupium-like egg-containing integumentary structures, or *Nectophrynoides occidentalis* which is ovoviviparous and develops true corpora lutea according to Gallien (1959).

2. Pars Intermedia

Aside from the chemical isolation of intermedin, most of the work with this hormone has utilized amphibian test animals. Swingle (1920), by implanting different lobes of pituitary tissue into hypophysectomized frog tadpoles, was the first to show that the pigmentary response is identifiable with the pars intermedia. Later work, during the 1920's, by Hogben and his collaborators firmly established the pars intermedia as the source of intermedin, developed the use of the frog for bioassay, and described in detail the reactions of the integumentary chromatophores.

Because of the large amounts of pituitary tissue required for chemical isolation and analysis, only the mammalian intermedins have been so studied. Two melanophore-dispersing polypeptides have been isolated from the pars intermedia of pig, beef, sheep, horse, whale, and man, and the sequences of their amino acids have been determined (Geschwind, 1959). The smaller molecule, α-MSH* contains 13 amino acids; the larger, β-MSH contains 18 amino acids. In addition it has been found in tests upon frog skin that mammalian ACTH has some intermedin-like activity. This is of interest because within the larger molecule of ACTH the amino acid sequence of α-MSH is completely reproduced. Even among the mammals there are small differences in amino acid composition of β-MSH. Hence it would be expected that the amphibian MSH might vary to an even greater degree from the mammalian pattern. According to Geschwind, crude amphibian MSH has chemical properties which clearly distinguish it from that of mammals.

The typical response to intermedin observed in amphibian skin is a dispersion of melanin granules in the melanophore and a concentration of guanophores, which are deeper (Bagnara and Neidleman, 1958). Amphibia differ from the fishes and reptiles in the lack of additional nervous control over melanophores. Hypophysectomy has been shown in many amphibian species to have the opposite effect, a concentration of melanin granules close to the nucleus of all melanophores, resulting in a generally lighter skin color. The deeper guanophores thus revealed are in the dispersed phase in hypophysectomized animals.

Two different kinds of actions of intermedin upon amphibian melanophores must be distinguished; a rapid effect upon dispersion of melanin granules, and a slower, more permanent effect upon the absolute number of these granules and/or the number of melanophores ("morphological", or "melanogenic" effect). The morphological effect of intermedin, or its lack, has been observed primarily in developing amphibians. Hypophysectomized tadpoles or larval urodeles, for example, are relatively deficient

* To specify the various polypeptides with intermedin activity, biochemists have preferred to use the abbreviation MSH (melanocyte-stimulating hormone). Since this implies that the hormonal action is restricted to the melanophore, its use should perhaps be limited to the identity of these polypeptides. Intermedin acts also upon guanophores and lipophores.

in numbers of melanophores (Blount, 1945; Burch, 1938; Eakin, 1939; Bagnara and Neidleman, 1958). On the other hand, Bagnara and Neidleman (1958) have found an absolute increase in the amount of guanine pigment in the skins of hypophysectomized frog tadpoles. Intermedin injection reverses these effects (Bagnara and Neidleman, 1958). The morphogenic effect is not restricted to developing organisms. In adult *Xenopus* kept permanently on a dark background so that the animal is presumably continually secreting intermedin to keep its skin appropriately dark, there is a net increase in the amount of melanin in the skin, compared with permanently light-adapted animals (Burgers, 1956).

The normal response mechanism resulting in release of intermedin when the amphibian is placed on a dark background is only partially understood (Rey and Chambon, 1960). Since the mechanism is inoperative in blinded animals, the eye must be the primary receptor organ. Attempts to trace a retino-hypophyseal nerve pathway have not yet succeeded. As has been mentioned before, the terminal part of this pathway, from the preoptic nucleus to the neurohypophysis and pars intermedia has been described. However, aside from the experiments of Etkin analyzing the relation of the hypothalamus to the pigmentary response, little has been done. Etkin and his collaborators have found that the normal influence of the hypothalamus upon intermedin secretion and release is inhibitory since transplanted pituitaries in frog tadpoles and *Ambystoma* larvae appear to secrete intermedin in great excess (Etkin, 1940; Etkin and Lehrer, 1960; Etkin and Sussman, 1961).

The amphibian melanophore response to intermedin is one which can be readily observed (Fig. 4) and accurately measured (Fig. 5) by photoelectric instruments. Hence, it is a convenient response to a hormone to subject to further analysis from a cellular physiological point of view. The resemblance between the reversible movement of pigment granules in the melanophore and muscular contraction (Spaeth, 1916) or mitoses has influenced such investigations to a certain extent. Colchicine, a mitotic

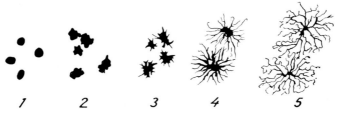

1   2   3   4   5

Fig. 4. The "Hogben melanophore index" (after Hogben and Slome, 1931). The "Hogben melanophore index" is a number system which refers to progressively greater degrees of dispersion of the melanin in melanophores.

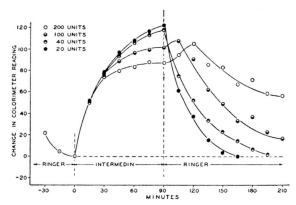

Fig. 5. Responses of melanophores during and following exposure to intermediate and large doses of intermedin. Each curve is an average of eight different tests. From Wright (1955).

poison, for example, prevents the reaggregation of melanophore pigment after removal of intermedin from the fluid bathing a piece of frog skin *in vitro* (Wright, 1955). By using a metabolic poison, iodoacetate, which inhibits glycolysis, Wright (1955) found that the melanophore is permanently expanded. If this can be interpreted to mean that the paling ("contraction") phase requires energy from intracellular glycolysis, then the role of intermedin might be to inhibit such glycolysis.

Another approach has been taken recently by Novales (1959) using isolated pieces of *Rana* skin in various media. He found that sodium-ion is required for skin darkening by intermedin, and that the action of the hormone is in proportion to the sodium concentration. He concluded that intermedin may act on the plasma membrane of the melanophore permitting local entry of sodium ion. Entry of the sodium ions may entrain water, and thus produce melanin dispersion through a gel-sol mechanism. An alternative explanation requires that a local electrical potential in the region of sodium ion entrance may set up a difference in electrical potential between the center and periphery of the melanophore. The melanin granules might then be dispersed by this potential, a sort of "intracellular electrophoresis." Such differences in potential have been actually demonstrated in the melanophores of fish by Kinosita (1953).

C. NEUROHYPOPHYSEAL HORMONES

It is known from numerous biological tests that the amphibian neurohypophysis contains hormonal factors which have pressor, antidiuretic and oxytocic activity (review in Sawyer *et al.*, 1960). By a combination of such tests, Sawyer *et al.* (1960) have identified the active substances

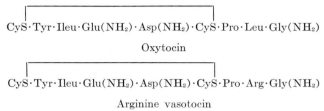

CyS·Tyr·Ileu·Glu(NH₂)·Asp(NH₂)·CyS·Pro·Leu·Gly(NH₂)

Oxytocin

CyS·Tyr·Ileu·Glu(NH₂)·Asp(NH₂)·CyS·Pro·Arg·Gly(NH₂)

Arginine vasotocin

Fig. 6. Molecular structures of oxytocin and arginine vasotocin.

in the amphibian pars nervosa as oxytocin and arginine vasotocin. Both of these are octapeptides. They differ only by the substitution of arginine for leucine at one position in the molecule (Katsoyannis and du Vigneaud, 1959) (Fig. 6). At least in the tested amphibian species there appears to be no vasopressin.

More recently, Acher *et al.* (1960) in a heroic experiment involving dissection of 20,000 pituitaries of *Rana esculenta* attempted a chemical separation and identification of neurohypophyseal hormones. They accumulated 2 gm of acetone-dried neurohypophysis-powder, and from this material by chromatography they separated three fractions. One fraction was identified as oxytocin; a second consisted mostly of arginine vasotocin; the third fraction, containing only slight biological activity, corresponded to arginine vasopressin.

The only physiological action which has been clearly identified with the neurohypophyseal hormones in the Amphibia is related to the movement of water and salts through certain membranes (Heller, 1945; Jorgensen, 1950; Ewer, 1952; Sawyer and Sawyer, 1952). The previously mentioned ability of vasopressin to induce molting in toads (Jorgensen and Nielsen, 1958) is believed to be an indirect effect, through stimulation of adenohypophyseal TSH-release. The effect upon water metabolism is produced by responses at three known sites: the mesonephros, the skin, the urinary bladder. More complete discussion of water and salt metabolism will be found in Chapter 5. The antidiuretic effect upon the mesonephros is measurable by a reduced volume of urine formed under standard conditions (Sawyer, 1956, 1957a,b) after injection of the hormone. The effect of neurohypophyseal hormone upon the skin can be demonstrated either in the intact animal by an increase in total body weight (the "Brunn effect," Brunn, 1921), or *in vitro* by mounting frog skin in a glass chamber which permits measurement of fluid volume transferred through the skin. The effect upon the bladder can be measured *in vitro* in a similar way to show net transfer (reabsorption) of fluid through the wall of the organ.

All three of the amphibian systemic responses to hormones of the pars nervosa are directed toward the hydration of the organism, or perhaps more exactly, toward counteracting dehydration. It is of interest that the fishes have these same hormones in their neurohypophyses but they do not respond to them in any of the three modes just described for the Amphibia (review in Pickford and Atz, 1957). In the phylogenetic sense, the class Amphibia is the first to be faced with the problem of water conservation. It is thus possible that the most primitive use of the hypothalamic-neurohypophyseal hormones is for "local" stimulation of adenohypophyseal secretion (Jorgensen and Larsen, 1960a). The pars nervosa, newly differentiated in the Amphibia for direct systemic distribution of these hormones may be, accordingly, the first morphological adaptation for the new endocrine mechanism for regulating water conservation (Sawyer and Sawyer, 1952; Sawyer, 1956; Wingstrand, 1959). In this same vein it is perhaps significant that aquatic amphibians are less responsive to neurohypophyseal hormones than terrestrial amphibians; aquatic tadpoles, although their pituitaries contain antidiuretic hormone, are relatively unresponsive to it until they approach metamorphosis (Howes, 1940; Delsol and Masnou, 1958).

Although it is possible that there may be in amphibians some kind of blood volume receptor (this question is discussed by Heller, 1957) it appears most likely that the stimulus to release of antidiuretic hormone is an increase in solute concentration in the body fluids. At least it has been found that injections of hypertonic salt solutions (which would *increase* body fluid volume) are the most effective stimulants for neurohypophyseal hormone release (Jorgensen and Rosenkilde, 1956; Eliassen and Jorgensen, 1951; Buchborn, 1956).

In earlier experiments in which the preoptico-hypophyseal tracts were cut near the median eminence of toads (Jorgensen and Rosenkilde, 1956) it was found that there is no diminished ability to react to dehydration, using the Brunn effect as the index. This paradoxical finding is apparently explained by later work of Jorgensen *et al.* (1960) who found that regeneration of a blood supply to the region of the cut ends of the preoptico-hypophyseal tract occurs within a few days. Thus, even though the original pars nervosa may degenerate, a new functional pars nervosa forms at a slightly removed site.

The manner in which antidiuretic hormone influences urinary water excretion has been the subject of much study (see review in Sawyer, 1957b). The observed reduction in urine volume could follow either or a decreased rate of glomerular filtration or an increased rate of tubular reabsorption or both. Actually both occur, although the response of the tubular phenomenon to antidiuretic hormone seems to predominate (Sawyer, 1957a,b). When the different amphibian neurohypophyseal hormones are tested separately for their antidiuretic action (Uranga and Sawyer, 1960) arginine vasotocin proves to be more than 500 times as effective as oxytocin, when tested in adult bullfrogs. Frog neurohypophysis extract has a similar 500-fold greater activity than oxytocin; this can be taken as another evidence for the identity of the amphibian antidiuretic principle with arginine vasotocin. The locus of hormonal action is the distal part of the nephron and only "osmotically free" water is involved (i.e.., water which would move in response to osmotic differences between blood and urine if the intervening membrane permitted). Thus, the hormone's action has been likened to an increasing in pore size of the cell membranes of the distal portion of the tubule.

A similarity has been found in the hormone responsiveness of the integument to antidiuretic hormone. In tests with intact animals, or with isolated amphibian skins *in vitro* (reviews in Heller, 1957) only the movement of osmotically free water can be accelerated by the hormone. If the external medium (on the outer surface of the skin) is isosmotic or hypertonic in comparison with the medium on the inside, the hormone stimulates no movement of water. It would seem that here, too, the hormone increases the relative permeability of the skin to water.

Recent work by Sawyer (1960a,b) on reabsorption of water from the urinary bladder of frogs under influence of antidiuretic hormone indicates that it, too, follows these principles.

Work by Ussing and his collaborators (see review by Ussing, 1960) as well as by others, has shown that isolated frog skins or urinary bladders are able to move sodium ion from the epidermal to dermal or serosal side by means of an active transport mechanism. This transport mechanism is associated with an electrochemical potential gradient, a "sodium battery" charge. Furthermore, the oxygen consumption of skin or urinary bladder is in direct proportion to the amount of sodium transported (Leaf and Dempsey, 1960; Leaf, 1960). Posterior pituitary extracts have been found to increase the active transport of sodium ion through skin, and through the urinary bladder of anurans, the so-called "natriferic" action (Acher *et al.*, 1960; Leaf and Dempsey, 1960; Sawyer, 1960a). Associated with the natriferic action of neurohypophyseal preparations is a precisely stimulated oxygen consumption. Leaf and Dempsey (1960) found that neurohypophyseal hormones stimulate oxygen consumption of isolated toad (*Bufo marinus*) bladders only if sodium is present in the bathing medium. A fixed proportion of 19 sodium ions was transported per molecule of O_2. Sawyer (1960b) identifies the natriferic principle in frog pituitaries as arginine vasotocin.

In summary, it appears that neurohypophyseal hormones act upon the skin, mesonephros, and urinary bladder to increase passive permeability of their membranes to water and salts and urea (Leaf, 1960), and to stimulate

TABLE I

MINIMAL EFFECTIVE DOSES OF ANTIDIURETIC HORMONE FOR RENAL ANTIDIURESIS
AND INCREASED INTEGUMENTARY WATER UPTAKE IN THE TOAD *Bufo bufo*[a]

	Commercial mammalian ADH (milliunits)	Mammalian ADH, extract of du Vigneaud (milliunits)
Renal antidiuresis	0.005	0.01
Increased integumentary water uptake	0.50	0.75

[a] From Buchborn (1956).

active transport of sodium. It is well to bear in mind that the adrenal corticoids, and perhaps thyroxine also, affect permeability of these membranes. Accordingly, discussion of endocrine control over these phenomena will be continued in later sections of this chapter.

Under conditions of minimal circulating levels of neurohypophyseal hormone it is of interest to know which of the targets of hormonal influence is the most sensitive. Using various doses of mammalian antidiuretic hormone and measuring the cutaneous and renal effects simultaneously, Buchborn (1956) found that the first renal response was obtained at a dose level $\frac{1}{75}$ to $\frac{1}{100}$ that required for the skin response (Table I). This would suggest that hormone-stimulated percutaneous transfer of water occurs only under extreme circumstances.

III. Thyroid Gland

A. MORPHOLOGY

The well known and spectacular action of the thyroid hormone upon amphibian metamorphosis (Chapter 8) has somewhat overshadowed the fact that little is known of the action of this hormone in adult amphibians. It remains to be shown clearly that the thyroid serves as important a role in adult amphibians as in mammals.

In almost all amphibian species the thyroid tissue is included in two well encapsulated distinctly separate organs. In Anura the glands usually are closely associated with a hyoid cartilage near the trachea, often being firmly bound to the cartilage by connective tissue. In many urodeles the glands are more widely separated and they are relatively superficial, just beneath the procoracoid, making them easy to remove surgically. The question of accessory thyroid tissue has been investigated rarely in Amphibia. Stone and Steinitz (1953) found numerous accessory thyroid follicles scattered among the muscles of the lower jaw and neck of *Triturus* (Fig. 7).

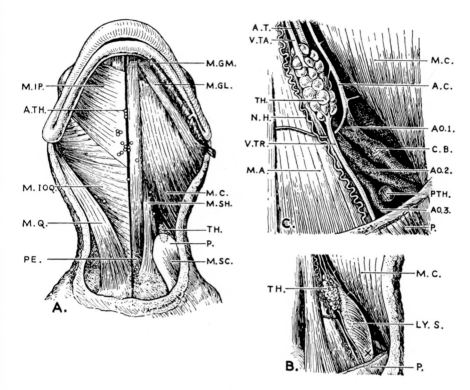

Fig. 7. A. Ventral view of lower jaw and pericardial region of *Triturus* with skin removed to reveal superficial muscle layer on right side and deeper muscle layer and site of thyroid gland (TH.) on left side. Sites of accessory thyroid follicles at varying depths are projected on surface as open circles (A.TH.).

B. Site of left thyroid gland (TH.) at higher magnification slightly tilted toward right. Large segment of cartilago procoracoidea (P.) is cut away to show relationship of thyroid gland (TH.) and lymph sac (LY.S.). Dorsal to the latter lie the carotid body and parathyroid gland (X) not shown in drawing.

C. At higher power same region as in "B" with lymph sac removed to show parathyroid (PTH.) and other details.

Abbreviations: A.C., A. carotis externa; A.T., A. thyreoidea; A.TH., Accessory thyroid follicles; AO.1, First aortic arch (= common carotid); AO.2, Second aortic arch (systemic); AO.3, Third aortic arch (= pulmo-cutan.); C.B., Carotid body; LY.S., Lateral lymph sac; M.A., M. abdominohyoideus; M.C., M. ceratohyoideus; M.GL., M. geniohyoideus lateralis; M.GM., M. geniohyoideus medalis; M.IOQ., M. inter ossa quadrata; M.IP., M. intermandibularis posterior; M.Q., M. quadratopectoralis; M.SC., M. supracoracoideus; M.SH., M. sternohyoideus; N.H., N. hypobranchialis; P., Cartilago procoracoidea; PE., Pericardium; PTH., Parathyroid gland; TH., Thyroid gland; V.TA., V. thyreoidea advehens; V.TR., V. thyreoidea revehens (= external jugular); X., Site of parathyroid gland behind lymph sac. From Stone and Steinitz (1953).

The interesting claim has been advanced for two species, *Typhlomolge rathbuni* and *Pelobates syriacus* (Uhlenhuth, 1923; Boschwitz, 1957) that the thyroid may be lacking altogether. In the case of *Typhlomolge* this was unconfirmed by later work (Gorbman, 1957), but the claim for *Pelobates* still stands. If this is so, then *Pelobates* is the only vertebrate known to be without a thyroid, and it is the only amphibian able to enter metamorphosis without one (Boschwitz, 1957).

B. THYROID GLAND FUNCTION

In microscopic structure it is difficult to distinguish the amphibian thyroid from that of other vertebrates. It is made up of vesicular follicles each of which consists of a single layer of epithelial cells surrounding a space filled with a viscous fluid, the colloid (Fig. 8). Research based principally upon the mammalian thyroid has shown that the glandular epithelium is able to transport iodide actively from the blood. The iodide

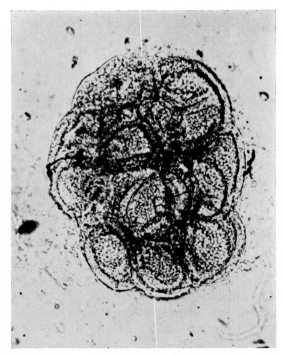

Fig. 8. Photograph of an entire lobe of thyroid gland of a tadpole of *Xenopus laevis*. In this semitransparent preparation the individual spherical follicles may be seen. Furthermore, it is clear that each follicle is lined by a cellular wall and is filled with a fluid (the "colloid"). Photograph by Prof. J. M. Dodd, Leeds.

is oxidized, and in the oxidized state it combines with tyrosine residues in the protein of the colloid. By condensation of pairs of iodinated tyrosines, thyroxine and triiodothyronine are formed, still attached to the protein (thyroglobulin). These two hormones are freed by intracolloidal hydrolysis of the thyroglobulin and they pass into the blood, apparently by diffusion.

Unfortunately, but few of these biochemical events in the synthesis of thyroid hormone have been investigated in amphibians. Numerous studies have been made of larval and adult Amphibia by means of radioautography of radioiodine (Gorbman and Evans, 1941; Dent and Hunt, 1952; Saxen et al., 1957). With the usual application of this technique the presence and distribution of protein bound radioiodine is revealed. Accordingly, such studies show that the amphibian thyroid, like that of all other vertebrates, accumulates and metabolizes iodine. The chemical form of this protein-coupled radioiodine in the thyroid of frogs, toads, and salamanders has been found to be iodotyrosine and a relatively small proportion of thyroxine, and perhaps triiodothyronine (Saxen et al., 1957; Donoso and Trivelloni, 1958b; Berg et al., 1959; Dundee and Gorbman, 1960). Thus, the available evidence indicates that the amphibian thyroid hormones are the same as those of other vertebrate animals.

In a quantitative sense, however, such experiments utilizing radioiodine have shown that the *level* of iodine metabolism in adult amphibians is extremely low. That is, the thyroid will accumulate only a very small fraction (usually less than 3%) of an administered dose of I^{131}. The most active amphibian thyroidal accumulation of radioactive iodine which has been reported is 9.3%, found by Donoso and Trivelloni (1958b) in adult toads. Only in frog tadpoles, for a brief period during the metamorphic climax (see Chapter 8) does the thyroid exhibit the great appetite for I^{131} that is found in many other vertebrates.

An interesting question with regard to thyroid function may be asked for those amphibian species which are truly neotenous (e.g., *Necturus*), or show at breeding age various anatomical signs of incomplete transformation from the larval form (e.g., *Amphiuma*). Neoteny, or partial neoteny could be due to either a failure to produce enough thyroid hormone or to an insensitivity of development to thyroid hormone. Swingle (1922) showed that the thyroids of *Necturus* contain enough hormone to cause metamorphosis when implanted into frog tadpoles, yet this species, as well as *Proteus*, is completely neotenous, and unresponsive to large doses of injected thyroid hormone. It was found by Schreiber (1933) that pieces of axolotl skin transplanted into thyroid-treated *Proteus* will undergo metamorphosis, though the surrounding host's skin remains "larval." This would seem to establish the fact that a low order of sensitivity, if not complete insensitivity, to thyroid hormone characterizes neotenous forms of the type like *Necturus* and *Proteus*. On the other hand, the neotenous Mexican axolotl, and certain neotenous cave salamanders (e.g., *Eurycea tynerensis*, Kezer, 1952) will respond to thyroxine by partial or complete metamorphosis (reviewed by Lynn and Wachowski, 1952). Accordingly, various grades of loss of thyroxine sensitivity may be found among amphibian species.

When the thyroids of neotenous species are analyzed for their content of newly labeled hormone (after I^{131} administration) it is found that such hormone is formed at an unusually slow rate when compared with other vertebrates. However, this rate of hormone formation is not particularly poor when compared with the same phenomenon in metamorphosing amphibian species (Kaye, 1961). The rate of thyroid hormone formation in adult *Necturus* and *Amphiuma* is so low that there seems to be good reason to suspect that this hormone plays no physiological role in these forms (Kobayashi and Gorbman, unpublished).

C. ACTION OF THYROID HORMONE IN ADULTS

Investigation of the action of thyroid hormone in postlarval amphibians has been confined largely to three areas: (a) action upon oxidative and other metabolism, (b) action upon integumentary structure, and (c) action upon nervous function.

In general, efforts to stimulate oxygen consumption in adult amphibians by treatment with thyroid hormone have been mostly unsuccessful (Gayda, 1922; Henschel and Steuber, 1935; Issekutz *et al.*, 1943). Accordingly, it has been concluded by most reviewers of this subject (von Buddenbrock, 1950; Lynn and Wachowski, 1951; Gorbman, 1959) that an influence of thyroid hormone upon oxygen consumption in Amphibia is uncertain. In any case, it is not as readily or as clearly demonstrable as in the warm-blooded vertebrates. The exceptional claims of thyroid stimulated respiratory metabolism that remain in the literature must be mentioned so their nature may be realized. Taylor (1939) found that oxygen consumption of thyroidectomized *Triturus* declined slowly after an initial rise just after the operation. Conversely, he found that thyroid implants increased oxygen consumption after an initial decline. Warren (1940) was able to increase oxygen consumption in *Rana pipiens* by thyroid hormone injection. Donoso and Trivelloni (1958a) have reported that thyroxine or triiodothyronine injections into adult *Bufo* stimulate oxygen consumption. Two unusual claims, both more than 25 years old, have been made with regard to the influence of thyroid hormone upon respiration of frog tissue slices. When thyroxine (10^{-8} to 10^{-18} M) was incubated with frog muscle slices, von Euler (1933) found no respiratory stimulus with

respect to controls unless the oxygen content of the atmosphere was reduced to 5 to 10%. This suggested a stimulus of anaerobic metabolism.
Haarman (1936) reported the curious fact that thyroxine in the incubating
medium of frog muscle tissue fragments *in vitro* stimulated oxygen consumption at a concentration of 10^{-16}, a remarkably low concentration,
but not at 10^{-15} or 10^{-17}! More recently Donoso (1960) measured the
respiration of tissue slices from thyroidectomized and thyroid hormone
injected toads (*Bufo paracnemis* and *B. arenarum*). Tissues (kidney,
heart, muscle, liver) from thyroidectomized animals did not differ from
controls. Kidney and heart slices from toads injected with 1.0 mg of
thyroxine or triiodothyronine (an extremely high dose) daily for 4 days
showed 40% and 23% increases in oxygen consumption, respectively, over
similar tissues from untreated toads. Respiration of muscle and liver,
the tissues contributing most to the mass of the animal, was not different
from controls. It is clear that the entire question of a respiratory metabolic effect upon amphibians of thyroid hormone *in vivo* or *in vitro* needs
careful study with modern procedures. The data we now have are inconsistent and cannot be related to findings in other vertebrate groups.

Only scattered evidence exists which relates thyroid function to other
phases of metabolism. Thyroid hormone increases the level of urinary
nitrogen in summer frogs, but not in winter frogs (Mansfeld and Lanczos,
1936). It is now well established that thyroid hormones cause dehydration of tadpoles at the time of metamorphic stimulation. It is not known
whether this effect is exerted through the mesonephros, or other endocrines,
or through a direct cellular action upon water metabolism and distribution. Another frequently reported observation is the body wastage in frogs
and salamanders given large dosages of thyroid hormone. The mechanism
of this easily observable consequence of thyroid hormone action is unknown. A suggestion may be found in the work of Levinsky and Sawyer
(1952) who reported that removal of the anterior pituitary prevents the
water uptake through the skin of frogs that were injected with an extract
of the neurohypophysis (i.e., adenohypophysectomy blocks the "water
balance response"). If such animals are given ACTH the water balance
response is partly restored; if they are given ACTH plus thyroxine it is
completely restored. Accordingly, thyroxine, together with the adrenocorticoids and neurohypophyseal hormones, may influence or condition
the permeability of cells of the skin, the mesonephros, or other organs, to
water and/or salts.

It may be mentioned at this point that thyroid hormones also have
been found to influence "maturation" of certain biochemical systems—a
not surprising finding in view of the general maturational action of these
hormones. Wald (1946) has observed in tadpoles that thyroid hormone

accelerates differentiation of the visual pigment of the eye from the larval type, porphyropsin, to the adult type rhodopsin. Paik and Cohen (1960) found that thyroxine treatment of tadpoles stimulated synthesis of carbamyl phosphate synthetase in the liver. This enzyme forms a part of Krebs Henseleit urea metabolic cycle which undergoes biochemical differentiation at metamorphosis.

The clear relationship between thyroid state and structure of the skin has been recognized in the amphibians—as in all other vertebrates—for many years. In both anurans and urodeles it is useful to separate the phenomenon of molting into two normally consecutive processes of epidermal proliferation and cornification on the one hand, and shedding or sloughing of cornified epidermis on the other hand. After thyroidectomy in most, but not all, adult amphibians periodic sloughing is inhibited or completely arrested. However, proliferation and cornification as a rule continue, and produce eventually a greatly thickened epidermis. The thickened epidermis is easily recognizable, by color and texture, to the unaided eye (Adams *et al.*, 1932; Adams and Grierson, 1932). The accumulation of epidermis after thyroidectomy raises the question of whether the rate of epidermal mitotic proliferation is affected by thyroid state. Data to clarify this question are relatively few but they indicate that thyroxine accelerates and thyroidectomy inhibits cellular hyperplasia (Quast, 1939). Thyroidectomy in newts has been found to have a complex effect, an initial acceleration followed eventually (140 days) by a slowing in epidermal mitotic activity (Taylor, 1936). Thyroxine treatment stimulates sloughing of superficial cornified layers of the skin in all amphibians, even in those in which sloughing persists after thyroidectomy (Ungar, 1933). A single thyroxine dosage of about 50 μg in either urodeles or anurans may produce a "burst of molts," a rapid succession of sloughings of epidermis. This has led Jorgensen and Larsen (1960b) to conclude that periodicity of molting in Amphibia is governed by absolute level of thyroid hormone and does not depend upon a cyclic release or increase of thyroid hormone. Jorgensen and Larsen (1960b) also have made the interesting observation that adrenocortical hormones are involved in epidermal sloughing in those anurans (species of *Bufo*) in which sloughing persists after thyroidectomy.

The action of thyroid hormone upon the nervous system is another important, but imperfectly understood topic. In other classes of cold-blooded vertebrates evidence for such an action has been adduced from behavioral changes which follow a change in thyroid level (reviewed in Gorbman, 1959). Observations upon such behavioral changes have not been made in the Amphibia, but other evidence of a fundamental relationship between thyroid and nervous function exists. The embryonic differentiation and development of the central nervous system in tadpoles is locally stimulated by implants of thyroxine-containing agar pellets into the brain. Using this procedure Kollros and his collaborators (Kollros, 1942, 1943, 1959; Kollros and Pepernik, 1952; Pesetsky and Kollros, 1956) have produced differentiation of the blink reflex, or of Mauthner's cells on one side of the brain when the "control" side, lacking a thyroxine pellet, remained in the relatively undifferentiated state. May and Mugard (1955) have found that the stimulating action of thyroid hormone upon the brains of frog tadpoles is paralleled by a stimulated mitotic rate. Evidence of thyroxine stimulation of threshold sensitivity of peripheral nerves of adult frogs has been furnished by LeGrand and Ajoulat (1931). They found that thyroid treatment lowers the chronaxie and rheobase of sciatic nerve-muscle preparations. Chronaxie and rheobase are expressions of sensitivity of nerve to minimal electrical stimuli.

It was claimed earlier that thyroxine has no effect upon the heart rate of frogs (Warren, 1940), as it does in mammals. In an older report, Davis and Hastings (1935) stated that the oxygen consumption of the isolated frog heart is stimulated by addition of thyroxine. More recently, Kleinfeld *et al.* (1958) showed that the isolated perfused frog heart is stimulated by triiodothyronine as well as by thyroxine. The stimulation appears to be relatively specific since it is not produced by thyronine.

It is generally agreed (Allen, 1918, 1929; Hoskins and Hoskins, 1919; Chang, 1955) that thyroidectomy of amphibians has relatively little effect upon reproductive development. This relative independence from thyroid state has been held to be at the basis for the neotenic condition (ability to reproduce despite a failure to metamorphose) in certain amphibian species. However, in a positive sense, it has been found that thyroid treatment of frogs will accelerate spermatogenesis (Warren, 1940), though the mechanism of this stimulation has never been further studied.

Limb regeneration in young salamanders has been found to be inhibited by thyroidectomy, or by hypophysectomy (Speidel, 1929; Richardson, 1940). Treatment of such animals with small doses of thyroid hormones restores regenerative capacity. Treatment with large doses of hormone does not further stimulate regeneration, but on the contrary is inhibitory because it causes premature differentiation of the undifferentiated blastema tissues which must be available for successful regeneration. It is of interest that lens regeneration has been found to be independent of thyroid state by Stone and Steinitz (1953).

IV. Parathyroid Glands

Aside from some older morphological studies, there has been surprisingly little attention paid to the parathyroid glands of Amphibia. They have been known for many years, since so designated by Maurer in 1887, as

Epithelkörperchen, or the English equivalent "epithelial bodies." In both anurans and urodeles Maurer has illustrated two pairs of parathyroids originating from the *ventral* wings of the third and fourth pharyngeal pouches, while thymus arises from the *dorsal* wings. The dorsoventral relationships of parathyroids and thymi in reptiles, birds, and mammals are just the reverse of this. Parathyroid tissue is unknown in the fishes, so that the Amphibia appear to be the first vertebrate group in which such glands are found as organized bodies.

Adult amphibians have two pairs of small encapsulated parathyroids which usually remain close to the external jugular vein, and lateral to it (Maurer, 1887; Scholz, 1933; Romeis, 1926; Waggener, 1929). In histological structure they are made up of whorls or cords of cells (Romeis, 1926; Waggener, 1929; Cortelyou *et al.,* 1960). There is a distinct annual cycle in histological structure. In winter frogs the parathyroids appear degenerate, with nuclei pycnotic and cytoplasm disorganized and highly vacuolated. A regeneration of normal structure occurs in the spring (Cortelyou *et al.,* 1960).

Waggener (1930) found that parathyroidectomized *Rana catesbeiana* survive less than 3 days. In the period preceding death they develop symptoms resembling those seen in parathroidectomized mammals, including nervous and muscular hyperirritability, prolonged contracture or tetanus of limb musculature, difficult locomotion and breathing. None of these symptoms was seen if only two of the four parathyroids were removed. In addition, Waggener found that the blood calcium level fell about 30%. In contrast, parathyroidectomized salamanders (*Salamandra atra* and *S. maculosa,* Scholz, 1933) and frogs (*Rana temporaria,* Romeis, 1926; *Hyla aurea,* Kuffler, 1945) have been reported to live for long periods, showing no symptoms like those described for *R. catesbeiana.*

The most careful study in this field is the recent one of Cortelyou *et al.* (1960). They found that completely parathyroidectomized frogs (*Rana pipiens*) displayed none of the external hypoparathyroid symptoms reported by Waggener. Tests of sensitivity and response of sciatic nerve-gastrocnemius muscle preparations showed no significant deviation from normal. On the other hand Cortelyou and his co-workers found that calcium metabolism was clearly disturbed. Blood calcium was greatly reduced and urinary excretion of calcium was increased after parathyroidectomy (Fig. 9), although the time required for development of these changes was much greater than usual. The plasma phosphorus is increased, but declines again several weeks after parathyroidectomy (Cortelyou, 1960). Urinary phosphorus excretion is increased, as in mammals, and the high level of phosphaturia is maintained for about 10 days. Repeated injections of a mammalian "parathormone" extract (Cortelyou, personal com-

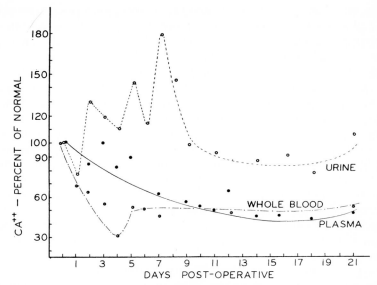

Fig. 9. Changes in urinary and serum calcium concentrations, in terms of per cent of the normal concentrations, after parathyroidectomy of the frog, *Rana catesbeiana*. From Cortelyou (1960a).

munication) into *R. pipiens* does not significantly alter plasma calcium concentrations, though it causes a sustained increase in urinary excretion of calcium. The parathormone injections cause a fall in plasma phosphorus, but no significant change in urinary phosphorus. These consequences of parathormone injection differ in some respects from those seen in mammals, and suggest basic differences between mammals and amphibians in calcium and phosphorus metabolism. Continued work in this field should be enlightening and of great interest.

There is clearly a need for further research to clarify the role of parathyroid hormone in the mineral metabolism and physiology of the Amphibia. This is of particular importance since it is in the amphibians, in the phylogenetic sense, that the parathyroid glands appear. Accordingly, their physiological adaptive value for amphibians would be essential to evaluate more accurately.

V. Islets of Langerhans

A. MORPHOLOGY

Among the amphibians, as well as in all other vertebrates, it is clear that the pancreatic islets of Langerhans, apparently through production of insulin, are concerned in the regulation of metabolism of carbohydrate. It is well to bear in mind that other endocrines also affect this phase of metabolism (hypophyseal ACTH and STH, adrenaline, glucagon, thyroxine, adrenal corticoids). Insulin is secreted into the hepatic portal system; thus, the most direct object of its action is probably the liver. However, the extent to which the hormone also influences peripheral utilization of glucose is imperfectly understood. Additional complexities in this picture are added by the variability in diet, stage of the life cycle, and season of the year as they frequently affect any of the above listed endocrine factors. The complexity of the analysis of the role of insulin in amphibian carbohydrate metabolism is mentioned at this point since it may be at the base of some of the apparently conflicting reports now in the literature. Furthermore, we must be prepared to find that somewhat different endocrine mechanisms regulate carbohydrate metabolism in different vertebrate groups. Indeed, such a claim has been made to explain certain differences between anurans and urodeles (Miller and Wurster, 1959).

The pancreatic islets of Amphibia are scattered histologically distinct cellular units within the pancreas. They were first described by Diamare (1899) in *Triton cristatus*. In contrast to the acinar exocrine tissue, they are composed of branching cords of cells which have no relation to the pancreatic ducts in adults. Their general anatomical characteristics have been studied in a variety of amphibian species (see references to earlier literature in Miller, 1960; Miller and Wurster, 1959; Seiden, 1945; Janes, 1938) and they have been found to be relatively uniform in this respect. From the physiological point of view it is important to know how many secretory cell types there are in the islets since the different types are now believed to secrete different hormones. In birds and mammals at least, appropriate staining reveals cells of the α-type which are believed to secrete glucagon, the hyperglycemic factor and β-cells which are generally agreed to be the source of insulin (Foa *et al.*, 1957).

Unfortunately there is little uniformity or conformity in the various descriptions of the islet cell types in different amphibians. This situation is summarized in Table II. A single cell type (*Taricha*) and as many as five types (*Rana temporaria*) have been reported. It is clear that further work is required to clarify the question, but a conservative tentative view based upon the most recent work is that there are two classes of amphibian islets. In one class (first two columns of Table II) there is only a single cell type or a principal cell type and a presumably inactive transitional type. In the second class (third column of Table II) there are two cell types. In the first class the cell type is most likely equivalent to the β-cell of mammals (Miller and Wurster, 1959); in the second class a small

TABLE II

NUMBERS OF PANCREATIC ENDOCRINE CELL TYPES

One	One and transitional	Two	Five
Taricha (*Triturus*) *torosa* (Miller, 1953)	*Triton cristatus* (Fischer, 1912) (Kolossow, 1927)	*Triton cristatus* (Diamare, 1899)	*Rana temporaria* (Saguchi, 1921)
		Rana japonica (Hirata, 1934)	
	Rana temporaria (Barrington, 1951)		
		Rana clamitans *Rana catesbeiana* *Rana sylvatica* *Hyla versicolor* (Janes, 1938)	
	Rana fusca (Fischer, 1912)		
		Rana pipiens (Seiden, 1945)	
		Rana catesbeiana (Wright, 1959)	
		Bufo viridis (Diamare, 1899)	
		Bufo arenarum (DeRobertis and Primavesi, 1939)	

proportion of α-cells is also present, particularly near the edges of the islets (see Seiden, 1945).

As in other vertebrate classes, the amphibian islet tissue develops from primitive pancreatic ducts. Completion of anatomical and functional differentiation of islets is relatively late in both urodele and anuran species (reviewed by Frye, 1959), approximately at the time of metamorphosis. Since most amphibian species feed actively during the long larval period it would be interesting to know how carbohydrate metabolism is regulated during the premetamorphic period.

B. FUNCTION OF ISLET TISSUE

Analysis of the endocrine role of the amphibian pancreas began with pancreatectomy experiments performed soon after the illuminating work of von Mering and Minkowski (1890) on the dog. Marcuse (1894) and Loewit (1910) showed that depancreatized frogs (*Rana temporaria*) de-

velop diabetes mellitus. In most instances in such frogs there was a gly-
cosuria within a day after pancreatectomy and a marked increase in urine
volume (polyuria) and at the same time a decrease in liver and muscle
glycogen.

Further analysis, mostly after 1925, was designed to probe into the roles
of the liver, the pituitary, and the adrenal glands in the diabetes of pancreatectomy. In the hands of B. A. Houssay and his students, the toad,
Bufo arenarum provided much information concerning endocrine regulation of carbohydrate metabolism, and this information served to orient
much of the research which followed in which mammals were used (this
work is reviewed in Houssay, 1959). A wide variety of amphibians, mostly
anurans, has been made diabetic by surgical pancreatectomy: *Rana temporaria, R. catesbeiana, R. pipiens, Bufo arenarum, B. marinus, B. paracnemis, B. d'Orbigny, Leptodactylus ocellatus, Ceratophrys ornata,* and
Taricha torosa. In most instances the diabetic condition terminates in
coma and death. The rate of development of diabetes and its fatal termination depends upon temperature (Houssay and Biasotti, 1931). Particularly in summer *Bufo,* recovery may frequently be observed, marked by
a return of normal blood sugar values. In such instances Dosne (1943)
reported that pancreatic and islet tissue regenerate from the biliary ducts.

It was found early that removal of the liver "protects" the depancreatized amphibian. That is, the liver is necessary for full development of the
diabetes (Wagner and Allen, 1929), since it serves, no doubt, as the
principal source of carbohydrate for the observed hyperglycemia and gly-
cosuria. The reduction in blood sugar by hepatectomy of diabetic toads is
proportional to the amount of liver removed (Foglia, 1942). Hepatectomy
alone lowers the blood sugar to minimum levels so that the animal dies in
a state of hypoglycemia. In fact, pancreatectomy appears to be the only
experimental means of raising blood sugar and lengthening survival of
hepatectomized toads. Anterior pituitary hormones, which will raise blood
sugar levels in depancreatized toads (see below) have no effect in hepatectomized animals (Houssay and Rietti, 1950).

One of the major contributions of the earlier work with *Bufo arenarum*
was the demonstration that hypophysectomy is an effective means of reducing blood sugar in diabetic toads after pancreatectomy (Houssay and
Biasotti, 1930, 1931). Anterior pituitary implants, or extracts, on the
other hand, aggravate the diabetes. The "diabetogenic factor" of the pars
distalis is not species specific since pituitaries of other amphibian species,
or of fish, reptiles, birds, and mammals are active in *Bufo arenarum*
(Houssay, 1959). When single purified mammalian pituitary hormones
are injected to learn which of them is diabetogenic it is found that growth
hormone, STH is most active, ACTH is slightly less active, and prolactin

has slight activity (Houssay and Anderson, 1949) in depancreatized anurans.

In the depancreatized salamander *Taricha* (*Triturus*), in contrast with the anurans just described, Miller and Wurster (1959) have found hypophysectomy relatively ineffective in reducing blood sugar level. Hypophysectomized *Taricha* have a very low blood glucose level of about 8 mg per 100 ml. Pancreatectomy performed within a month after hypophysectomy causes a rise in blood glucose to levels about the same as pancreatectomy alone will produce (170–200 mg per 100 ml). However, if the pancreatectomy is delayed until 2 or 3 months after hypophysectomy then somewhat less severe hyperglycemias result (70 to 140 mg per 100 ml). Since during this interval the interrenal (adrenal) gland of hypophysectomized *Taricha* regresses, Miller and Wurster (1959) suggest that the interrenal is the pituitary-dependent diabetogenic agent in *Taricha*. That this is a reasonable suggestion is indicated by the diabetogenicity of pure ACTH and of adrenal glucocorticoids, particularly hydrocortisone (Houssay, 1959; Miller and Wurster, 1959).

Differences between *Taricha*, as described by Miller, and other amphibians (principally anurans) extend also to their responses to insulin and alloxan. In frogs insulin produces a hypoglycemia but requires about 24 hours (Hemmingsen, 1925). In *Taricha* the hypoglycemia is produced more quickly and responses are obtained to doses as low as 10 units per kilogram of body weight. The β-cells of the pancreatic islets are injured by alloxan and a hyperglycemia usually follows in frogs and toads (Seiden, 1945; Houssay, 1959). In *Taricha* alloxan affects neither islet structure nor blood sugar.

Although the islet β-cells of *Taricha* are unresponsive to alloxan, they are caused to lose their cytoplasmic granules by artificially created high levels of blood sugar after glucose injection. Hydrocortisone, which causes blood sugar to more than double, also leads to β-cell degranulation (Miller and Wurster, 1959). Glucagon, the hyperglycemic factor of mammals, has no effect upon *Taricha*. It is of great interest that alloxan injected into an amphibian which has been reported to have α-cells in its pancreatic islets, *Rana catesbeiana*, causes a rapid development of hyperglycemia (Wright, 1959).

Very little research has been done with amphibians in analysis of the mechanism of action of insulin. The direct nature of this action upon the liver was shown by Kepinov (1938) who perfused insulin through isolated toads' livers and found that it caused a drop in the amount of glucose in the effluent fluid. In summer frogs' livers this response was obtained within a half hour. In livers from winter frogs it was necessary to perfuse the insulin for more than 4 hours before hepatic glycogenolysis was affected.

Furthermore, adrenaline and insulin are directly antagonistic when tested on the isolated toad's liver. Perfusion with adrenaline leads to a release of about 6.7 mg of glucose per 100 ml of perfusion fluid. Addition of insulin to the medium reduces this to 0.4 mg of glucose.

More recently Norman and Hiestand (1960) have studied the effect of insulin *in vitro* upon the penetration of the unmetabolized sugar xylose into frog muscles (*R. pipiens*). As little as 4 milliunits per milliliter of mammalian insulin in the incubation medium produced a relatively rapid penetration of xylose into the muscle cells when certain control materials (cortisol, thyronine) were without effect. However, during the time of active penetration by sugar (glucose was also included in the incubation medium) there was no change in muscle glycogen, according to Norman and Hiestand. This apparent difference from mammalian insulin-induced sugar penetration and subsequent glycogenesis has no ready explanation. In other *in vitro* studies (Gourley, 1957; Manery *et al.*, 1956) it has been found (as in mammals) that insulin increases muscle tissue oxygen consumption.

VI. Adrenal Gland

A. MORPHOLOGY

In the Amphibia, as well as in the teleostean fishes, the adrenal tissue is more intimately associated with the kidney than it is in other vertebrate groups. In the anurans adrenal tissue is found as two strips recognizably different in color and texture in the ventral surface of each kidney (Fig. 10). The urodele adrenal is not so consolidated. Instead it is found in the form of islets upon the ventral surface, or embedded in the kidney, or lying between the two kidneys. Adrenalectomy is extremely difficult because of the injury to the kidney which these anatomical relationships make unavoidable. However, in some amphibians seemingly successful adrenalectomy, or at least adrenal insufficiency has been imposed by cautery of the adrenal tissue.

At least three kinds of cells have been described in amphibian adrenal tissue. In one type the "chromaffin" staining reaction may be produced, and such cells may be considered equivalent to the medullary adrenal tissue of higher vertebrates. A second type of cell contains numerous lipid inclusions and may be considered equivalent to the interrenal or cortical adrenal tissue of other vertebrates. A third type, the "summer cells of Stilling" contain densely eosinophilic material, which may be glycoprotein in nature (Verne and Delsol, 1956) stainable by the PAS reaction (Maillet, 1960). The cells of Stilling vary greatly in proportion to the other types and may be absent, apparently, from urodele amphibian adrenals. *Rana esculenta*

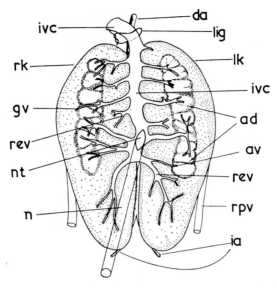

Fig. 10. Diagram of the anatomical relations of the amphibian adrenal glands, and the method of ligation of caval vein for cannulation of adrenocorticoid—containing blood. Abbreviations: ad, adrenal gland; av, adrenal efferent veins; da, dorsal aorta; gv, gonadal vein; ia, iliac arteries; ivc, inferior vena cava; lig, ligature; lk, left kidney; n, needle of syringe; nt, tip of needle; rev, renal efferent vein; rk, right kidney; rpv, renal portal vein. From Chester Jones *et al.* (1959).

has been described as having a particularly high proportion of these cells (Stilling, 1898), most abundant in the summer time. There is no known equivalent for the cells of Stilling in the adrenals of other vertebrate groups, and their function is completely unknown. The possibility that they may serve as part of an integrated endocrine mechanism is raised by the fact that they seem responsive to pituitary ACTH. Maillet (1960) reports that their glycoprotein (PAS-positive) granules are depleted in *R. esculenta* after treatment with ACTH.

The chromaffin cells of the amphibian adrenal tissue are neuro-ectodermal, being derived from the embryonic neural crest. The cortical-equivalent cells and the Stilling cells are mesodermal in origin.

B. CHROMAFFIN TISSUE

The chromaffin tissue was so named because of the brownish color produced in it after treatment with chrome salts and other reagents. It is known from more recent work that the chromaffin reaction is due to the formation of brown melanin-like substances (Bennett, 1941) and that the probable precursor materials for this pigment are the easily oxidized substances adrenaline and noradrenaline (West, 1955).

Adrenaline was the first hormone to be isolated (1901) and synthesized (1904). The demonstration and isolation of noradrenaline followed after a period of about 45 years. The proportion of adrenaline to noradrenaline in adrenal medullary tissue varies widely with species, age, and physiological state. West (1955) has found approximately equal amounts of adrenaline and noradrenaline in adrenal tissue of a frog and a toad. In this sense these amphibians fall approximately midway in a range in which avian and elasmobranch adrenals contain 60% to 80% noradrenaline, and rabbits and guinea pigs as little as 2%. Since the pharmacological properties of adrenaline and noradrenaline are somewhat different when tested in mammals and birds, the interesting question remains whether different cells are responsible for secretion of the two substances, and whether they can be released separately. Other complicating factors in the analysis of adrenal medullary physiology are the presence of accessory parabangliar chromaffin tissue which also forms catechol amines of unknown adrenaline-noradrenaline ratio, and the contribution of the sympathetic nerve endings of catechol amines, presumably mostly noradrenaline. The latter possibility was demonstrated in the classic work of Loewi (1936) using the isolated double frog heart preparation. Stimulation of the sympathetic nerve of one heart causes the second heart to bet faster, even though it is connected to the first heart only by perfusion fluid. Even before Loewi, O'Connor (1912) used the Löwen-Trendelenburg frog leg preparation (see below) to show that an adrenaline-like substance is released after stimulation of the splanchnic nerve. Another related amine, 5-hydroxytryptamine or serotonin, which resembles adrenaline in some of its actions, is in relatively high concentration in parts of the central nervous system and in amphibian skin. The discussion of the relationship of adrenal medullary tissue and nervous system cannot be included here, but may be found in recent reviews (Welsh, 1959).

Because of the early availability of pure adrenaline, this substance has been tested extensively for its action in amphibians, particularly with respect to integumentary pigmentation and cardiovascular functions. Relatively little is yet known of the action of noradrelanine.

The fatal dose of adrenaline injected into frogs (Bayer, 1929) has been found to be 0.25 to 0.1 mg per kilogram. Most effects of adrenaline observed in experiments using amphibians or isolated amphibian tissues require concentrations of approximately $1:10^5$ or $1:10^6$. However some responses have been reported at extraordinarily low concentrations: $1:10^8$ can affect the heart (Sollman and Barlow, 1926) or increase permeability of frog skin to salts (Jorgensen, 1947). Oxygen consumption of minced frog muscle tissue was found increased by an adrenaline concentration as low as $1:10^{11}$ (Ahlgren, 1925). Within this great range it is clear that some of the observed responses to adrenaline must be considered by pharmacological interest only, and it may be thought doubtful whether they occur under any normal circumstances.

Much attention has been paid to the actions of adrenaline on the amphibian cardiovascular system. The Löwen-Trendelenburg test for adrenaline was frequently used in earlier research and was based on the readily observed (Löwen, 1904) vasoconstriction in the web of the frog's foot and in other parts of the leg after infusion with the hormone. In the Löwen-Trendelenburg test the abdominal aorta is perfused at a constant pressure with saline solutions containing various concentrations of hormone, and the rate of fluid effluent is measured in the anterior abdominal vein. The usual response is a decreased flow rate due to vasoconstriction. A minimum dose of 1.0 ml of $1:10^5$ adrenaline injected into the dorsal lymph space of anurans (Schneider, 1926) has been found effective. However, under certain circumstances adrenaline perfusion of amphibian tissues has been found to produce vasodilation (Wehland, 1922; Kono, 1938). The blood vessels of various internal visceral structures consistently respond to adrenaline in a manner different from the Löwen-Trendelenburg system. Amphibian adrenal vessels dilate (Wertheimer, 1922) as do hepatic vessels (Morita, 1915). There is disagreement concerning the adrenaline vasomotor response in lung, Adler (1921) and Rothlin (1920) having observed slight vasodilation in *Rana esculenta*, while Matsumoto (1940) reported vasoconstriction in a toad. The digestive tract of frogs was found by Dixon (1902) to respond to adrenaline, as to sympathetic stimulation, by vasoconstriction. However in the esophagus the opposite has been observed in frogs and toads (Boruttau, 1899).

In general, adrenaline has been found to cause constriction of the glomerular arterioles of the amphibian kidney (Zuckerstein, 1917; Wertheimer, 1922). The renal effect is of obvious importance with respect to excretory function. Richards and his collaborators (1927) found that adrenaline given to frogs intravenously in doses as small as 1.0 ml of $1:10^6$ caused dilation of glomerular capillaries due to a valve-like constriction of efferent vessels. Larger doses, by this means reduce the number of "active" glomeruli and the number of open pathways in any one glomerulus.

The nature of the action of adrenaline upon the amphibian heart *in situ*, or *in vitro*, has been found to depend upon dose or concentration of the hormone. Aside from Loewi's (1936) general observations of cardiac stimulation others have described similar phenomena and even refined the experimental conditions so that the frog's heart could be used for bioassay of adrenaline (e.g., Lutz, 1933; Satow, 1938; Lissak, 1939a,b). The variable dose-response effects of adrenaline in isolated frog hearts, with actual injury at higher dose levels, have been described by Sollman and Barlow (1926) and Colombini (1940). Tiffeneau and Beauvallet (1938) described the gradual decrease in response by the perfused frog's heart when the same adrenaline solution is continually recirculated through the heart. They found that this "inactivated" cardiac perfusion fluid was similarly inactive when tested in a fresh heart but that it had undiminished potency when tested for ability to elicit upon intestinal mucular contraction. They therefore proposed that a cardiac inhibitor or adrenaline antagonist was formed by the perfused frog's heart.

Vascular permeability is another phase of adrenaline action in amphibians which has been investigated although, unfortunately, there is not complete agreement in reported observations. The permeability of vessels in various frog tissues (muscle, skin, intestine) is decreased by lower concentrations ($1:10^7$) and increased by higher concentrations ($1:10^6$) (Gellhorn, 1933; Parrot et al., 1944). Kiuchi (1936) found the reverse true by testing the permeability of frog mesenteric vessels to Congo red within a narrow range of concentrations near $1:10^6$; a slightly higher concentration of adrenaline *decreased* permeability to Congo red; a slightly lower concentration increased it.

It is well known that adrenaline ($1:10^4$ solution) causes a blanching in color of amphibians due to concentration of the pigment in integumentary melanophores (Lieben, 1906). Such blanching is temporary and is reversed in a few hours. Some earlier workers claimed that this effect was produced through stimulation of nerve fibers, and therefore requires an intact animal. However, it has become well established that melanophores in isolated pieces of frog skin *in vitro* respond readily to adrenaline (Wright, 1947, 1955; Novales, 1959) by melanin concentration (color lightening), and, thus, it is a direct cellular response to the hormone. The color responses of certain intact amphibians to adrenaline are sometimes complex and do not conform to these generalizations. For example, Geiringer (1938) found in a European frog that adrenaline causes a brief blanching, and then a prolonged darkening. Since the secondary darkening is preventable by atropine treatment Geiringer believed it was due to reflex parasympathetic stimulation. In those frog species which respond suitably to rough handling, an "excitement pallor" is often induced (Parker and Scatterty, 1937). In *Xenopus laevis*, on the contrary, excitement causes a darkening of the skin. In this species Burgers et al. (1953) have found that treatment of the skin or isolated limbs with adrenaline also causes melanophore dispersion (darkening). Why the melanophore response of *Xenopus* to adrenaline should be the opposite of that of other amphibians is not clear.

Adrenaline affects other phases of integumentary function. The secretory activity of glands in the skin of toads and frogs is under certain circumstances greatly increased (Ehrmann, 1905a,b; Wastl, 1921), particularly on the dorsum, by this hormone. However, the parotid glands of toads are relatively unaffected by adrenaline. Jorgensen (1947) has shown that permeability of frog skin to movement of salts is extremely sensitive to adrenaline, even in concentrations as low as $1:10^8$.

Adrenaline also causes a shift in position of retinal pigment in the frog's eye (Sima, 1939; Akagi, 1943). The dilatation of the pupil of the frog's eye, whether isolated *in vitro* or in its normal site, is a well established response to adrenaline. It has been used for bioassay of this hormone (Ehrmann, 1905a,b) since it is sensitive to concentrations as low as $1:2 \times 10^7$. However the nonspecificity of the reaction of the frog's eye (Waterman and Boddaert, 1908) and its sensitivity to hydrogen-ion concentration (McCarrison, 1923), reduce its usefulness as a bioassay system.

Although there is ample information concerning the action of adrenaline upon nervous function and upon metabolism in other vertebrate groups, these problems have been studied only rarely in Amphibia. Oti (1940) found that adrenaline can inhibit the spinal reflex in toads and frogs, and he has interpreted this to mean that the myoneural junction may be the site of action of the hormone. Adrenaline reduces the fatiguability of frog muscle and reduces the chronaxie (sensitivity to electrical stimulus) which usually is raised in fatigued muscles (Ruf, 1937). The oxygen consumption and carbon dioxide production of minced frog muscle is stimulated by adrenaline concentrations in the range $1:10^7$ to $1:10^{11}$ (Ahlgren, 1925). As it does in mammals, adrenaline causes a hyperglycemia in urodele and anuran amphibians (Miller and Wurster, 1959; Wright, 1959).

In mammals, in which most of such research has been done, it is known that hypoglycemia stimulates the release of adrenaline and noradrenaline into the blood. However, if the spinal cord is cut at the lowest cervical segment in dogs, or if the splanchnic nerve is sectioned, the reflex release of adrenaline does not occur. Similar experiments have been done with toads (Inoue, 1959). Section of the splanchnic nerve, or of the spinal cord at the level of the second spinal roots, prevents the release of adrenaline in toads made hypoglycemic by insulin injection. Hemisection of the cord blocks adrenal release only in the same side (determined histochemically); hence, there is no decussation of the descending spinal pathway of the adrenaline secretory fibers. The location of the hypoglycemia-sensitive nervous center is not yet known.

C. CORTICAL TISSUE

Although research defining the properties of amphibian cortical tissues and their hormones has been broad in scope, in most areas it has been shallow in depth. The technically easy aspects (e.g., effects of injections of hormones) have been relatively well investigated. The technically difficult aspects have been largely neglected.

A seasonal cycle of gross and histological structure of the adrenal has been observed frequently in Amphibia (Stilling, 1898; Holzapfel, 1937; Beatty, 1940; Miller, 1953; Chester Jones et al., 1959). In both urodeles and anurans the adrenal tissue becomes brightly orange colored and prominent in parallel with breeding activity. Later it becomes duller in color, often yellowish, and more flattened.

Dependence of the adrenal upon the pituitary also has been well established. Hypophysectomy produces atrophic or degenerative changes in adrenal histology and prevents proper differentiation of the adrenal in young animals (Houssay, 1949; Sluiter et al., 1949; Miller, 1953). Conversely, administering of pituitary extracts or of ACTH stimulates adrenal morphological changes and functional changes presumed to depend on increased adrenal hormone secretion (Atwell, 1935; Marenzi, 1936; Villee, 1943; Cicardo, 1947; Myers et al., 1955; Macchi, 1956; Inoue, 1959; Chester Jones et al., 1959; Carstenson et al., 1959). These experiments will be discussed further in later parts of this section. On the other hand it appears that amphibian adrenocortical function is not completely dependent upon the pituitary since survival (Atwell, 1935) and muscular chemical changes (Fowler, unpublished work cited by Chester Jones, 1957) are not as severely affected after hypophysectomy as after adrenalectomy.

Because the adrenal stores little hormone, and because of its small size in Amphibia, it has been difficult to identify the steroids produced, even with the sensitive chromatographic techniques available. Chester Jones and associates (1959) by collecting venous effluent blood from the adrenal, identified hydrocortisone in such blood in Xenopus, and hydrocortisone plus corticosterone in the blood of Amphiuma. They found no aldosterone, but they suggested that an aldosterone-like steroid must exist in amphibans because of the great disturbance of hydromineral metabolism after adrenalectomy and the relative ineffectiveness of the two steroids they did find in hydromineral metabolism. Thus, it is of great interest that Carstenson et al. (1959) more recently found that aldosterone is the most abundant hormone formed when bullfrog (Rana catesbeiana) adrenal tissue is incubated in vitro with ACTH. Corticosterone they found to be less abundant, and they could demonstrate no hydrocortisone. Ulick and Solomon (1960) found that bullfrog adrenal tissue incubated with C^{14}-labeled progesterone forms labeled aldosterone as readily as does bovine adrenal tissue under the same conditions.

Thus, it would appear that in general the same adrenal corticoids may be found in Amphibia as in other vertebrates. Many questions remain: whether extraction from blood yields different corticoids than incubation of adrenal tissue, whether there are seasonal, species, or sex differences in distribution of adrenal corticoids, and whether the relative proportions of these hormones may change under different circumstances. It may be hoped that these questions, which are difficult to study even in larger animals, will be clarified eventually for the Amphibia.

Although identification of the amphibian adrenal corticoids is still incomplete much more information is available concerning the physiological action of these substances. Most of this information is based upon experiments utilizing adrenalectomized animals or injection of hormones. Much attention has been paid to the role of adrenal hormones in distribution and movement of sodium, potassium, and water in the tissues (muscle, liver), blood, skin, and kidney. Carbohydrate absorption and metabolism also have been studied, as have been the physiological properties of the circulatory, nervous, and reproductive systems in different functional states of the adrenals. The relation of adrenal corticoids to metamorphosis also has been an interesting topic for research. Several authors (see especially Chester Jones, 1957) have emphasized that at the basis of much of the disagreement in the published literature in this field may be the factor of seasonal variability. As was mentioned earlier, the changes in functional state in amphibian adrenal tissue in different seasons are so great as to be visible even grossly. Accordingly, it might be expected, for example, that the effect of adrenalectomizing a summer animal may have consequences which differ in nature, or in extent, from adrenalectomy of a winter animal.

A part of the difference between summer and winter animal experiments may be ascribed merely to environmental temperature. Both Maes (1937) using *Rana*, and Fustinoni (1938a,b) using *Bufo*, found that survival of adrenalectomized animals was prolonged by keeping them at 5°C. At higher temperatures they survive for only a few days. Chester Jones *et al.* (1959) found that although summer *Rana temporaria* die within 48 hours after surgical adrenalectomy, winter frogs survive for long periods, and 35 days after the operation they show only minor changes in mineral constituents in blood and muscle.

An early symptom in the adrenalectomized anuran is a generalized and progressing asthenia, characterized by torpor and muscular weakness (Maes, 1937; Fustinoni, 1938a,b). Muscles of adrenalectomized frogs tested either in the intact animal, or in isolated preparations, show a reduced capacity (as much as 40%) for work (Ochoa, 1932; Wacholder and Morgenstern, 1933; Lang, 1934). Work capacity is increased by pretreatment of the adrenalectomized frog with adrenal cortical extracts. Csik and Ludany (1933) found that the pattern of muscle contraction (shape of the contraction curve) also is affected by the adrenal state. Several workers have found that cortical extracts will improve the work capacity of even normal frog muscles until they exceed normal values by more than 30% (Lang, 1934). Furthermore, the responsiveness of muscles to electrical stimuli is reduced after adrenalectomy. Hoppe and Vogel (1951) found the chronaxie raised.

These visible changes of muscular ability, as might be expected, are the symptoms of basic biochemical changes. The most common finding after adrenalectomy, especially in summer animals, is a gain in muscle weight due to an increase in both intracellular and extracellular fluid. At the same time there is a loss of sodium ion and a gain in potassium ion (Chester Jones, 1957). The increased water content of muscle is accompained by hydration of other tissues as well (e.g., liver) and a generalized edema produces body weight increases of 22% by 2 days after adrenalectomy (Fowler and Chester Jones, 1955) or of 28% to 33% by 1 to 2 weeks after adrenalectomy of frogs (Angerer and Angerer, 1942, 1949). It is of course necessary for such hydration that the frog be kept in water. Chester Jones (1957) found that although water-immersed adrenalectomized frogs become hydrated, they are less able to withstand dehydration than normal frogs. Hyman and Chambers (1943) noted that adrenal corticoids reduced the tendency of intravascularly perfused leopard frog legs to become edematous due to uptake of water from the perfusate. Angerer and Angerer (1941) and Cavalli and Occialini (1940) showed a similar property in isolated frog muscles placed in Ringer's solution. Those from adrenalectomized frogs took up more water and gained more in weight than did normals.

Marenzi and Fustinoni (1938) found an increase in the potassium content of heart and liver in adrenalectomized toads, but no change in muscle. This would seem to disagree with the earlier cited data of Chester Jones (1957) but it must be noted that Chester Jones found no real change in muscle potassium in winter adrenalectomized *Rana*. At least a part of the changes in muscle are due primarily to the shifts in salts and water between the animal and his environment. This is indicated by experiments described by Chester Jones (1957) who placed adrenalectomized frogs in isotonic salt solution. When so kept they survived well and the chemical changes in their tissues were minimized. It is of interest that the adrenalectomized rat, too, can be maintained by increasing its salt (sodium chloride) intake.

Many of the disturbances in water and mineral metabolism after hypophysectomy resemble those which follow adrenalectomy (Marenzi, 1936). Either implantation of toad anterior pituitaries (Marenzi, 1936) or injection of purified ACTH will correct these changes, indicating that they are due to failure of adrenal secretion after hypophysectomy. However, hypophysectomized anurans survive longer than adrenalectomized ones

(Atwell, 1935; Scheer and Bishop, 1960). Also, the fall in muscle sodium is not as great after hypophysectomy as after adrenalectomy (Chester Jones, 1957). These facts suggest that some residual level of adrenal function continues after hypophysectomy.

The effects of injections of pure adrenal hormones has not been well studied in relation to the phenomena just described. Clark *et al.* (1944) found that deoxycorticosterone, an artificially synthesized corticoid, is relatively ineffective in prolonging life in adrenalectomized frogs, or in preventing the usual changes in water and mineral content of muscle. Fustinoni (1938a,b) was not able to increase survival in adrenalectomized toads with adrenal extracts. Scheer and Bishop (1960) have reported that hydrocortisone alone or "adrenal cortical extracts" actually delay the recovery of normal physiological properties in the skin (sodium transport) of adrenalectomized frogs. However, repeated injections of a mixture of aldosterone and hydrocortisone accelerate this recovery. It seems clear that further study is necessary to decide which are the essential adrenal corticoids that are lacking after adrenalectomy in amphibians.

It appears from direct perfusion experiments (e.g., Hyman and Chambers, 1943; Cicardo, 1947) that the site of action of adrenocortical hormones in producing shifts of hydromineral metabolism may be the muscular and other generalized tissues of the organism perhaps through an effect upon cell permeability to metabolites. Some further support for this idea may be found in the work of Norman and Hiestand (1960) who have studied recently the question of hormonal control of permeability of frog muscle cells to xylose, sodium, and potassium. In their tests, cortisol had no effect, but deoxycorticosterone produced a retention of sodium ion and had no apparent action on potassium ion distribution. Neither hormone affected the rate of cell penetration of the nonmetabolized sugar, xylose. On the other hand, a large body of information has accumulated which demonstrates that adrenocortical hormones also act by regulating those organs through which salt and water are exchanged with the environment: the skin, and the mesonephros.

The concentrations of water and salts in the blood are useful indices of the shifts in hydromineral metabolism in different adrenal functional states. Unfortunately, few such measurements have been made. Urechia et al. (1937) and Marenzi and Fustinoni (1938) found a 34% rise in serum potassium and a 25% fall in serum sodium in adrenalectomized *Bufo*. Erythrocytes are decreased in concentration after adrenalectomy in the toad according to Fustinoni and Parodi (1938) while a slight increase in blood volume (hemodilution) occurs. In later phases of adrenalectomy blood becomes very viscous (hemoconcentration) and, with the added effects of a slower heart beat, hemostasis occurs frequently in certain organs, as well as congestion of blood vessels in the viscera (Chester Jones, 1957). Various authors have reported a slight hypoglycemia after adrenalectomy, and Chester Jones (1957) states that, conversely, ACTH will produce hyperglycemia in frogs.

Although the changes in concentration of glucose in the blood are relatively slight, there are important, although incompletely characterized, general changes in carbohydrate metabolism of adrenalectomized amphibians. Even initial absorption from the intestine is affected, as Minibeck (1939) found in adrenalectomized or hypophysectomized frogs that the ability to selectively absorb certain sugars is lost. However Houssay et al. (1941) found no such clear relation in similarly treated Bufo arenarum. Muscle and liver glycogen become gradually depleted after adrenalectomy (Fernandez et al., 1934; Fustinoni, 1938a,b). The ability to produce lactic acid in the contracting isolated frog muscle is reduced after adrenalectomy (Ochoa, 1932), as is the blood concentration of lactate (Arvay and Lengyel, 1931). There is at the same time a reduction in creatine phosphate in the muscle (Lang, 1931; Ochoa, 1932; Moschini, 1934). Since such changes indicate an altered system of phosphorylation and energy transfer within muscle, it seems reasonable to agree with those authors who have placed most of the blame for the asthenia after adrenalectomy in amphibians on changes in carbohydrate metabolism.

Hydrocortisone treatment of the salamander Taricha causes a hyperglycemia which is severe enough to produce simultaneously a degranulation of β-cells in the pancreatic islets and Wurster and Miller, 1960). Miller (1960) considers that the adrenal has a major role in maintaining the blood sugar level of Taricha.

However, at least a part of the basis for the asthenic condition resides in changes in the nervous system (Cerf, 1955), as well as in the vascular system. Both Maes (1937) (Rana temporaria) and Odoriz (1941) (Bufo arenarum) found a lower rate of nerve fiber impulse conduction after adrenalectomy. Odoriz, furthermore, found that the difference between normal and adrenalectomized animals was greater at 30°C (normal, 42 meters per second, adrenalectomy 34 meters per second) than at 5°C (normal 13.5 meters per second, adrenalectomy 11.6 meters per second). Spike amplitude also was affected. Correlated with these deficiencies in function are some measurable changes in chemical constitution of nervous tissues in adrenalectomized amphibians. Potassium is reduced 32% in brain and 48% in peripheral nerve (Urechia et al., 1937).

Heart beat rate is decreased after adrenalectomy in frogs and toads (Loewi and Gettwert, 1914), and there is an accompanying reduction in cardiac muscle glycogen and increase in chronaxie (Fustinoni and Cicardo, 1937). Loewi and Gettwert found that, at death, hearts of adrenalectomized frogs are in diastole and can be revived by atropine.

The vascular congestion mentioned previously is especially marked in the digestive tract, producing extreme dilatation of vessels (Houssay *et al.*, 1941). The question of vascular permeability also has been investigated. Rauchschwalbe (1940) found that an increased tendency for methylene blue to leave blood vessels after adrenalectomy was checked by adrenal cortical extracts. Zweifach and Chambers (1942) showed that the hyperemic tissue capillary bed in frogs induced by histamine treatment could be returned to normal by dehydrocorticosterone.

At this point it is useful to return to the question of control by adrenal corticoids over those organs through which water and salts are exchanged with the environment. This question is a complex one because other hormones, particularly the neurohypophyseal factors and thyroxine also affect this exchange in the skin and mesonephros. It must be kept in mind that the doses of neurohypophyseal substances needed to affect amphibian skin permeability are so large as to lead some workers to question whether such hormonal concentrations can be achieved under normal physiological conditions (Boyd and Young, 1940).

Normal frog skin is relatively impermeable to water and sodium, thus preventing loss of body salt and entrance of blood-diluting water in response to the osmotic gradient. Ussing (1952, 1960) has shown that an inward active transport of sodium ion occurs in normal frog skin, and correlated with this transport is an electrochemical potential (Fuhrmann and Ussing, 1951; Scheer and Bishop, 1960). Posterior pituitary hormones increase the electrical potential (Jorgensen and Rosenkilde, 1956) and the penetration of osmotically free water, as well as sodium (Sawyer, 1956; Capraro and Garampi, 1956). Adrenalectomized amphibians also show an increase in penetration of the skin by water, but a loss of sodium through the skin, and a decrease in electrical potential (Jorgensen, 1947; Scheer and Bishop, 1960). It may be concluded, then, that adrenocorticoids decrease penetration of the skin by water, and that they promote the inward transport of sodium. Dow and Zuckerman (1939) were able to show only a slight decrease in body weight (hence, skin permeability to water) in axolotls treated with deoxycorticosterone (DCA) or cortical extracts. Others have been unable to demonstrate a significant effect of adrenocorticoids upon integumentary water transfer of frogs (at least as judge by body weight changes, Hsieh, 1950) or upon isolated skins (Huf and Wills, 1953). Pretreatment of the animal with ACTH increases sodium transport by axolotl skins (Johnsen and Ussing, 1949) and frog skin (Myers *et al.*, 1955; Scheer and Bishop, 1960).

Taylor and Weinstein (1952) and others have found that DCA, aldosterone, and other steroids increase both frog skin potentials and sodium transport. Thus, it is difficult to reconcile the fact that the actions of corticoids and posterior pituitary hormones seem to be opposed with respect to water movement through amphibian skin; yet they have a similar effect upon sodium and electrochemical potential. It is of interest, and perhaps of significance, that the neurohypophyseal hormones appear to have no action in adrenalectomized amphibians or animals whose anterior pituitary (hence ACTH) (Jones and Steggerda, 1935) was removed. This ability is restored by ACTH injection (Levinsky and Sawyer, 1952). On the other hand, the effects of adrenalectomy or adrenocorticoids on skin permeability are produced even in the complete absence of the pituitary (Chester Jones, 1957; Scheer and Bishop, 1960).

Studies of the action of adrenocorticoids upon urine formation are much less complete than those just cited for skin. Hsieh (1950) found that both pitressin (vasopressin) and DCA inhibit the flow of urine in frogs given a measured volume of water by mouth. When given together their effects are not additive. Chester Jones (1957) cites some unpublished experiments of Fowler in which sodium "loads" were administered to normal and adrenalectomized frogs. Loss of sodium, partly through the kidney and partly through the skin, was more rapid from the adrenalectomized frog.

In general, morphological effects by the adrenocorticoids are few. Various authors have shown that adrenal steroids will inhibit metamorphosis if given to young frog tadpoles (Gasche, 1945; Kobayashi, 1958) but will stimulate metamorphosis if given to older tadpoles (Gasche, 1945; Campora, 1926; Bock, 1938; Eskin, 1932; Kobayashi, 1958), or if given at any time together with small amounts of thyroxine. Kobayashi (1958) suggests that the early inhibitory effect of adrenal steroids is due to the inhibition of thyroidal differentiation. Later, when the thyroid is already secreting, the corticosteroids potentiate thyroid hormone action, since they seemingly have no metamorphic action alone. Furthermore, Kobayashi (1958) points out that corticosteroids synergize the destructive phases of metamorphosis: emergence of forelegs by precocious opercular perforation, shrinking of the tail, and shortening of the trunk. DCA actually inhibits growth of limbs at a time when, given with thyroxine, these destructive phenomena are accelerated.

References

Abel, J. J., and Macht, D. I. (1912). Two crystalline pharmacological agents obtained from the tropical toad, *Bufo agua*. *J. Pharmacol. Exptl. Therap.* **3**, 319–377.

Abelous, J. E., and Langlois, P. (1891). La mort des grenouilles aprés la déstruction des deux capsules surrénales. *Compt. Rend. Soc. Biol.* **43**, 855–857.

Acher, R., Chauvet, J., Lenci, M. T., Morel, F., and Maetz, J. (1960). Présence d'une vasotocine dans la neurohypophyse de la grenouille (*Rana esculenta* L.). *Biochim. Biophys. Acta* **42**, 379–380.

Adams, A. E., and Grierson, M. C. (1932). Cornification and molting in *Triturus*. *Proc. Soc. Exptl. Biol. Med.* **30**, 341–344.

Adams, A. E., Kunder, A., and Richards, L. (1932). The endocrine glands and molting in *Triturus viridescens*. *J. Exptl. Zool.* **63**, 1–55.

Adler, L. (1921). Untersuchungen zur Pharmakologie der Gefässe. I. Die Wirkung von Giften auf die Arteria pulmonalis und die Arteria cutanea magna von *Rana esculenta. Arch. Exptl. Pathol. Pharmakol. Naunyn-Schmiedeberg's* **91,** 110–124.

Ahlgren, G. (1925). Microspirometric investigation of the action of hormones: Adrenalin. *Skand. Arch. Physiol.* **47,** 275–280.

Akagi, T. (1943). Influence of sunlight, X-rays, and adrenaline of the shifting of the retinal pigment in the different developmental stages of the frog embryo. *Folia Pharmacol. Japon.* **39,** 229–243.

Allen, B. M. (1916). The results of extirpation of the anterior lobe of the hypophysis and of the thyroid of *Rana pipiens* larvae. *Science* **44,** 755–757.

Allen, B. M. (1918). The results of thyroid removal on the larvae of *Rana pipiens. J. Exptl. Zool.* **24,** 499–520.

Allen, B. M. (1929). The influence of thyroid gland and hypophysis upon growth and development of amphibian larvae. *Quart. Rev. Biol.* **4,** 325–352.

Angerer, C. A. (1950). Body weight survival times, coloration, and water content of skeletal muscles of adrenalectomized frogs. *Ohio J. Sci.* **50,** 103–105.

Angerer, C. A., and Angerer, H. (1941). Weight variations of muscles of adrenalectomized frogs in normal and hypotonic Ringer's solution. *Am. J. Physiol.* **133,** 197–198.

Angerer, C. A., and Angerer, H. (1942). The effect of dehydration on the viability of adrenal-insufficient frogs. *Federation Proc.* **1,** 3.

Angerer, C. A., and Angerer, H. (1949). The rate and total loss of body water in the survival time of adrenalectomized frogs. *Proc. Soc. Exptl. Biol. Med.* **71,** 661–665.

Aron, M. (1928). Le fonctionnement du pancréas chez les larves d'amphibiens. *Compt. Rend. Soc. Biol.* **99,** 213–215.

Arvay, A., and Lengyel, L. (1931). Die Milchsäurebildung bei Muskelarbeit nach Entfernug der Nebennieren. *Biochem. Z.* **239,** 128–137.

Atwell, W. J. (1935). Effects of thyrotropic and adrenotropic principles on hypophysectomized amphibia. *Anat. Record* **62,** 361–379.

Atwell, W. J. (1937a). Functional transplants of the primordium of the epithelial hypophysis in Amphibia. *Anat. Record.* **68,** 431–447.

Atwell, W. J. (1937b). Effects of administering thyrotropic and adrenotropic extract to thyroidectomized and hypophysectomized tadpoles. *Am. J. Physiol.* **118,** 452–456.

Atwell, W. J., and Halley, E. (1936). Extirpation of the pars intermedia of the hypophysis in the young amphibian with subsequent silvery condition and metamorphosis. *J. Exptl. Zool.* **73,** 23–41.

Bagnara, J. T., and Neidleman, S. (1958). Effect of chromatophorotropic hormone on pigments of anuran skin. *Proc. Soc. Exptl. Biol. Med.* **97,** 671–673.

Barlow, D. W., Vigor, W. N., and Peck, R. I. (1931). The action of insulin on the frog, the influence of dosage, temperature, excision of the liver, administration of glucose, sodium bicarbonate and calcium gluconate on the reaction of the frog to insulin. *J. Pharmacol. Exptl. Therap.* **41,** 229–243.

Barrington, E. J. W. (1951). The specific granules of the pancreatic islet tissue of the frog (*Rana temporaria*). *Quart. J. Microscop. Sci.* **92,** 205–220.

Bayer, G. (1929). Nebennieren. *In* "Handbuch der Inneren Sekretion." Max Hirsch, ed., C. Kabitzsch, Leipzig.

Bayer, G., and Wense, V. D. (1938). Physiologie des Nebennierenmarks. *Zwangl. Abhand. inn. Sekret.* **6.**

Beatty, B. (1940). A comparative account of the adrenal glands in *Rana temporaria* and *Rana esculenta. Proc. Leeds Phil. Lit. Soc.* **3,** 633–643.

Bennett, H. S. (1941). Cytological manifestations of secretion in the adrenal medulla of the cat. *Am. J. Anat.* **69,** 333–381.

Berg, O. A., Gorbman, A., and Kobayashi, H. (1959). The thyroid hormones in invertebrates and lower vertebrates. *Comp. Endocrinol., Proc. Columbia Univ. Symp. Cold Spring Harbor N.Y.* 1958, pp. 302–319.

Biasotti, A., and Porto, J. (1945). Influencia del aloxano en el *Bufo arenarum* (Hensel). *Rev. Soc. Arg. Biol.* **21,** 63–73.

Blount, R. F. (1945). The interrelationship of the parts of the hypophysis in development. *J. Exptl. Zool.* **100,** 79–102.

Bock, K. A. (1938). Die Einwirkung von Nebennierenrindenextrakt auf den Ablauf der Thyroxinmetamorphose bei Froschlarven und beim Axolotl. *Klin. Wochschr.* **17,** 1311–1314.

Boruttau, H. (1899). Experiments on the adrenals. *Arch. Ges. Physiol. Pflüger's* **78,** 97–128.

Boschwitz, D. (1957). Thyroidless tadpoles of *Pelobates syriacus* Boettger. *Copeia* pp. 310–311.

Boyd, E. M., and Young, F. M. (1940). Optical stimuli and water balance in frogs. *Endocrinology* **27,** 137–143.

Brunn, F. (1921). Beitrag zur Kenntnis der Wirkung von Hypopysenextrakten auf den Wasserhaushalt des Frosches. *Z. Ges. Exptl. Med.* **25,** 170–175.

Buchborn, E. (1956). Zur Kinetik des amphibischen Wasserhaushaltes bei der Kröte. *Pflüger's Arch. Ges. Physiol.* **262,** 377–394.

Burch, A. B. (1938). Suppression of the pars intermedia of the pituitary body in *Hyla regilla* by operations upon the gastrula. *Proc. Soc. Exptl. Biol. Med.* **38,** 608–610.

Burgers, A. C. J. (1956). Investigations into the action of certain hormones and other substances on the melanophores of the South African Toad, *Xenopus laevis.* Thesis, Utrecht. G. W. van der Wiel, Arnhem, Netherlands.

Burgers, A. C. J., Boschman, T. A., and van de Kamer, J. C. (1953). Excitement darkening and the effect of adrenaline on the melanophores of *Xenopus laevis. Acta Endocrinol.* **14,** 72–82.

Burgos, M. H. (1959). Histochemistry and electron microscopy of the three cell types in the adrenal gland of the frog. *Anat. Record* **133,** 163–185.

Campora, G. (1926). Ricerche comparative con alimentazioni mono e pluriglandolari in larve di anfibi (timo, surrence corticale, ipofisi anteriore e ipofisi totale). *Pathologica* **18,** 602–610.

Capraro, V., and Garampi, M. L. (1956). The hormonal control of water and salt-electrolyte metabolism studies with isolated frog skin. *Mem. Soc. Endocrinol.* **5,** 60–71.

Carstenson, H., Burgers, A. C. J., and Li, C. H. (1959). Isolation of aldosterone from incubates of adrenals of the American bullfrog and stimulation of its production by mammalian adrenocorticotrophin. *J. Am. Chem. Soc.* **81,** 4109–4110.

Cerf, J. (1955). Note de Cerf, J., présentée par Bremer, F. Corrélation des troubles électrolytiques humoraux et des altérations fonctionnelles du nerf périphérique chez la Grenouille surrénalectomisée. *Compt. Rend. Soc. Biol.* **149,** 615–618.

Chadwick, C. S. (1940). Identity of prolactin with water drive factor in *Triturus viridescens. Proc. Soc. Exptl. Biol. Med.* **45,** 335–337.

Chang, C. Y. (1955). Hormonal influences on sex differentiation in the toad. *Anat. Record* **123,** 467–478.

Charipper, H. A., and Corey, C. (1930). Studies on amphibian endocrines. *Anat. Record* **45,** 258–270.

Chester Jones, I. (1957). "The Adrenal Cortex." Cambridge Univ. Press, Cambridge, Massachusetts.

Chester Jones, I., Philips, J. G., and Holmes, W. N. (1959). Comparative physiology of the adrenal cortex. *Comp. Endocrinol., Proc. Columbia Univ. Symp. Cold Spring Harbor N.Y.* 1958, pp. 582–612.

Cicardo, V. A. (1947). "Importancia biologica del potasio." El Ateneo, Buenos Aires.

Clark, W. G., Brackney, E. L., and Miliner, R. A. (1944). Adrenalectomy in frogs and toads. *Proc. Soc. Exptl. Biol. Med.* **57**, 222–224.

Colombini, N. (1940). L'azione dell'adrenalin sul cuore isolaro degli anfibi, considerata nel quandro di una recente concezione. *Arch. fisiol.* **40**, 449–472.

Cortelyou, J. R. (1960). Plasma and urine phosphorus changes in totally parathyroidectomized *Rana pipiens. Anat. Record* **137**, 346 (abstr.).

Cortelyou, J. R., Hibner-Owerko, A., and Mulroy, J. (1960). Blood and urine calcium changes in totally parathyroidectomized *Rana pipiens. Endocrinology* **66**, 441–450.

Csik, L., and von Ludany, G. (1933). Die Zuckungskurve des Muskels nach Exstirpation der Nebennieren. *Pflüger's Arch. Ges. Physiol.* **232**, 187–198.

Davis, J. E., and Hastings, A. B. (1935). Relation of thyroxin to the metabolism of tissues. *Proc. Central Soc. Clin. Res.* **504**, 123–130.

Dawson, A. B. (1953). Evidence for the termination of neurosecretory fibers within the pars intermedia of the frog (*Rana pipiens*). *Anat. Record* **115**, 63–69.

Delsol, M., and Masnou, F. (1958). Dosage de l'hormone antidiuretique hypophysaire et capacité réactionelle a cette hormone chez les "*Alytes obstetricans*" au cours de la métamorphose. *Actes Soc. Linn. Bordeaux* **97**, (Suppl. Colloque sur les Métamorphoses).

Dent, J. N., and Hunt, E. L. (1952). An autoradiographic study of iodine distribution in larvae and metamorphosing specimens of anura. *J. Exptl. Zool.* **121**, 79–98.

De Robertis, E., and Primavesi, L. (1939). Les celulas de las ilotes de Langerhans del *Bufo arenarum* (Hensel). *Rev. Soc. Arg. Biol.* **15**, 474–481.

Deulafeu, V., and Duprat, E. (1944). Basic constituents of the venom of some South American toads. *J. Biol. Chem.* **153**, 459–463.

Diamare, V. (1899). Studii comparativi sulle isoli del Langerhans de pancreas. *Intern. Monatsschr. Anat. Physiol.* **16**, 155–209.

Dierickx, K., and van den Abeele, A. (1959). On the relations between the hypothalamus and the anterior pituitary in *Rana temporaria. Z. Zellforsch. Mikroskop. Anat.* **51**, 78–87.

Dierickx, K., van den Abeele, A., and Rysenaer, M. (1960). Phénomènes d'activité cyclique dans le système hypothalamohypophysaire de *Rana temporaria*. Données nouvelles. *Arch. Anat. Microscop. Morphol. Exptl.* **49**, 73–88.

Dixon, W. E. (1902). The innervation of the frog's stomach. *J. Physiol. (London)* **28**, 57–75.

Donoso, A. O. (1960). Action des hormones thyroidiennes sur le métabolisme des tissus isolés de crapaud. *Compt. Rend. Soc. Biol.* **154**, 832.

Donoso, A. O., and Trivelloni, J. C. (1958a). Hormones tiroideas y metabolismo del sapo. *Rev. Soc. Arg. Biol.* **34**, 46–52.

Donoso, A. O., and Trivelloni, J. C. (1958b). Yodo radioactivo y funcion tiroidea en el sapo. *Rev. Soc. Arg. Biol.* **34**, 64–69.

Dosne, C. (1943). Study of interrelationship of pancreatic diabetes with endocrine glands in the toad. *Endocrinology* **33**, 224–228.

Dow, D., and Zuckerman, S. (1939). The effect of vasopressin, sex hormones, and adrenal cortical hormones on body water in axolotls. *J. Endocrinol.* **1**, 387–398.

Dundee, H., and Gorbman, A. (1960). Utilization of radioiodine by thyroid of neotenic salamander, *Eurycea tynerensis* Moore and Hughes. *Physiol. Zool.* **33**, 58–63.

Eakin, R. M. (1939). Correlative differentiation of the intermediate lobe of the pituitary in *Triturus torosus*. *Growth* **3**, 373–380.

Ehrmann, R. (1905a). Über eine physiologische Wertbestimmung des Adrenalins und seinen Nachweis im Blut. *Arch. Exptl. Pathol. Pharmakol. Naunyn-Schmiedeberg's* **53**, 97–111.

Ehrmann, R. (1905b). Über die Wirkung des Adrenalins auf die Hautdrüsentätigkeit des Frosches. *Arch. Exptl. Pathol. Pharmakol. Naunyn-Schmiedeberg's* **53**, 137–139.

Eliassen, E., and Jorgensen, C. B. (1951). The effect of increase in osmotic pressure of the body fluid on the water balance in anurans. *Acta Physiol. Scand.* **23**, 143.

Eskin, J. A. (1932). Über den Einfluss der Nebenniere auf die Metamorphose bei Amphibien. *Endokrinologie* **11**, 249–260.

Etkin, W. (1940). Developmental relationship between pars intermedia of pituitary and brain in tadpoles. *Proc. Soc. Exptl. Biol. Med.* **44**, 471–473.

Etkin, W. (1958). Independent differentiation in components of the pituitary complex in the wood frog. *Proc. Soc. Exptl. Biol. Med.* **97**, 388–393.

Etkin, W., and Lehrer, R. (1961). Excess growth in tadpoles after transplantation of the adenohypophysis. *Endocrinology* **67**, 457–466.

Etkin, W., and Sussman, W. (1961). Hypothalamo-pituitary relationships in metamorphosis of *Ambystoma*. *Gen. Comp. Endocrinol.* **1**, 70–79.

Etkin, W., and Rosenberg, L. (1938). Infundibular lesion and pars intermedia activity in the tadpole. *Proc. Soc. Exptl. Biol. Med.* **39**, 332–334.

Ewer, R. F. (1952). The effects of posterior pituitary extracts on water balance in *Bufo carens* and *Xenopus laevis* together with some general considerations of Anuran water economy. *J. Exptl. Biol.* **29**, 429–439.

Fernandez, R., Foglia, V. G., Leloir, L. F., and Novelli, A. (1934). Cortico-surrénale et formation de glycogène musculaire aux dépens du glucose. *Compt. Rend. Soc. Biol.* **115**, 334–337.

Fischer, H. (1912). Über die Langerhanschen Inseln im Pankreas von Amphibien. *Arch. Mikroskop. Anat. Entwicklungsmech.* **9**, 276–306.

Foa, P. P., Galansino, G., and Pozza, G. (1957). Glucagon, a second pancreatic hormone. *Recent Progr. Hormone Res.* **13**, 473–510.

Foglia, V. (1942). Masa hepatica e intensidad de las diabetes pancreatica y hipofisaria. *Rev. Soc. Arg. Biol.* **18**, 5–19.

Fowler, M. A., and Chester Jones, I. (1955). The adrenal cortex in the frog *Rana temporaria* and its relation to water and salt-electrolyte metabolism. *J. Endocrinol.* **13**, 6–7.

Frieden, E., and Naile, B. (1955). Biochemistry of amphibian metamorphosis. I. Enhancement of induced metamorphosis by glucocorticoids. *Science* **121**, 37–39.

Frye, B. E. (1958). Development of the pancreas in *Ambystoma opacum*. *Am. J. Anat.* **102**, 117–139.

Frye, B. E. (1959). The development of function in the islets of Langerhans. *Comp. Endocrinol., Proc. Columbia Univ. Symp. Cold Spring Harbor N.Y. 1958*, pp. 681–696.

Fuheman, F. A., and Ussing, H. H. (1951). A characteristic response of the isolated frog skin potential to neurohypophysial principles and its relation to the transport of sodium and water. *J. Cellular Comp. Physiol.* **38**, 109–130.

Fustinoni, O. (1938a). Survie des crapauds aprés déstruction des surrénales. *Compt. Rend. Soc. Biol.* **128**, 1137–1138.

Fustinoni, O., (1938b). La astenia de la insufficiencia del sapo. *Rev. Soc. Arg. Biol.* **14**, 304–313.

Fustinoni, O., and Cicardo, V. H. (1937). Modifications cardiaques dans l'insuffisance surrénale du crapaud. *Compt. Rend. Soc. Biol.* **126**, 829–830.

Fustinoni, O., and Parodi, S. A. (1938). Morfologia de las glandulas adrenales del sapo *Bufo arenarum* Hensel. *Rev. Soc. Arg. Biol.* **14**, 215–221.

Gallien, L. (1959). Endocrine basis for reproductive adaptations in Amphibia. *Comparative Endocrinol., Proc. Columbia Univ. Symp. Cold Spring Harbor N.Y. 1958*, pp. 479–487.

Ganong, W. F. (1959). Adrenal-hypophyseal interrelations. *Comparative Endocrinol., Proc. Columbia Univ. Symp. Cold Spring Harbor N.Y. 1958*, pp. 187–201.

Gasche, P. (1945). Einwirkung von Desoxycorticosteron-Acetat auf Larven von *Xenopus laevis* in den verschiedenen Metamorphosestadien. *Helv. Physiol. Acta* **3**, C10–C11.

Gayda, T. (1922). Contributi allo studio della fisiologia della tiroide delle rana. *Arch. Fisiol.* **20**, 267–285.

Geiringer, M. (1938). Die synergistische Wirkung des Adrenalins und des Thyroxins auf den Farbwechsel der Amphibien und der Fische. *Arch. Intern. Pharmacodyn.* **60**, 251–258.

Gellhorn, E. (1933). The effect of hormones on cellular permeability. *Ann. Internal Med.* **7**, 33–44.

Gerschmann, R. (1943). Variaciones estracionales o por hipofisectomia de los elementos minerales del plasma del sapo. *Rev. Soc. Arg. Biol.* **19**, 172–184.

Geschwind, I. I. (1959). Species variation in protein and polypeptide hormones *Comp. Endocrinol.* (A. Gorbman, ed.), pp. 471–443. John Wiley, New York.

Geyer, G. (1959). Histochemische und elektronenmikroskopische Untersuchungen an der Nebenniere von *Rana esculenta. Acta Histochem.* **8**, 234–288.

Gorbman, A. (1941). Comparative anatomy and physiology of the anterior pituitary. *Quart Rev. Biol.* **16**, 294–310.

Gorbman, A. (1957). The thyroid gland of *Typhlomolge rathbuni. Copeia* **8**, 41–43.

Gorbman, A. (1959). Problems in the comparative morphology and physiology of the vertebrate thyroid gland. *Comp. Endocrinol.* (A. Gorbman, ed.), pp. 266–282. John Wiley, New York.

Gorbman, A., and Evans, H. M. (1941). Correlation of histological differentiation with beginning of function of developing thyroid gland of frog. *Proc. Soc. Exptl. Biol. Med.* **47**, 103–106.

Gourley, D. R. H. (1957). Combination of insulin with frog skeletal muscle. *Am. J. Physiol.* **189**, 489–494.

Grant, W. C., and Grant, J. A. (1958). Water drive studies on hypophysectomized efts of *Diemyctilus viridescens*. Part L. The role of lactogenic hormone. *Biol. Bull.* **114**, 1–9.

Green, J. D. (1947). Vessels and nerves of amphibian hypophyses. *Anat. Record* **99**, 21–53.

Green, J. D. (1951). The comparative anatomy of the hypophysis with special reference to its blood supply and innervation. *Am. J. Anat.* **88**, 225–312.

Green, J. D., and Maxwell, D. S. (1959). Comparative anatomy of the hypophysis and observations on the mechanism of neurosecretion. *Comp. Endocrinol.* (A. Gorbman, ed.) pp. 368–392.

Gudernatsch, J. F. (1912). Feeding experiments on tadpoles. I. The influence os specific organs given as food on growth and differentiation. A contribution to the knowledge of organs with internal secretion. *Arch. Entwicklungsmech. Organ.* **35,** 457–483.

Haarman, W. (1936). Uber den Einfluss von Thyroxin auf den Sauerstoffverbrauch überlebender Gewebe. *Arch. Exptl. Pathol. Pharmakol. Naunyn-Schmiedeberg's* **180,** 167–182.

Harris, G. W. (1955). "Neural Control of the Pituitary Gland." Edward Arnold, London.

Harris, G. W. (1959). Neuroendocrine control of TSH regulation. *Comp. Endocrinol., Proc. Columbia Univ. Symp. Cold Spring Harbor N.Y. 1958,* pp. 202–222.

Hartman, F. A., Lewis, L. A., Gabriel, J. E., Spoor, H. J., and Brownell, K. A. (1940). The effect of cortin and the Na factor on adrenalectomized animals. *Endocrinology* **27,** 287–296.

Heller H. (1945). The effect of neurohypophyseal extracts on the water balance of lower vertebrates. *Biol. Rev. Cambridge Phil. Soc.* **20,** 147–157.

Heller, H. (1957). "The Neurohypophysis" (H. Heller, Ed.), Butterworths, London.

Hemmingsen, A. M. (1925). The action of insulin in the frog and some invertebrates. *Acta Physiol. Scand.* **46,** 56–63.

Henschel, H., and Steuber, M. (1935). Über die Bedeutung der Schilddrüse für den Stoffwechsel der Amphibien. *Arch. Exptl. Pathol. Pharmakol. Naunyn-Schmiedeberg's* **177,** 418–431.

Herlant, M. (1954). Anatomie et physiologie comparées de l'hypophyse dans la série des vertebrés. *Bull. Soc. Zool. France* **79,** 256–281.

Hild, W. (1951a). Vergleichende Unterschungen über Neurosekretion im Zwischenhirn von Amphibien und Reptilien. *Z. Anat. Entwicklungsgeschichte* **115,** 450–469.

Hild, W. (1951b). Experimentell-morphologische Untersuchungen über das Verhalten der "neurosekretorischen Bahn" nach Hypophysenstieldurchtrennungen, Eingriffen in den Wasserhaushalt und Belastung der Osmoregulation. *Arch. Pathol. Anat. Physiol. Virchow's* **319,** 526–548.

Hild, W. and Zetler, G. (1951). Über das Vorkommen der Hypophysenhinterlappenhormone im Zwischenhirn. *Arch. Exptl. Pathol. Pharmakol. Naunyn-Schmiedeberg's* **213,** 139–153.

Hirata, K. (1934). On the histogenesis of the island of Langerhans in *Rana japonica* (Gunther). *Sci. Rept. Tohoku Univ. Fourth Ser.* **9,** 159–182.

Hisaw, F. L. (1959). Endocrine adaptations of the mammalian estrous cycle and gestation. *Comp. Endocrinol., Proc. Columbia Univ. Symp. Cold Spring Harbor N.Y. 1958,* pp. 533–552.

Hogben, L., and Slome, D. (1931). The pigmentary effector system. VI. The dual character of endocrine coordination in amphibian color. *Proc. Roy. Soc.* **B108,** 10–53.

Holzapfel, R. A. (1937). The cyclic character of hibernation in frogs. *Quart. Rev. Biol.* **12,** 65–85.

Hoppe, G., and Vogel, G. (1951). Der Einfluss der Adrenalektomie auf den Zeitwert der muskulären Erregbarkeit. *Arch. Ges Physiol. Pflüger's.* **253,** 518–532.

Hoskins, E. R., and Hoskins, M. M. (1919). Growth of amphibia after thyroidectomy. *J. Exptl. Zool.* **29,** 1–69.

Houssay, B. A. (1949). Hypophysial functions in the toad *Bufo arenarum* Hensel. *Quart. Rev. Biol.* **24,** 1–27.

Houssay, B. A. (1959). Comparative physiology of the endocrine pancreas. *Comp. Endocrinol., Proc. Columbia Univ. Symp. Cold Spring Harbor N.Y. 1958,* pp. 439–667.

Houssay, B. A., and Anderson, E. (1949). Action diabétogène de l'hormone de croissance, l'adrénocorticotrophine et la prolactine. *Compt. Rend. Soc. Biol.* **143,** 1262–1264.

Houssay, B. A., and Biasotti, A. (1930). Hipofisectomia y diabetes pancreatica en el sapo. *Rev. Soc. Arg. Biol.* **6,** 8-24.

Houssay, B. A., and Biasotti, A. (1931). Hypophysektomie und Pankreasdiabetes bei der Kröte. *Arch. Ges. Physiol. Pflüger's* **227,** 239–250.

Houssay, B. A. and Biasotti, A. (1933). Role de l'hypophyse et de la surrénale dans le diabète pancréatique du crapaud. *Compt. Rend. Soc. Biol.* **123,** 497–500.

Houssay, B. A., and Biasotti, A. (1936). Influencia de la hipofisis y la suprarenal sobre la diabetes pancreatica del sapo. *Rev. Soc. Arg. Biol.* **12,** 104–111.

Houssay, B. A., and Mazzocco, P. (1933). L'adrénaline de la surrénale des Chiens hypophysoprives. *Compt. Rend. Soc. Biol.* **114,** 722–723.

Houssay, B. A., and Rietti, C. T. (1924). Accion de la insuline sobre algunos vertebrados poiquilothermos. *Compt. Rend. Soc. Biol.* **91,** 27–29.

Houssay, B. A., and Rietti, V. M. (1950). Action de l'insuline et de la "pars distalis" de l'hypophyse sur la courbe de tolérance au glucose du crapaud. *Compt. Rend. Soc. Biol.* **144,** 1230–1232.

Houssay, B. A., and Sara, J. G. (1945). Accion de aloxano an el sapo *Bufo aranarum. Rev. Soc. Arg. Biol.* **21,** 74–80.

Houssay, B. A., Biasotti, A., and Sammartino, R. (1935). Modifications fontcionelles de l'hypophyse après les lésions infundibulotubériennes chez le crapaud. *Compt. Rend. Soc. Biol.* **120,** 725–727.

Houssay, B. A., Foglia, V. G., and Fustinoni, O. (1941). Intestinal absorption of sugars in the toad with hypophyseal or adrenal insufficiency. *Endocrinology* **28,** 915–922.

Houssay, B. A., Gerschman, R., and Rapela, C. E. (1950). Adrenalina y noradrenalina en la suprarenal del sapo normal o hipofisoprivo. *Rev. Soc. Arg. Biol.* **26,** 29–38.

Howes, B. N. (1940). The response of the water-regulating mechanism of developmental stages of the common toad *Bufo bufo* L. to treatment with extracts of the posterior lobe of the pituitary body. *J. Exptl. Biol.* **17,** 128–138.

Hsieh, K. M. (1950). Increase in weight of frogs after DOCA administration. *Federation Proc.* **9,** 63–64 (abstr.).

Huf, E. G., and Wills, J. (1953). The relation of sodium uptake potassium rejection, and skin potential in isolated frog skin. *J. Gen. Physiol.* **36,** 473–487.

Hunt, E. L., and Dent, J. N. (1957). Iodine uptake and turnover in the frog tadpole. *Physiol. Zool.* **30,** 87–91.

Hyman, C., and Chambers, R. (1943). Effect of adrenal cortical compounds on edema formation of frog's hind limbs. *Endocrinology* **32,** 310–318.

Inoue, M. (1959). Descending spinal pathway subserving adrenaline secretion of the adrenal gland in the toad. *Tohoku J. Exptl. Med.* **70,** 319–324.

Issekutz, B. von (1935). Über den Angriffspunkt des Thyroxins. *Wien. Klin. Wochschr.* **48,** 1325–1330.

Issekutz, B. von, and Issekutz, A. M. von (1935). Wirkungsort des Thyroxins. *Arch. Exptl. Pathol. Pharmakol. Naunyn-Schmiedeberg's* **177,** 442–449.

Issekutz, B. von, Tukats-Leinzinger, M., and Issekutz, A. M. von, (1943). Über die Wirkung des Thyroxins, β-Phenylisopropylamins, und des Adrenalins auf den Gasstoffwechsel des Frosches. *Arch. Exptl. Pathol. Pharmakol. Naunyn-Schmiedeberg's* **201,** 334–345.

Janes, R. G. (1938). Studies on the amphibian digestive system. III. The origin and development of pancreatic islands in certain species of Anura. *J. Morphol.* **62,** 375–391.

Johnsen, V. K., and Ussing, H. H. (1949). The influence of the corticotropic hormone from the ox on the active salt uptake in the axolotl. *Acta Physiol. Scand.* **17,** 38–47.

Jones, M. E., and Steggerda, F. R. (1935). Studies on water metabolism in normal and hypophysectomized frogs. *Am. J. Physiol.* **112,** 397–400.

Jorgensen, C. B. (1947). Influence of adenohypophysectomy on the transfer of salt across frog skin. *Nature* **160,** 872.

Jorgensen, C. B. (1950). The amphibian water economy with special regard to the effect of neurohypophyseal extracts. *Acta. Physiol. Scand.* **22,** (Suppl.) 78.

Jorgensen, C. B., and Larsen, L. O. (1960a). Effect of neurohypophyseal principles on adenohypophyseal activity in toads. *Proc. Soc. Exptl. Biol. Med.* **103,** 685–688.

Jorgensen, C. B., and Larsen, L. O. (1960b). Hormonal control of moulting in amphibians. *Nature* **185,** 244–245.

Jorgensen, C. B., and Nielsen, L. (1958). Effect of synthetic lysine-vasopressin on adenohypophysial activity in toads. *Proc. Soc. Exptl. Biol. Med.* **98,** 393–395.

Jorgensen, C. B., and Rosenkilde, P. (1956). Relative effectiveness of dehydration and neurohypophyseal extracts in enhancing water absorption in toads and frogs. *Biol. Bull.* **110,** 306–309.

Jorgensen, C. B., Larsen, L. O., Rosenkilde, P., and Wingstrand, K. G. (1960). Effect of extirpation of median eminence on function of pars distalis in the toad *Bufo bufo* (L.). *Comp. Biochem. Physiol.* **1,** 38–43.

Katsoyannis, P. G., and du Vigneaud, V. (1959). Arginine vasotocin. *Nature* **184,** 1465.

Kaye, N. W. (1961). Interrelationships of the thyroid and pituitary in embryonic and premetamorphic stages of the frog *Rana pipiens. Gen. Comp. Endocrinol.* **1,** 1–19.

Kaye, N. W., and Le Bourhis, E. E. (1958). Uptake and turnover of a single injected dose of I[131] in tadpoles of *Rana clamitans. Zoologica* **43,** 73–76.

Kepinov, L. (1938). Nouvelles recherches sur l'action antiglycogénolytique de l'insuline. *Compt. Rend. Soc. Biol.* **128,** 331–334.

Kezer, J. (1952). Thyroxin-induced metamorphosis of the neotinic salamanders *Eurycea tynerensis* and *Eurycea neotenes. Copeia* pp. 234–237.

Kinosita, H. (1953). Studies on the mechanism of pigment migration within fish melanophores with special reference to their electrical potentials. *Annotationes Zool. Japon.* **26,** 115–127.

Kiuchi, S. (1936). The action of adrenalin, pituitrin, and histamine on the permeability of the blood vessel wall to dyes. *Sei-i-kai Med. J.* **55,** 1354–1364.

Kleinfeld, M. A., Rosenthal, A., and Stein, E. (1958). Comparative effects of D-thyronine, L-triiodothyronine, and L-thyroxine on the isolated perfused frog heart. *Am. J. Physiol.* **195,** 63–65.

Kobayashi, H. (1958). Effect of desoxycorticosterone acetate on metamorphosis induced by thyroxine in anuran tadpoles. *Endocrinology* **62,** 371–377.

Kollros, J. J. (1942). Localized maturation of lid closure reflex mechanism by thyroid implants into tadpole hind brain. *Proc. Soc. Exptl. Biol. Med.* **49,** 204–206.

Kollros, J. J. (1943). Experimental studies on the development of the corneal reflex in Amphibia. II. Localized maturation of the reflex mechanism effected by thyroxin-agar implants into the hind brain. *Physiol. Zool.* **16,** 269–279.

Kollros, J. J. (1959). Thyroid gland function in developing cold-blooded vertebrates. *Comp. Endocrinol., Proc. Columbia Univ. Symp. Cold Spring Harbor N.Y. 1958,* pp. 340–350.

Kollros, J. J., and Pepernik, V. (1952). Hormonal control of the size of the mesencephalic V nucleus in *Rana pipiens*. *Anat. Record* **113**, 527 (abstr.).

Kolossow, N. G. (1927). Über die morphologische Bedeutung der Langerhansschen Inseln (der Einfluss des Zuckers auf die Inselelemente). *Z. Mikroskop. Anat. Forsch.* **11**, 43–66.

Kono, M. (1938). The influence of adrenaline, pituitrin and histamine on the passage of water through the walls of blood vessels. *Sei-i-kai Med. J.* **57**, 5–6.

Kuffler, S. W. (1945). Excitability changes at the neuromuscular junction during tetany. *J. Physiol. (London)* **103**, 403–411.

Kurotsu, T., and Kondo, H. (1941). Über die Beziehungen zwischen dem Jahreszyklus und der feineren Zellstruktur des Nucleus praeopticus magnocellularis bei *Bufo vulgaris japonicus*. *Japan. J. Med. Sci.* **9**, 64–65.

Lang, K. (1931). Nebennierenrinde und Muskelchemismus. *Arch. Ges. Physiol. Pfluger's* **229**, 60–85.

Lang, K. (1934) Über die Veränderung des Muskelstoffwechsels im Zusammenhang mit der Steigerung der Arbeitsleistungen des Muskel durch Nebennierenrindenhormon. *Naturwissenschaften* **22**, 91–92.

Leaf, A. (1960). Some actions of neurohypophyseal hormones on a living membrane. *J. Gen. Physiol.* **43**, 175–189.

Leaf, A., and Dempsey, E. (1960). Some effects of mammalian neurohypophyseal hormones on metabolism and active transport of sodium by the isolated toad bladder. *J. Biol. Chem.* **235**, 2160–2163.

Leblond, C. P. and Noble, G. K. (1937). Prolactin-like reaction produced by hypophysis of various vertebrates. *Proc. Soc. Exptl. Biol. Med.* **35**, 517–518.

Le Grand, A., and Ajoulat, L. (1931). Action de la thyroidectomie sur la rhéobase et la chronaxie de *Rana temporaria*. *Compt. Rend. Soc. Biol.* **108**, 1263-1264.

Levinsky, N. G., and Sawyer, W. H. (1952). Influence of the adenohypophysis on the frog water balance response. *Endocrinology* **51**, 110–115.

Lieben, S. (1906). Über die Wirkung von Extrakten chromaffinen Gewebes (Adrenalin) auf die Pigmentzellen. *Zentr. Physiol.* **20**, 108–117.

Lissak, K. (1939a). Effects of extracts of adrenergic fibers on the frog heart. *Am. J. Physiol.* **125**, 778–785.

Lissak, K. (1939b). Liberation of acetylcholine and adrenalin by stinulating isolated nerves. *Am. J. Physiol.* **127**, 263–271.

Loewi, O. (1936). Qualitative und quantitative Untersuchungen über den Sympatheticusstoff. *Arch. Ges. Physiol. Pflüger's.* **237**, 504–514.

Loewi, O., and Gettwert, W. (1914). Über die Folgen der Nebennierenexstirpation. *Arch. Ges. Physiol. Pflüger's* **158**, 29–40.

Loewit, M. (1910). Diabetesstudien. III. Der Pankreasdiabetes beim Frosche. *Arch. Exptl. Pathol. Pharmakol. Naunyn-Schmiedeberg's* **62**, 47–91.

Löwen, A. (1904). Quantitative Untersuchungen über die Gefässwirkung von Suprarenin. *Arch. Exptl. Pathol. Pharmakol. Naunyn-Schmiedeberg's* **51**, 415–441.

Lutz, B. R. (1933). The effect of adrenalin chloride and toad venom on the blood pressure and heart rate of the tropical toad, *Bufo marinus*. *Biol. Bull.* **64**, 299–303.

Lynn, W. G., and Wachowski, H. E. (1951). The thyroid gland and its functions in cold blooded vertebrates. *Quart. Rev. Biol.* **26**, 123–168.

McCarrison, R. (1923). The function of the adrenal gland and its relation to concentration of hydrogen-ion. *Brit. Med. J.* **I**, 101–102.

Macchi, I. A. (1955). *In vitro* ACTH stimulation of incubated frog adrenals. *Biol. Bull.* **109**, 373–374.

Macchi, I. A. (1956). *In vitro* ACTH action on reducing substance and QO₂ in frog adrenal tissue. *J. Clin. Endocrinol. Metab.* **16**, 942 (abstr.).

Maes, J. (1937). Study of the syndrome of adrenal insufficiency in the frog. *Arch. Intern. Physiol.* **45**, 135–188.

Maillet, M. (1960). Action de l'hormone adrénocorticotrope hypophysaire sur les cellules positives à la réaction de MacManus de la surrénale de *Rana esculenta*. *Compt. Rend. Soc. Biol.* **154**, 582–583.

Manery, J. F., Gourley, D. R., and Fisher, K. C. (1956). The potassium uptake and rate of oxygen consumption of isolated frog skeletal muscle in the presence of insulin and lactate. *Can. J. Biochem. Physiol.* **34**, 893–902.

Mansfeld, G., and Lanczos, A. (1936). Stoffwechselwirkung des Thyroxins am Kaltblüter. *Arch. Exptl. Pathol. Pharmakol. Naunyn-Schmiedeberg's* **183**, 267–273.

Marcuse, W. (1894). Über die Bedeutung der Leber für das Zustandekommen des Pankreasdiabetes. *Z. Klin. Med.* **26**, 225–257.

Marenzi, A. D. (1936). Chemical changes in the muscle of the hypophysectomized toad. *Endocrinology* **20**, 184–187.

Marenzi, A. D., and Fustinoni, O. (1938). Potassium of the blood and tissues of the adrenalectomized toad. *Rev. Soc. Arg. Biol.* **14**, 118–122.

Matsumoto, S. (1940). Untersuchungen über die Wirkung von Azetylcholin und Adrenalin auf die Lungengefässe der Kröten. *Okayama Igakkai Zasshi* **52**, 1585–1593.

Maurer, F. (1887). Schilddrüse, Thymus und Kiemenreste der Amphibien. *Morphol. Jahrb.* **13**, 296–382.

May, R. M., and Mugard, H. (1955). Action de l'ingestion de poudre de thyroide sur la multiplication cellulaire dans l'encéphale des têtards de *Rana temporaria*. *Ann. Endocrinol. Paris* **16**, 46–66.

Mazzi, V. (1947). Attività secretoria nel nucleo magnocellulari preottico di *Triturus cristatus carnifex*. *Atti. Accad. Naz. Lincei, Rend. Classe Sci. Fis. Mat. Nat.* [8], **3**, 155–161.

Miller, M. R. (1953). Experimental alteration of the adrenal histology of the urodele amphibian *Triturus torosus*. *Anat. Record* **116**, 205–225.

Miller, M. R. (1960). Pancreatic islet histology and carbohydrate metabolism in amphibians and reptiles. *Diabetes* **9**, 318–323.

Miller, M. R., and Wurster, D. H. (1959). The morphology and physiology of the pancreatic islets in urodele amphibians and lizards. *Comp. Endocrinol., Proc. Columbia Univ. Symp. Cold Spring Harbor N.Y. 1958.* pp. 668–680.

Minibeck, H. (1939). Die selektive Zuckerresorption beim Kaltblüter und ihre Beeinflussung durch Nebennieren- und Hypophysenextirpation. *Pflüger's Arch. Ges. Physiol.* **242**, 344–353.

Money, W. L., Lucas, V., and Rawson, R. W. (1955). The turnover of radioiodine by the *Rana pipiens* tadpole. *J. Exptl. Zool.* **128**, 411–421.

Morita, S. (1915). Pharmakologische Untersuchungen an den Portalgefässen der Froschleber. *Arch. Exptl. Pathol. Pharmakol. Naunyn-Schmiedeberg's* **78**, 232–244.

Moschini, A. (1934). Le phosphogène musculaire aprés destruction totale des surrénales chez la grenouille. *Compt. Rend. Soc. Biol.* **115**, 215–218.

Myers, R., Fleming, W. R., and Scheer, B. T. (1955). Pituitary-adrenal control of sodium flux across frog skin. *Endocrinology* **58**, 674–676.

Nogaki, S. (1924). On the influence of removal of the hypophysis and adrenals on the iritability of frog vessels. *Arch. Exptl. Pathol. Pharmakol. Naunyn-Schmiedeberg's* **103**, 147–162.

Norman, D., and Hiestand, W. A. (1960). Hormones and sugar penetration in skeletal muscle. *Comp. Biochem. Physiol.* **1**, 167–179.

Novales, R. R. (1959). The effects of osmotic pressure and sodium concentration on the response of melanophores to intermedin. *Physiol. Zool.* **32**, 15–28.

Ochoa, S. (1932). Über die Energetik der anaeroben Kontraktion von isolierten Muskeln nebennierenloser Frosche. *Pflüger's Arch. Ges. Physiol.* **231**, 222–233.

O'Connor, J. M. (1912). Über den Adrenalingehalt des Blutes. *Arch. Exptl. Pathol. Pharmakol. Naunyn-Schmiedeberg's* **67**, 195–232.

Oti, Y. (1940). The influence of acetylcholine and adrenaline on the spinal reflex. *Okayama Igakkai Zasshi* **52**, 2591–2597.

Paik, W. K., and Cohen, P. P. (1960). Biochemical studies on amphibian metamorphoses. I. The effect of thyroxine on protein synthesis in the tadpole. *J. Gen. Physiol.* **43**, 683–696.

Parker, G. H., (1948). "Animal Color Changes and Their Neurohumours." Cambridge Univ. Press, Cambridge, Massachusetts.

Parker, G. H., and Scatterty, L. E. (1937). The number of neurohumors in control of frog melanophores. *J. Cellular Comp. Physiol.* **9**, 297–314.

Parrot, J. L., Lavolloy, H., and Galmiche, P. (1944). Sur la viatmine P. Action de l'épicatéchine sur la résistance des capillaires. *Compt. Rend. Soc. Biol.* **138**, 179–181.

Pasqualini, R. Q., and Resau, J. C. (1951). Action de la désoxycorticostérone sur l'absorption cutanée chez le crapaud. *Compt. Rend. Soc. Biol.* **146**, 604–606.

Pesetsky, I., and Kollros, J. J. (1956). A comparison of the influence of locally applied thyroxine upon Mauthner's cell and adjacent neurones. *Exptl. Cell. Res.* **11**, 477–482.

Pickford, G., and Atz, J. W. (1957). "The Physiology of the Pituitary Gland of Fishes." New York Zoological Society, New York.

Rauchschwalbe, H. (1940). Permeabilitats-Studien mit Cortidyn. *Arch. Exptl. Pathol. Pharmakol. Naunyn-Schmiedeberg's* **195**, 425–438.

Rey, P., and Chambon, M. A. (1960). Influence de l'eclairement sur les manifestations histologiques de la secretion dans le complexe hypothalamo-neurohypophysaire et dans le lobe intermédiare de *Rana viridis* Linne. *Acta Endocrinol.* **35** (Suppl. 51), 109 (abstr.).

Richards, A. N., and Schmidt, C. F. (1924). A description of the glomerular circulation in the frog's kidney and observations concerning the action of adrenalin and various other substances upon it. *Am. J. Physiol.* **71**, 178–208.

Richards, A. N., Barnwell, J. B., and Bradley, R. C. (1927). The effect of small amounts of adrenalin upon the glomerular blood vessels of the frog's kidney perfused at a constant rate. *Am. J. Physiol.* **79**, 410–418.

Richardson, D. (1940). Thyroid and pituitary hormones in relation to regeneration. I. The effect of anterior pituitary hormone on regeneration of the hindleg in normal and thyroidectomized newts. *J. Exptl. Zool.* **83**, 407–429.

Rokhlina, M. L., and Petrovskaya, O. A. (1939). Effect of the suprarenal cortex on the metamorphosis of the axolotl. (translation). *Probl. Endokrinol.* **4**, 3–16.

Romeis, B. (1926). Morphologische und experimentelle Studien uber die Epithelkörper der Amphibien. *Z. Anat. Entwicklungsgeschichte* **80**, 547–578.

Rothlin, E. (1920). Experimentelle Studien uber die Eigenschaften uberlebender Gefässe unter Anwendung der chemischen Reizmethode. *Biochem. Z.* **111**, 219–256.

Ruf, H. (1937). Untersuchungen über die Muskelfunktion nach Adrenalektomie mit Hilfe des Aktionsstroms. *Z. Biol.* **98**, 154–162.

Saguchi, S. (1921). Cytological studies of Langerhans' islets with special reference to the problem of their relation to the pancreatic acinous tissue. *Am. J. Anat.* **28**, 1–57.

Satow, Y. (1938). On the action of adrenaline of the toads heart *in situ*. *Tohoku J. Exptl. Med.* **32**, 20–26.

Sawyer, W. H. (1956). The hormonal control of water and salt-electrolyte metabolism with special reference to the Amphibia. *Mem. Soc. Endocrinol.* **5**, 44–56.

Sawyer, W. H. (1957a). Increased renal reabsorption of osmotically free water by the toad *Bufo marinus* in response to dehydration and neurohypophyseal extracts. *Am. J. Physiol.* **189**, 564–568.

Sawyer, W. H. (1957b). The antidiuretic action of neurohypophysial hormones in Amphibia. *In* "The Neurohypophysis" (H. Heller, ed.), pp. 171–179. Butterworths, London.

Sawyer, W. H. (1960a). Evidence for the identity of natriferin, the frog water-balance principle, and arginine vasotocin. *Nature* **187**, 1030–1031.

Sawyer, W. H. (1960b). Increased water permeability of the bullfrog (*Rana catesbeiana*) bladder *in vitro* in response to synthetic oxytocin and arginine vasotocin and to neurohypophysial extracts from nonmammalian vertebrates. *Endocrinology* **66**, 112–120.

Sawyer, W. H., and Sawyer, M. K. (1952). Adaptive responses to neurohypophyseal fractions in vertebrates. *Physiol. Zool.* **25**, 84–98.

Sawyer, W. H., Munsick, R. A., and Van Dyke, H. B. (1959). Pharmacological evidence for the presence of arginine vasotocin and oxytocin in neurohypophysial extracts from cold-blooded vertebrates. *Nature* **184**, 1463–1464.

Sawyer, W. H., Munsick, R. A., and Van Dyke, H. B. (1960). Antidiuretic hormones. *Circulation* **21**, 1027–1037.

Saxen, L., Saxen, E., Toivonen, S., and Salimaki, K. (1957). Quantitative investigation on the anterior pituitary-thyroid mechanism during frog metamorphosis. *Endocrinology* **61**, 35–44.

Scharrer, B. (1959). The role of neurosecretion in neuroendocrine integration. *Comp. Endocrinol., Proc. Columbia Univ. Symp. Cold Spring Harbor N.Y. 1958*, pp. 134–148.

Scharrer, E. (1959). General and phylogenetic interpretations of neuroendocrine interrelations. *Comp. Endocrinol., Proc. Columbia Univ. Symp. Cold Spring Harbor N.Y. 1958*, pp. 233–249.

Scharrer, E., and Scharrer, B. (1954). Neurosekretion. *In* "Handbuch der mikroskopischen Anatomie des Menschen" (W. von Möllendorff, ed.), Vol. III, Pt. 5, pp. 953–1066. Springer, Berlin.

Scheer, B. T., and Bishop, W. R. (1960). Pituitary-adrenal control of active transport across frog skin. *Acta Endocrinol.* **35** (Suppl. 51), 225.

Shellabarger, C. J., Gorbman, A., Schatzlein, F. C., and McGill, D. (1955). Some quantitative and qualitative aspects of I131 metabolism in turtles. *Endocrinology* **59**, 331–339.

Schneider, W. (1926). Die Wirkung von Hormonen auf den Kapillarkreislauf unter möglichst physiologischen Bedingungen. *Biochem. Z.* **173**, 111–138.

Scholz, V. (1933). Morphologische Untersuchungen über die Epithelkörper der Urodelen. *Z. Mikroscop. Anat. Forsch.* **34**, 159–200.

Scholz, J. (1935). Die Wirkung der Parathyreoidektomie bei Urodelen. *Wilhelm Roux Arch. Entwicklungsmech. Organ.* **132**, 752–762.

Schreiber, G. (1933). Ricerche sperimentali sulla neotenia degli Urodeli. L'azione della tiroxina sugli innesti xenoplastici di pelle. *Arch. Zool. Ital.* **27**, 181–215.

Seiden, G. (1945). The response of the pancreatic islands of the frog (*Rana pipiens*) to alloxan. *Anat. Record* **91**, 187–197.

Shapiro, B. G. (1933). The topography and histology of the parathyroid glandules in *Xenopus laevis*. *J. Anat.* **68**, 39–44.

Sima, I. (1939). Über den Einfluss von verschiedenen Hormonen auf die retinale Pigmentverschiebung nach Ausschaltung der Nebennierenfunction. *Arch. Intern. Pharmacodyn.* **62**, 168–174.

Sluiter, J. W., Mighorst, J. C. A., and van Oordt, J. T. (1949). The changes in cytology of the adrenals of *Rana esculenta* following hypophysectomy. *Koninkl. Ned. Akad. Wetenschap. Proc.* **52**, 1214–1219.

Smith, P. E. (1916). Experimental ablation of the hypophysis in the frog embryo. *Science* **44**, 280–282.

Sollman, T., and Barlow, D. H. (1926). The effect of epinephrine and prolonged accelerated stimulation on the response of the frog's heart to stimulation of the cardio-inhibitory nerve. *J. Pharmacol. Exptl. Therap.* **28**, 159–164.

Spaeth, R. A. (1916). Evidence proving the melanophore to be a disguised type of smooth muscle cell. *J. Exptl. Zool.* **20**, 193–215.

Speidel, C. C. (1929). Studies of hyperthyroidism. VI. Regenerative phenomena in thyroid-treated amphibian larvae. *Am. J. Anat.* **43**, 103–165.

Stilling, H. (1898). Zur Anatomie der Nebennieren. *Arch. Mikroskop. Anat. Entwicklungsmech.* **52**, 176–195.

Stone, L. S., and Steinitz, H. (1953). Effects of hypophysectomy and thyroidectomy on lens regeneration in the adult newt, *Triturus viridescens*. *J. Exptl. Zool.* **124**, 469–504.

Swingle, W. W. (1919). Iodine and the thyroid. III. The specific action of iodine in accelerating amphibian metamorphosis. *J. Gen. Physiol.* **1**, 593–606.

Swingle, W. W. (1920). Iodine and the thyroid. IV. Quantitative experiments on iodine feeding and metamorphosis. *J. Gen. Physiol.* **2**, 161–171.

Swingle, W. W. (1922). Thyroid transplantation and anuran metamorphosis. *J. Exptl. Zool.* **37**, 219–257.

Taylor, A. (1936). Athyroidism in the salamander *Triturus torosus* Rathke. *J. Exptl. Zool.* **73**, 153–181.

Taylor, A. (1937). The effect of athyroidism on the rate of cell division. *J. Exptl. Zool.* **75**, 239–244.

Taylor, A. (1939). The effect of athyroidism and hyperthyroidism on the oxygen consumption of the adult salamander. *J. Exptl. Zool.* **81**, 135–146.

Taylor, A. B., and Weinstein, I. (1952). The effect of desoxycorticosterone glucoside (dog) upon the potential of isolated frog skin. *Anat. Record* **113**, 611.

Thurmond, W., and Eakin, R. M. (1959). Implantation of the amphibian adenohypophysial anlage into albino larvae. *J. Exptl. Zool.* **140**, 145–168.

Tiffeneau, R., and Beauvallet, M. (1938). Cessation spontanée des effects de l'adrénaline sur le coeur de Grenouille. Formation probable d'une substance antagoniste. *Compt. Rend. Soc. Biol.* **138**, 226–227.

Uhlenhuth, E. (1923). The endocrine system of *Typhlomolge rathbuni*. *Biol. Bull.* **45**, 303–324.

Ulick, S., and Solomon, S. (1960). The synthesis of aldosterone from progesterone by the amphibian adrenal. *J. Am. Chem. Soc.* **82**, 249.

Ungar, I. (1933). La cause de la production d'une pellicule cutanée, chez le Crapaud hypophysoprive ou à tuber lésé. *Compt. Rend. Soc. Biol.* **112**, 504–506.

Uranga, J., and Sawyer, W. H. (1960). Renal responses of the bullfrog to oxytocin, arginine vasotocin, and frog neurohypophyseal extract. *Am. J. Physiol.* **198,** 1287–1290.

Urechia, C. I., Benetato, G., and Retezeanu, M. (1937). Nouvelles recherches sur le potassium dans l'insuffisance surrénale. *Compt. Rend. Soc. Biol.* **125,** 191–192.

Ussing, H. H. (1952). Ion transport across living membranes. *Conf. Renal Function, Trans. 4th Conf.*

Ussing, H. (1960). The frog skin potential. *J. Gen. Physiol.* **43,** 135–148.

van Oordt, G. J., van Oordt, P. G. W. J., and van Dongen, W. J. (1959). Recent experiments on the regulation of spermatogenesis and the mechanism of speriation in the common frog, *Rana temporaria. Comp. Endocrinol., Proc. Columbia Univ. Symp. Cold Spring Harbor N.Y. 1958,* pp. 488–498.

Verne, J., and Delsol, M. (1956). Les cellules positives à la réaction de MacManus dans la surrénale de *Rana esculenta* L. *Ann. Histochim.* **32,** 91–97.

Verney, E. B. (1947). The antidiuretic hormone and the factors which determine its release. *Proc. Roy. Soc.* **B135,** 25–34.

Villee, C. A. (1943). The effect of adrenocorticotrophic hormone on the interrenals (cortical tissue) of *Triturus torosus. J. Elisha Mitchell Sci. Soc.* **59,** 23–26.

Vivien, J. H., and Schott, J. (1958). Contribution a l'étude des corrélations hypothalamopituitaires chez les batraciens. Le controle de l'activité gonadotrope. *J. Physiol. (London)* **50,** 561–563.

von Buddenbrock, W. (1950). "Vergleichende Physiologie," Vol. IV. Birkhauser. Basel.

von Euler, U.S. (1933). Thyroxin und Gewebsoxydation. *Klin. Wochschr.* p. 671.

von Mering, I., and Minkowski, O. (1890). Diabetes mellitus nach Pankreasextirpation. *Arch. Exptl. Pathol. Pharmakol. Naunyn-Schmiedeberg's* **26,** 371–387.

Wachholder, K., and Morgenstern, V. (1933). Der Einfluss von Wirksubstanzen der Nebennierenrinde und von Adrenalin auf die Leistungen der Muskeln normaler und nebennierenloser Frösche. *Arch. Ges. Physiol. Pflüger's* **232,** 444–453.

Waggener, R. A. (1929). A histological study of the parathyroids in the Anura. *J. Morphol. Physiol.* **48,** 1–44.

Waggener, R. A. (1930). An experimental study of the parathyroids in the Anura. *J. Exptl. Zool.* **57,** 13–55.

Wagner, R. J., and Allen, F. M. (1929). Gaseous and carbohydrate metabolism in bullfrogs after removal of the liver and the pancreas. *Am. J. Physiol.* **90,** 548–549.

Wald, G. (1946). *Harvey Lectures Ser.* **41,** 117–134.

Warren, M. R. (1940). Studies on the effect of experimental hyperthyroidism on the adult frog *Rana pipiens. J. Exptl. Zool.* **83,** 127–159.

Wastl, H. (1921). Über die Wirkung des Adrenalins auf die Drüsen der Krötenhaut. *Z. Biol.* **74,** 77–80.

Waterman, N., and Boddaert, R. J. (1908). Über den Nachweis von Nebennierenprodukten im Blut und Harn. *Deut. Med. Wochschr.* **34,** 1102–1103.

Wehland, N. (1922). Action de l'atropine sur les effects exercés par l'adrénaline sur les vaisseaux sanguins. *Compt. Rend. Soc. Biol.* **87,** 774–776.

Welsh, J. H. (1959). Neuroendocrine substances. *Comp. Endocrinol., Proc. Columbia Univ. Symp. Cold Spring Harbor N.Y. 1958,* pp. 121–133.

Wertheimer, E. (1922). Untersuchungen am intakten Kreislauf verschiedener Organe beim Frosch. *Arch. Ges. Physiol. Pflüger's.* **196,** 412–422.

West, G. B. (1955). The comparative pharmacology of the suprarenal medulla. *Quart. Rev. Biol.* **30,** 116–137.

Wilson, L. O., Weinberg, J. A., and Bern, H. A. (1957). The hypothalamic neurosecretory system of the tree frog *Hyla regilla. J. Comp. Neurol.* **107,** 253–272.

Wingstrand, K. G. (1959). Attempts at a comparison between the neurohypophysial region in fishes and tetrapods, with particular regard to amphibians. *Comp. Endocrinol., Proc. Columbia Univ. Symp. Cold Spring Harbor N.Y. 1958*, pp. 393–403.

Witschi, E. (1953). The experimental adrenogenital syndrome in the frog. *J. Clin. Endocrinol.* **13,** 316–329.

Witschi, E., and Chang, C. Y. (1959). Amphibian ovulation and spermiation. *Comp. Endocrinol., Proc, Columbia Univ. Symp. Cold Spring Harbor, N.Y. 1958*, pp. 149–160.

Wright, P. A. (1947). Antagonism of adrenalin and intermedin on the melanophores of frog skin *in vitro. Anat. Record* **99,** 595.

Wright, P. A. (1948). Photoelectric measurement of melanophoral activity of frog skin induced *in vitro. J. Cellular Comp. Physiol.* **31,** 111–123.

Wright, P. A. (1955). Physiological responses of frog melanophores *in vitro. Physiol. Zool.* **28,** 204–218.

Wright, P. A. (1959). Blood sugar studies in the bullfrog *Rana catesbeiana. Endocrinology* **64,** 551–558.

Wurster, D. H., and Miller, M. R. (1960). Studies on the blood glucose and pancreatic islets of the salamander *Taricha torosa. Comp. Biochem. Physiol.* **1,** 101–109.

Zuckerstein, S. (1917). Die Wirkung des Adrenalins auf die Gefässe verschiedener Abschnitte der Niere des Frosches und die Veränderungsfähigkeit dieser Wirkung. *Z. Biol.* **67,** 293–306.

Zwarenstein, H. (1933). Metabolic changes associated with endocrine activity and the reproductive cycle in *Xenopus laevis*. Part 2. The effect of hypophysectomy on the potassium content of the serum. *J. Exptl. Biol.* **10,** 201–203.

Zwarenstein, H., and Bosma, L. P. (1932). The influence of hypophysectomy on the blood sugar and glucose tolerance in *Xenopus* laevis. *Quart. J. Exptl. Physiol.* **22,** 45–48.

Zweifach, B. W., and Chambers, R. (1942). Responses of the capillary bed in the frog to adrenal-cortical hormones. *Anat. Record* **84,** 461.

8

METAMORPHOSIS

William Etkin

I. Introduction

A. NATURE OF METAMORPHOSIS

By metamorphosis we shall understand a postembryonic period of extensive morphological change by which a larva adapted to one mode of life is transformed into an adult with a different manner of living. Amphibians, except for a few with specialized life histories, begin life as free-living aquatic organisms called larvae, which subsequently transform at metamorphosis into more or less terrestrial adults. The nature of this transformation varies considerably with the degree of specialization of each phase for its own ecological niche.

The anurans are the most highly specialized of the amphibians in this respect. Their larvae, called tadpoles, usually differ from the adult not only in manner of respiration as is necessary for the difference in environment but also in manner of locomotion, feeding, sensory apparatus, etc. Hence, in this group metamorphosis involves the most radical transformation of the organism. Urodele larvae on the other hand, are generally more or less similar to the adults except for respiratory apparatus and skin and consequently show a less highly developed metamorphic pattern. The Apoda show some transformation in development similar to metamorphosis (Klumpp and Eggert, 1934) but being a little studied group will not enter into our discussion. The specialized life histories will be discussed separately below.

Our concern in this chapter is to try to understand the physiological mechanisms which regulate the process of metamorphosis. The previous discussion makes it evident that anuran metamorphosis provides the best material for experimental analysis with the urodeles and forms having the specialized life histories offering supplemental information. Since this field has been reviewed periodically we shall not attempt here to develop the subject historically or to document the conclusions drawn from earlier studies. Instead, we shall concentrate our attention upon the aspects of the experimental analysis which have received particular attention during the last 10 years. Where conclusions and concepts derived from earlier work are not specifically documented the reader will find the evidence specified in one of the reviews listed (Bounhiol, 1942; Lynn and Wachowski, 1951; Etkin, 1955; Roth, 1956a; Kollros, 1959). The biochemical aspects of amphibian metamorphosis have recently been given detailed treatment by Frieden (1961).

B. ANURAN METAMORPHOSIS

For an appreciation of the physiological analysis it is necessary to have a clear concept of the morphological transformations involved in metamorphosis particularly their sequential and temporal relations. In this section we shall briefly consider metamorphic change as found in typical anurans, of which *Rana pipiens* may be considered the paradigm since it is the most extensively studied of American anurans. The temporal sequence of metamorphic events has been described for this and related Ranidae (Etkin, 1932), and Taylor and Kollros (1946) have provided an admirably illustrated description of postembryonic development in numbered stages. In Table I these studies are summarized and supplemented in terms of days before and after the critical event of emergence of the forelegs (for other species see reviews, also Nieuwkoop and Faber, 1956).

In summary we may briefly characterize the principal stages of anuran development as follows. At the end of the embryonic period (about 8 days at 23°C) the animal has assumed the definitive larval form with an oval body (head-body) region and a muscular tail nearly twice the body length (Fig. 1). It maintains this tadpole form without essential change for the following 5 or 6 weeks (23°C) while the total length of the animal increases from about 12 to 55 mm and its weight from less than 0.01 grams

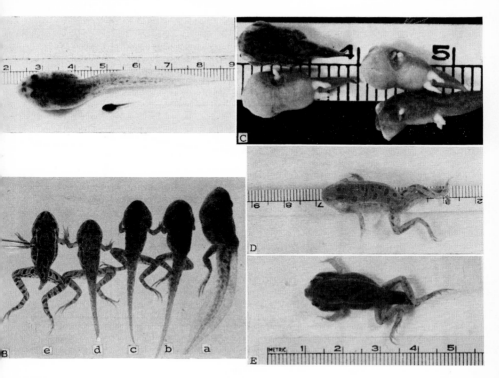

Fig. 1.   A. Normal tadpoles (*Rana pipiens*), smaller, at beginning of tadpole stage, larger, 5 weeks older, at beginning of prometamorphosis.   B. Normal tadpoles near and in metamorphic climax; a = day before emergence of foreleg (E − 1); b = E + 0; c = E + 1; d = E + 2; e = E + 4.   C. Results of treating early tadpoles with strong concentrations of thyroxine (243 p.p.b.). Note distorted metamorphosis since all tissue changes are induced at the same time instead of being properly spaced out in time.   D. Result of treating a large thyroidectomized tadpole with a patterned sequence of increasing thyroxine concentrations. Note essentially normal morphology.   E. Results of treating a large hypophysectomized tadpole as in D.

to about 1.0 grams. Meanwhile the hind legs have grown at a rate only slightly greater, than the body and have reached about 4 mm and differentiated into three basic regions. The ratio of hind leg to body length increases from about 0.1 in the 40 mm. tadpole to 0.2 (Fig. 2 and Table I). This period is the premetamorphic or larval period and is characterized by much growth with very little developmental change. It is followed by the first metamorphic period, called prometamorphosis, during which growth continues but differential development of parts begins to transform the organism to the adult form. Initially the most conspicuous change is the differential acceleration of hind leg growth whereby these structures grow

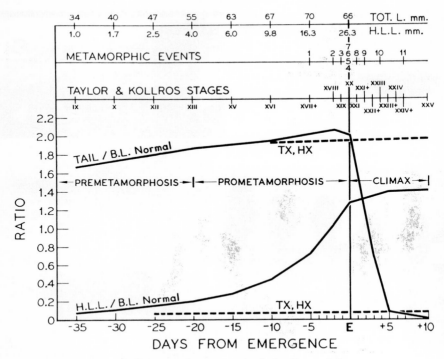

Fig. 2. Pattern of metamorphosis in *Rana pipiens*

The data summarized in Table I are here presented graphically. Twenty animals from one batch were raised individually in fingerbowls and fed canned spinach. The temperature was 23°C ± 1. Time on the abscissa is given in days before or after the emergence of the second foreleg (E), which is taken as the beginning of metamorphic climax. Although in our experience the absolute values of size and rate of tadpole growth vary considerably from batch to batch, the relative values of hind leg length (H.L.L.) to body length (B.L.) and of tail length (T.L.) to body length and the timing of gross morphological change are relatively uniform between groups. We therefore find it convenient to evaluate the developmental stage of tadpoles before metamorphosis according to the T and K stages, during prometamorphosis by the ratio of H.L.L. to B.L. (lower curve, solid line) and during climax by the ratio of T.L. to B.L. (upper curve, solid line). Additional checks are afforded by the T and K stages during metamorphosis and by the morphological data summarized in the last column of the table and shown as numbered metamorphic events in the figure (key to the numbers given at end of this legend). It must be emphasized that no one criterion is applicable to all stages although in the experimental literature frequent attempts to apply one criterion such as the ratio of tail to leg length have been made.

By the use of this figure and accompanying Table I the progress of a tadpole in metamorphosis can be evaluated on a time axis. In this way data derived from the study of animals sacrificed at varying stages can be interpreted in terms of growth curves showing the rate of change of the items studied. Also the time at which a specific tadpole may be expected to reach a particular status in metamorphosis may be estimated for normal conditions.

rapidly to about 20 mm while the total length of the animal increases to about 68 mm. The ratio of the hind leg length to body length increases in this period from 0.2 to about 1.2. The ratio of the tail to body length remains approximately constant near 2.0. Prometamorphosis lasts about 3 weeks during which time a definite sequence of relatively inconspicuous changes occur as listed in the legend for Fig. 2 and in Table I. With the emergence of the forelegs (E) through an opening developed by degeneration in one corner of the opercular skin (skin window of foreleg, SWFL) prometamorphosis may be said to terminate. It is followed by a period of very rapid and profound morphological change called metamorphic climax (Fig. 1). This lasts about 1 week. During this period the narrow mouth of the tadpole transforms to the wide frog mouth, the tongue increases to more than double its initial length, the gills and the remains of the operculum are resorbed, and most conspicuously the tail undergoes complete resorption, losing about half its length in the 2 days E + 2 to E + 4.

It is well to note that although resorption phenomena are most conspicuous during climax and growth changes during prometamorphosis, neither of these processes is confined to one period; in fact, the attainment of the appropriate change in each period requires the coordination of both resorptive and growth changes. Thus from Table I it can be seen that ACP (anal canal piece) and SWFL constitute resorptive changes in prometamorphosis and that the jaws, tongue, and tympanic apparatus grow during climax. The nature of metamorphic change is thus specific for each tissue. An analysis of metamorphosis should encompass the entire range of changes and their complex of sequential and temporal interrelations.

C. URODELE METAMORPHOSIS

Among urodeles metamorphic transformation is not as dramatic or complex as in the anurans since the tail is retained in the adult and the legs do not undergo any marked changes, having completed their morphological differentiation in late embryonic stages. Skin changes involving loss of the larval Leydig cells, growth of glands and pigmentary developments, the reduction of the external gills and of the fin of the tail are the characteristic changes of salamander metamorphosis. It is well to note that amphibian

---

Comparable data for thyroidectomized animals (TX) and hypophysectomized animals (HX) are shown by broken lines.

The metamorphic events indicated in the figure by number are the following: 1. Anal canal piece—first definite reduction. 2. Anal canal piece reduction completed. 3. Skin window for the forelegs clearly apparent. 4. Loss of 2nd (both) beaks, in experimental animals this is the most satisfactory criterion for the beginning of climax (E). 5. Emergence of first foreleg to appear. 6. Emergence of second foreleg. 7. Mouth widened to level of nostril. 8. Mouth widened to level between nostril and eye. 9. Mouth widened to level of anterior edge of eye. 10. Mouth widened past level of middle of eye. 11. Tympanum definitely recognizable.

TABLE I

NORMAL PATTERN OF METAMORPHOSIS IN *Rana pipiens* AT 23°C

Days	T. and K. stage	Average total length (mm)	Average body length (mm)	Average hind leg length (mm)	Ratio: tail to body length	Ratio: hind leg to body length	Gross morphological changes since previous time
Premetamorphosis							
E − 35	IX	34	10	1.0	1.66	—	—
E − 30	X	40	13	1.7	1.73	0.10	—
E − 25	XII	47	17	2.5	1.81	0.15	—
Prometamorphosis							
E − 20	XIII	55	20	4.0	1.85	0.20	—
E − 15	XV	63	23	6.0	1.90	0.28	—
E − 10	XVI	67	24	9.8	1.94	0.42	—
E − 5	XVII+	70	25	16	1.97	0.73	ACP definitely begun
E − 2	XVIII	70	25	22	2.03	1.01	ACP completely reduced. SWFL usually clear
E − 1	XIX	68	25	25	2.05	1.18	SWFL definitely clear
E + 0	XX	66	25	27	2.03	1.25	Loss of 2 beaks, emergence of 2 forelegs, mouth to nostril
Metamorphic Climax							
E + 1	XXI	—	—	—	1.66	—	Mouth between nostril and eye
E + 2	XXI+	—	—	—	1.26	—	Mouth to anterior eye
E + 3	XXII+	—	—	—	0.68	—	Mouth slightly past mid eye
E + 4	XXIII	—	—	—	0.39	—	Mouth definitely past mid eye
E + 5	XXIII+	—	—	—	0.14	—	Tympanum beginning. Tail conical stub (no fin)
E + 6	XXIV	—	—	—	—	—	Opercular membrane completely resorbed
E + 7	XXIV+	—	—	—	—	—	Tympanum definitely recognizable
E + 10	XXV	—	—	—	—	—	Black stub of tail gone completely

larvae generally already possess lungs in larval stages. Metamorphic transformation in urodeles occurs in a short period generally of a few days duration.

On morphological grounds the metamorphosis of the salamander seems to correspond to metamorphic climax in anurans. The two periods are alike in the resorption of the gills and of tail structures, in the cessation of feeding and reconstruction of the gut, and in the general intensity of morphological change at this time. In this interpretation a period of prometamorphosis is absent in urodeles, the rapid leg growth so characteristic of this period in anurans being independent of metamorphosis in urodeles and the skin changes characterizing late prometamorphosis in anurans being incorporated in the brief but highly active metamorphic period of urodeles.

As we shall see there is reason to think that the mechanisms regulating urodele metamorphosis correspond to those of anuran climax and not to those of prometamorphosis. Presumably the urodele condition is the more primitive, that of the anurans evolving with the development of a life history in which the larva has a very different ecological adaptation from that of the adult.

The fossil record gives us but little direct evidence on this matter. However, the commonly accepted concept of the origin of the Devonian amphibians (Stegocephalia) from lung-possessing Crossopterygii suggests that in the most primitive form of the amphibian life history the aquatic stage differed from the adult chiefly in the extent to which the lung was used in respiration rather than as a hydrostatic organ. In this view separate evolutionary paths of specialization for the larva and adult became possible with the evolution of an endocrine mechanism by which a definite transformation of one state to the other was regularized. It is this mechanism which will be considered in this chapter. If we may anticipate our conclusion in order to apply it to the general evolutionary considerations before us, we may say that one mechanism, namely that of anuran climax, was evolved by the common ancestor of urodeles and anurans and thus is now possessed by both groups. The second, that of prometamorphosis, was subsequently developed by anurans and is now found exclusively in this group.

D. ABERRANT LIFE HISTORIES

The specialized life histories found in amphibians are of two forms; (1) direct development and (2) neoteny. Direct development consists in the suppression of the free-living larval stage so that the young become free of the parent as miniature adults. Such life histories are found chiefly among anurans. Two such forms which have been extensively studied are the tropical American genus *Eleutherodactylus* and the South African genus *Arthroleptella*. In both a fairly typical tadpole develops from the large egg but this undergoes precocious metamorphosis within the egg membrane "aquarium" in which it lies. Direct development has also been described for a urodele (Dent, 1942).

In neoteny, on the contrary, it is the "adult" terrestrial stage which is suppressed and reproduction occurs in the larval form. Metamorphosis does not occur where neoteny is complete but in some forms skin or other structures may show typical transformation without gill reduction or other metamorphic changes. This type of life history is fairly common among urodeles, some species being definitively neotenous and not showing metamorphosis under any circumstances. Other species are facultatively neotenous showing transformation only in some circumstances in nature or in the laboratory. The analysis of aberrant life histories throws light on the normal physiology of metamorphosis and upon the evolutionary pathways by which the developmental mechanisms have been transformed.

II. Thyroid Action in Metamorphosis

A. INTRODUCTION

The central role of the thyroid-pituitary axis in regulating amphibian metamorphosis was clearly established in the first quarter of this century and extended in detail during the next 25 years. From this work the following concepts may be accepted as the basis for an examination of modern studies: (1) Metamorphic change in the tissues is activated primarily by the hormone or hormones produced by the thyroid gland. (2) The metamorphic activity of the thyroid gland is controlled by a specific thyroid stimulating hormone (TSH or thyrotropin) secreted by the anterior lobe of the pituitary.

B. CHEMICAL NATURE OF THE THYROID HORMONE

Contemporary work indicates that the principal hormone secreted by the mammalian thyroid is thyroxine (TX) with variable amounts of the lower iodinated thyronines particularly triiodothyronine (T3) playing a subsidiary role by reason of their low concentrations (Barker, 1954; Pitt-Rivers and Tata, 1959). This appears to be true of the amphibian thyroid as well (Donoso, 1958; Shellabarger and Brown, 1959). The great activity of thyroxine when dissolved in the external medium on metamorphosis has long been known. Recent studies indicate that T3 is more active than thyroxine by a factor variously estimated as 4 to 8 times (Bruice *et al.*, 1954; Roth, 1954; Shellabarger and Godwin, 1954; Money *et al.*, 1958, 1960). In this respect the tadpole resembles various mammalian test objects. However, other modifications of the central diphenol molecule yield in a few instances, compounds even more active in the tadpole test than T3 although these do not show such excess activity in the mammal. Thus the propionic acid analogue is reported as much as several hundred times as active as TX by the tadpole test though by mammalian tests it is no more active than T3 (Bruice *et al.*, 1954; Money *et al.*, 1960). Other discrepancies between tadpole and mammalian tests are reported by Lardy (1955), Roth (1956b), and Tomita and Lardy (1956). However, these results must be regarded with caution because Frieden (1961) has recently reported that the differences may depend upon the manner of application of the compound—immersion in the tadpole test and injection in mammals. When injected into tadpoles, he finds some of these compounds to exhibit much the same relative potencies as in mammals.

The greater activity of T3 as compared with TX has been interpreted as due to its greater penetrance into cells and the suggestion has been made that TX is enzymically converted to T3 in the periphery and the latter is the active substance (Gross and Pitt-Rivers, 1953). In this event it is conceivable that the regulation of metamorphosis might, in part, result from a shift in the nature of the hormone produced by the gland at different times. However, the study by Shellabarger and Brown (1959) noted above indicates that TX was predominant at all stages studied and no important qualitative changes in the hormone were noted. The studies by Kaltenbach with different thyroid analogues applied locally to produce metamorphic change (Kaltenbach, 1959a) may throw further light on the possible physiological role of these modifications of the thyroxine molecule which show such surprising activities. But to date, we have no reason to believe that qualitative changes in thyroid hormone production are important influences in governing metamorphosis and we must regard thyroid activity in metamorphosis as essentially the result of thyroxine secretion.

C. INFLUENCE OF OTHER HORMONES ON THYROID ACTION

There has been renewed interest in the possibility that thyroid action in metamorphosis is influenced by other endocrine glands. On *a priori* grounds such an influence might be expected from the adrenal steroids because of the extensive changes in water, salt, and protein metabolism occurring at metamorphosis and because of the similarity of resorption phenomena at metamorphosis to inflammatory tissue responses. Perhaps the most definitive study associating corticosteroids and thyroid action is that of Kobayashi (1958), who reported that deoxycorticosterone acetate (DCA) potentiates degenerative changes and antagonizes certain growth changes induced by thyroxine. Results with adrenal steroids, however, are not consistent. Wurmbach and Haardick (1952) for example found DCA without marked effect on metamorphosis. Frieden and Naile (1955) and Kaltenbach (1958) found an enhancement of induced metamorphosis by glucocorticoids but Dastoli and Tector (1959) report an opposite effect. Gonadal steroids have generally shown inhibitory effects on thyroid activity (Roth, 1941, 1950; Gallien, 1950), although some workers report little or no effect from them (Vegmitalluri and Padoa, 1953; Schubert, 1957; Kobayashi, 1958). Unfortunately in the studies with thyroxine-steroid combination normal tadpoles were used so that indirect effects upon the animal's own endocrine system have not been excluded. In any case, the ready response of tissues to local thyroxine application (see Section II,F below) and the sensitivity of hypophysectomized animals to thyroxine (publication in preparation) argue against any essential role for adrenal or gonadal steroids in metamorphosis. We must conclude, therefore, that whatever pharmacological interactions may occur, no physiological role in the normal metamorphic process has been demonstrated for any of the steroid hormones. We are thus led to look to quantitative variations in the thyroid hormone, rather than to complex interactions between many hormones, for an understanding of the patterning of metamorphic events.

D. LEVEL OF THYROID HORMONE IN NORMAL METAMORPHOSIS

Early morphological studies of the thyroid during metamorphosis had indicated that the gland is activated at the time of metamorphosis. In the salamander (*Ambystoma*) the rather large and well developed follicles of the larval gland show extreme activation not only in increased height of the cells and vacuolization of colloid but in an extensive evacuation of the colloid and collapse of the follicles. In anurans the activation is less extreme but equally unequivocal. The premetamorphic gland is small and by histological criteria appears inactive. During prometamorphosis it grows rapidly both absolutely and relative to body size. Epithelial height and other indices attest to increasing activity at this time. At the beginning of climax the gland is large, epithelial height is maximal, and colloid vacuolization is extensive. In some species (*Xenopus*) extensive evacuation of colloid occurs (Saxen *et al.*, 1957a, b), but in most this is not conspicuous. The morphological picture clearly suggests the similarity of anuran climax with salamander metamorphosis in respect to extreme activation of the thyroid. This substantiates the concept of the comparability of these two developmental phases suggested above on the basis of the similarity of metamorphic events. At the end of climax (E + 7) the gland appears quite inactive, again with flattened epithelium and follicles distended with dense acidophilic colloid. This picture has been interpreted as indicating an activation of the gland at the beginning of prometamorphosis, with the level of activity increasing to a maximum at the beginning of climax and subsequent sudden reduction to minimal activity at the end of metamorphosis (Etkin, 1936).

With the availability of radioiodine (I^{131}) the problem of quantifying thyroid activity in relation to metamorphosis has been restudied by a number of workers. One conclusion which has clearly emerged is that the thyroid gland of the premetamorphic animal is functional in trapping and releasing iodine although the rate of activity at this time is very low (Gorbman and Evans, 1941; Schmidt, 1956; Saxen et al., 1957a, b; Hunt and Dent, 1957; Kaye, 1961). This concept of functional activity before metamorphosis begins is supported by studies of the effect of thiouracils and other goitrogenic drugs as discussed below in Section III. The slight difference in hind leg to body ratio between normal premetamorphic tadpoles and hypophysectomized and thyroidectomized animals of comparable size as seen in Fig. 2 also suggests the effects of very low concentrations of thyroxine in the animals during the premetamorphic period.

It is also clear from recent work with I^{131} that the activity of the gland at metamorphic climax is very high although exact quantitative figures are difficult to arrive at. The studies of Saxen et al. (1957a, b) and of Kaye (1961) are most precise here. Saxen's results indicate that the climax gland in *Xenopus* has an activity only about three times that of the premetamorphic gland as measured by the protein-bound iodine level in the body tissues.

The chemical data regarding the activity of the prometamorphic gland in anurans are not as clearly interpretable. In their study Saxen et al. did not detect any increase over the premetamorphic gland in any of the measures they used and interpret the activity of the thyroid at this time as one of storage rather than secretion of the hormone. Since, however, it is clear that prometamorphic change is dependent upon increased thyroid activity (see Fig. 1) we are inclined to view their results as indicating only that the increase in activity over the premetamorphic gland is not large enough to be detected by the chemical tests used. On the other hand in terms of I^{131} uptake Kaye (1961) found a 10-fold increase in prometamorphosis (T.K. stage XII–XIV) and a 40-fold increase near climax (T.K. stage XX). These results (Fig. 3) are in close agreement with morphological studies and with the matching experiment discussed below.

This problem was recently approached in our laboratory by attempting to match the rate of change characteristic of different stages of normal metamorphosis by applying exogenous hormone to young tadpoles. It was found that concentrations as low as 1 part per billion (p.p.b.) of thyroxine induce appreciable differential hind leg growth at a rate higher than that characterizing the premetamorphic animal. Using the criterion of growth

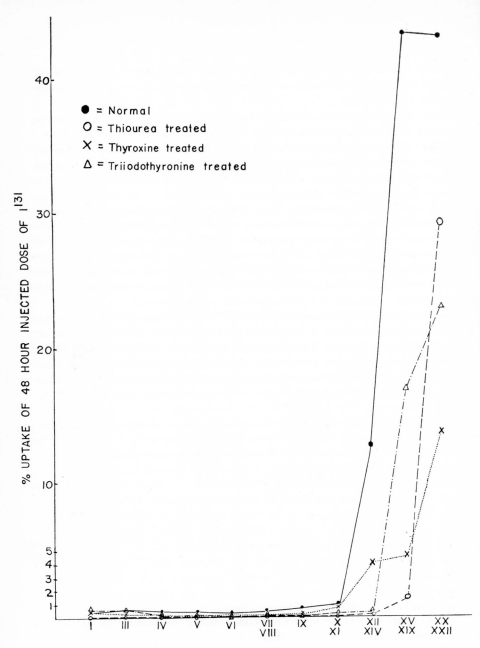

Fig. 3. Mean thyroidal uptake of I¹³¹ 48 hours after a single injection of radioiodine. The treatment with thiourea, thyroxine, and triiodothyronine was begun 2 days before radioiodine injection. Abscissa given in terms of T and K stages: Stages I–XI = premetamorphosis; XII–XIV = early prometamorphosis; XV–XIX = late prometamorphosis; XX–XXII = climax. From Kaye (1961).

rate suppression, Steinmetz (1954) also concluded that the thyroxine level in the premetamorphic animal was less than the equivalent of 1 p.p.b. With 3 p.p.b. we found that the rate of hind leg growth relative to the body approaches that found in early prometamorphosis. The concentration of thyroxine which produces the maximum rate of leg growth obtained in this experiment was 27 p.p.b. although at 9 p.p.b. the rate was not much lower. On the other hand tail resorption at the rate seen in the normal animal 2 to 4 days after foreleg emergence required 243 p.p.b. These data indicate that the normal pattern of metamorphic change is produced by an activation of the gland which increases its rate of hormone release somewhat as follows. During premetamorphosis the rate of hormone production is equivalent to less than 1 p.p.b. During the 3 weeks of prometamorphosis the rate of hormone production rises from the equivalent of 3 p.p.b. to about 20 p.p.b. At about the time of foreleg emergence the rate rises abruptly to about 200 p.p.b. and remains high until tail resorption is complete (E + 5) when, as the morphological evidence indicates, it appears to drop to a low level again.

In a study of the effects of different concentrations of thyroxine on metamorphic change (Etkin, 1935) the concept was developed that no single concentration of thyroxine produces a normal time pattern of metamorphic change but that such a pattern can be produced by a regulated increase in concentration during the course of the artificially induced metamorphosis. Figure 1 shows examples of thyroidectomized and hypophysectomized animals which were brought through a nearly normal pattern of metamorphosis by being treated to increasing concentrations of thyroxine. In contrast examples of the distorted animals resulting from treatment with single high concentrations of the hormone are also shown.

E. MODE OF ACTION OF THE THYROID HORMONE

1. Introduction

Our previous discussion emphasized the central role of thyroxine in inducing metamorphic transformation. In the present section we will consider experiments bearing on the problem of the mechanism of action of this substance.

2. Continuity of Action

In a general way it has long been recognized that continuity of thyroid hormone action is necessary for the persistence of metamorphic activity since animals transforming under thyroxine stimulation become static when the stimulus is removed (Moser, 1950; Blaizot and Blaizot, 1951; Kollros and Kaltenbach, 1952). There are also occasionally instances of partial neoteny among untreated animals which appear to result from inactivation of the thyroid during metamorphosis (Tiovonen, 1952).

We have recently studied this phenomenon in *Rana pipiens* in some detail by two methods; (1) temporary immersion in various concentrations of thyroxine and (2) thyroidectomy at different stages in metamorphosis. Hind leg growth induced by low concentrations (3 p.p.b.) ceases in 2 to 4 days after transfer to spring water without thyroxine. If strong concentrations (81 or 243 p.p.b) are used and the animals removed when tail resorption is initiated the tail resorption ceases immediately, mouth widening persists for 2 or 3 days and leg growth may continue for as long as a week. It would thus appear that the thyroid level in the animal drops gradually after removal from the thyroxine solution and therefore the more sensitive tissues persist in metamorphic change for some time. If the thyroid glands are removed from a tadpole on the day before or on the day of foreleg emergence, mouth widening persists for about 2 days so that the mouth reaches about half way to completion before stasis sets in. Tail resorption, on the other hand, is not appreciably initiated and the animal remains at this "half-way mark" as long as kept alive (in our material over 1 month). If the thyroids are not removed until 2 days after emergence of the forelegs, at which time tail reduction has already advanced about one-quarter toward completion, tail resorption proceeds to the conical bud stage normally and mouth widening to completion before stasis sets in.

A remarkable instance involving continuity of thyroid action is reported by Kollros and McMurray (1956). They find that the neurons of the mesencephalic V nucleus (presumably the proprioceptor neurons for the jaw muscles) not only respond by growth to the action of thyroxine but regress when the hormone action ceases. To this reviewer's knowledge this is the only instance known of regression in a metamorphic change upon removal of the stimulus. This dependence does not, however, continue into the postmetamorphic period (Kollros, 1957). It is possible, therefore, that the dependence is not upon the hormone per se, but upon the peripheral connections which had not differentiated in the experiments with early stages.

Taken as a whole, the evidence for the necessity of continuity in thyroid action suggests that the hormone takes a direct part in the chemical changes involved in metamorphic transformations perhaps as a prosthetic group in an enzyme system as suggested by Frieden and Winzler (1949).

3. Threshold versus Stoichiometric Action of Thyroid Hormone

A fundamental question to which considerable attention has been given is whether there is a threshold for stimulation by thyroid hormone for each tissue or whether on the contrary the tissues respond at all levels of hormone with an increase in rate as the concentration of the hormone rises (stoichiometric interpretation). On the basis of their early work both Allen (1932) and Etkin (1935) decided in favor of the stoichiometric interpretation. Their view was that each tissue had a different total thyroxine requirement for the accomplishment of its metamorphic change, this total being satisfied either by higher concentration acting in a shorter period or a lower one over a longer time. This concept has recently been called into question by Kollros (1959, 1961) in his painstaking studies with very low concentrations of thyroid acting on hypophysectomized tadpoles over periods of many months duration. Since this problem is of fundamental theoretical interest it is desirable to analyze it in some detail.

It is generally agreed that empirically a threshold-like effect is seen where, after subjecting the animal to thyroid treatment, the experimenter simply observes the occurrence or absence of a metamorphic change at a given time. As was recognized by Allen who employed this method, the appearance of thresholds under these conditions may be simply the mechanical effect of the manner of experimentation since the procedure provides no evidence that change had ceased at the time of sacrifice of the animals. Recognizing this, both Etkin and Kollros have followed metamorphic change continuously in their animals. Using a variety of hormone levels on thyroidectomized animals Etkin (1935) concluded that, within practical limits, any concentration will produce any and all metamorphic events if it acts long enough. Kollros, on the other hand, reports that low concentrations bring the animal to a particular point in metamorphosis at which they remain as long as the concentration is not raised. With each rise in concentration the animal moves to a more advanced level and again stops (Table II).

According to the stoichiometric view the timing of metamorphic events

TABLE II
Hormone Concentration Related to Terminal Metamorphic State Achieved[a]

Concentration of DL-thyroxine (μg/liter)	Maximum stage	Days of treatment
0.002	IX+	395
0.02	XI− to XV	360–425
0.04	XII+ to XV	365–410
0.2	XV to XIX	275–305
0.4	XIX and XX	42–111
0.6	XX to XXI+	52–150

[a] From Kollros (1961).

in the normal animal results from the fact that early events have low total thyroxine requirements and later events have successively higher requirements. As the hormone level in the blood rises during metamorphosis in accordance with the pattern of activation of the thyroid gland, as discussed above (Section II,D), the requirement for active leg growth (the most sensitive of tissue responses) is reached early, anal canal piece resorption later, and only after extreme thyroid activity has been maintained for some days is the very high total requirement for the late climax events such as tail resorption achieved. Of course, other factors such as the latent period for the manifestation of an induced change also enter into the picture but, basically, the stoichiometric view is that the normal time pattern of metamorphosis results from the rate at which the pattern of development of thyroid activity provides the necessary total thyroxine requirements for each tissue.

The concept of thresholds implies, on the other hand, that the pattern of normal metamorphosis results from the fact that the continuously rising concentration of thyroid hormone serves to trip a series of threshold levels for the different metamorphic events. Both theories therefore, are based on the concept of an increase in thyroxine level during metamorphosis. The difference between the two concepts is of fundamental importance from the point of view of the mode of action of the hormone in metamorphosis. The stoichiometric view implies that the hormone enters directly on a molar basis into the biochemical activities producing the morphological changes. In my view the threshold concept on the other hand, implies that the hormone acts more as a stimulus does in nerve-muscle physiology to release an endogenous mechanism which proceeds thereafter independently of the stimulus. However, Kollros regards his threshold findings somewhat differently. He writes (personal communication) "not only is there release of a 'mechanism,' but the continued function of the 'mechanism' requires the maintenance of at least that minimal or threshold level of thyroid hormone. It is not simply a triggering."

Since the evidence for the threshold concept has not yet been published in detail it cannot be here analyzed as to its adequacy either technically or statistically. Summary tables such as given in Table II here indicate the nature of the evidence. A different level of hind leg differentiation is seen to be induced by different concentrations of thyroxine. Such differentiations are reported to remain stable in hypophysectomized animals over periods of months and to respond by further development to increases in the level of external thyroxine. Our own studies, both those published earlier and those summarized above in connection with the concentration-matching and continuity experiments, were done with concentrations higher than those used by Kollros and the events studied though including hind leg growth were largely later metamorphic changes. Other conditions were also not comparable as we did not use hypophysectomized animals, nor did we run the experiments for the very long periods used by Kollros. It is, therefore, difficult to make a direct comparison. With respect to leg growth it should be pointed out that the lowest concentrations used in our studies though producing growth at the rate characteristic of early prometamorphosis gave no evidence of stasis at any point. When using low thyroxine concentrations on thyroidectomized animals we have observed an apparent stasis of metamorphosis at forelimb emergence such as Kollros also mentions. We believe this appearance can be understood stoichiometrically in terms of the high thyroxine requirement for late climax events. This requirement cannot be provided at low concentrations since the animals stop feeding when climax is initiated. It would appear that further work is necessary before definitive conclusions can be drawn. At present, however, we regard the evidence as on the whole supporting the stoichiometric interpretation and in line with other evidence suggesting the direct participation of the thyroxine molecule in the biochemical changes basic to metamorphic transformation.

4. Influence on Metabolic Rate

The characteristic effect of thyroid hormone on raising the over-all metabolic rate in mammals has led many investigators to consider the metabolic effect as central to the mode of action of the hormone (Barker, 1951). There have been repeated efforts to detect such effects in metamorphosis in amphibians (see also Chapter 7). Although earlier results in this area were conflicting it was commonly recognized that if, in fact, thyroid hormone action did raise the metabolic rate such increase was not essential to metamorphosis since other agents with considerably greater influence on metabolic rate are not effective metamorphic stimulants. Supportive evidence on this point is seen in the lack of effect of antipyretic substances on tadpole metamorphosis (Wilhelmi, 1957). Nonetheless recent developments in thyroid hormone theory, particularly enzyme activities such as the uncoupling effects of thyroxine on oxidative phosphorylation in mitochondria (Lardy *et al.*, 1960), suggest that the hormone may act on basic processes regulating energy transfer and have led to renewed attempts to restudy this subject. We may consider these under three headings.

a. Studies in Animals Undergoing Normal Metamorphosis. In an extensive study of oxygen consumption in normally metamorphosing tadpoles (*Xenopus laevis* and *Rana temporaria*), Fletcher and Myant (1959) found no increase in metabolic rate before or during metamorphosis. The oxygen consumption remained constant per unit dry or wet weight. The few data on normal metamorphosis in *R. grylio* reported by Lewis and Frieden (1959) also show no evidence of metabolic increase. Thus for the normally metamorphosing animal recent evidence supports the earlier interpretation (Etkin, 1934) that no over-all change in oxygen consumption occurs at metamorphosis.

b. Studies on Thyroid-Treated Animals. Lewis and Frieden (1959) found pronounced increases in oxygen consumption following thyroidization of tadpoles. In the Fletcher and Myant study (1959) on the other hand, a decrease in Q_{O_2} was found under similar conditions with other species. Unfortunately in both studies thyroid treatment was not regulated to produce a normal pattern of metamorphic change by gradually increasing dosages. It is difficult to say therefore to what extent the results may represent activities compensatory to the stress of abnormal development. It is further regrettable that the modern studies use Warburg techniques involving the shaking of the animals instead of methods permitting a closer approach to basal conditions as stressed in earlier studies.

c. Tissue Studies. In vitro studies on isolated tissues would seem a hopeful approach to this problem. Barch (1953) made an extended investigation of metabolic rate in dorsal skin isolated from animals undergoing normal and artificially induced metamorphosis. She found an increase in oxygen consumption per unit dry weight during the progress of normal metamorphosis and after thyroid treatment of tadpoles. Furthermore she stressed the fact that the increase occurring after thyroidization was found before morphological change (gland and collagen development) occurred in the skin. These results were interpreted as supporting the theory of a metabolism regulating effect of thyroid hormone in amphibian tissues. However, we must consider that the skin of this region shows a specific growth response to thyroxine and since synthetic biochemical activities necessarily precede their morphological expression, the early appearance of the increase in metabolism is not convincing evidence that the effect of the hormone is primarily upon metabolic stimulation rather than on the specific synthetic activities peculiar to that tissue. Furthermore the data indicate that the metabolic increase persists for several weeks after normal metamorphosis during which time the thyroid level in the animal has presumably dropped (Section II,D). An extension of this type of investigation into a variety of tissues showing differing morphological response is very much needed. In summary, we believe that presently available evidence does not support the concept that the mode of action of the thyroid hormone in amphibian tissues undergoing metamorphic transformation can be profitably interpreted in terms of a common metabolic stimulating effect.

5. Influence on Enzymic Activities

Recent developments of biochemical and histochemical techniques permitting the quantitative assessment of enzymic activities in tissues and cells suggest methods for the analysis of thyroid action in metamorphosis at the enzymic level. Some of the enzymic changes which have been found may be considered to be the consequence of developmental transformation of the tissues rather than part of the mechanisms of thyroid action on the tissues. The increased activity of the digestive glands is presumably an example of such change (Gennaro, 1953).

Many enzymic and other biochemical transformations which have been described in recent years hold considerable interest when viewed in terms of the shift in the animal's adaptation from the water to the land environment. Thus we know that the tadpole excretes much of its nitrogen in the form of ammonia whereas the frog converts the ammonia to urea before excreting it. The development of the enzyme system in the liver which makes this conversion possible has been followed in several species (literature in Underhay and Baldwin, 1955; Paik and Cohen, 1960). The great increase in albumins in the serum of tadpoles during metamorphosis described by Frieden et al. (1957) is clearly adaptive to the osmotic requirements attendant upon emergence upon land. During metamorphosis porphyropsin, the retinal protein of the tadpole, is largely replaced by rhodopsin, the adult protein (Wald, 1958). In this instance the biological significance of the change is not clear. Our knowledge of such enzymic changes during metamorphosis has been extensively analyzed by Frieden (1961) from the point of view of the adaptive significance of these changes. It should be recognized, however, that such evolutionary considerations do not constitute a physiological explanation of the metamorphic change and leave the question of the mechanisms of action by which the adaptation is achieved in abeyance. It is, of course, to the latter problem that we would wish to direct our attention here. Unfortunately current work in this field, although it has uncovered many specific facts, has not yet led to a clear over-all picture of the relation of tissue and enzyme changes. Since the subject has been reviewed in detail by Bennett and Frieden (1962) and Kaltenbach (1958) it will not be extensively treated here. It may be profitable however, to consider briefly tail resorption as an example of the possibilities of the analysis.

The histolytic reduction of the tail in metamorphosis suggests the action of proteolytic enzymes and this is borne out by enzyme analysis. Various acid proteases increase markedly at metamorphosis (for literature see Frieden, 1961). An increase of over twenty times in the cathepsin activity of tail tissue at this time was reported by Weber (1957; also De Cesaris

Coromaldi, 1959). Weber regards this as evidence that the cathepsins act primarily in tissue lysis rather than in synthesis. However, it is apparent in Weber's data that cathepsin activity undergoes a moderate rise in the weeks before "metamorphosis." Since in Weber's terminology "metamorphosis" is considered to begin with forelimb emergence (i.e., metamorphic climax), the period in question corresponds to that described above as prometamorphosis. It will be recalled that during this period the thyroxine level in the animal also shows a moderate rise followed by a sudden 10-fold increase at climax (Section II,D). It thus appears that cathepsin activity in the tail closely parallels the level of thyroid activity irrespective of the absence of tail resorption during prometamorphosis. Weber's results, therefore, suggest a direct relation of cathepsin with thyroid hormone level rather than with tissue lysis. Yamamoto (1960), on the other hand, reports little change in proteases in tadpole tails during resorption. He finds a reduction in succinic and glutamic dehydrogenases and regards the consequent limitation in available energy as the basis of tissue decomposition. Whatever the relation of cathepsins to tissue lysis, the fact that recent cytological study ascribes their localization in the cell to the so-called lysosomes (see Novikoff, 1959) suggests the possibility of following the analysis of thyroid action at this point to the level of cytoplasmic components.

F. ROLE OF TISSUE SENSITIVITY

1. Variation in Sensitivity

The striking fact that the different tissues of the larval amphibian body show specific differential sensitivity to the thyroid hormone has, of course, been obvious from the earliest studies. Although the tissues of the embryo are insensitive to thyroxine such sensitivity appears abruptly in tadpoles toward the end of embryonic development at embryonic stage 23 (P and M stages, Etkin, 1950; Moser, 1950). It was our impression that the external events observed in this experiment were, at least qualitatively, the same in early and late premetamorphic tadpoles. Moser, however, reports differences in the time of appearance of responsiveness in different tissues and Kollros (1959) finds that the responsiveness of the mesencephalic V nuclei cells to thyroxine does not appear until mid-tadpole stages and increases as the animals develop. A novel concept has been proposed by Pesetsky (1962) for the Mauthner's neuron. He regards this as acquiring thyroxine dependence as a result of thyroid action during metamorphosis. The normal postmetamorphic degeneration of this cell he regards as a consequence of the withdrawal of thyroid activity at the end of metamorphosis. A general reexamination of changes in the sensitivity of tissues to thyroid action is sorely needed at this time.

Since the legs decrease their growth rate sharply at the beginning of climax (see Fig. 2) when the thyroxine level in the animal rises very sharply, it might be supposed that they lose their sensitivity to thyroxine as is characteristic of other persistent adult structures such as the tongue. None of these respond to seasonal variations in thyroid activity in adult life. However, no specific analysis of this loss of sensitivity is known to this reviewer and other possibilities of action cannot be excluded.

Occasionally untreated animals are seen which show aberrant conditions of tissue sensitivity, particularly involving the opercular skin. Thus an instance of the failure of the skin window for the forelegs to form was reported by Richardson and Barwick (1957) and, in our material, we have seen several instances of the opposite condition consisting of a hyperdegeneration of the operculum that laid bare the entire gill chamber in preclimax tadpoles.

Wide differences in sensitivity between comparable tissues in different species have been known and appear to form the basis of the neotenic condition of such salamanders as *Necturus* in which the tissues are insensitive to the hormone. Recently, however, metamorphic change has been induced in a specimen of the normally neotenous salamander *Typhlomolge rathbuni* by high doses of thyroxine (Dundee, 1957). In this species, as in the well known case of facultative neoteny in the axolotl, the tissues retain their capacity to respond to thyroxine although in *Typhlomolge*, to judge from the scanty evidence, a partial loss of sensitivity has occurred.

The contrary situation is reported for the anuran *Eleutherodactylus martinicensis* by Lynn and Peadon (1955). In this species development is considered to be direct. While still within the egg membranes the larva assumes a tadpole-like form. Before hatching, however, it transforms to the adult condition. By treating the larva with thiouracil or with thyroxine, Lynn and Peadon showed that such early metamorphic changes as leg and skin gland growth are independent of thyroid. On the other hand the resorption of the tail and certain other resorptive phenomena are thyroid-dependent.

If we assume that the thiouracil completely suppressed thyroid hormone production in these experiments it would appear that the prometamorphic changes which are dependent on low thyroxine levels in other anurans have become independent of the hormone in this species whereas at least some climax phenomena retain their dependence upon the thyroid hormone. It is thus apparent that some evolutionary changes in the life history of various amphibians have come about through changes in tissue responsiveness to the thyroid hormone.

2. *Direct versus Indirect Action of the Thyroid Hormone*

From the early studies of Helff and others, it was clear that whereas some tissue changes in metamorphosis are direct responses by the tissue to thyroid hormone, others are mediated by inductive effects from neighboring structures.

The most important recent advances in this area have followed the exploitation, particularly in the laboratories of Kollros and of Kaltenbach, of the use of pellets containing thyroxine to induce local change, a method introduced by Hartwig (1940). By slow diffusion from the pellet a local area of high concentration of hormone is produced. While some hormone is carried throughout the body by the circulation, adequate management of the pellet minimizes this. A clear distinction in metamorphic status between the local area and the general body tissues is thus created. Metamorphic differentials thus produced locally are interpreted by these workers as evidence that the tissue involved is responding directly to the hormone. It is well to note the limitation of the above interpretation.

Whereas general systemic effects such as action through other endocrine glands or other general factors, are clearly isolated by the technique, the possibility of indirect effects within the local area itself as for example the influence of the tympanic cartilage on the overlying skin (Helff, 1940) are not necessarily ruled out. Within the limitations of this understanding we may recognize that numerous tissue responses have been shown to be direct responses to thyroid hormone. Among the non-nervous tissues of *Rana pipiens* thus shown to respond directly are the labial fringes and teeth, dermal plicae, hind limbs, and tail fin (Kaltenbach, 1953a, 1959b). The eyelids, nictitating membrane, cornea, and extrinsic muscles of the eye likewise respond to locally applied thyroxine pellets (Kaltenbach, 1953b). Whether or not these responses are independent of each other is not entirely clear since a certain degree of coordination among the parts of the eye is apparent in the described results.

The formation of the skin window for the foreleg has been much studied in this connection. Helff had presented evidence to indicate that this formation is secondarily induced by degenerating gill tissue. In subsequent studies, however, he concluded that both direct and indirect action of the hormone are involved (literature in Etkin, 1955). By use of the thyroxine pellet technique Kaltenbach (1953c) was able to demonstrate clearly that this skin degeneration can be produced by direct local action of thyroxine. That the phenomenon is complex, however, in indicated by the fact that the SWFL (skin window of foreleg) which appears before climax $(E - 2)$ is only the initial response of the skin of the operculum. Subsequently $(E + 2)$ the rest of the opercular skin undergoes degeneration while the gills are being resorbed. The interplay of direct thyroxine action and indirect inductive effects in the opercular area deserves further study.

Local effects of thyroid hormone are of special interest in the nervous system where the interaction of central and peripheral structures is of fundamental importance. Weiss and Rossetti (1951) reported a striking contrast in the response of different cells in the hind brain to locally applied thyroxine. Ependymal and certain nerve cells showed marked growth whereas the Mauthner neurons atrophied as in normal metamorphosis. Pesetsky and Kollros (1956) confirmed these findings for the non-Mauthner cells. Their results for the Mauthner neurons, however indicate that a complex interaction of higher concentrations of thyroxine with possibly peripheral influences occurs. As mentioned above, Pesetsky (1962) now believes, on the basis of indirect evidence, that this neuron degenerates in response to hormone withdrawal rather than to its presence. By implantation of a thyroxine pellet on one side of the midbrain Kollros (1958) was also able to produce a precocious unilateral maturation of the corneal reflex, thus demonstrating its independence, at least initially, of peripheral differentiation.

III. Pituitary-Thyroid Interrelations during Metamorphosis

Recent studies of the interrelation of pituitary and thyroid in relation to metamorphosis commonly make use of the following concepts of pituitary-thyroid physiology. (1) The anterior lobe of the pituitary produces a specific thyrotropic hormone (thyroid-stimulating hormone or TSH). This hormone is probably produced by the aldehyde-fuchsin positive basophils present in the gland in the rat although this identification may not be applicable in other animals (Barrnett et al., 1956; Purves and Griesbach, 1956; Ortman and Griesbach, 1958). (2) There is a feedback or "thyrostat" mechanism by which the thyroxine level, when it exceeds a given value, inhibits TSH production. Thus for each "setting" of the thyrostat a constant level of thyroxine and TSH is maintained in the blood. (3) Certain goitrogenic chemicals (thiouracil, etc.) interfere with the formation of thyroid hormone and thereby produce a hypothyroid condition. This, by eliminating feedback, leads to increased release of TSH, which in turn stimulates the thyroid cells and produces a hyperplastic goiter.

Since the thyroid differentiates in a normal manner in the hypophysectomized amphibian and shows minimal activity, it might be thought that this gland is independent of the pituitary in premetamorphic stages. However, good evidence to the contrary exists. Goitrogens induce hyperplasia of the thyroid in premetamorphic tadpoles (Gordon et al., 1945; Blackstad, 1949; Delsol, 1952; Copenhaver, 1955; Iwasawa, 1956) although Delsol's study suggests this is true only in later premetamorphic stages. Thyroxine inhibits I^{131} uptake by the thyroid in early premeta-morphic tadpoles (Bowers *et al.*, 1959; Kaye, 1961; see Fig. 3). Thyro-trophic cells are identifiable in the pituitary of premetamorphic tadpoles and salamanders although they are relatively few and poorly granulated (Toney, 1954; Pasteels, 1957; Saxen, 1958). Furthermore, the production of TSH begins in the as yet undifferentiated gland since it has been dem-onstrated that a locally effective thyrotropic field exists around the em-bryonic pituitary (Etkin, 1939; Kaye, 1961).

Taken altogether, this evidence strongly indicates that the pituitary-thyroid axis including its feedback feature is fully functional before metamorphosis. Therefore, the low level of thyroid hormone in this period cannot result from any inability of the pituitary to secrete enough hormone to produce a higher level of thyroid activity, but must be the consequence of the restraint upon TSH production by the feedback mechanism. As we shall see below (Section IV) the pituitary before climax is not dependent upon hypothalamic contact. The feedback effect of thyroxine must, there-fore, be operating directly upon the thyrotrophs of the pituitary rather than upon the hypothalamic mechanism in inhibiting TSH production. We, therefore, conclude that the thyrotrophs of the premetamorphic animal are extremely sensitive to thyroxine feedback and that it is this condition that keeps the thyroid hormone level so low before metamorphosis.

The dependence of the thyroid upon the pituitary during prometa-morphosis and climax was clearly demonstrated in early studies with hypophysectomized animals. Such animals fail to metamorphose and their thyroids do not undergo the normal growth phase during pro-metamorphosis. These deficiencies are remedied by pituitary injections or implantation (for literature see reviews). Recent confirmation of this concept comes from the success in inhibiting metamorphosis by chemicals which are believed to be specific inhibitors of the thyrotropic hormone (Loeser *et al.*, 1955; Iwasawa, 1958). The rate of thyroid activity during prometamorphosis and climax must, therefore, be a reflection of the changing activity of the pituitary in TSH production. In their study of the pituitary-thyroid axis during metamorphosis in *Xenopus*, Saxen and co-workers (Saxen *et al.*, 1957a, b; Saxen, 1958) found cytological evidence in support of this concept. The granulation of the thyrotropic cells and the size of their nuclei increase during prometamorphosis and undergo an abrupt decrease during the climax. These workers interpret this as indi-cating that during prometamorphosis there is much storage of the hormone and at climax an abrupt release occurs. This picture is consistent with the concept developed above (Section II,D) that thyroid hormone production rises only moderately during prometamorphosis but abruptly shoots to high levels at the beginning of climax.

With respect to the thyrostat mechanism we must conclude that the sensitivity of the thyrotrophs to thyroxine feedback undergoes a moderate reduction during prometamorphosis. At climax, a major, perhaps total, release of the cells from feedback control occurs. It is possible that a positive stimulus to TSH release is also received by the pituitary at this time. The reduction in thyroid activity, which comes at the end of metamorphosis (Section II,D) implies that the cells regain their sensitivity to feedback control again at that time.

IV. Pituitary-Hypothalamic Interrelations in Metamorphosis

The relation of the pituitary to the hypothalamus has recently been a productive area of endocrinological research. A general concept that has developed and has been widely if not universally accepted is as follows. Various nuclei in the hypothalamus contain neurosecretory neurons whose axons bring their products to the region of the median eminence of the hypothalamus. Here the secretions are picked up by the blood and conveyed through portal veins into the sinusoids of the anterior pituitary. gland. There they influence the secretion of tropic hormones by the pituitary. More specifically with relation to the pituitary-thyroid axis, there is much evidence in mammals and birds that a low level of TSH production is maintained by the pituitary independently of its hypothalamic connection, but that higher levels of such activity are dependent upon hypothalamic control (Assenmacher, 1958; D'Angelo, 1958; Harris, 1959). The feedback inhibition of TSH by thyroxine operates upon both the pituitary and the hypothalamic mechanisms with some evidence that the former is the more sensitive area (von Euler and Holmgren, 1956; Yamada, 1959; Bogdanove and Crabill, 1960). These studies used thyroid morphology or I^{131} metabolism as a measure of thyroid activity rather than any physiological tissue response.

In the adult frog the interrelation of the hypothalamus and pituitary appears to conform to this pattern. The median eminence and hypothalamo-hypophyseal portal system are well developed. The production of ACTH is known to be under hypothalamic control through this apparatus in the toad (Jorgensen and Larsen, 1960). Dawson (1957) described supposed thyrotrophs of the adult *Rana pipiens* as being distributed along the ventral border area of the pars anterior in close association with the portal vessels. However, Ortman and Lannen (1963) were unable to confirm this identification of thyrotrophs by bioassay methods. Pasteels (1957, 1960) found that the thyrotrophs are not maintained after transplantation in the salamander, *Pleurodeles waltlii* and regards this as evidence of their dependence upon hypothalamic stimulation.

The problem of hypothalamic control of the pituitary in relation to

metamorphosis was first studied in frog embryos (*R. pipiens*) by transplanting the primordium of the adenohypophysis into the animal's own
tail before it had assumed its definitive relationship to the hypothalamus
(Etkin, 1938). Most transplants showed no capacity for inducing metamorphosis. Some stimulated metamorphic change, at a maximum up to
forelimb emergence. The prometamorphosis induced by such grafts was,
however, late in beginning and usually proceeded much more slowly than
in the normal animal. We have recently repeated this work with identical
results (Fig. 4) and have found the grafts, whether inducing metamorphosis or not, to approximate normal size and to present a healthy histological picture (Etkin and Ortman, 1960). Since these grafts induced body growth
in excess of normal it is apparent that they were capable of hormone production (Etkin and Lehrer, 1961). The metamorphosis induced, therefore,
must be ascribed to the capacity of the graft pituitary to function independently of the hypothalamus, rather than to the release of stored hormone by degeneration of the pituitary cells. By transplanting differentiated
pituitaries from donors in metamorphic climax into hypophysectomized
tadpoles we have found these also occasionally induce metamorphosis up
to early climax (paper in preparation). However, after foreleg emergence
the host animals enter metamorphic stasis and progress only very slowly
if at all through climax changes (Figs. 4 and 5). Although their mouths
may widen slowly, their tails show little resorption even 10 days after the
emergence of the forelegs. Histological study of the grafts again showed
healthy anterior lobe tissue. Furthermore, pars intermedia function is
still active in these animals as is evidenced by their intensely black color.
These results, thus, confirm and extend our experience with grafts of the
primordia and clearly show that the pituitary is able to produce enough
TSH to carry the host through prometamorphosis without hypothalamic
connection, although such connection does facilitate the development of
TSH function. But they also indicate that without association with the
hypothalamus the gland is not able to produce enough TSH to support
metamorphic climax, particularly tail resorption. The control of anuran
metamorphosis is thus seen to be biphasic; prometamorphosis is fundamentally independent of the hypothalamus although facilitated by it, and
climax is entirely dependent upon hypothalamic control of the pituitary.

Working on the embryo of the Japanese toad, Uyematsu (1940) succeeded in removing the primordium of the hypothalamus and producing
tadpoles in which the adenohypophysis developed without the normal
connection to this organ. Such animals began metamorphosis, proceeding
through the stage of foreleg emergence, but thereafter entered a period of
stasis and did not resorb their tails. From his histological study of these
isolated pituitaries he concluded that at the climax of metamorphosis the

Fig. 4. A. Tadpole with own pituitary primordium transplanted to tail. Top (A1) shows hind leg development at total length of 86 mm (normals metamorphosed at about 65 mm). Middle (A2) shows same animal 25 days later. Bottom (A3) shows same animal 38 days after top. Note slow but definite progress through prometamorphosis. B. *Upper* (dark) animal. Tadpole with own pituitary primordium transplanted to tail, no hind leg growth despite attainment of large size. *Lower* (light) animal. Normal at beginning of prometamorphosis. C. Hypophysectomized animal with graft of pituitary from climax donor. Upper picture (C1) taken at day of foreleg emergence, 19 days after implantation. Lower picture (C2) taken 9 days later. Note progress in leg, mouth, and eyes but failure of tail to regress. The dark color in all graft animals indicates persistence of pars intermedia activity at high rate.

isolated anterior lobe underwent degeneration and loss of function. It is not clear to what extent the initial TSH function displayed by his grafts could be ascribed to the release of hormone by the degenerating gland. The American toad tadpole is reported to show considerable hind leg growth in the absence of thyroid (Allen, 1925) and, therefore, it is possible that very little TSH was secreted by the isolated pituitary in Uyematsu's experiment. Uyematsu himself appears to have regarded the failure of the animals to proceed through metamorphosis to be due to the lack of a formative influence exerted by cells migrating from the hypothalamus, rather than to physiological governance of the pituitary by the hypothalamus. It should be noted that this work anteceded modern concepts of the neurosecretory regulation of the pituitary.

We have been able to repeat Uyematsu's experimental results on *Rana pipiens*. Witschi and Chang (1959) briefly mention similar successes obtained in their laboratory and Pesetsky, in this laboratory (personal communication), has likewise done so. At least some metamorphic change

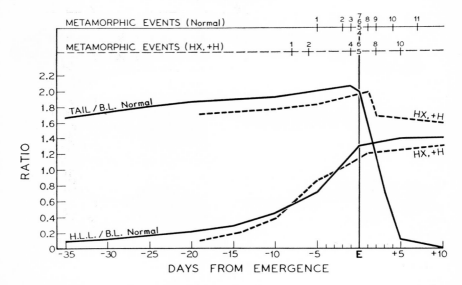

Fig. 5. Metamorphic patterns. Solid lines = normal animals as in Fig. 2. Broken lines = hypophysectomized animal with graft as in Fig. 4C. Note that graft animal showed nearly normal hind leg growth, slightly protracted prometamorphic changes, and mouth widening but very little tail resorption.

has been seen by all workers in these animals. In our experiments, the animals deprived of their infundibula showed prometamorphic changes but with delay in initiation of the process and some slowing of time relations. Just before or after foreleg emergence, however, they ceased to progress appreciably and remained in stasis more than 10 days at which time they were sacrificed. Since some of these animals showed excess pigmentation, similar to that of animals with transplanted primordia, we infer that the pars intermedia developed fully and maintained its excess activity until sacrifice. On histological examination the glands were seen to be isolated from the brain and appeared healthy (publication in preparation). The results are thus seen to be entirely consistent with our findings with graft glands and to support the inferences drawn from that work. First, the pituitary can develop some thyrotropic function independently of its contact with the brain. This development of function is generally subnormal. It varies from none to that level which induces the completion of prometamorphic change. Second, without contact with the hypothalamus the pituitary is not able to produce (or release) enough thyrotropin to induce the events of metamorphic climax which have a high thyroid requirement.

Recently Voitkevich (1962) has summarized a series of studies done in the U.S.S.R. by himself and Ivanova on metamorphic control through the brain that has led them to much the same viewpoint as advocated here. Voitkevich showed that whereas removal of the telencephalon does not interfere with metamorphosis (climax phenomena) removal of the diencephalon with the telencephalon does reduce metamorphic change. Transplantation of the area of the diencephalon with the preoptic nucleus restores metamorphic activity. There is increased neurosecretory activity in this nucleus at the time of metamorphic climax at which time transplants are most effective. Cytological studies indicate the dependence of basophils (PAS-positive cells) upon neurosecretions conveyed by the pituitary portal system. Voitkevich interprets his results as indicating control by the hypothalamus of the pituitary activity necessary for intestinal and tail reduction (climax) but not for leg growth (prometamorphosis). Confirmation of the importance of the diencephalon for metamorphosis was also found by Srebo (1961), Remy (1962), and Bounhiol and Remy (1962) who inhibited this process by lesions in that area of the brain.

As explained in Sections I and II, the metamorphosis of typical salamanders corresponds, in respect to morphological changes and level of thyroid activity, to the climax phase of anuran metamorphosis. The concept developed above, that anuran climax is dependent upon activation of the pituitary through the hypothalamus, therefore, suggests that such dependence might be expected to apply to urodele metamorphosis as a whole. This concept was analyzed experimentally by cutting the connection of the pituitary to the hypothalamus in fully grown larvae of the salamander. *Ambystoma maculatum*, and maintaining the separation by implanting a barrier to prevent regeneration of the hypophyseal portal vessels (Etkin and Sussman, 1961). It was found that where the separation of the two organs was entirely successful, no metamorphosis ensued. In the experimental animals which did metamorphose, regenerated blood vessels were seen to have connected the hypothalamus and pituitary. Thus urodele metamorphosis and anuran metamorphic climax, both of which are dependent upon a very high level of thyroid activity, are seen to require intact connections between hypothalamus and pituitary. It is furthermore clear that in the salamander, at least, this connection is sufficient if made by the vascular system and not directly by nerves. This suggests that some substance passing from the hypothalamus to the pituitary by way of the pituitary portal blood vessels leads to activation of the pituitary which then stimulates the thyroid to the requisite high level of function for inducing metamorphosis in salamanders or climax in anurans.

The biphasic concept of anuran metamorphosis as developed above raises the question of how the first phase of low level, semiautonomous

pituitary activity is coordinated with the second phase of high level hypo-
thalamus-controlled activity to produce the normal integrated pattern of
metamorphosis. Studies of the development of the median eminence and
the hypothalamo-hypophyseal portal blood vessels in normal and thyroidectomized tadpoles provides a clue to this problem. We have found
that in the premetamorphic tadpole (*Rana catesbeiana and R. pipiens*)
the anterior pituitary has a broad area of contact with the very thin floor
of the infundibulum (infundibular stem) with which it is connected by
intervening capillaries. These, we believe, constitute a diffuse portal system bringing neurosecretion from the infundibular stem to the anterior
pituitary. During prometamorphosis the anterior part of the infundibular
stem develops into the more highly specialized median eminence by
considerable thickening and vascularization of the infundibular floor and
a concentration of the connecting blood vessels to a small area of contact
at the anterior tip of the pars distalis. In the normal animal this process
is well advanced, although not completed, by the beginning of metamorphic climax (also Voitkevich, 1962; Etkin, 1963a, b; see also Fig. 6).

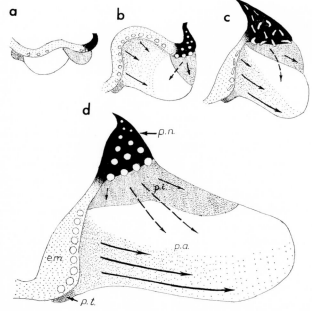

Fig. 6. Schema of development of the pituitary gland in *Pelobates fuscus*. (a). In
larva long before metamorphosis. (b). Before metamorphosis (climax). (c). At the
end of metamorphosis. (d). Adult frog. KEY TO LABELS: p.a., pars anterior; p.t., pars
tuberalis; p.i., pars intermedia; p.n., pars nervosa; e.m., eminentia mediana. Zone of
predominance of the basophile cells is dotted. Arrows indicate the direction of proliferation in two lobes of the adenophypophysis. (From Voitkevich, 1962.)

In the thyroidectomized tadpole the formation of the median eminence does not occur and the region remains in the premetamorphic status indefinitely. When large thyroidectomized animals are treated with graded doses of thyroxine to produce a normal pattern of metamorphosis the median eminence differentiates as in normal metamorphosis. It therefore appears that thyroid activity during prometamorphosis has a positive feedback effect, inducing the development of the neurosecretory-median eminence system. It appears likely that these morphological developments are part of a physiological maturation of the hypothalamus by which its capacity to effect climax activation of the pituitary-thyroid mechanism is achieved. The activation of the hypothalamus by the positive feedback effects of low thyroid hormone levels during prometamorphosis thus leads to the high level activation of the pituitary at the appropriate time.

Another problem raised by the biphasic theory is that of the variability of thyrotropic function in the isolated gland. Why does the lower level of TSH activity characteristic of prometamorphosis develop only in some isolated pituitaries and not in others? And when developed why is it generally delayed and subnormal in rate?

Insight into the relation between the pituitary and the hypothalamus in the tadpole before metamorphosis was provided by a study on the growth rate in tadpoles bearing grafts of their own pituitary primordia (Etkin and Lehrer, 1960). Such animals were found to grow faster than normal indicating an excessive production of growth factors. This suggests that the hypothalamus does exert an influence over the premetamorphic pituitary. It restrains the production of a growth factor. Cytological evidence indicates that the growth factor is produced by certain acidophils since the graft glands show an excess of such cells. In the normal premetamorphic gland these acidophils are found concentrated in the region of the gland most remote from the border that adjoins the hypothalamic stalk (Etkin and Ortman, 1960). The inference drawn from these studies is that the hypothalamus produces some substance which restrains the production of the growth factor by inhibiting the differentiation of the acidophils. The presence of such a relation between the hypothalamus and pituitary in the premetamorphic animal suggests that the hypothalamus, by the same or other substances, may favor the differentiation of the thyrotrophs directly or, indirectly, by inhibiting the tendency of the isolated gland to differentiate excessively in the direction of acidophils. Since, as seen in Section III, the thyrotrophs of the premetamorphic pituitary are extremely sensitive to thyroxine feedback, the influence of the supposed hypothalamic substances might operate at least in part by reducing this sensitivity. This mode of action of the hypothalamus has been proposed for the rat by Reichlin (1960). In this way, the normal animal would regularly enter prometamorphosis at the appropriate time, whereas the animal with the isolated pituitary would show varying degrees of pituitary insufficiency depending upon the extent to which its differentiation capacities are influenced by its situation. That some grafts do induce prometamorphic change may be related to the fact brought out in Section III that the difference in activity level of the pituitary between premetamorphosis and prometamorphosis is not great. Such a difference may be bridged by the variability of the cells when developing in an abnormal situation or by variability in the amount of neurosecretion reaching them through the systemic circulation.

V. A Theory of the Metamorphosis-Activating Mechanism

The experimental results discussed above suggest a coherent hypothesis on the interaction of thyroid, pituitary, and hypothalamus which may be summarized as follows: As the embryonic pituitary differentiates, it forms thyrotrophs and secretes thyrotropin from earliest tadpole stages on. The thyrotrophs are extremely sensitive to feedback inhibition by thyroxine and thus the thyroxine concentration in the animal is kept at a very low level, equivalent to less than 1 p.p.b. (part per billion) of external thyroxine. The neurosecretory mechanism of the hypothalamus also differentiates in the embryo and, through a diffuse vascular connection with the pars distalis, sends neurosecretions to the latter. These substances desensitize the thyrotrophs to thyroxine feedback and promote their differentiation. Thyroxine, however, acts upon the hypothalamus in a positive feedback manner to induce further differentiation of the hypothalamic mechanism particularly the median eminence and thus accelerates its stimulating effect upon the thyrotrophs of the pituitary. Consequently, a chain reaction or self-accelerating system is set up in which thyroid hormone increases hypothalamic activity and this in turn leads to more thyroid activity, etc. (Fig. 7).

Because the initial level of thyroxine is so low this system accelerates only very slowly at first. Consequently, there is a long period during which the level of thyroid hormone remains so low that the differentiation of the general tissues is not clearly affected and the normal and thyroidectomized animal do not differ markedly. This is the premetamorphic period.

Eventually the rate of thyroxine secretion reaches the level at which it induces leg growth at a rate clearly above that of the thyroidectomized animal. The animal is then said to enter prometamorphosis. During this period the positive feedback of thyroxine upon the hypothalamus is more effective than previously since the thyroxine level is now higher. The system, therefore, accelerates rapidly. As the concentration of thyroxine rises through levels estimated as the equivalents of 5 to 25 p.p.b. the normal sequence of prometamorphic changes is induced in the animal's

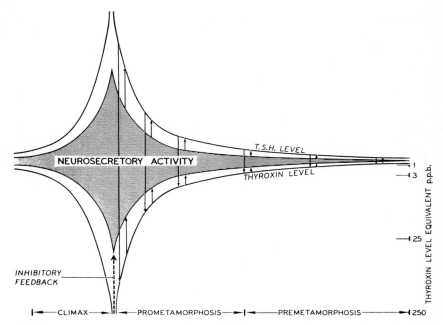

Fig. 7. Schema of the thyroid-pituitary-hypothalamic neurosecretory activity during development of the tadpole. The initial thyroid activity is shown (arrow) feeding back to the hypothalamic neurosecretory (NS) mechanism particularly the median eminence and serving to accelerate its development. The NS substance acts upon the TSH cells of the pituitary to reduce their sensitivity to inhibition by thyroxine feedback thereby permitting them to release more TSH. This in turn stimulate more thyroxine production thereby producing a self-accelerating cycle of activity. Starting with thyroxine at less than 1 p.p.b. level this cyclic system builds up slowly during the premetamorphic period (about 5 weeks in *Rana pipiens* at 23°C) to about 3 p.p.b. By the time this level is reached the effect of thyroxine in stimulating leg growth is apparent and the tadpole enters prometamorphosis. Also, at this level of thyroid hormone, the positive feedback of the hormone on the hypothalamus proceeds more rapidly leading to an explosive release of TSH at the end of prometamorphosis (after 3 weeks). This TSH release produces an extreme activation of the thyroids and thyroxine levels jump to about 250 p.p.b. equivalent. The general tissues of the tadpole are then quickly brought through the changes of metamorphic climax by this very high level of thyroid hormone. The mature neurosecretory system now becomes sensitive to negative feedback by the high level of thyroxine and its secretory activity is inhibited. As a result the TSH cells regain their sensitivity to thyroxine feedback and they cease activity. The thyroid therefore returns to an inactive state marking the close of metamorphosis.

tissues, including the emergence of the forelegs and the initiation of mouth changes.

At this point a critical level in hypothalamic activity is reached and the now fully differentiated thyrotrophs of the pituitary are completely released from inhibition by thyroxine feedback. The consequent release of large quantities of TSH brings about a sudden increase in thyroid activity, often accompanied by extensive evacuation of colloid. As a result, the thyroxine level in the body jumps by a factor of about ten times to the level of over 200 p.p.b. in the course of a day or two. This high thyroxine level brings on tail resorption and other climax events at their appropriate rates. The now differentiated hypothalamic mechanism, like other differentiated tissues, loses its former sensitivity to thyroxine and no longer shows the positive feedback response to this hormone. Instead, the high level of thyroxine acts in the negative feedback manner familiar in mammalian physiology to inhibit hypothalamic secretion. With the loss of hypothalamic secretion the thyrotrophs regain their sensitivity to negative thyroxine feedback and the system returns to the low level characteristic of the end of metamorphosis. Presumably, it remains subject to the two linked negative feedback systems operating on the hypothalamus and on the thyrotrophs as is thought to be the case in mammals.

This theory is readily applied to urodele metamorphosis. Whereas in the urodeles the tissues including the hypothalamus do not undergo any morphological development under the low thyroid levels operating during the period of larval life, the hypothalamus may be assumed to show functional development under such stimulation. Consequently, there is no observable transformation as the positive feedback system builds up in the hypothalamus to the critical point. Complete activation of the TSH mechanism then occurs as in anuran climax. All the tissues are thus activated to transform to the adult status by the flooding of the body with thyroid hormone at this time.

VI. Environmental Influences on the Metamorphosis-Activating System

A number of environmental factors have been found to influence amphibian metamorphosis. Unfortunately this aspect of the problem of metamorphosis has received inadequate attention in recent years and there is little to add to the information summarized in older reviews. In the present context we may discuss three factors in terms of contemporary neuroendocrine theory.

The central role of the neurosecretory centers of the nervous system in integrating developmental and other endocrine-mediated responses of animals to environmental changes has been emphasized recently by Scharrer and Scharrer (1963). The positive feedback concept of metamorphic activation as developed above suggests that environmental influences can affect metamorphosis by acting indirectly by way of hypothalamic inhibition of growth factor production with coordinate promotion of TSH production. In this event, a reciprocal action on growth and metamorphosis is to be expected. Where one is favored the other should be restrained. Of course, influences impinging directly upon the pituitary rather than through the brain might influence all its activities in a like manner.

Starvation before middle prometamorphosis inhibits further metamorphic progress in the tadpole (D'Angelo *et al.*, 1941). Growth, of course, also ceases in such animals. This effect, therefore, presumably results from the direct inhibition of all pituitary functions following the cachexia of inanition, an effect familiar in mammalian physiology.

The finding of D'Angelo and co-workers that after mid-prometamorphosis starvation accelerates rather than retards metamorphosis, however, holds more interest in the present context. Starvation at this time probably does not lead to inanition cachexia because the tadpoles store considerable fat in the fat body and the intestine does not empty itself for a week or two after feeding stops. It is possible that the cessation of feeding acts neurogenically upon some behavior-sensitive brain mechanism. This then stimulates the hypothalamus to the production of its pituitary controlling factors which accelerate metamorphosis at the expense of growth.

Another effect that may operate through the hypothalamic mechanism is that of crowding. This factor is well known to inhibit growth and leads to metamorphosis at a reduced size but with much variability among the animals (Adolph, 1931). It appears to act principally by way of a water-borne product of the animal's own metabolism (Rose, 1960). In crowding, the behavior of the animals also changes. They constantly arouse each other and interfere with the normal quiet feeding pattern (Holder, 1958). Here again the effective agents may act through the hypothalamus to inhibit growth and stimulate metamorphosis as suggested above in late starvation.

The effect of temperature on growth and metamorphosis appears to be a complex one (literature in reviews). In our experience, within the range of 15 to 30 degrees C metamorphosis is accelerated by increased temperature more than is growth and the animals metamorphose at a smaller size. This appears to be true also in *Ambystoma* (Uhlenhuth, 1919). Higher temperatures thus favor TSH over growth factor production in the pituitary. This could be accounted for by a neurogenic stimulation of hypothalamic development resulting from a temperature-sensitive mechanism in the brain. However, another mechanism is suggested by the reported observations that at low temperatures the animal's tissues become insensitive to thyroxine. If this reduction in sensitivity applies to the hypothalamus it is evident that the positive feedback mechanism postulated in our theory would be less and less effective with decreasing temperature with a consequent favoring of growth over metamorphosis. The tendency of the facultatively neotenous salamander, *Ambystoma tigrinum*, to be neotenous in cold but not warm lakes can be understood as a special case of this differential effect of temperature on thyroxine sensitivity.

In the absence of an adequate experimental exploration of the influence of environmental factors on metamorphosis the suggestions made above must be considered speculative. It is perhaps worth while to note, however, that the starvation, crowding, and temperature effects are adaptive in relation to the animals' mode of life. Starvation and crowding promote emergence of animals from ponds which have become nutritionally inadequate or overcrowded late in the season. The temperature effect promotes emergence from ponds during the warm part of the year, particularly if the pond begins to dry out and become overheated. The same mechanism inhibits emergence during the inappropriate cold seasons. The concept of a positive feedback mechanism in the metamorphosis activating system is thus consistent with the concept of the hypothalamus as a funnel through which environmental influences bear upon the endocrine system to produce adaptive modifications in development.

References

Adolph, E. (1931). Body size as a factor in the metamorphosis of tadpoles. *Biol. Bull.* **61**, 376–386.

Allen, B. M. (1925). The effects of extirpation of the thyroid and pituitary glands upon the limb development of anurans. *J. Exptl. Zool.* **42**, 13–30.

Allen, B. M. (1932). The response of *Bufo* larvae to different concentrations of thyroxin. *Anat. Record* **54**, 45–65.

Assenmacher, Y. (1958). Recherches sur le contrôle hypothalamique de la fonction gonadotrope préhyphysaire chez le canard. *Arch. Anat. Microscop. Morphol. Exptl.* **47**, 447–572.

Barch, S. H. (1953). Oxygen consumption of normal and thyroxin-stimulated *Rana pipiens* skin. *Physiol. Zool.* **26**, 223–231.

Barker, S. B. (1951). Mechanism of action of the thyroid hormone. *Physiol. Rev.* **31**, 205–243.

Barker, S. B. (1954). The circulating thyroid hormone. *Brookhaven Symp. Biol.* **7**, 74–89.

Barrnett, R., Ladman, A., McAllister, N., and Siperstein, E. (1956). The localization of glycoprotein hormones in the anterior pituitary glands of rats investigated by differential protein solubilities, histological stains and bio-assays. *Endocrinology* **59**, 398–418.

Bennett, J. P., and Frieden, E. (1962). *In* "Comparative Biochemistry" (M. Florkin, and H. S. Mason, eds.), Vol. IV, p. 483. Academic Press, New York.

Blackstad, T. W. (1949). Depigmentation in *Rana temporaria* tadpoles as a result of methylthiouracil treatment. *J. Endocrinol.* **6**, 23–27.

Blaizot, S., and Blaizot, J. (1951). Recherches sur la métamorphose du crapaud commun. (*Bufo vulgaris* Laur.). *Physiol. Comparata Oecol.* **2**, 210–223.

Bogdanove, E., and Crabill, E. (1960). Thyroid pituitary feed-back. Direct thyroid hormone inhibition of the pituitary-thyroidectomy reaction in the rat. *Mem. Soc. Endocrinol.* **9**, 54–59.

Bounhiol, J. J. (1942). "Le déterminisme des métamorphoses chez les amphibiens." Hermann, Paris.

Bounhiol, J. J., and Remy, C. (1962). Nouvelles observations sur le freinage de la morphogénèse chez le têtard privé de diencéphale. *Compt. rendu. Soc. Biol.* **156**, 2037–2039.

Bowers, C. Y., Segaloff, A., and Brown, B. (1959). Factors affecting the thyroid gland uptake of I^{131} of the *Rana catesbeiana* tadpole. *Endocrinology* **65**, 882–888.

Bruice, T., Winzler, R., and Kharasch, N. (1954). The thyroxine-like activity of some new thyroxine analogues in amphibia. *J. Biol. Chem.* **210**, 1–9.

Copenhaver, W. M. (1955). Growth of thyroid tissue in the gills of *Amblystoma punctatum* reared in propylthiouracil. *J. Exptl. Zool.* **129**, 291–308.

D'Angelo, S. A. (1958). Role of the hypothalamus in pituitary-thyroid interplay. *J. Endocrinol.* **17**, 286–299.

D'Angelo, S. A., Gordon, A. S., and Charipper, H. A. (1941). The role of the thyroid and pituitary glands in the anomalous effect of inanition on amphibian metamorphosis. *J. Exptl. Zool.* **87**, 259–277.

Dastoli, F. R., and Tector, A. J. (1959). The effect of cortisone on amphibian metamorphosis. *Bios. (Mt. Vernon, Iowa)* **30**, 27–32.

Dawson, A. B. (1957). Morphological evidence of a possible functional interrelationship between the median eminence and the pars distalis of the anuran hypophysis. *Anat. Record* **128**, 77–89.

De Cesaris Coromeldi, L. (1959). Studio delle attività autoletiche nello sviluppo embrionale e nella metamorfosi di *Bufo vulgaris. Rev. Biol. (Perugia)* **51**, 327–340.

Delsol, M. (1952). Action du thiouracil sur les larves de batraciens. Néoténie expérimentale. Rôle de l'hypophyse dans ce phenomène. *Annee Biol.* **28**, 175–189.

Dent, J. (1942). The embryonic development of *Plethodon cinereus* as correlated with the differentiation and functioning of the thyroid gland. *J. Morphol.* **71**, 577–601.

Donoso, A. O. (1958). Yodo radioactiva y funcion tiroidea en el sapo. *Rev. soc. Arg. Biol.* **34**, 65–69.

Dundee, H. A. (1957). Partial metamorphosis induced in *Typholomolge rathbuni. Copeia* pp. 52–53.

Etkin, W. (1932). Growth and resorption phenomena in anuran metamorphosis I. *Physiol. Zool.* **5**, 275–300.

Etkin, W. (1934). The phenomena of anuran metamorphosis II. Oxygen consumption during normal metamorphosis. *Physiol. Zool.* **7**, 129–148.

Etkin, W. (1935). The mechanisms of anuran metamorphosis I. Throxine concentration and the metamorphic pattern. *J. Exptl. Zool.* **71**, 317–340.

Etkin, W. (1936). The phenomena of anuran metamorphosis III. *J. Morphol.* **59**, 69–90.

Etkin, W. (1938). The development of thyrotropic function in pituitary grafts in the tadpole. *J. Exptl. Zool.* **77**, 347–377.

Etkin, W. (1939). A thyrotropic field effect in the tadpole I. *J. Exptl. Zool.* **82**, 463–496.

Etkin, W. (1950). The acquisition of thyroxine sensitivity by tadpole tissues. *Anat. Record* **108** (3) (abstr.).

Etkin, W. (1955). Metamorphosis. *In* "Analysis of Development" (B. H. Willier, P. A. Weiss, and V. Hamburger, eds.), pp. 631–663. Saunders, Philadelphia, Pennsylvania.

Etkin, W. (1963a). Maturation of the hypothalamic neurosecretory mechanism by thyroid feedback in the frog. *Life Sci.* **2**, 125–18.

Etkin, W. (1963b). The metamorphosis activating system of the frog. *Science* **139**, 810–814.

Etkin, W., and Lehrer, R. (1960). Excess growth in tadpoles after transplantation of the adenohypophysis. *Endocrinology* **67**, 457–466.

Etkin, W., and Ortman, R. (1960). Cellular differentiation in relation to growth-promoting activity of pituitary grafts in tadpoles. *Anat. Record* **137**, 353.

Etkin, W., and Sussman, W. (1961). Hypothalamo-pituitary relations in metamorphosis of *Ambystoma*. *Gen. Comp. Endocrinol.* **1**, 70–79.

Fletcher, K., and Myant, N. B. (1959). Oxygen consumption of tadpoles during metamorphosis. *J. Physiol.* (*London*) **145**, 353–368.

Frieden, E. (1961). Biochemical adaptation and anuran metamorphosis. *Am. Zoologist* **1**, 115–151.

Frieden, E., and Naile, B. (1955). Biochemistry of amphibian metamorphosis I. Enhancement of induced metamorphosis by glucocorticoids. *Science* **121**, 37–39.

Frieden, E., and Winzler, R. J. (1949). Competitive antagonists of thyroxine and structurally related compounds. *J. Biol. Chem.* **179**, 423–433.

Frieden, E., Herner, A., Fish, L., and Lewis, E. (1957). Changes in serum proteins in amphibian metamorphosis. *Science* **126**, 559–560.

Gallien, L. (1950). Action inhibitrice de l'éthinyl-testostérone sur la thyroïde larvaire et le développement des amphibiens anoures. *Arch. Anat. Microscop. Morphol. Exptl.* **39**, 102–109.

Gennaro, J. F. (1953). Quantitative studies on the distribution of phosphorus[32] in metamorphosing tadpoles, *Rana sylvatica*. *Univ. Pittsburgh Bull.* **49**, 1.

Gorbman, A., and Evans, H. M. (1941). Correlation of histological differentiation with beginning of function of developing thyroid gland of frog. *Proc. Soc. Exptl. Biol. Med.* **47**, 103–106.

Gordon, A. S., Goldsmith, F. D., and Charipper, H. A. (1945). The effects of thiourea on amphibian development. *Growth* **9**, 19–41.

Gross, J., and Pitt-Rivers, R. (1953). 3:5:3¹-Triiodothyronine. II. Physiological activity. *Biochem. J.* **53**, 652–657.

Harris, G. W. (1959). Neuroendocrine control of TSH regulation. *In* "Symposium on Comparative Endocrinology" (A. Gorbman, ed.), pp. 202–222. John Wiley and Sons, New York.

Hartwig, H. (1940). Metamorphose-Reaktionen auf einen localisierten Hormonreiz. *Biol. Zentr.* **60**, 473–478.

Helff, O. M. (1940). Studies on amphibian metamorphosis XVII. *J. Exptl. Biol.* **17**, 45–60.

Holder, F. (1958). Untersuchungen über den Crowd-Effekt an Kaulquappen von *Rana temporaria* L. *Rev. Suisse Zool.* **65**, 350–359.

Hughes, A., and Astwood E. (1944). Inhibition of metamorphosis in tadpoles by thiouracil. *Endocrinology* **34**, 138–139.

Hunt, E., and Dent, J. (1957). Iodine uptake and turnover in the frog tadpole. *Physiol. Zool.* **30**, 87–91.

Iwasawa, H. (1956). Effects of thiourea upon the development of anuran larvae. *Endocrinol. Japon.* **3**, 169–175.

Iwasawa, H. (1958). Effects of parahydroxypropiophenone on the secretion of hypophyseal hormones in frog larvae. *Endocrinol. Japon.* **5**, 163–165.

Jorgensen, C. B., and Larsen, L. O. (1960). Hormonal control of moulting in amphibians. *Nature* **185**, 244–245.

Kaltenbach, J. C. (1953a). Local action of thyroxin in amphibian metamorphoses. I. Local metamorphosis in *Rana pipiens* larvae effected by thyroxin-cholesterol implants. *J. Exptl. Zool.* **122**, 21–39.

Kaltenbach, J. C. (1953b). Local action of thyroxin on amphibian metamorphosis. II. Development of the eyelids, nictitating membrane, cornea, and extrinsic ocular muscles in *Rana pipiens* larvae effected by thyroxin-cholesterol implants. *J. Exptl. Zool.* **122**, 41–51.

Kaltenbach, J. C. (1953c). Local action of thyroxin on amphibian metamorphosis. III. Formation and perforation of the skin window in *Rana pipiens* larvae effected by thyroxin-cholesterol implants. *J. Exptl. Zool.* **122**, 449–467.

Kaltenbach, J. (1958). Direct steroid enhancement of induced metamorphosis in peripheral tissues. *Anat. Record* **131**, 569.

Kaltenbach, J. (1959a). Thyroxin-like activity of iodophenols in anuran larvae. *Anat. Record* **134**, 589.

Kaltenbach, J. C. (1959b). Local action of thyroxin on amphibian metamorphoses. IV. Resorption of the tailfin in anuran larvae effected by thyroxin-cholesterol implants. *J. Exptl. Zool.* **140**, 1–17.

Kaye, N. (1961). Interrelationships of the thyroid and pituitary in embryonic and premetamorphic stages of the frog, *Rana pipiens*. *Gen. Comp. Endocrin.* **1**, 1–19.

Klumpp, W., and Eggert, B. (1934). Die Schildrüse und die branchiogenen Organe von *Ichthyophus glutinous* L. *Z. Wiss. Zool.* **146**, 329–381.

Kobayashi, H. (1958). Effect of desoxycorticortisone acetate on metamorphosis induced by thyroxine in anuran tadpoles. *Endocrinology* **62**, 371–377.

Kollros, J. (1957). Influence of thiourea on growth of cells of midbrain in frogs. *Proc. Soc. Exptl. Biol. Med.* **95**, 138–141.

Kollros, J. (1958). Hormonal control of onset of corneal reflex in the frog. *Science* **128**, 1505.

Kollros, J. (1959). Thyroid gland function in developing cold blooded vertebrates. *In* "Symposium on Comparative Endocrinology". (A. Gorbman, ed.), pp. 340–350. John Wiley and Sons, New York.

Kollros, J. (1961). Mechanisms of amphibian metamorphosis: hormones. *Am. Zoologist* **1**, 107.

Kollros, J., and Kaltenbach, J. (1952). Local metamorphosis of larval skin in *Rana pipiens*. *Physiol. Zool.* **25**, 163–170.

Kollros, J., and McMurray, V. M. (1956). The mesencephalic V nucleus in anurans. II. The influence of thyroid hormone on cell size and cell number. *J. Exptl. Zool.* **131**, 1–26.

Lardy, H. (1955). The biological activity of *O*-methyl thyroxine. *Endocrinology* **57**, 566–570.

Lardy, H., Lee, Y., and Takemori, A. (1960). Enzyme responses to thyroid hormones. *Ann. N. Y. Acad. Sci.* **86**, 506–511.

Lewis, E., and Frieden, E. (1959). Biochemistry of amphibian metamorphosis. Effect of triiodothyronine, thyroxine, and dinitrophenol on the respiration of the tadpole. *Endocrinology* **65**, 273–282.

Loeser, A., Mikulicz, K., and Ritter, K. (1955). Hemmung der Metamorphose durch *Lithospermum officinale*. *Acta Endocrinol.* **20**, 293–296.

Lynn, W. G., and Peadon, A. (1955). The role of the thyroid gland in direct development in the anuran. *Eleutherodactylus martinicensis*. *Growth* **19**, 263–286.

Lynn, W. G., and Wachowski, H. F. (1951). The thyroid gland and its functions in cold-blooded vertebrates. *Quart. Rev. Biol.* **26**, 123–168.

Money, W., Meltzer, R., Young, J., and Rawson, R. (1958). The effect of change in chemical structure of some thyroxine analogues on the metamorphosis of *Rana pipiens* tadpoles. *Endocrinology* **63**, 20–28.

Money, W. L., Kumaoka, S., Rawson, R., and Kroc, R. (1960). Comparative effects of thyroxine analogues in experimental animals. *Ann. N. Y. Acad. Sci.* **86,** 512–544.

Moser, H. (1950). Beiträge zur Analyse der Thyroxinwirkung im Kaulquappenversuch. *Rev. Suisse Zool.* **57** (Suppl. 2), 3–144.

Nieuwkoop, P. D., and Faber, J., eds. (1956). "Normal Table of *Xenopus laevis* (Daudin). "North-Holland Publ. Co., Amsterdam, Holland.

Novikoff, A. (1959). The intracellular localization of chemical constituents. *In* "Analytical Cytology" (R. C. Mellors, ed.), pp. 69–169. McGraw-Hill, New York.

Ortman, R., and Griesbach, W. E. (1958). The cytology of the pars distalis of the Wallaby pituitary. *Australian J. Exptl. Biol. Med. Sci.* **36,** 609–618.

Ortman, R., and Lannen, J. A. (1963). Bioassay data bearing on the localization of thyrotroph cells in *Rana pipiens. Anat. Record* **145,** 268.

Paik, W. K., and Cohen, P. (1960). Biochemical studies on amphibian metamorphosis. I. The effect of thyroxine on protein synthesis in the tadpole. *J. Gen. Physiol.* **43,** 683–696.

Pasteels, J. L. (1957). Recherches expérimentales sur le rôle de l'hypothalamus dans la différenciation cytologique de l'hypophyse, chez *Pleurodeles waltlii. Arch. Biol. (Liege)* **68,** 65–114.

Pasteels, J. (1960). Etude expérimentale des différentes catégories d'éléments chromophiles de l'hypophyse adulte de *Pleurodeles waltlii,* de leur fonction et de leur contrôle par l'hypothalamus. *Arch. Biol. (Liege)* **71,** 409–468.

Pesetsky, I. (1962). The thyroxine-stimulated enlargement of Mauthner's neuron in Anurans. *Gen. Comp. Endocrinol.* **2,** 229–235.

Pesetsky, I., and Kollros, J. (1956). A comparison of the influence of locally applied thyroxine upon Mauthner's cell and adjacent neurones. *Exptl. Cell Res.* **11,** 477–482.

Pitt-Rivers, R., and J. R. Tata (1959). "The Thyroid Hormones." Pergamon, New York.

Purves, H. D., and Griesbach, W. E. (1956). Changes in the basophil cells of the rat pituitary after thyroidectomy. *J. Endocrinol.* **13,** 365–375.

Reichlin, S. (1960). Thyroid response to partial thyroidectomy, thyroxine and 2,4-dinitrophenol in rats with hypothalamic lesions. *Endocrinology* **66,** 327–339.

Remy, C. (1962). L'ablation du diencephale empeche la métamorphose chez le têtard du crapaud accoucheur, *Alytes obstetricans* (Laur.). *Compt. Rend. Acad. Sci.* **254,** 567–568.

Richardson, L. R., and Barwick, R. E. (1957). Faulty eruption of the forelimb in *Hyla aurea. Trans. Roy. Soc. New Zealand* **84,** 941–942.

Rose, S. M. (1960). A feedback mechanism of growth control in tadpoles. *Ecology* **41,** 188–199.

Roth, P. (1941). Action antagoniste due propionate de Testostérone dans le métamorphose expérimentale des batraciens provoquée par la thyroxine. *Bull. Museum Natl. Hist. Nat.* (Paris) **13,** 500–502.

Roth, P. (1950). Sur l'action des hormones sexuelles dans la métamorphose des amphibiens hypophysoprivés. *Bull. Museum Natl. Hist. Nat. (Paris)* **22,** 67–72.

Roth, P. (1954). Action threshold of 3:5:3 L-triiodothyronine on the metamorphosis of *Rana temporaria* tadpoles. *Ann. Endocrinol.* **15,** 767–770.

Roth, P. (1956a). Les métamorphoses des batraciens et leur signification pour la biologie générale. *Scientia* **91,** 151–155.

Roth, P. (1956b). Semil d'action de la tétraiodo des aminothyroxine sur la métamorphose des tétards de *Rana temporaria* L. *Ann. Endocrinol.* **17,** 725–728.

Saxen, L. (1958). The onset of thyroid activity in relation to the cytodifferentiation of the anterior pituitary. Histochemical investigation using amphibian embryos. *Acta Anat.* **32**, 87–100.

Saxen, L., Saxen, E., Toivonen, S., and Salimaki, K. (1957a). Quantitative investigation on the antero pituitary-thyroid mechanism during frog metamorphosis. *Endocrinology* **61**, 35–44.

Saxen, L., Saxen, E., Toivonen, S., and Salimaki, K. (1957b). The anterior pituitary and the thyroid function during normal and abnormal development of the frog. *Ann. Zool. Soc. Zool. Botan. Fennicae Vanamo* **18**, 1–44.

Scharrer, E., and Scharrer, B. (1963). "Neuroendocrinology." Columbia Univ. Press, New York.

Schmidt, A. (1956). Thyroid function in the Northwestern salamander, *Ambystoma gracile* (Baird). *J. Exptl. Zool.* **133**, 539–558.

Schubert, G. (1957). Die Aktivität von Hypophyse, Thyroidea, Epiphyse und ihre Beeinflussung durch Parahydroxy-propiophenon, Östradiol und Testosteron während der Larval-entwicklung von *Bufo bufo* L. *Wilhelm Roux, Arch. Entwicklungsmech. Organ.* **150**, 1–47.

Shellabarger, C. J., and Brown J. (1959). The biosynthesis of thyroxine and 3:5:3 triiodothyronine in larval and adult toads. *J. Endocrinol.* **18**, 98–101.

Shellabarger, C. J., and Godwin, J. T. (1954). Effects of triiodothyroxine on tadpoles. *Endocrinology* **54**, 230–232.

Srebro, Z. (1961). The influence of brain injuries on the development of *Xenopus laevis. Folia Biol. (Warsaw)* **9**, 119–129.

Steinmetz, C. H. (1954). Some effects of thyroxine and antithyroid compounds on tadpoles and their relation to hormonal control of growth. *Physiol. Zool.* **27**, 28–40.

Taylor, A. C., and Kollros, J. J. (1946). Stages in the normal development of *Rana pipiens* larvae. *Anat. Record* **94**, 7–23.

Toivonen, S. (1952). Ein Fall von partieller Neotenie by *Xenopus laevis* Daudin und experimentelle Untersuchungen zu seiner kausalen Erklärung. *Arch. Soc. Zool. Botan. Fennica Vanamo* **6**, 107–123.

Tomita, K., and Lardy, H. (1956). Synthesis and biological activity of some triiodinated analogues of thyroxine. *J. Biol. Chem.* **219**, 595–604.

Toney, M. (1954). Histology of the anterior pituitary gland of the frog during normal development. *Growth* **18**, 215–225.

Uhlenhuth, E. (1919). Relation between metamorphosis and other developmental phenomena in amphibians. *J. Gen. Physiol.* **1**, 525.

Underhay, E., and Baldwin, E. (1955). Nitrogen excretion in the tadpoles of *Xenopus laevis* Daudin. *Biochem. J.* **61**, 544–547.

Uyematsu, T. (1940). Experimentelle Untersuchungen über die Entwicklung der Hypophyse bei Anuren *(Bufo). Okajimas Folia Anat. Japon.* **19**, 391–457.

Vegmitalluri, M., and Padoa, E. (1953). L'organo del Bidder nei gerini di *Bufo viridis* trattate con Testosterone. *Monit. Zool. Ital.* **61**, 186–197.

Voitkevich, A. A. (1962). Neurosecretory control of the amphibian metamorphosis. *Gen. Comp. Endocrinol. Suppl.* **1**, 133–147.

von Euler, C., and Holmgren, B. (1956). The role of hypothalamo-hypophysial connections in thyroid secretion. *J. Physiol. (London)* **131**, 137–146.

Wald, G. (1958). The significance of vertebrate metamorphosis. *Science* **128**, 1481.

Weber, R. (1957). On the biological function of cathepsin in tail tissue of *Xenopus* larvae. *Experientia* **13**, 153–155.

Weiss, P., and Rossetti, F. (1951). Growth responses of opposite sign among different neuron types exposed to thyroid hormone. *Proc. Natl. Acad. Sci. U.S.* **37**, 540–556.

Wilhelmi, G. (1957). Zur Frage einer thyrostatischen Wirkung von Antipyretics. (Metamorphose-Versuche an Froschlarven). *Arch. Intern. Pharmacodyn.* **112**, 155–173.

Witschi, E., and Chang, C. Y. (1959). *In* "Symposium on Comparative Endocrinology" (A. Gorbman, ed.), pp. 149–160. John Wiley and Sons, New York.

Wurmbach, H., and Haardick, H. (1952). Steuerung von Wachstum und Formbildung durch Wirkstoffe. II. Die Wirkung von Vitamin E (*dl-α*-tocopherol) im Kaulquappenversuch. *Wilhelm Roux' Arch. Entwicklungsmech. Organ.* **116**, 68–95.

Yamada, T. (1959). Studies on the mechanism of hypothalamic control of thyrotropin secretion. Comparison of the sensitivity of the hypothalamus and of the pituitary to local changes of thyroid hormone concentration. *Endocrinology* **65**, 920–925.

Yamamoto, K. (1960). Changes in activities of succinic and glutamic dehydrogenases, aspartic-*α*-ketoglutaric transaminase and proteolytic enzyme in tadpole tail tissue of *Rana japonica* during induced metamorphosis. *Endocrinol. Japon.* **7**, 8–12.

9

THE DEVELOPMENTAL PHYSIOLOGY
OF AMPHIBIA

Lucena Jaeger Barth

I. Introduction

A fundamental distinction between developmental physiology and the physiology of adult organ systems stems from the element of change with time during development. The embryo must develop or die. The adult organism also must change, i.e., adapt its physiological regulatory mechanisms to cope with temporary changes in external and internal environments; but the normal result of such regulatory mechanisms is return to the former state of dynamic equilibrium. "It is the non-repetitive character of the responses of embryonic segregation that really sets them apart from functional responses, such as the contraction of a muscle cell. . . . Ontogeny is a moving equilibrium, which involves all fundamental physiological processes at each stage" (Lillie, 1927). We may thus come to understand the physiology of an embryo at any specified "stage" of development (its energy sources, responses to chemical and physical factors in the environment, its biochemical composition, etc.), yet the physiological factors causally involved in the transition from one phase of development to the next may still elude us. The phrase "developmental physiology" thus expresses an inherent contradiction unless the definition of physiology here be broadened to include a new order of events, emergence of new sets of physiological properties in causal and sequential order.

The following account will take as the major problems of amphibian developmental physiology the questions: (1) What is the nature of the nucleocytoplasmic interactions that accompany the origin of differences between cells? (2) What developmentally significant reactions between cells and cell groups characterize amphibian differentiation and embryogenesis? The conventional divisions of physiology will be included only as they apply to these central problems. The discussion will be restricted to researches on early development. Growth *per se* (increase in mass, cell number, etc.) is excluded, as are the problems presented by metamorphosis and regeneration, which are ably dealt with in other chapters. Special processes such as fertilization and the mechanism of cleavage similarly are omitted in the interest of concentration upon the central problem of embryonic development: the origin of differences between the cells that arise from cleavage of the activated egg.

The scope of the present chapter precludes extensive coverage of the literature in any given area of developmental physiology. Reviews, technical papers, and books will be cited where much more complete and authoritative presentations are to be found. The writer has attempted to bring together in somewhat orderly fashion the approaches of many different schools and individuals, in preference to limiting the chapter to a detailed review of the most recently published data.

Beyond the scope of the present chapter, but of great significance to the student of general biology, are the contributions of amphibian embryonic material to the fields of ecology and evolution. The remarkable adaptation of amphibia in range of temperature tolerance and rates of development to the temperatures of their normal environments is a case in point. Balinsky (1957) has correlated his observations on South African frog species with the North American data reported by Moore (1939). Not only are the temperature limits for development of the South African species at a higher level on the whole, but some South African species (*Pyxicephalus adspersus*, for example) are characterized by a brief larval period, which adapts them to surmount the danger of evaporation of the warm, shallow rain pools in which their eggs develop.

Significant contributions toward understanding the evolutionary history and systematics of the Amphibia are resulting from the work of Moore (1955) on the viability of hybrid embryos prepared from frogs gathered in different geographic areas. Breeding and migration habits of these characters upon speciation problems are being studied by Twitty (1959).

The amphibian embryo occupies a unique place in the history of developmental physiology. Many of the basic problems and concepts of development first were formulated in terms of the amphibian embryo. Although many investigators have turned to "simpler" organisms to study various subcategories of the developmental process, the student of amphibian development will not be satisfied until the results of all these studies can be integrated into a causal analysis of the whole harmonious phenomenon of normal development.

Some properties of the amphibian egg responsible for its early and continuing popularity as an experimental object may be mentioned here. (1) Relatively large size of the eggs: although the eggs of different groups of Amphibia vary widely in diameter, species are found in all parts of the world whose eggs are of a convenient size (1–2 mm) for microsurgery. (2) Absence of heavy shells or elaborate embryonic membranes: the various types of jelly coats of amphibian eggs are readily removed by chemical and mechanical means. (3) Availability of early stages: unlike the hen egg, the amphibian embryo may be studied from the very initiation of development onward. With pituitary-induced ovulation and artificial insemination (Rugh, 1934) in the hands of a careful investigator nearly 100% normal development may be obtained in *Rana pipiens* from about mid-October through May. Since each female contains approximately 2000 ripe ova, large numbers of embryos are available for biochemical studies at specific stages depending upon the temperature at which they are raised. (4) Self-sufficiency as to energy sources: the fact that amphibian eggs contain sufficient yolk reserves in the form of platelets to carry them through early development and hatching is an advantage in some types of experiments since there is no need to supply exogenous metabolites. A brief but enlightening survey of amphibian gametes together with references to the original literature can be found in Moore (1955).

II. Nuclear-Cytoplasmic Interactions in Development of the Amphibian Embryo

A. HISTORICAL FORMULATIONS OF BASIC PROBLEMS

Historically the first basic embryological problems to be formulated concerned the role of the nucleus in cellular differentiation. The story of the conceptual and experimental beginnings of developmental physiology has been well documented by a number of distinguished workers (Spemann, 1938; Huxley and De Beer, 1934; Raven, 1954, among others). The present account is intended merely as a guide into an area that may not be well known to students in other areas of physiology.

1. Weismann's Theory

The last quarter of the nineteenth century was a period in biology during which great strides were made by a number of mutually stimulating workers. Rapid progress was made toward an understanding of chromosome behavior in mitosis and meiosis, and in the correlation of chromosome behavior with inheritance. In this intellectual context both Roux and Weismann posed fundamental questions that laid the groundwork for experimental embryology. Weismann, the theoretician, proposed that the germplasm was "set aside" early in development, insulated in some unspecified manner from change so as to account for parent-offspring resemblances. Somatic cells, on the other hand, were the recipients of particulate components segregated out in an orderly fashion from the zygote nucleus and distributed unequally among the daughter nuclei during cleavage. The classic experiments whereby Weismann's theory of unequal distribution of nuclear determinants was considered to have been refuted are especially well described in the writings of Spemann, Huxley and De Beer, and Raven referred to above.

2. Experimental Refutations of Weismann's Theory

The most conclusive of these experiments were designed to test the nonequivalence of nuclei resulting from the early cleavages—a necessary consequence if Weismann were correct. The results were negative (any early cleavage nucleus functioned to produce normal embryos in a certain number of instances). These experiments gave the first hint that cytoplasmic differences between various regions of the fertilized ovum were developmentally significant. Eggs of the newt (*Triton taeniatus*) and of the toad (*Bombinator pachypus*) used in various experiments gave no differences in principal results.

Roux stimulated an active era of work in this area and his contemporaries and successors were able to show that if the first two blastomeres of a urodele or anuran egg were completely separated by constriction in a certain plane, two half-sized but otherwise normal embryos developed. Spemann performed similar constriction experiments before first cleavage (Spemann, 1914, 1928) and at blastula and early gastrula stages (Spemann, 1901, 1902). When a loose ligature was tied around the fertilized egg of the newt in such a manner as to trap the zygote nucleus in one half of the egg, cleavage continued in the nucleated half. When the latter had divided into as many as 16 cells the nucleus nearest the bridge would wander into the bridge. At telophase of the next mitosis a daughter nucleus would move into the previously enucleate half egg, whereupon cleavage there was initiated and normal development ensued. Such "delayed nucleation" experiments indicated that the early cleavage nuclei were equivalent to the original zygote nucleus in their capacity to evoke normal differentiation.

Another experimental device employed was compression of the frog egg between two glass plates with the result of forcing the cleavage planes to form perpendicularly to the glass surfaces and thereby distributing the daughter nuclei into abnormal loci of cytoplasm. Development was nonetheless normal when the compression was removed, another indication of nuclear equivalence incompatible with Weismann's theory.

These experiments and many others naturally led to a devaluation of the significance of the nucleus for embryonic development, and a corresponding insistence upon the importance of the differential distribution of cytoplasmic constituents. This prejudice remained unchallenged for more than 50 years before the issue of nuclear differentiation was revived (Section II,C,3). One cannot escape the impression that some of the experiments comprising the prolific literature of early experimental embryology would bear reinterpretation in the light of contemporary information and concepts. A case in point concerns some constriction experiments on *Triton* (Spemann, 1928). As mentioned above the common impression among embryologists is that a $\frac{1}{16}$ nucleus is able to ensure development. Not so widely recognized, however, is the fact that this statement must be qualified. A $\frac{1}{16}$ nucleus cannot promote development past late gastrula or rarely early neurula if the constriction had been tied in the frontal plane and the zygote nucleus had been trapped in the ventral half embryo. Interpreting these facts in 1934 Huxley and De Beer blamed the cytoplasm for this deficiency, suggesting that the dorsal half of an embryo is more susceptible than a lateral half to absence of a nucleus and is no longer able to respond fully when a $\frac{1}{16}$ nucleus belatedly wanders into its confines.

On the basis of recent advances in our knowledge of the extensive interchanges that occur between nuclear and cytoplasmic constituents during mitosis (Section II,C,3), it seems at least equally plausible that the chromosomes replicating a ventral half embryos found inadequate components for complete and normal replication. It is known now from the work of Briggs and King (1955) that blastula nuclei are able to support development of freshly enucleated, activated frog's eggs. The latter therefore have no cytoplasmic deficiency. Would a $\frac{1}{16}$ ventral nucleus obtained by constriction support development of a freshly enucleated, activated frog egg?

That reanalysis of classic experiments may necessitate revisions of and additions to their conclusions is suggested also by newer studies on the effects of total constriction on blastula and gastrula stages of the newt (Brice, 1958). Both dorsal and ventral halves were found capable of extensive regulation toward fairly normal neurulae in contrast to the firmly entrenched impression gained from the literature that a ventral half produces only a "Bauchstück" or belly piece with no structuration period.

Dollander (1950) also noted the formation under certain circumstances of a complete embryo from a ventral blastomere at the two-cell stage. It is an unfortunate consequence of the difficulty of the technique that the conclusions of Brice were based upon relatively few operations. Dollander (1952) concluded that the center of the clear crescent of the *Triturus* species used marks the approximate center of the primitive dorsal side 85% of the time. Regulation in ventral halves following frontal constriction of young blastulae in Brice's experiments occurred in six cases out of eight (75%). It is probable then that the constrictions actually did separate dorsal and ventral halves, and that the regulatory abilities of the egg exceed what was earlier reported.

Returning to the question of the equivalence of nuclei, the work of Boveri (1910, quoted in Spemann, 1938, p. 31) weakened Weismann's postulate of differential distribution of nuclear determinants for differentiation. In effect, then, the early work in experimental embryology discredited the notion that differentiation is to be accounted for upon the basis of changes in the nuclei in the different presumptive tissues. Attention was focused upon cytoplasmic differentiation.

B. CYTOPLASMIC DIFFERENTIATION IN THE EGG AND EARLY EMBRYO

Although exceptions come to mind (the egg of *Fucus*, for example), most eggs have to begin with a polarity in the form of graded distributions of their inclusions, both visible and at the molecular level detectable by biochemical analysis. This is especially well established for the "mildly telolecithal" eggs of many amphibians which have been studied from this point of view. The fact that the embryologist must start with an object already exhibiting a degree of differentiation has led some students of developmental physiology to turn to materials other than eggs in the quest for an absolute zero or baseline in differentiation. Although the latter trend only recently has become popular, it was suggested and implemented by Child over 40 years ago. In 1941 he summarized the working hypothesis that had guided his choice of experimental materials as follows. "Pattern is already present in eggs—often advanced in development—when what we commonly call 'development' begins, and the ovarian developmental period is at present almost inaccessible to analytic experiment. If we are to be consistent, we must admit that embryonic development in general is by no means the only material of developmental physiology" (Child, 1941, p. v).

1. Descriptive Studies of Organization: Morphological

Earlier descriptions of amphibian egg structure emphasized the location of various "plasms" (Lehmann, 1945) characterized by the possession of different ratios of pigment and yolk. Thus Lehmann distinguishes in the fertilized axolotl egg a yolky vegetal plasm, a central plasm, a marginal plasm, and a light plasm representing the residue of the germinal vesicle contents. The most superficial layer of some amphibian eggs has been named the "coat" by Holtfreter (1943a), who uses its cohesive properties to account for many of the coordinated morphogenetic movements exhibited during early development. In *Rana pipiens*, however, the existence of a noncellular *pigmented* coat layer is dubious since the pigment is an intracellular constituent of the outermost layer of cells of the animal hemisphere.

The existence of a surface coat more or less continuous with the intercellular matrix has been demonstrated by Bell (1960). This "thin, filmy membrane," separated by ultrasound, consists primarily of mucopolysaccharide, lacks sulfur-containing amino acids and contains little or no ribonucleic acid. Structureless initially (as judged by electron microscope photographs), the coat develops fibrils at stages just prior to hatching, according to Bell. It remains to be shown whether this surface coat plays a role in morphogenesis comparable to that assigned to the RNA-protein-calcium complex described by Brachet (1959) and by Curtis (1958).

In many amphibian eggs shifts in the plasms are visible upon fertilization or activation because of differences in pigmentation. Thus in *Rana pipiens* a shift in surface materials relative to underlying yolk results in the appearance of the so-called gray crescent. In *Triturus* sp. a yellowish or clear crescent is seen. In a high percent of instances these crescents are natural markers for the future dorsal side of the embryo. That the shift in pigmentation represented by the gray or clear crescent in some species may be merely a secondary symptom of an earlier existing organization of the egg was indicated by Fankhauser (1930, 1948) on the basis of a series of constrictions performed on *Triton* eggs at intervals ranging from 10 min to 4 hr from fertilization. The results of the early constrictions did not differ from the later, although the gray crescent in species possessing this marker requires about an hour and a half after fertilization to appear. This was taken to mean that implicit in the fundamental egg structure of some species at least is the future dorsoventral axis of the embryo.

That the determination of the future dorsal region of the embryo, however, is to some extent labile in the early stages following fertilization has been suggested by Løvtrup and Pigon (1958). These workers oriented eggs at the two-cell stage in narrow tubes with the plane of cleavage parallel to the axis of the tube. They report a significant preponderance of dorsal lips forming on the side of the egg nearest the open end of the tube. This observation was used to lend some support to Løvtrup's hypothesis that gray crescent formation involves stretching of the surface coat with accompanying increased permeability and accelerated oxygen-dependent reactions in this region.

Worth mention in this connection however are unpublished studies by the writer in which eggs of *Rana pipiens* just after gray crescent formation were oriented in a gradient chamber so that the gray crescent area was bathed in 10% Ringer's solution while the presumptive ventral lip was exposed to various test compounds such as adenosine triphosphate, nucleotides, sulfhydryl-containing compounds, etc. Under these conditions it was possible to shift the position of the dorsal lip of the blastopore approximately 45 degrees from the center of the gray crescent area to one of its lateral borders. There was no evidence however for conversion of presumptive ventral lip into dorsal lip material in this species where the gray crescent is easily seen in most batches of eggs. In the eggs used by Løvtrup and Pigon the gray crescent is not visible, orientation of the egg with respect to the dorsoventral axis presumably is at random, and the higher incidence of dorsal lip formation on the side toward greater oxygen availability might represent the kind of partial shift observed in our extensive experiments with *Rana pipiens* eggs.

Lehmann (1956) has compared the egg organizations found in various echinoderm, mollusc, and annelid eggs with that characteristic of amphibian eggs. In all types of eggs he distinguishes two principal regions: (1) a cortex, relatively stable to centrifugation; (2) an endoplasm with various inclusions such as yolk distributed between a marginal-animal region (fated to become chordamesoderm and ectoderm) and a vegetal area later to become endoderm. This unremarkable picture of the egg cell recalls a comment by Holtfreter (1948): "The architecture of any cell from early amphibian embryos closely resembles the general organization found in *Amoeba proteus.*"

Descriptions of egg organization lose much of their force when confronted with the fact of lability in developmental potentialities. Among the classic experiments of developmental physiology are those of Spemann (1903) who demonstrated that in several species of newts each of the first two blastomeres can under certain circumstances form half-sized but structurally normal embryos. Fusion of two newt eggs at the two-cell stage resulted in development of a large but normally constructed embryo (Mangold and Seidel, 1927).

It is nonetheless true that an interaction of some constituents of the "plasms" may be a controlling factor in development of the amphibian (Pasteels, 1958). In *Xenopus* and in the frog by mild centrifuging of the inverted, unsegmented egg Pasteels (1951) was able to produce a larva with inverted cephalo-caudal polarity. This morphological abnormality was correlated with displacement of ribonucleic acid-containing granules toward the vegetal pole of the inverted, centrifuged egg. Inversion without centrifugation produced less drastic segregation of the inclusions and resulted in the production of two or three new "marginal zones" whose composition in terms of RNA-rich granules and yolk platelets resembled that of the normal marginal zone. Double and triple embryos were formed. That the two types of granules must interact was further indicated by the hypomorphic embryos that developed when the uncleaved egg was centrifuged in normal position in such way as to segregate the RNA granules at the animal (centripetal) pole and the yolk platelets at the vegetal (centrifugal) pole.

The importance of an animal-vegetal balance for normal development in *Rana pipiens* has been demonstrated also by Paterson (1957). Paterson's interesting experiments revealed that the middle third of an early gastrula could regenerate an organizer region and develop into a swimming tadpole. An animal third developed abnormally unless generalized heat or better a thermal gradient were applied, after which treatments restoration of animal-vegetal balance occurred and development proceeded normally.

The relatively labile character of determination in the amphibian egg thus discourages any sort of visualization of static components. When, however, the higher resolution afforded by electron microscopy became available it was applied to the problem of egg organization. Weber and Boell (1955) have photographed mitochondria from unfertilized eggs of *Xenopus*. Structurally they resemble mitochondria from liver homogenates (Weber, 1954) and from gastrular ectoderm photographed by Eakin and Lehmann (1957). Such resemblances do not encourage the view that ultrastructure *per se* will provide clues as to morphogenetic potentials in all types of eggs. In *Tubifex* (Lehmann, 1956) endoderm-forming and mesoderm-forming somatoblasts can be distinguished by characteristic differences in their cytoplasmic fine structure—but this may be after the fact, symptomatic rather than casual for differentiation. Kemp (1956) has made a beautiful study of growing oöcytes of *Rana pipiens* in which increasing differentiation of cortical cytoplasm coincides with the synthesis of fat droplets and yolk granules. While not directly concerned with development, this study yielded electronphotomicrographs of the cortical structure of the frog egg that should stimulate a study of its appearance after centrifugation or inversion of the egg. Further, Kemp figures the endoplasmic reticulum, sparse at first, as later occurring throughout the cytoplasm.

Little seems to have been gained by mearly looking at the fine structure of egg and early embryonic cells at a higher level of magnification. It might be hoped that a combination of electron microscopy with experimental modifications of development might prove more fruitful. It is, of course, entirely within the realm of possibility that the developmentally significant constituents are below the resolution even of the electron microscope or are not present after materials have been prepared for electron microscopy. It appears improbable that a static picture no matter how highly magnified can reveal causal factors in development. Brachet (1950a) has stressed the value of comparing normal with experimentally modified embryos in respect to any parameter being studied.

In recent years the question of continuity of the "germ plasm" between generations has been revived. Limiting our discussion to the amphibian egg we note that Blackler (1958) has provided a histological study of the "germinal cytoplasm" of anuran eggs as a result of which he concludes that material later to be localized in the oöcytes already is present near the vegetal pole shortly after fertilization. It is interesting that this germinal cytoplasm is associated with large numbers of mitochondria and that just before gastrulation cells containing this type of oöplasm show mitotic inhibition and retention of intact yolk platelets as opposed to platelet breakdown in other cell types. Fischberg and Blackler (1961) have suggested that the function of the germ plasm is "to prevent germ cell nuclei from undergoing changes during development." Revival of interest in the germ track problem has been accompanied by development of new techniques for tracing cells, most notable of which is use of the one-nucleolus marker, a genetic character found in one strain of *Xenopus laevis* (Fischberg *et al.*, 1958a).

2. Descriptive Studies of Organization: Chemical

Studies of the enzymic properties and protein-synthesizing capacities of subcellular fractions and changes in these properties with stage of development and after experimental modification of development may be expected to give a more subtle description of the raw materials available for differentiation. The question will still need to be answered of how the appropriate reactions are triggered at the "right" time and place for normal development. Already it is known that mitochondria isolated from *Ambystoma* and *Xenopus* embryos at successive stages of development show increasing cytochrome oxidase activity per unit protein nitrogen (Boell and Weber, 1955). It is suggested that a given cell may contain diverse species of mitochondria, and that any individual mitochondrion may exhibit differentiation with time. Pasteels' centrifugation and inversion experiments again come to mind as material for such investigations. What new enzyme system are activated when new contacts are established between subcellular structures by centrifugation at 400 g for 2 minutes?

Pasteels (1951) does not hesitate to assign to the ultracentrifugable granules the role of the biochemical basis of "morphogenetic potential."

There is need for a detailed census and biochemical characterization of the fine structures implicated, as well as proof that both normal and experimentally modified amphibian development witness changes in the distribution and/or activities of these organelles.

The discovery of lysosomes in adult cells (de Duve, in Brachet, 1960a) led to the speculation that some embryonic processes such as liberation of masked inductor substances might be set in motion by breakdown of these enzyme-containing bodies. Thus far however it has not been possible to demonstrate the presence of lysosomes in amphibian eggs (Brachet *et al.*, 1958).

Ficq (1961) has demonstrated that oöcytes of *Bufo* and *Triton* contain several types of ribonucleic acids whose localizations and properties are consistent with the roles of structural, messenger, and ribosomal nucleic acids in contemporary schemes of nuclear control of the synthesis of specific proteins.

Pasteels (1958) has reviewed critically the methods of study currently in use. He encourages in particular the use of isotope incorporation and immunological methods for the localization *in situ* of proteins. It has been known since the pioneer work of R. S. Cooper (1948) that the frog egg already contains some of the antigens present in the blood serum of the adult. More recently Nace (1958) has used an immunological method in which oöcytes were stained with fluorescent anti-adult frog sera. This author observes that "... macromolecules possessing the serological specificity of adult frog serum assume typical patterns of localization in the growing oöcyte and ... these patterns are characteristic of specific stages." There is a need for similar studies during early embryogenesis of the amphibian egg. Immunological studies on amphibian eggs made thus far include the works of Flickinger and Nace (1952) and Clayton (1953). Nace and his colleagues (1961) have followed a highly specific antigen from follicle cells and oviduct of *Rana pipiens* into the oöcyte. They suggest that this protein may serve to "mature" (render fertilizable) the egg.

Protein differentiation in various embryonic tissues of *Pleurodeles* has been studied by Denis (1961) by means of electrophoresis on cellulose acetate of saline extracts. Significant changes in the protein constitution of localized areas of gastrula and neurula stages were found. The paper of Denis includes references to the work of previous investigators on protein differentiation during early amphibian development.

When, during the 1930's and early 1940's, ultramicrochemical and cytochemical methods began to be applied to the amphibian egg and embryo, the existence of gradients in a variety of constituents and activities was demonstrated—glycogen, —SH groups, ribonucleic acids, alkaline phosphatase activity, and oxygen consumption, to mention only a few. These are best discussed in connection with the metabolism of the embryo in Section III,A,3.

To summarize, then, the developmental physiologist who chooses the amphibian egg as his object of study begins with a degree of complexity that has been described physically at various levels of magnification and biochemically by several techniques. Experimental manipulation of this structure has indicated, however, that the egg's organization is highly modifiable without deteriment to normal morphogenesis. The various levels of resolution at which structure thus can be viewed do not give a clue as to the nature of such "regulation" after experimental disturbance of normal egg organization.

C. THE ROLE OF THE NUCLEUS REEXAMINED

1. Genes and Early Development

Although the earliest experimental embryological studies tended to emphasize the decisive role of cytoplasmic segregation in differentiation and to minimize the significance of the nucleus except as the vehicle for continuity between generations, dissenters to this point of view were not lacking. Goldschmidt (1927) accepted the concept of qualitative identity of all the cleavage nuclei and went on to postulate two mechanisms whereby differentiation might still involve gene function. (1) Each gene enters into activity at a rate, and therefore at a time, proportional to a precisely regulated initial quantity. (2) There exists between each gene and its appropriate cytoplasmic "substrate" a "lock-and-key" specificity such that a given gene is inactive except in the presence of the cytoplasmic constituent whose stereochemical configurations match those of the gene. Both concepts rest upon the assumption that there are specific genes for all the characteristics of each stage of development and that all other genes exist in a latent state at a given stage.

The first postulate has not received experimental verification, but the second has survived in a modified and more sophisticated form as a working hypothesis implicit in many contemporary investigations. The principal difficulty with this concept seems to be its postulation of the very situation which it is asked to explain. This becomes clear when one considers a statement of Sewell Wright (1945), who sees the ". . . activity of the genes during development dependent upon the physical and chemical environment in the cell—an environment for which the genes themselves are largely responsible. A sort of cyclical feedback occurs between genome and its ever-changing chemical environment so that the changing interactions between gene and environment provide the motive power for driving embryonic cells along their diverse paths of differentiation."

It is conceded that the egg possesses an initial cytoplasmic organization due in part to the genetic composition of the female producing the eggs. The problem significant for differentiation, however, begins at this point. The same criticism applies today to the concept that development is to be explained in terms of gene activation by specific substrates to produce specific proteins (induced enzymes). One needs to account for the presence at the right time and place and in correct quantity of the substrate appropriate to a given gene. Ephrussi (1953) has pushed the problem of embryonic differentiation back to the role of genetic mechanisms in oögenesis that lead to polarity of the egg. It seems to the writer, however, that oögenesis is best considered an example of terminal differentiation, in the same sense as eye color. It is in such situations that the role of the gene has been elegantly demonstrated as a result of the early studies of Ephrussi, Beadle, etc. (Needham, 1942, p. 408 *et seq.*). For a number of reasons, among them the lability of polarity and symmetrization in the early amphibian embryo, the student of developmental physiology prefers to *begin* his studies with the activated ovum.

A discussion of the role of the nucleus during development appears called for, centered about two questions: (1) role of the nucleus in enhancing cytoplasmic diversity; (2) possibility of cytoplasmic influence upon diversification of nuclei during development.

To the geneticist, accustomed as he is to the use of "pure" strains of organisms, the amphibian embryologist's practice of disregarding the genetic makeup of the parent organisms appears a shocking lapse. Amphibia are in general difficult to raise to maturity in the laboratory, and the materials of the amphibian embryologist interested in primary morphogenesis have consisted mainly of embryos gathered in nature or obtained by artificial insemination from randomly selected males and females brought to the laboratory. The fact that development proceeds normally in such a high percent of cases cannot be taken to mean, however, that such mutations as may be carried in the parent organisms are insignificant for the developmental process. That this is not the case is proved by the impressive catalogue of mutants (particularly in mice) affecting every stage of embryonic development where they have been looked for. For an early review of genes in development Needham (1942, p. 365 *et seq.*) may be consulted. More recent reviews may be found in Hadorn (1958) and Gluecksohn-Waelsch (1953). In wild populations of frogs such mutations would be expected to occur but if they are lethal or harmful they would be selected against both in nature and in the laboratory where the investigator chooses for his experimental material only those clutches of eggs that exhibit a high percent of fertilization and normal development. When, as rarely, deliberately searched for, the existence of recessive lethal genes with morphogenetic effects has been confirmed in amphibia (Humphrey, 1948). A viable mutant strain of *Xenopus laevis* bearing the cytological marker of absence of a nucleolus has been developed by Fischberg *et al.* (1958a). This mutant provides an excellent means of identifying various cell types as they participate in developmental processes under experimental modification.

A more direct approach to the role of the nucleus becomes possible when, after deliberate alterations are made in either quantity or quality of nuclear materials, changes in the morphogenetic processes result. It will be the purpose of the following section to outline some of the experimental results obtained from this type of program. For full and authoritative discussions the reader is referred to Fankhauser (1955), Needham (1942), Moore (1955), Baltzer (1952), and King and Briggs (1956).

2. The Effect of Quantitative Variations in Nuclear Material upon Development of the Eggs

a. Development without a Nucleus. The influence of the nucleus cannot be entirely eliminated since the long sojourn (3 years in *Rana* species) of the oöcyte in the ovary is a period of intense synthetic activity during which the cytoplasm becomes highly differentiated both ultrastructurally (Kemp, 1956) and biochemically (Grant, 1953). In addition, breakdown of the germinal vesicle during maturation releases nuclear constituents to the cytoplasm. These facts may underlie the ability to support mitosis during cleavage that is seen in amphibian eggs deprived of the nucleus, since the egg is in this respect an exception to other cells.

An ingenious method was employed by Briggs *et al.* (1951) to deprive *Rana pipiens* eggs of functional chromosomes. When sperm are heavily X-irradiated their chromosomes are inactivated for participation in cleavage although such sperm are still capable of activating the egg and contributing a division center. The egg nucleus can be removed surgically after insemination with irradiated sperm. Proof that the sperm chromosomes actually were inactivated came from the use of a lethal hybrid cross. Sperm from *Rana catesbeiana* will not carry *R. pipiens* eggs past early gastrula stage; such hybrids die. Irradiated *R. catesbeiana* sperm however permit development of the *R. pipiens* egg to larval stage with characteristics of the haploid syndrome. If the same irradiation of *R. catesbeiana* sperm is followed by enucleation of the *R. pipiens* egg the latter should contain no functional chromosomes. Such eggs developed into partial blastulae in which cleavage was restricted to a variable portion of the animal hemisphere, plus a portion of the upper vegetal hemisphere on one side of the egg. Cleavage soon ceased, no further differentiation occurred, and death ensued after 1 to 4 days. Synthetic activities, cell division, and differentiation therefore require the presence of the nucleus.

The inadequacy of the achromosomal cells in the present experiments could not be alleviated by grafting them to a normal embryo, a fact the authors interpreted as ruling out diffusibility as a property of the missing nuclear (chromosomal) component. The fact that these achromosomal eggs cleave at all probably is to be attributed to the ability of the sperm after this dosage of irradiation to contribute a division center, a hypothesis fortified by experiments in which toluidine blue treatment of sperm produced first chromosomal dysfunction and, with greater exposure, damage to the sperm's capacity to form a division center. Of more interest, however, is the localization of the cleavages that did occur in the achromosomal embryos, namely, animal hemisphere and a portion of the upper vegetal hemisphere on one side of the egg. One would like to know whether the cleaved areas of these partial blastulae coincide with the localization of sulfhydryl groups and ribonucleoproteins so extensively studied by Brachet (1940) in eggs of *Triton* and *Pleurodeles*.

As Brachet (1957) emphasizes, the cleavage-initiating capacity of granules from late blastula stages might be correlated with the inclusion in this granular fraction of Palade's RNA-rich "small granules" which Brachet contends are the best candidates known at present for the role of "plasmagenes." Such granules, Shaver found, must undergo progressive differentiation, activation, or stabilization, since fractions obtained from stages earlier than late blastula are unable to initiate cleavage (Shaver, 1953; cf. Bogucki, 1923, on cell-free extracts in parthenogenesis). If, as in the enucleation experiments, the "small granules" are permitted to remain *in situ*, their possible lability thus protected from extraction and handling injuries, they might account for the limited cleavage observed. Cytochemical analysis of the enucleate embryos of Briggs *et al.* would be of interest.

Experiments with *Triturus palmatus* and *T. viridescens* (Fankhauser, 1929, 1934; Fankhauser and Moore, 1941) gave advanced blastulae as the terminal stage of development for non-nucleated eggs. Although in the axolotl (*Ambystoma mexicanum*) an apparently normal blastula could develop from an egg lacking chromosomes, gastrulation was not initiated (Stauffer, 1945). The conclusion is that the nucleus is essential for the initiation of differentiation at gastrulation.

b. Development of Haploid Embryos. Elimination of either paternal or maternal chromosomes from participation in development, achieved at the turn of the century in echinoderms, was obtained shortly thereafter in Amphibia. The method employed was parthenogenetic stimulation of the egg by pricking with a needle contaminated with adult blood or tissue fluids (Guyer, 1907). Even more ingenious methods for bringing about haploid androgenesis or gynogenesis were devised and may be found summarized in Fankhauser (1955, p. 132) and in Moore (1955). Spontaneous haploidy in salamanders occurs at a frequency of 0.1–0.2% (Fankhauser, 1955).

As in achromosomal eggs, nuclear products from oögenesis and germinal vesicle breakdown are present in the cytoplasm; but haploid embryos demonstrate the effect of the nucleus by permitting development to more advanced albeit still abnormal stages. Fankhauser summarized the general characteristics of the "haploid syndrome" as follows ". . . the development of the haploid embryos is usually retarded and abnormal from an early stage on. In many cases the development of the archenteron is subnormal, leading to various degrees of microcephaly. The body remains short and broad, blood circulation is usually deficient, edema and ascites are common, and motility and general reactivity are reduced. The great majority of embryos die before they reach the feeding stage" (Fankhauser, 1955, p. 130). For a detailed description of the androgenetic haploid embryo of *Rana pipiens* Porter (1939) may be consulted.

None of the hypotheses advanced by several workers to account for haploid inviability has been universally accepted. Presence of a recessive lethal unmasked by haploidy is refuted by the normal development obtained when haploids regulate to the diploid condition by a nuclear division not followed by cell division (Parmenter, 1933). Furthermore, as pointed out by Moore (1955), every gamete, male or female, would have to carry a lethal recessive since no haploid ever survives; yet in the ordinary diploid population of embryos obtained by artificial insemination 99–100% normal development can occur, an improbable situation were the expected proportion of diploid homozygous lethals present.

The hypothesis that the low nuclear-cytoplasmic ratio in haploids leads to developmental arrest receives some support from the superior development and survival of small haploids over large haploid eggs (Briggs, 1949).

c. Polyploidy. Any explanation based upon rigidly quantitative ratios between nuclear and cytoplasmic constituents collapses in the face of the normal development of polyploid embryos of either spontaneous or experimental origin. Normal development through hatching and even later has been observed variously in triploid, tetraploid, and pentaploid embryos of frogs and salamanders (Fankhauser, 1955). A most interesting feature of organ formation in polyploid embryos is their adjustment of cell size to cell number resulting in normally proportioned organs despite the absolute number of cells participating in a specific organogenesis.

d. Aneuploidy. The developmental effects of unbalanced chromosome complements have been studied by Fankhauser and his colleagues and summarized by Fankhauser (1955). Suffice it to repeat here that, "In contrast to most balanced polyploids, aneuploids have a greatly reduced viability and are usually abnormal in appearance." The abnormalities reported become manifest during development of the circulatory system, hence rather too late to be of interest to the student of primary morphogenesis. In mammals, moreover, the chromosome number may vary from cell to cell within the same tissue (Beatty, 1954), a fact which Waddington (1956) suggests may be a very late event in development, or may indicate diffusibility of vital gene products from cell to cell.

Beetschen (1958, 1959) has made a cytological study of lethal heteroploids of *Pleurodeles waltlii* produced by hypothermic shock to fertilized, unsegmented eggs. Those embryos surviving the shock cease development during blastula or gastrula stages and show the high nuclear RNA content observed by Brachet in lethal hybrids. Beetschen proposes to use autoradiography to analyze the details of the disharmony in nucleocytoplasmic relationships.

e. Conclusions. Quantitative variation of the nuclear materials (not all of them necessarily genic) has been shown to lead to abnormality and often death of the embryo at an earlier or later stage. While indicating that a "proper balance" between nuclear products and cytoplasmic products is essential to support normal morphogenesis, purely quantitative alterations of nuclear-cytoplasmic factors can provide information of limited scope. Another approach that already has yielded valuable information will be discussed in the following section.

3. The Effect of Qualitative Variation in Nuclear Materials

a. Analytical Methods. (1) Xenoplastic transplantations. Among the most frequently cited groups of experiments from the early years of classic experimental embryology are those concerning the developmental effects of fusing parts of amphibian embryos taken from different species, genera, and even orders. When the hereditary characters of the two groups differ it is possible to distinguish between the contribution of the respective tissues to a given organ or tissue, and thus to make a tentative judgment as to the role of genes in differentiation.

Among the best known of such experiments was that concerning the induction of head and mouth structures in reciprocal transplants between urodele and anuran gastrular tissues. The larvae of these two orders differ in head and mouth structures in that the urodeles possess a balancer on each ventrolateral side of the head and dentine teeth, whereas anuran larvae develop mucous glands (suckers) and horney denticles. In transplantation experiments performed by Spemann and his colleagues (cited in Holtfreter and Hamburger, 1955) ventral ectoderm of an anuran gastrula placed in the prospective head region of a urodele gastrula was induced by the urodele tissues to form suckers and horney denticles in the mouth region. In the reciprocal transplantation a salamander's ventral ectoderm was induced by head structures of the frog to form salamander-type organs. These transplantation experiments were highly significant to an interpretation of induction as a general "release" mechanism, and they also reinforced the embryologists' prejudice that genes in the developmental process affected only terminal superficial characters. Other instances in which nuclear factors have been shown to be directly involved in later stages of differentiation of, for example, pigment cell pattern distribution (Twitty, 1936), will not be discussed here.

Clearly, a different type of experiment was called for to test the role of the nucleus in primary morphogenetic events. To a certain extent analysis of the modifications in development that occur when lethal genes are present has contributed to our knowledge as to the time and place at which genes intervene in normal developmental processes. A more precise distinction between nuclear and cytoplasmic factors in specific developmental events is available, however, from the use of interspecific hybridization. The type of embryo resulting from hybrid cross may be expected to reflect different distinctive features characteristic of either of the two parents, hence an indication is provided of whether nucleus or cytoplasm played the controling role.

(2) *Hybridization.* A motive for making some of the earlier hybrid crosses in amphibia was the question of which aspects of early development were under nuclear and which under cytoplasm control. Since a high percentage of diploid hybrids was found capable of some development, but various hybrids blocked at different stages, the answer was plainly not a simple one. In each particular hybrid cross only an analysis by every technique available of the precise morphogenetic event(s) that fails can provide insight into the long-standing basic questions of when and how genes intervene in morphogenesis and differentiation, and what the relative roles of nucleus and cytoplasm are (Hadorn, 1958).

If, furthermore, reciprocal crosses gave different developmental results, cytoplasmic factors mediated through the ovum (since the chromosome complements of such diploid hybrid reciprocal crosses would be identical) were implicated as playing the preponderant role. Baltzer (1940, 1950, 1952) and his students made many of the early experiments on hybridization in urodeles. Reviews of hybridization experiments are found in Needham (1942, p. 358), Moore (1955), and Fankhauser

(1955, p. 141). The present brief discussion will be based upon several examples cited in Moore (1955) of hybridization between non-European species.

Of the 140 diploid crosses tabulated by Moore, 91% gave some development and 42% of the latter formed normal tadpoles or even reached the adult stage. The more useful hybrid crosses, of course, are those which block at an earlier stage of development—late blastula, gastrula, or neurula—permitting analysis of their defects by classic methods of experimental embryology. It had previously been thought that such early developmental blocks in hybrids precluded decision as to the respective contributions of nucleus and cytoplasm to particular developmental processes because the hybrids died before the stage at which the differential characters between the parent species begin to show (Baltzer, 1920, cited in Raven, 1954, p. 84). Earlier workers had circumvented this difficulty in part by grafting hybrid primordia into normal embryos where the hybrid tissues survived long enough for them to be characterized as maternal or paternal in type (see Raven, 1954, for references). Moore, utilizing the informational background offered by his extensive studies on developmental rate at different temperatures in different species, could use rate of development as a criterion for the relative effects of nuclear and cytoplasmic factors in the early embryogenesis of hybrids (see also Porter, 1941, 1942). In general, Moore found that in those diploid hybrids which blocked at early gastrula stage the rate of development corresponded to that of the maternal parent species. In those hybrids in which development continued beyond the gastrula stage its rate at first during cleavage and gastrulation approximated that of the maternal species but was altered in the paternal direction at neurula stages and later.

No generalization can be made from this finding, however, since in other hybrid crosses (Hamburger, 1935, 1936) between *Triton taeniatus* and *T. cristatus*, for example, development appeared almost completely maternal until the limb bud stage, only after which an effect of paternal chromosomes became manifest in comparative length of the embryo and pigmentation. Reciprocal crosses between *Triton taeniatus* or *T. palmatus* × *T. cristatus* gave different developmental results, hindlimb abnormalities being typical when a *T. cristatus* male provided the paternal chromosomes but absent when *T. cristatus* eggs were fertilized with *T. palmatus* sperm.

Moore (1947, 1948) augmented his early hybrid studies by tests of the inductive capacities and competence of dorsal lip and presumptive epidermis respectively. After transplantation of lethal hybrid tissue into normal host embryos a partial "revitalization" was effected, suggesting diffusibility of vital gene-induced substances. The grafted hybrid tissues, however, showed less than normal competence and inductive ability (cf. Hadorn, 1937). Grafts of lethal hybrid ectoderm from gastrulae obtained in the cross of *Rana pipiens* ♀ × *R. sylvatica* ♂ were made into normal neurulae of *R. palustris* or *Ambystoma maculatum*. Such grafts exhibited lowered competence to form neural tissue and sense organs. Grafts of dorsal lip regions from hybrid to normal gastrulae showed reduced inductive power in terms of both frequency and quality of the secondary embryos induced. Brachet (1945, cited in Moore, 1955) reported more normal inductive ability in dorsal lip tissue from the *R. esculenta* ♀ × *R. fusca* ♂ hybrid.

Another type of hybridization experiment has been performed for a large number of frogs collected in different geographic locations (see Moore, 1955, for references). Among the important findings are the specific early developmental disturbances in reciprocal crosses between northern and southern forms of *Rana pipiens*. When northern eggs are fertilized with southern sperm, developmental rate is retarded and the head is abnormally large. The reciprocal cross produces hypomorphisms in head structures. Other such intraspecific hybrids show developmental interferences at earlier and later stages.

Even a scanty review of experiments thus illustrates that: (1) the introduction of foreign chromosomes into the cytoplasm of an egg has widely varying results ranging from no detectable effect upon development to cytolysis and death in late blastula or early gastrula. (2) The time at which incompatibility of nuclear and cytoplasmic components becomes manifest in hybrids varies in reciprocal crosses. The cytoplasmic "determination" of morphogenetic processes thus indicated must originate during oögenesis. Its ability to support normal development depends sooner or later upon cooperation with the "proper" nuclear components.

Whiteley and Baltzer (1958), after an extensive study of respiratory rate and DNA content in sea urchin hybrid development, have compared their findings with the amphibian hybrid studies. These authors suggest two interpretations for alteration in hybrid respiration: "... that the hybrid respiration is controlled by averaging of the genetic influences of the two parental genomes or that it is the result of development disharmony (incompatibility between the A nucleus and P cytoplasm)." (A = *Arbacia*; P = *Paracentrotus*).

A further instructive attack upon the problem of nucleocytoplasmic relationships became possible with the study of androgenetic haploid hybrids. Whereas in a diploid hybrid the foreign chromosomes are challenged not only with host cytoplasm but also with the maternal nucleus, an enucleate ovum produced by removal of the second maturation spindle together with all the maternal chromosomes affords a better opportunity for demonstration of the foreign chromosomes' ability to function in the milieu of host cytoplasm of a different species.

As general conclusions from the results of many crosses by a number of workers (see Moore, 1955, for references) it may be said that (1) androgenetic hybrids do not develop quite as well or survive as long as their corresponding diploid hybrids but there is fair correlation when they are divided into classes in terms of survival. Thus "when androgenetic hybrids fail in the late blastula stages, the diploids are incapable of developing beyond an early gastrula stage" (Moore, 1955). Absence of competition from host nuclear components apparently permits a slightly earlier and somewhat stronger effect of foreign nuclear materials. (2) Moreover, "these interspecific androgenetic hybrids do not develop as well as the gynogenetic or androgenetic haploids formed of a nucleus and cytoplasm of the same species." The "haploid syndrome" described by a number of workers is here intensified by virtue of qualitative incompatibilities between nucleus and cytoplasm.

b. The Question of Nuclear Differentiation. (1) Nuclear transplantation, normal and hybrid. In 1938 Spemann (p. 211) suggested an experiment which appeared at that time to be "somewhat fantastical," namely the introduction of nuclei from blastula and later stages into an enucleated egg. "This experiment might possibly show," he predicted, "that even nuclei of differentiated cells can initiate normal development in the egg protoplasm." If so, Spemann argued, decisive information would thereby be provided as to whether every cell of the differentiated body contains the whole complement of hereditary determinants. Leaving aside for the moment the validity of the argument, let us review some of the experimental results on nuclear transplantation which have followed introduction of successful techniques by Briggs and King.

In their earlier experiments Briggs and King (1952, 1953, 1955) showed that living nuclei of blastula and early gastrula cells of *Rana pipiens* upon transplantation to activated, enucleated eggs could support cleavage and development into normal embryos in as high as 40% of the instances. When late gastrula cells were tested a low percentage of host eggs receiving nuclei from chordamesoderm and presumptive neural plate achieved various degrees of development, demonstrating that at least some of the late gastrula nuclei were equivalent to cleavage nuclei in respect to ability to support embryogenesis. Since negative results were open to criticism because of the possibility of nuclear damage during manipulation, Briggs and King (1957) improved their techniques by using trypsin-versene treatment rather than a glass needle in the isolation of donor nuclei. They could then extend their tests to nuclei from later stages of development. Endoderm nuclei (selected because this germ layer is determined early in development and because its cells are relatively large) from late gastrula, mid-neurula, and tailbud stages were transplanted into enucleated eggs of *Rana pipiens*. Gradual restriction of the capacity of the nuclei to elicit cleavage and to promote normal development was noted. For example, while late gastrula nuclei promoted cleavage to the blastula stage in 50% of the trials, development was arrested somewhat later and the arrested embryos showed deficiencies in ectodermal derivatives. Mid-neurula endoderm nuclei showed further reduction in ability to initiate cleavage and to support formation of ectodermal and ectomesenchymal structures. And finally, endoderm nuclei from tailbud embryos produced a very low percent cleavage in enucleated eggs, and those which did begin development usually failed at early gastrula. Briggs and King thus have presented compelling evidence for "a gradual restriction of nuclear potencies so that eventually the nuclei would be capable of engaging only in those types of activities characteristic of given cell types," a contemporry rewording of the Roux-Weismann theory of differentiation.

Further experiments involving serial transplantation of endoderm nuclei (King and Briggs, 1956) indicated that the nuclear changes (not changes in mere chromosomes number) were stable through three generations. Clonal descendants of a single endoderm nucleus promoted a "relatively uniform type of developmental abnormality in contrast to the diverse developmental abnormalities observed in eggs injected with nuclei from different donor endoderm cells." In all the nuclear transplantation experiments a scatter in behavior of nuclei from a given source always was observed, indicating that the nuclear changes described do not occur in all cells at once but that within a "determined" organ area the component cells are in different stages of differentiation. In interpreting the apparent specificity of nuclei from the several germ layers it is necessary to determine to what extent the abnormalities shown by the injected embryos are due to gross interferences with normal morphogenetic movements as opposed to strictly nuclear differentiation. Thus, neuro-ectodermal deficiencies would be expected if invagination were impaired, quite irrespective of whether the endoderm nuclei had lost their original capacity to support the differentiation of structures in all germ layers.

An analysis of the lethal hybrid cross *Rana pipiens* ♀ × *R. catesbeiana* ♂ by the nuclear transplantation method (King and Briggs, 1953) showed that nuclei are able to function, i.e., promote normal cleavage and blastula formation, "well after the onset of the arrest of development." The block in development thus is not attributable to nuclear failure alone.

but to disharmony between nucleus and foreign cytoplasm. The resulting deficiencies cannot be alleviated by grafting hybrid tissue to normal embryos. In this respect the *R. pipiens* × *R. catesbeiana* cross differs from some other hybrids.

Attempts have been made to extend the Briggs and King method to the transfer of embryonic nuclei in eggs of the newt *Triturus* (Waddington and Pantelouris, 1953; H. E. Lehman, 1955). Technical difficulties and peculiarities of the species appear to account for the lower degree of success achieved with the newt. Fischberg *et al.* (1958a) using *Xenopus* obtained some normal tadpoles from injection of ectoderm nuclei of late gastrula. Gurdon (1962) has demonstrated that even as late as hatched tadpole stage some of the gut-cell nuclei from *Xenopus* are capable of supporting development of a normal adult frog.

Moore (1958a,b) has advanced the analysis of the hybrid block still further. Nuclear transplantations were made between *Rana pipiens* and *R. sylvatica*, whose diploid hybrids block at the early gastrula stage. Transplantation of a *R. sylvatica* blastula nucleus into an enucleated *R. pipiens* egg resulted in development as far as late blastula stage. The reciprocal transplantation gave the same results. Each type of nucleus thus appeared able to replicate in the foreign cytoplasm, a fact that does not give a hint as to the underlying cause of the developmental block. By an ingenious modification of this experiment, however, Moore has opened up new horizons to be explored. He made androgenetic haploid hybrids by fertilizing enucleated *Rana sylvatica* ova with *R. pipiens* sperm. Cleavage to late blastula stage ensued involving 14 to 15 mitotic divisions, and repeated *R. pipiens* chromosome replication took place in the foreign cytoplasm. A haploid nucleus from the hybrid blastula then was transplanted into an enucleated *R. pipiens* ovum. The resulting development was abnormal; more than half the eggs blocked at gastrula and underwent a characteristic pattern of cytolysis involving primarily the marginal zone and vegetal hemisphere. The highly significant conclusions drawn from this result are that the *R. pipiens* chromosomes were profoundly changed by the *R. sylvatica* cytoplasm during the 14–15 replications they underwent in this foreign environment. Repeated backtransfer into *R. pipiens* cytoplasm of haploid *R. pipiens* nuclei that had replicated in *R. sylvatica* cytoplasm failed to improve the quality of development supported by the changed nuclei (Moore, 1960). The manner in which the cytoplasm brings about this genic change and its implications for the manner of chromosome replication are under investigation and some early results will be mentioned in Section II,C,4.

Models of gene action worked out for microorganisms (Jacob and Monod, 1961) have been applied to some problems of developing embryos in an interesting paper by Moore (1962). Moore cites several examples from classic experimental embryology which indicate that the "action of genes is a function of their location in a specific cytoplasm." He emphasizes the role of non-chromosomal elements and conditions in controlling the action of the structural genes and thus ultimately the synthesis of specific proteins.

(2) *Cytological indications.* It is apparent to the most elementary student of histology that nuclei differ in appearance in the cells comprising different tissues. The gross *appearance* of nuclei, however, cannot be taken to indicate their functional capacities any more than can visible *cytoplasmic* differentiation of cells permit inferences as to the genic composition of their nuclei. "Cells may be highly differentiated cytoplasmically yet be undifferentiated in their nuclei, which (may) retain a full complement of genes" (Child, 1941, p. 229). Too little as yet is known about what components of nuclei may be associated with changes during differentiation.

Cytological evidence that chromosome structure varies from tissue to tissue and within a given tissue in various phases of activity has been presented in several widely cited works, among which are Beerman (1956) and Breuer and Pavan (1955). Although in the polytene chromosomes of insect larvae the distribution of the Feulgen-positive bands is highly constant at all stages of growth and in all organs analyzed, the formation of "puffs" by certain euchromatic bands varies widely from one tissue to another and within the same tissue in various states of metabolic activity and stages of development (larval and pupal periods). The loops of "lampbrush" chromosomes in amphibian oöcytes undergo characteristic changes during meiosis (Gall, 1958) which may be associated with synthetic activities. Since no permanent genetic change obviously can occur during these meiotic activities, Gall cites this as an instance of a change in chromosome structure associated with the functional state of the cell independent of the genetic character of the cell.

(3) *Nuclear chemistry.* The protein and enzyme content of isolated nuclei from several adult tissues show some specific differences (Mirsky and Allfrey, 1958). Hemoglobin is present in the avian erythrocyte nucleus. Myoglobin is absent from the nucleus of the heart muscle cell. Mammalian liver and calf kidney nuclei have a high arginase content, while avian kidney nuclei are very low in this enzyme (Stern *et al.*, 1952). Similar analyses of nuclear enzyme composition are needed for the amphibian embryo. Direct chemical analysis of nuclei and chromosomes from various differentiated cells or tissues also have furnished evidence that chromosomes undergo differentiation in some of their components at least, notably RNA and residual protein (Allfrey *et al.,* 1955).

4. Mechanisms for Nuclear-Cytoplasmic Interactions

a. Biochemical Studies on Hybrids. (1) Energy metabolism. The early hope that differences in metabolism between normal and hybrid amphibian embryos might reveal which biochemical reactions crucial for differentiation represent the results of nuclear-cytoplasmic interaction has thus far received but limited encouragement from actual experimental results. This is by no means to say, however, that the cause is hopeless, because the comparative normal-hybrid studies must select as the modality of comparison those aspects of metabolism that have been studied by descriptive biochemical analyses of normal development. As the biochemistry of normal embryogenesis becomes better known, we may hope for more hints as to what differences may be looked for in hybrid metabolism. On the other hand, ". . . it seems likely that each hybrid cross will have its own biochemical peculiarities. . . . They may have an importance in unravelling the chemistry of development similar to that which the many metabolic poisons have had for cellular biochemistry" (Moore, 1955).

The metabolic poisons referred to in this analogy are those which interfere with the energy-yielding processes of the cell. That a simple correlation between hybrid block and energy failure cannot be made is indicated by the dissociability of rate of oxygen consumption from developmental arrest when various hybrid crosses are compared. In the *Rana pipiens* ♀ × *R. sylvatica* ♂ hybrid, for example, oxygen consumption shows no further increase after the time of developmental arrest, whereas in the *Rana pipiens* ♀ × *R. clamitans* ♂ cross where development likewise stops at the beginning of gastrulation, the rate of oxygen consumption continues to rise normally (Barth and Barth, 1954; Healy, 1952). Work with hybrid crosses between European species of frogs and newts (Brachet, 1957, p. 393 *et seq.*) confirms the lack of a universal correspondence between rate of oxygen consumption and developmental arrest. In the lethal hybrid cross *Triton* ♀ × *Salamandra* ♂ the oxygen consumption is already somewhat lower from the first appearance of cytological abnormalities in the blastula and remains at this low level in the blocked gastrulae while in the controls it rises steadily (Chen, 1953). In the cross *Rana esculenta* ♀ × *R. temporaria* ♂ studied by Brachet and also in frog eggs fertilized with nitrogen mustard-treated sperm, respiration of the blocked blastulae rises at rates comparable to those of controls (Brachet, 1957). When developmental arrest is accompanied by a block to oxygen consumption all regions of the arrested gastrulae reflect the lower respiration (Sze, 1953a).

The oxidative metabolism of the amphibian embryo both normal and hybrid has been documented in detail by several writers to whose publications the reader is referred (Brachet, 1950a, 1957; Barth and Barth,

1954). In the last cited reference, L. G. Barth has discussed the relation between developmental blocks and changes in respiration. If the block in metabolism is assumed to precede the block in development he suggests that any of three vulnerable points in the chain between energy source and developmental event may be at fault in the hybrid. (1) The energy-yielding reaction(s) may be blocked. Gregg (1948) had suggested a failure in the reaction diphosphoglyceraldehyde plus oxidized diphosphopyridine nucleotide (DPN) to give phosphoglyceric acid and reduced DPN. Brachet (1957) suggested failure in DPN synthesis. In either case oxygen consumption would be depressed concomitantly with the developmental block. (2) A block may occur in the energy transfer system, whereupon "the respiration may be unaffected, yet a block to development would occur as a result of a decrease in the availability of energy." (3) "Finally, the block in metabolism may occur in the terminal reactions that accept energy from the reactions which transfer energy from respiration. The respiration then will be normal, the phosphates present in full complement, but an enzyme or substrate for a reaction leading to the synthesis of a compound may be inhibited or missing."

As a result of the work of a number of investigators (Barth and Jaeger, 1947; Cohen, 1953; Kutsky, 1950) it appears well established that phosphorylating glycolysis provides at least one type of energy transfer system for development. The nature of the energy acceptors remains obscure. An attempt (Barth and Barth, 1954) to demonstrate a protein acceptor for the energy from ATP analogous to the ATP-actomyosin system of muscle was perhaps premature since so little is known even yet about the nature of the stage- and region-specific proteins that must arise or increase in amount during development. It is to be hoped that as progress is made in understanding the biochemical properties of the various subcellular structures the several types of lethal hybrids will not be overlooked as materials for comparative studies of such properties as isotope incorporation and enzyme composition.

An entirely new point of view has been expressed by Gregg (1960), who has made a number of investigations of the respiratory metabolism of normal and hybrid frog embryos. Gregg believes that the normal increase in respiration with stage of development occurs in response to increasing energy demands imposed by the developmental process accompanied by ATP breakdown and a corresponding increase in respiration for rephosphorylation of ADP. Thus respiration increases because more energy is needed for development. Hybrid *Rana pipiens* ♀ × *R. sylvatica* ♂ embryos do not develop past gastrula stage and do not show the increased respiration characteristic of normal embryos after this time. Yet according to Gregg's observations on homogenates (Gregg and

Ray, 1957) hybrids have the respiratory machinery to support a normal respiratory rate, and respiration of intact gastrulae responds equally well as controls to the uncoupling agent dinitrophenol. Gregg believes that one aspect of biochemical differentiation may consist of intracellular changes in particulate structure that increasingly facilitate substrate-enzyme union.

This hypothesis provides a reasonable explanation for the lack of correspondence between hybrid arrest and change in respiration noted in several different hybrid crosses. The respiratory machinery may be un-impaired but some deficiency in enzyme-substrate contact or enzyme-transfer mechanisms may arise in hybrids. As Gregg points out, studies of the biochemical properties of cell particulates of various hybrid crosses are much needed.

Some observations of Mirsky and Allfrey (1958) might be applied to the problem of hybrid blocks. These workers report that in nuclei isolated from the thymus gland DNA (deoxyribonucleic acid) is a "cofactor" for the synthesis of ATP (adenosine triphosphate), which in turn is required as an energy source for RNA (ribonucleic acid) and protein synthesis within the nucleus. How specific the DNA must be to serve in the above capacity has not been determined since it is not known whether the same products are formed when a polynucleotide or a foreign DNA is substi-tuted for the normal DNA. If we attribute specificity to this function of DNA, however, and if nuclei of the gastrula possess a system similar to that of thymus nuclei, interference with ATP synthesis and hence with RNA and protein synthesis in the nuclei might occur when nuclear DNA is confronted with a DNA or its components of foreign origin. The "wrong kind" of DNA thus could interfere both with energy sources and with specific syntheses. If Mirsky and Allfrey's method could be applied to nuclei isolated from the *Rana pipiens* gastrula and deprived of their DNA by deoxyribonuclease it might be possible to test the ability or lack of ability of *R. sylvatica* DNA to restore their nuclear ATP and RNA. The system described for thymus nuclei requires oxygen. We know that under anaerobic conditions hybrid eggs and eggs fertilized with nitrogen mustard-treated sperm (Barth and Jaeger, 1947; Brachet, 1957) show a decreased ability for keeping ATP in the phosphorylated form. These speculations represent simply another attempt to translate into specific terms the hypothesis advanced by Moore (1955) that the foreign chromo-somes might be acting to produce "abnormal substances, which would act as competitive metabolites to the normal gene products, or even ... poisons."

(2) *Nucleic acids and protein synthesis.* In any case the problem of

lethal hybrid blocks is fundamentally a matter of disharmony between nuclear and cytoplasmic systems of the hybrid embryo. A more direct approach to the problem is becoming conceivable as advances are made in understanding the interconnected roles of RNA and DNA in nuclear and cytoplasmic synthetic processes. Most of the work in this field has used microorganisms and adult organs of mammals as experimental objects. A discussion by Spiegelman (1957) has pointed up the state of incompleteness of available information as to the precise molecular mechanism for protein synthesis according to the widely favored template hypothesis, a state of affairs which he believes will soon be improved.

Two main schools of thought exist as to the processes of protein synthesis in embryonic cells (Caspersson, 1950; Brachet, 1950a, 1952, and 1958). Both accept the euchromatin (DNA and histone are its principal constituents) as self-replicating and involved in the synthesis of chromosomal patterns, and both assign to RNA an essential role in protein synthesis. The heterochromatin rich in RNA and associated with the nucleolus is thought by Caspersson to produce proteins that are stored in the nucleolus from which they later diffuse to the nuclear membrane just outside of which the production of RNA-proteins is intense. The latter are considered to be the main sources of cytoplasmic proteins. Brachet has emphasized the importance of cytoplasmic RNA-rich granules (the microsomes of the endoplasmic reticulum or ergastoplasm) for protein synthesis. After an extensive review of the literature including work done on nonembryonic cells, Brachet (1957) makes the interesting suggestion that since nuclear RNA has a different base composition from cytoplasmic RNA it may not be able to serve as precursor for the latter. While the concept of cytoplasmic RNA particles as "gene-initiated plasmagenes" appears quite plausible, the possibility of the existence of non-gene-initiated plasmagenes, i.e., self-replicating, nucleus-independent RNA particles has not been disproved. If substantiated, this mechanism for RNA synthesis then coexists with another mechanism whereby RNA is synthesized in the nucleus. How much cytoplasmic RNA is of nuclear origin and how much may be formed independently by cytoplasmic RNA synthesis are problems for the future to solve. Also unsettled is the question of possible control of nuclear RNA synthesis by DNA. Brachet (1957) has marshaled an impressive array of new information on RNA, DNA, and protein metabolism and has integrated it in masterful fashion from the viewpoint of developmental physiology. For a comprehensive review of the experimental observations on protein and nucleic acid metabolism of normal and lethal hybrid amphibian embryos the reader is referred to his book (Brachet, 1957).

As to the nucleic acid metabolism in lethal hybrids Brachet (1957, p. 416) mentions several valuable findings. "It is likely that the RNA synthesized in the abnormal nucleus cannot be properly utilized by the cytoplasm.... RNA synthesis and morphogenesis are closely linked; this is in contrast with the dissociation between DNA synthesis and development, the former still proceeding when the latter is blocked." We owe the latter information to Gregg and Løvtrup (1955) as a result of their study of DNA synthesis in normal and hybrid embryos from the *Rana pipiens* × *R. sylvatica* cross. There is need for more studies of nucleic acid metabolism in the different hybrid crosses—particularly those in which the energy metabolism has been investigated.

b. Radioautographic Studies. An important new approach to the problem of the nucleic acid metabolism of the embryo has been undertaken by B. C. Moore (1960). Moore earlier had found by autoradiography that tritium-labeled thymidine injected into the female was later incorporated into the nuclei of the developing eggs obtained from that female. She has now extended her studies in an ingenious manner by comparing the incorporation of H^3-cytidine and H^3-uridine injected directly into embryos at different stages of development. The presence or absence of labeling was studied in DNA, nuclear RNA, and cytoplasmic RNA. Labeling at all three sites proceeded more rapidly in the case of cytidine than with uridine. A stage difference in incorporation of cytidine into cytoplasmic RNA was observed: mid-gastrulae had not become labeled in this region after 2 hr, while the cytoplasmic RNA of neural fold embryos had become labeled during the same interval. When injected gastrulae were allowed to develop to late gastrula or early neural fold stages they showed moderate incorporation of the labeled cytidine into cytoplasmic RNA. Nuclear RNA was rapidly and strongly labeled by both compounds, particularly at neural fold stage. The different relative activities of the nuclear and cytoplasmic RNA's in rate of incorporation of the labeled nucleotides is consistent with the higher specific activity of nuclear RNA observed in isotope experiments with $C^{14}O_2$ (Brachet and Ledoux, 1955).

If in the present experiments the lag in labeling of cytoplasmic RNA is not to be attributed to its formation in the nucleus and diffusion thence to the cytoplasm, the findings are consistent with Brachet's hypothesis that nuclear and cytoplasmic RNA's are different in the amphibian embryo as in other tissues. The fact that uridine was incorporated into DNA suggests some doubt as to the specificity of this base as a precursor for RNA.

The incorporation of H^3-uridine into partially dissociated amphibian egg cells has been studied by Bieliavsky and Tencer (1960), who employed citrate to bind calcium, thereby rendering the surface coat permeable. Uridine incorporation occurred principally into deoxyribonucleic acid uridine into both nuclear and cytoplasmic ribonucleic acid.

The technique of autoradiography although not quantitative has proved so effective in illuminating the mechanism of chromosome replication (Taylor *et al.*, 1957) that it may also help clear up some of the puzzles of nuclear-cytoplasmic interactions, particularly in embryos in which "chromosome juggling" has been done. A case in point is the question of the nucleotide composition of *R. pipiens* nuclei which after a sojourn in *R. sylvatica* cytoplasm can no longer support normal development when transferred into an enucleated *R. pipiens* ovum (Section II,C,3).

Although chemical analogues of purines and pyrimidines have been found to stop amphibian development at stages characteristic for each compound (Liedke *et al.*, 1954), there has been some question as to whether the compounds actually were effective on the basis of their molecular similarity to the natural bases, since reversal of inhibition could not always be brought about by supplying the natural compound. Whether or not chromosomes in foreign cytoplasm are altered in a fashion similar to what was expected from the chemical analogues might be revealed if a cytoplasmic label appeared in the nucleus of a lethal hybrid. A comparison of incorporation of labeled nucleotides into cytoplasmic RNA of haploid hybrids (which block at blastula) and diploid hybrids (which gastrulate slightly) has been promised by B. C. Moore. One might anticipate that if the foreign chromosomes cause production of an "analogue" of cytoplasmic RNA, the latter might differ in its ability to incorporate labeled nucleotides from the cytoplasmic RNA of a normal diploid embryo. One would also like to follow a label from a normal gastrula when the latter "revitalizes" a graft from a lethal hybrid embryo. Similarly it would be interesting to learn what passes from normal to aneuploid member during parabiosis as in the experiments of Gallien (1959).

Many phases of nuclear-cytoplasmic interaction in development have necessarily been omitted in the above brief treatment, and a minute fraction only of the available experimental results could be included. The problem of nuclear-cytoplasmic interaction is of course shared by all cells and is the property of biochemists, microbiologists, cytochemists, etc. For this reason alone it would appear likely that the mode of interaction of nucleus and cytoplasm will be understood long before problems that are peculiar to developing systems have even approached the stage where questions may be framed in exact biochemical terms. The remainder of this chapter will be an attempt to outline some of these problems peculiar to developing systems and in particular to the amphibian embryo.

III. Interactions between Cells in the Development of the Embryo

A. EMBRYONIC INDUCTION

1. Classic Experiments and Concepts

For approximately 40 years the concept of organizers in embryonic induction has dominated amphibian embryology. From the beginning a few workers were skeptical of the interpretation of major developmental phenomena solely in terms of specific inductors. The principal alternative suggested, however—patterning based upon quantitative activity gradients—was much less susceptible of experimental analysis than the relatively straightforward idea that certain regions of the developing embryo come to contain specific substances that can be passed to neighboring regions and there direct the pathway of differentiation.

Surely it is more than coincidence that those investigators who have limited their experiments to amphibian embryos have led the ranks of the specific inductor school of thought, while other workers who have employed developing systems wherever they be found, from plant through invertebrate and vertebrate materials, have tended to form the opposition to a rigorous adherence to the organizer concept. The present chapter doubtless suffers a similar handicap, since it is by request limited to a discussion of *amphibian* development.

The frustrating search for the chemical identity of the naturally occurring "primary organizer" of the dorsal lip of the amphibian embryo has faltered to a halt in all but a few laboratories, and attention is now turning to other possible interpretations of the rich body of information that accumulated as a result of the ingenious and skillful experiments of classic amphibian embryology.

For every stage of this search masterful reviews by outstanding workers in the field are available. Spemann (1938) presents the results of some 35 years of experiments by himself and his associates performed in order to answer the general question "whether and in what manner the larger partial processes of development are connected among themselves, whether one causes and conditions the other, or whether they proceed side by side independent of each other." Here are to be found data which any final theory of development must explain. A succinct review of amphibian developmental physiology—experimental and theoretical—is to be found in Holtfreter and Hamburger (1955), both of whom have made vast experimental contributions to this field. Huxley and De Beer's (1934) excellent book still is valuable both for its account of the results of classic embryology and for its attempt to reconcile the concept of "organizers" with those of fields and gradients. Child's (1941) book synthesizes much of the earlier literature on developing systems from a characteristically original viewpoint. The writer is strongly convinced that the body of information to be found in these books and the literature they cite should be part of the mental equipment of any student of developmental physiology, since it may be reinterpreted from time to time as information accumulates at different levels of analysis and can serve to provide familiar test objects for new hypotheses. On the chemical side two classic books are available: Needham (1942) and Brachet (1950a), both with comprehensive bibliographies. The latter author more recently (Brachet, 1957) has integrated cytostructural and biochemical aspects of development in a manner that raises new hope for more rapid progress in this field.

a. A First Analysis of Induction: Development of the Eye. It is important to recall that Spemann (1938) himself urged caution in the use of the term "organizer," which he chose to apply to the transplanted dorsal lip that formed a secondary embryonic axis in part from materials of the host. That the normal dosal lip left *in situ* constitutes a "center of organization" was, he believed, an unproven assumption. He furthermore emphasized the role of the reacting tissue in induction and stressed the idea of induction as a releasing process.

Even before 1900 the results of blastomere isolation and constriction (Section II,A,2) had forced the formulation of a fundamental question: to what extent are the parts of the fertilized egg "determined" for their future development and independent of one another, and to what extent does normal development depend upon interactions between the several parts. During the first decade of the twentieth century the vertebrate eye was the object of numerous investigations whose object was to permit a choice between these two alternatives. In Spemann's first experiments with *Rana fusca* removal of the optic cup rudiment at neural plate resulted in later absence of lens, an apparently clear-cut demonstration of a causal relation between these two primordia of the eye. The issue was soon beclouded when the experiments were extended to eye rudiments from other species of amphibia, until finally it could be reported than an entire range of dependence existed, grading from a highly differentiated eyeless lens in *Rana esculenta* and *Ambystoma maculatum*, through lentoids formed in the absence of optic cup by *Bombinator, Rana temporaria,* and *R. catesbeiana,* to no lens without optic cup in species of *Triton* and in *Pleurodeles.* A reinvestigation of this striking species difference by Ten Cate (1956) has shown that the previous temperature history of *Rana esculenta* was decisive for lens determination, self-origination of a lens being the general rule in embryos reared at 12°C while no lenses formed without optic cups in embryos raised at 25°C. The precise mechanism whereby determination and morphological stage thus were dissociated is not clear, since *explants* of presumptive lens ectoderm developed no lenses even if they were made from cooled embryos.

In any case, although the early studies on the vertebrate eye could not lead to unambiguous generalizations because of species differences, they did point up some crucial issues. Action and reaction systems were distinguished. The principle of "double assurance" was formulated from the fact that a small eyeless lens can be formed in *Rana esculenta*, yet the optic cup is able to induce a lens in epidermis not destined for this fate.

b. The "Primary Organizer." The experiments upon which the concepts of "organizer" and "embryonic induction" were founded are now part of the heritage of every student of developmental physiology. Spemann (1938) has left a complete description of his first experiment, with Hilde Mangold, in which, through the use of a compatible but distinctively pigmented host and donor, the composition of a secondary embryo could be analyzed. When a piece of dorsal blastoporal lip of a *Triton cristatus* gastrula was implanted into a ventral or lateral position of a *Triton taeniatus* or *T. alpestris* gastrula it turned inside, developed into notochord and somites, and induced the overlying host ectoderm to form a neural tube. The chimeric nature of the small secondary embryo extended even to its parts, the induced neural plate, for example, containing also some cells of graft origin. Substantiation for the causal role of presumptive notochordal material in neural differentiation came also from experiments in which no nervous system was formed when the presumptive neural plate was deprived of contact with underlying archenteron roof due to exogastrulation.

The vast literature of experimental embryology subsumed under the title of "Entwicklungmechanik" testifies to the enormously stimulating effect of these classic experiments extending over a period of more than three decades. From the first, however, problems of methodology and interpretation arose which have continued to plague workers in this field. To mention only two of these: (1) criteria for a physiological "neutral" medium for the culture of isolated embryonic regions; (2) the extent to which inferences as to normal developmental processes can be made upon the basis of the results of sometimes drastic experimental interference with normal development, exogastrulation being a case in point. Neither of these difficulties is, of course, peculiar to differentiating systems, and indeed they are examples of what Mazia (1959) has labeled "the uncertainty principle in biology." The question of culture medium will be discussed in Section III,A,5. The citation of absence of neural tissue in exogastrulae as proof that the archenteron roof is needed for neural differentiation has been criticized. Child (1941) questioned whether the means whereby exogastrulation was experimentally brought about (exposure of denuded embryos to a 0.35% NaCl solution) may not have inhibited the ectoderm's capacity to differentiate by some sort of injury since the number of survivors was small. In *Rana pipiens*, exogastrulation of the degree pictured by Holtfreter is extremely rare. Holtfreter (in Holtfreter and Hamburger, 1955) presents drawings of various degrees of hypomorphism produced by brief alkaline treatment, but even the most abnormal of *R. pipiens* embryos do not resemble his urodele exogastrulae in degree of mesodermal and endodermal stretching and differentiation. Recently in *R. pipiens* we have observed (Barth and Barth, unpublished) exogastrulation of a degree comparable to the urodele situation. In these experiments LiCl was added to the culture medium. Lithium suppresses neuralization in small explants of *Rana pipiens* presumptive epidermis and directs differentiation toward neural crest derivatives (Barth and Barth, 1959). Thus an agent that produces exogastrulation is known also to alter the differentiation tendencies of cells. The correlation noted by Holtfreter between extent and type of ectodermal differentiation and the amount of invagination strongly favors his interpretation, however.

c. *Regional Differences in the Organization Center.* Although any portion of the early ectoderm can be induced to form either head or tail structures, in normal development the neural axis is patterned in a cephalocaudal direction which suggested qualitative differences in the inductors of the archenteron roof. The work of many investigators (summarized by Holtfreter and Hamburger, 1955) has supported this supposition that differences in specific induction capacities exist between head and trunktail levels of the archenteron roof. These differences are not, however, sharply delimited and their borders overlap—a fact that has made inevitable two alternative interpretations: quantitative variation in a single inducing agent as opposed to a segregation of qualitatively different specific inductors. The reacting ectoderm must also possess a certain specificity since a so-called "trunk inductor" implanted at the head level can induce head structures. The same question arises in connection with mediolateral organization of the mesoderm in the neurula stage. We shall return to this point in Section III,A,4, because the regionally specific action of inductors from adult tissues is almost the last stand of those who support the concept of specific inductors.

d. *Homeogenetic Induction.* That the same experimentally observable facts have been variously interpreted is nowhere more strikingly clear than in the demonstration that neural plate having been induced by chordamesoderm, now itself can induce neural plate when transplanted beneath presumptive epidermis of an early gastrula. This interpretation presented by Holtfreter and Hamburger (1955) is that the same inducing substances are active both in the artificial situation of homeogenetic induction and in the normal induction of ectodermal placodal structures by neural plate. The different results in two instances reflect changes with time in competence of the ectoderm (e.g., ectoderm of a neurula has lost its competence to respond to these inductors in any manner other than formation of head structures such as nose, lens, and otocyst.). Child (1941) emphasized the lack of species-specificity in this phenomenon as an indication of the activating character of induction as opposed to transfer of specific substances. It should be noted, however, that the neural plate shows regional specificity when tested for homeogenetic inductive ability (Mangold and Spemann, 1927). The superficial resemblance of homeogenetic induction to viral infectivity suggests still another interpretation. It might be supposed that activation of specific protein synthesizing mechanisms associated with the microsomes of the endoplasmic reticulum (Brachet, 1957) is followed by invasion of the overlying host cells by these "plasmagenes" when grafted into the blastocoele. Rose (1957) has discussed homeogenetic induction in connection with his specific inhibition theory (Section IV,B,2).

  e. *Some Basic Concepts.* Among the many discoveries of classic experimental embryology was the fact that various regions of the amphibian embryo are capable of more varieties of differentiation than is apparent from their behavior in normal development. Even so cursory a review as the present one cannot fail to include the concepts that were designated as "prospective fate" and "prospective potency." The former was demonstrated by the vital staining experiments of Vogt (1929) which revealed the regularity with which various regions moved gradually into their final positions to form specific structures, unvaryingly under normal conditions. That the state of "determination" suggested by this behavior was labile was shown by Holtfreter's (1938a,b) explantation experiments in which the potencies of the ectodermal and dorsal lip regions were found to differ from their prospective fates. In the case of early gastrula ectoderm, isolated fragments cultured in Holtfreter's standard solution formed only epidermis. The dorsal lip region, however, exceeded its prospective fate when cultured *in vitro*, forming not only notochord and somites but also neural and epidermal structures. Endoderm by the experimental criteria imposed was determined and its potencies already restricted. In view of later experiments to be described in Section III,A,5, it appears at least possible that by suitable alterations of the culture medium but without addition of complex specific inductors, a wider range of potencies may be demonstrated for the presumptive epidermal cells of an early gastrula. It should be added that "potency" here is defined in terms of ability of cells of a region to form various cell types when isolated in a "neutral" medium. In a broader sense by using the technique of transplantation instead of isolation, cells of the presumptive epidermis of the early gastrula can be demonstrated to have the "potency" to participate in formation of any organ or tissue except endoderm. The question of how these potencies are evoked or restrained in normal development must be approached by asking how they may be controlled in experimental situations.

In conclusion, the prolific and stimulating school of "Entwicklungsmechanik" provided us with an embryo whose morphogenetic properties possess from one point of view a semi-anatomical character in their pattern of distribution. On the other hand, there were revealed astounding regulative powers first in large parts of the embryo, later in two of the three germ layers, and finally in organ-forming rudiments. These are among the properties that render developmental physiology a unique discipline.

Historically, after the principle of primary induction had been described, the efforts of a number of investigators were concentrated upon the problem of the chemical nature of inductors and the biochemistry of the early embryo in general. Needham (1942) is the most comprehensive source of information for the early period of investigations in biochemical embryology.

2. Early Search for the Chemical Nature of "the Organizer"

The confidence with which at least some embryologists attacked the problem of the chemical nature of the organizer is recorded in a footnote in Huxley and De Beer (1934, p. 12) where it is stated that, "Already it is known that the organising action is due to a substance which is almost certainly lipoidal and probably a sterol. ..." Thirty years later it is generally accepted that the sterol theory of Waddington et al. (1935) represented but one stage in the long and frustrating search.

That a substance responsible for induction is contained in the dorsal blastoporal region first was suggested by the fact that this region retained its inductive capacity after killing by heat, cold, or alcohol (Bautzmann et al., 1932). The most important experiments that followed upon this initial discovery are summarized by Holtfreter and Hamburger (1955); to Holtfreter we owe much of what is known in this area. The original test system was the early gastrula of *Triturus* into the blastocoele of which materials were inserted that through normal gastrulation movements later came to underlie the presumptive epidermis. The use of ectodermal "sandwiches," in which test materials were placed between two pieces of presumptive epidermis for culture *in vitro*, later was introduced by Holtfreter (1933a). The most alarming aspect of the early tests was the finding that noninductive regions of the gastrula (ectoderm and endoderm) acquired inductive power after killing. This introduced the possibility that any effective agent might simply be working indirectly, killing some cells, which in turn served as inductors for the remaining cells. This idea in somewhat modified form lingers on in the conception of "sublethal cytolysis" (Holtfreter, 1947a), according to which reversible cell injury is supposed to liberate the neural (but not the mesodermal) evocator.

These pioneer experiments also revealed the greater sensitivity of mesodermizing over neuralizing agents to killing procedures, as well as the loss of regional specificity by killed neural inductors, both of which phenomena since have been so extensively studied by the Japanese and Finnish schools (Section III,A,4).

Holtfreter also addressed himself to the question of how widely inductor substances are distributed in nature and "took up the task of testing practically the whole animal kingdom, from the tapeworm up to man, as to inductive agencies" (Spemann, 1938). Other workers followed suit with the result that numerous lists including the most bizarre items appeared in the literature as possessors of neural (not mesodermal) inductor ability. The inductive responses varied in strength, complexity, and frequency, and not *every* tissue and substance tested possessed inductive power. The latter nonetheless appeared remarkably widespread in both embryonic and adult fresh and killed tissues of many groups of animals.

It was logical then that extracts should be prepared from the inductive tissues in the hope of identifying the active principle. Other workers tested a variety of chemical compounds with the results that the active principle was variously identified as glycogen, fatty acids, sterols, cephalin, nucleoprotein, etc. When, furthermore, an entirely foreign substance, methylene blue, was found to stimulate neuralization of ectoderm a reevaluation of the entire problem was made (Waddington et al., 1936). Methylene blue, these workers postulated, must release the organizer from a bound, inactive form in which it occurs in the ectoderm. Thus any of the other compounds that had acted as inductors might have done so by the same indirect mechanism. It was also recognized (Barth and Graff, 1938) that toxic compounds or drastic treatments both may produce cytolysis and thereby stimulate neuralization (cf. Barth, 1941).

After this impasse was reached the analysis of tissue extracts was dropped by most workers for about a decade and a new front was opened as ultramicrochemical and histochemical methods became available for studying the metabolism of the parts of the embryo.

3. Metabolism of the Embryo

There were several stimuli for an attack upon the biochemistry of the amphibian embryo. If an inactive evocator complex did indeed exist throughout the embryo the explanation of why in normal development it was broken down in the dorsal marginal region might be sought in some metabolic peculiarity of that region. On the other hand, the frustrations associated with the attempt to nominate a specific compound as neural or mesodermal inductor had led numerous investigators to consider more closely the nature of the reacting tissue itself. An extreme of this viewpoint is to be found in Child (1941, p. 480) who stated: "The spatial pattern, whether we call it a gradient, a gradient system, or something else, is the real organizer. In the amphibian the natural inductor does not orginate this pattern but is a part of it and plays a role in modifying it." While few workers would have endorsed this opinion without reservation, it was generally conceded that the time had arrived for a detailed survey of the biochemistry of the early embryo in the hope of discovering either qualitative or quantitative differences or both among its various parts. This endeavor is still proceeding as advances in the biochemistry of protein synthesis in particular suggest new components to be localized in the embryo, and as new methods to make the necessary measurements and determinations are developed.

Since it is impossible to present here a complete survey of biochemical studies on the amphibian embryo the decision has been made to mention only some of those studies in which regions of the embryo have been analyzed by either ultramicrochemical or histochemical methods. For a complete survey of these studies and of the work done on whole embryos at progressive stages of development the reader may refer to Brachet (1950a, 1957). Løvtrup (1955) has made an extensive survey of enzyme activity during amphibian development.

One of the most intensively investigated metabolic properties of the embryo is its rate of oxygen consumption. The idea that the organizer region might be characterized by intense metabolic activity may have stemmed originally from its greater susceptibility to toxic agents and its more rapid rate of anaerobic dye reduction (Child, 1941; Bellamy, 1919; Piepho, 1938).

When sensitive and accurate enough methods were used for reliable measurements of small regions of the gastrula the picture was at first confused by seeming species differences and by the standards of reference used by various investigators for computing the rates of respiration. The conclusion finally reached after the efforts of several investigators had been applied to the problem for some 20 years (Boell et al., 1939; Boell, 1948; Barth, 1942; Sze, 1953b; Gregg and Løvtrup, 1950) was that there are no quantitative differences in the rates of respiration of the parts of the gastrula when the Q_{O_2} is calculated upon the basis of extractable (cytoplasmic) nitrogen. The differences earlier reported among regions of the gastrula were attributable to the fact that they were calculated upon the basis of reference standards which themselves are distributed in gradients within the gastrula as a whole (Barth and Barth, 1954, p. 58). This is not to say, however, that the gradients in oxygen consumption are meaningless, for particularly when total nitrogen (mainly a measure of yolk content) is used as the reference standard the respiratory gradients represent closely the actual situation in the living egg. The embryo, unlike the investigator, does not "correct for" yolk content.

A by-product of these researches was the designation of local differences within the gastrula in components and activities other than respiratory activity (e.g., dipeptidase activity, phosphoprotein phosphatase activity, lipid and carbohydrate content). The precise significance of these variables for development has not, however, been clarified.

The importance of carbohydrate as an energy source for development has been recognized since the earliest studies (Needham, 1942; Brachet, 1950a) and has received confirmation from many investigators using a variety of amphibian embryos and various methods and types of experiments. All the evidence points toward the amphibian embryo's possession of en-zymic machinery for phosphorylating glycolysis similar to that found in muscle and other adult animal tissues. The glycolytic and respiratory mechanisms seem to be qualitatively the same throughout the embryo, as evidenced by similar response in dorsal and ventral regions of the early gastrula to a variety of inhibitors (Ornstein and Gregg, 1952). Gastrulation is halted by respiratory and glycolytic inhibitors, and the partial processes which together form the basis for gastrulation (Holtfreter, 1943b, 1944c) also are inhibited or suppressed by various of these poisons (Gregg and Ornstein, 1953). For earlier work see Brachet (1950a, pp. 388–390). The hypothesis that intensive glycolysis during invagination of the organizer region plays a directly causal role in induction has not received experi-mental support (Jaeger, 1945).

Returning to the fundamental problem of the origin and nature of developmentally significant differences between the parts of the gastrula, it was recognized (Boell, 1955; Løvtrup, 1955; Barth and Barth, 1954) that purely "descriptive" analyses of lipids, proteins, enzyme activities of various regions were liable to run into the same dead end as had the studies of respiration and glycolysis. Several workers reported electrophoretic studies on protein fractions of embryos at various stages of development, but again these were essentially descriptive studies and no really helpful leads came from this technique. What needed to be looked for were the proteins that could accept the energy and perform embryological work in the form of morphogenetic movements or the synthesis of new specific compounds.

Thus far acceptors of energy after the pattern of actomyosin have not been detecteed in embryos. There have indeed been few attempts to look for them. One would expect in any event that such acceptors would be transient and therefore difficult to capture in the embryo's constantly changing chemodifferentiation. A more promising inroad is being made in the case of protein-synthesizing mechanisms where such rapid advances are being made by biochemists and microbiologists (Spiegelman, 1957). Some representative methods being focused upon the problem in amphibian embryos are: (1) cytochemical studies, for which Brachet (1957, 1958, 1960a,b) is an excellent source of references to the literature concerning the correlation between RNA content and protein synthesis in many types of cells; (2) isotope incorporation into cell structures and subcellular fractions, and into RNA, DNA, and proteins; (3) localization of specific proteins by immunological methods.

Almost 20 years ago cytochemical studies by Brachet and by Caspersson led them to postulate that RNA is concerned with protein synthesis. Later Brachet followed the distribution of sulfhydryl-ribonucleoproteins in a large number of urodele and anuran embryos at various stages of development. The sulfhydryl groups in most species are not demonstrable until after denaturation so that what is actually detected are proteins rich in potential —SH groups. The most important observations made by Brachet were that the —SH ribonucleoproteins were synthesized during development and that the localization of the syntheses coincided with the regions of most active morphogenesis at any particular stage of development. There was a striking correspondence between the ribonucleoproteins' graded distribution and the animal-vegetal and dorsoventral double gradient system postulated by embryologists. These chemical gradients later were confirmed by quantitative estimations.

That this localization of at least part of the machinery required for protein synthesis is significant and is actually being put to use during development was further indicated by studies with radioactive glycine, methionine, and $C^{14}O_2$ (Brachet, 1957, pp. 398–399). At the gastrula stage incorporation of these tracers into proteins was higher in the dorsal lip region as compared to the ventral ectoderm. The incorporation of $C^{14}O_2$ into proteins and nucleotides (Flickinger, 1954) in the different regions of the gastrula followed the same double gradient pattern as the ribonucleoproteins studied by Brachet.

We have recognized that the direction of a quantitative gradient depends entirely upon the standard of reference, so that the incorporation gradients also might simply reflect differences in the amount of non-yolk active cytoplasm. Thus a region such as the dorsal blastoporal area at a high point in a gradient possesses this quantitative advantage by virtue of containing a high ratio of active cytoplasm:inert yolk. This does not detract from the significance of the gradient, however, for we must accept the fact that in the amphibian embryo we have even at the outset in the unfertilized ovum heterogeneity between the regions. The task is to see how these initially heterogeneous regions become even more varied through either competitive or inhibitory interaction. If active cytoplasm with all its components is synthesized at the expense of yolk reserves (a possibility difficult to demonstrate because the high yolk content will obscure small decreases) the distribution of yolk, inert though it may be in terms of oxygen consumption, isotope incorporation, etc., is nonetheless significant. That yolk is not in itself a homogeneous constituent was demonstrated by Panijel's (1950) chemical analyses of platelets belonging to different size (mass) categories. Flickinger (1957) postulates that "the primary organizer region forms where the first and most active conversion of yolk to cytoplasm occurs." Of course we have not yet the information to explain why *qualitatively* different kinds of protein synthesis go on at various levels of the gradients, but Rose's (1957) theory of specific inhibition is an attractive one. The products of the most active region suppress like protein syntheses in areas they "dominate." This concept will be discussed in Section IV,B,2.

Serological methods recently have begun to be used in amphibian embryology. Immunological studies on *Rana pipiens* proteins bearing "brain determinant groups" revealed that these proteins are situated throughout the embryo at gastrula and even after hatching (Flickinger, 1958). It is perhaps premature to draw final conclusions as to the significance of this finding until the absolute specificity of the methods has been proven. Earlier immunological studies are cited in Brachet (1957, pp. 397, 422).

Brachet (summarized in 1950a, 1957, 1960a,b) has accumulated over the past 20 years massive quantities of evidence that the RNA gradients are causally significant for morphogenesis, without, however, insisting that RNA acts alone in this capacity. This indeed is the reason why Brachet's theory holds especial promise as a guide in future investigations. It will be recalled that embryologists, especially those of the "Entwicklungmechanik" school, have been reluctant to give any credence to the gradient theory of Child. Spemann (1938) expressed the reasons for this reluctance. Since he could not conceive how qualitative differences arise from purely quantitative ones Spemann preferred to view metabolic gradients as simply releasing factors for pre-formed differences within the egg. Brachet's gradients may represent differences in the whole complex protein-synthesizing machinery of the egg, including the various types of ultracentrifugable granules and ergastoplasm. These too probably differentiate with time (Weber and Boell, 1955), although more evidence is needed on this point. The qualitative differences derived during differentiation concern proteins. Hence Brachet's ribonucleoprotein gradients may be found to represent quantitative gradients that very well could give rise to qualitatively different cytoplasms in the various regions of the embryo. One needs, of course, to present the protein-synthesizing systems with (1) some initial cytoplasmic differences (and these in amphibian eggs certainly are present in the form of concentration of yolk as well as composition of the yolk platelets); (2) some mode of self-limiting interaction such that more than one type of protein can be synthesized. Brachet speaks of competition between plasmagenes, which he equates with different kinds of ergastoplasm. Brachet in postulating specific RNA's cites evidence that nuclear and cytoplasmic RNA's do not have the same base ratios. The fact that with the amphibian embryo we must fall back upon preformed qualitative differences in the ovum which cannot as yet be specified completely explains in part the recent trend in developmental biology toward the use of simpler organisms and the study of secondary induction phenomena.

When the biosynthesis of proteins is clarified no doubt the clues we need to attack protein synthesis in the embryo will be at hand. Meanwhile there is need for systematic investigation in amphibian embryos of the incorporation of protein and nucleic acid precursors into cellular particulates and visible structures at different stages and in different regions of the embryo.

4. The Problem of Specificity in Neural and Mesodermal Inductors

Early in the course of studies on the primary organizer a distinction was made between "head-organizer" and "trunk-organizer." In the intact gastrula the distinction was obscured by host "interference" with the grafted anterior or posterior prospective archenteron roof. "Trunk-organizer" transplanted to host head level induced head, and acted as "trunk-organizer" only at more posterior host levels. In isolated ectoderm, however, a more or less clear cephalocaudal qualitative difference in inductive power was observable (see Holtfreter and Hamburger, 1955 for references).

When foreign tissues began to be tested for inductive ability, while most of the effective ones were inductors of cephalic structures a few tended to induce spinocaudal structures. Chuang (1940) pressed the question further using mouse kidney and Triturus liver as inductors and found differences in their ability to induce cephalic and caudal structures in jackets of Triturus gastrula ectoderm. He further demonstrated that the mesodermizing power of the inductors was far more sensitive to heat (boiling) than was their neuralizing power. Since these beginnings there has accumulated a bewildering mass of information about a completely improbable situation—since it is scarcely to be expected that specific compounds characteristic of adult liver and kidney are present in the archenteron roof. The exhaustive nature of such information is exemplified anew (Iyeiri and

Kawakami, 1962) in experiments that tested the inductive effects of 23 kinds of tissues or organs of the rat, with the result that "no noticeable relation was found between inductive specificities of tissue and their embryological origin or physiological function." As Niu (1959) stated with good humor: "The discovery that different adult tissues could induce the presumptive ectoderm to develop into different structures was a great stride toward understanding the complexity of the induction problem." Efforts to extract region-specific compounds from the archenteron roof are indeed conspicuous by their absence from the literature of this field (see Holtfreter and Hamburger, 1955, p. 254). In a thought-provoking review of the early development of special proteins Nace *et al.* (1961) theorize that "since identical macromolecules [of the amphibian archenteric roof and from mammalian tissue extracts] are probably not being compared, . . . the significant units of action are not the macromolecules themselves, but rather the reactive sites on the macromolecules. . . . Their specific interaction would result in modification of the tertiary characteristics of the macromolecules, and the morphological response which is eventually observed would depend upon the modified character of the responding macromolecule and upon the milieu within which it acts." Such a substitution of "reactive sites" for entire macromolecules still leaves us with the longstanding question of the nature of the developmentally significant modifications produced in the reacting (molecular) system itself. The reason for reviewing the abnormal inductor story is the hope that some clue to the normal induction process can be ferreted out.

Three groups of investigators have been the principal contributors and have arrived at theoretical interpretations of inductive specificity which are not entirely incompatible. Toivonen and his school (see Toivonen and Saxén, 1955; Toivonen, 1958) conceive that the normal regional specificity of the embryonic axis arises as a result of the interaction between two gradients. The "neuralizing principle" has its highest concentration on the dorsal side of the embryo and grades off laterally. The "mesodermalizing principle," chemically distinct from the neuralizing principle, occurs in a caudocranial gradient. In anterior regions the neuralizing principle acts unimpeded to induce head (archencephalic) structures. In more posterior regions the mesodermalizing inductor interacts with the neuralizing one to produce deuterencephalic (mid- and hindbrain) structures; even more posteriorly where the mesodermal gradient has its peak, spinocaudal differentiations are induced. Toivonen found that alcohol-treated bone marrow from the guinea pig was a highly specific inductor of purely mesodermal structures when implanted into the blastocoele of *Triturus vulgaris*. Bone marrow then contains something equivalent in action to the postulated mesodermalizing principle of the living archenteron roof. Guinea pig liver, on the other hand, has the neuralizing capacities assigned to the postulated neuralizing principle and when used along with bone marrow produces all types of regional differentiation.

Yamada (1958) and his group also use a double gradient theory to interpret their data. Although their method of test, sandwiching the inductor between two pieces of presumptive epidermis, and the species used, *Triturus pyrrhogaster*, differ from Toivonen's, many points of similarity occur in the results of the two schools. In one set of experiments, for example, Kawakami and Yamada (1959) applied simultaneously crude pentose-nucleoprotein fractions from bone marrow and liver tissues of the guinea pig. Instead of purely mesodermal structures expected from bone marrow or archencephalic structures which liver alone induces, deuterencephalic-spinocaudal structures were induced. When bone marrow and kidney nucleoprotein fractions were combined, spinocaudal structures were evoked. These observations and many others made by this group are readily interpretable in terms of the interaction of fairly specific mediators distributed in cephalocaudal and dorsoventral gradients. The result of an induction depends upon the ratio between the two factors. It should be kept in mind that the gradients are purely hypothetical as regards their possible occurrence in the archenteron roof. The inductive effects of abnormal inductors upon isolated presumptive epidermis are the only real facts known. Toivonen (1953) has been quite explicit in theorizing about the situation in the living archenteron roof where he attributes specificity not to any great differences in regional distribution of the active components but rather to regional differences in permeability of the cells from which active substances must diffuse.

The chemical identity of the factors involved has been much in dispute—in particular the question of whether the guinea pig liver inductor owes its effectiveness to its ribonucleic acid or its protein component. The earlier clear-cut characterization of the archencephalic inductor as pentose nucleic acid and the spinocaudal inductor as protein (Kuusi, 1953) appears to have been premature. The use of enzymes (ribonuclease and proteases) of doubtful purity has contributed to the confusion.

A third group, headed by Nieuwkoop, involved with the problem of regional specificity of induction has used living notochord as the inductor. Without going into the details of their experimental evidence (for which see Nieuwkoop, 1952; Nieuwkoop and Nigtevecht, 1954) their main theoretical divergence from the other schools of thought rests upon the postulation of only one factor which first "activates" the presumptive epidermis to form neural tissue and afterward brings about "transformation" into more posterior and mesodermal structures. These concepts are similar to the two-step process designated by Waddington (1932) as evocation plus individuation. Toivonen (1958) has shown, however, that his purely mesodermal inductor from bone marrow induces mesoderm after as little as 2-hr contact without going through a preliminary phase of neuralization (activation).

More recently Toivonen (1961) and Saxén and Toivonen (1961) have strengthened their evidence for the existence of two qualitatively distinct inductors. Nonheated HeLa cells (spinocaudal inductors) were mixed with heated cells (archencephalic inductors) in increasing amounts. The resulting cell mixtures were tested by implantation into *Triturus* early gastrulae. The regional types of induction produced by such mixtures represented a progressive shift from archencephalic through deuterencephalic to largely spinocaudal types of differentiation. Using the "sandwich" test method on alcohol treated HeLa and bone marrow tissues respectively, these workers were able to reverse the usual neural-mesodermal sequence of differentiation. When bone marrow (a mesodermal inductor) was removed after 3 hr and replaced with heat-treated HeLa cells (neural inductors) deuterencephalic structures (hindbrain and ear) were evoked from presumptive epidermis. While admitting "that the difference between the views of Nieuwkoop *et al.* on the one hand, and of myself and my co-worker on the other, is largely a terminological one. . . ." Toivonen (1961) believes that the case for two qualitatively distinct regionally specific inductors is good.

An entirely new light has been shed on the problem by Yamada (1958) in a study of heat lability of the bone marrow factor. The instability of mesodermal inductors to heat was early recognized and repeatedly confirmed. That it is not an all-or-none phenomenon, however, was shown by Yamada, who steamed thin layers of bone marrow tissue for very brief intervals before testing their inductive capacity. As the duration of heating was extended from 25, 40, 60, through 150 *seconds* an orderly sequence of shifts in regional specificity of heated inductor occurred. The mesodermal character of the inductions became first modified toward spinocaudal, then deuterencephalic, and finally archencephalic inductive ability before complete loss of activity occurred. Yamada is tempted to assume "that the protein molecule responsible for induction goes through a series of changes in configuration . . . which are reflected in the regional effects." He points out further that the arrangement of prospective areas above the dorsal lip of the blastopore in the living gastrula follows the same dorsoventral sequence as does susceptibility of the regional inductive characteristics of bone marrow upon the level of differentiation achieved within a region. Although the method is not strictly quantitative, high concentrations of bone marrow factor induced notochord and somites, while low concentrations induced blood islands and mesothelium.

Mifune (1959) also reports a progressive shift in regional effects when bone marrow protein is stored in cold ethanol before being tested for inductive activity.

These experiments are reminiscent of Yamada's well known work with the mesodermal mantle in which more ventral regions of the mesoderm could be shifted in differentiation capacity toward more dorsal types of differentiation by combining the former with notochord in explants. Thus prospective blood islands plus notochord gave rise to pronephros; prospective pronephros plus notochord formed some muscle. Taken together these observations suggest a graded distribution of a mesodermalizing factor. Whether the latter acts as a stimulator or as a specific inhibitor in Rose's (1957) sense of the term is not clear. That gradual shifts in type of differentiation in explanted presumptive epidermis can be brought about by graded concentrations of an inorganic ion is reported by Barth et al. (1960). As the concentration of LiCl added to the culture medium is raised differentiation of nerve decreases until finally ectomesenchyme (pigment cells and mesenchyme) is obtained at high LiCl concentrations. This sequence is the same as that for the change in competence of ectoderm during aging observed by Holtfreter (1938c).

The use of foreign tissues and extracts has not solved the problem of the nature of the normal inductors or even whether these exist. The results have strengthened the case for the gradient and field properties of the developing system without, however, solving the problem of *what* is distributed within the gradients in the normal embryo.

5. The Means of Induction

a. The Question of Transfer of Material during Induction. Several experimental tools have been applied to the question of whether embryonic induction involves an actual passage of material. If this does occur in normal primary induction it must be a rapid process since a contact between inductor tissue and competent ectoderm of only 3- to 4-hr duration has been found sufficient to permit induction in *Triturus* and *Pleurodeles* (Johnen, 1956; Denis, 1956–1957). Holtfreter (1933a) interposed vitelline membrane between graft and organizer region and induction failed to occur. Brachet (1950b) found that neither inductive influence nor neutral red, a vital dye, would pass through a cellophane sheet interposed between inductor and competent ectoderm. The dye is bound by cytoplasmic granules since free neutral red passes readily through a cellophane membrane. When porous membranes were used instead of cellophane, induction could occur if the pores were large enough; in those positive instances filaments were observed to extend inside the membrane (Brachet and Hugon de Scoeux, 1949). Ordinary light microscopy revealed no protoplasmic continuity between the chordamesoderm and ectoderm so their interaction was considered by some investigators to be mediated through the intercellular matrix (Grobstein, 1954). When electron microscopy was applied to this question bridges and canals were observed between chordamesoderm and presumptive neural plate of the gastrula at the time of induction (Eakin and Lehmann, 1957). The surface coat of the ectoderm, whose permeability properties are not agreed upon, proved permeable to the inductive stimulus (Brahma, 1957) and neural tubes were induced in presumptive epidermal grafts when the surface coat of the graft was in immediate contact with axial mesoderm. The apparent necessity for close physical contact has been reexamined by Brahma (1958), who concludes that it has not yet been proven conclusively. A recent study by Saxén (1961) on transfilter neural induction of amphibian ectoderm also led to the conclusion that direct cellular contact is not necessary.

More decisive evidence has been sought through the use of isotopes and serological studies. In the former category, although labeled compounds from a graft have been shown to enter host tissues which are induced to form a neural tube, whether or not the label has marked the active principle of the inductor and in what form the label is actually diffusing remain unsettled points (see Sirlin *et al.*, 1956, for a review of earlier work by other investigators). There is some recent quantitative evidence for passage of some ribonucleoprotein during induction (Rounds and Flickinger, 1958), a finding consistent with earlier cytochemical observations (Brachet, 1950a). Flickinger *et al.* (1959) employed an ingenious serological method for detecting passage of *Rana pipiens* chordamesoderm antigens into *Taricha torosa* ectoderm during culture of fused explants for 3–4 days. Although such passage did occur, there was no quantitative increase when the ectoderm was cultured for a further period of time, a finding mediating against the possibility that autoduplicating particles or compounds had been transferred. In view of what we know of the incompatibility between species hybrids in chromosomal replication, this test for cytoplasmic autoduplicating particles is perhaps inconclusive for what may happen after normal induction. A technical difficulty in all experiments in which labeled material is grafted is the possibility of breakdown of some of the cells of the graft, liberation of the label from a macromolecule, and incorporation of the small molecular breakdown products into compounds being synthesized or exchanging. The question of the transfer of an inductor of macromolecular dimensions thus remains open.

Grobstein (1961) has reviewed the history and current status of the contact conception in relation to embryonic induction. In his opinion the "initial critical events in induction and hence in cytodifferentiation" may well take place in the "microenvironment" of the cells. The concept of microenvironment to replace that of direct cell contact (Weiss, 1958b) postulates a "heterogeneous molecular population which exists between cells." This idea has especial appeal as interpreted by Grobstein because it invokes the potency of simple variations in pH, ionic strength, etc., as factors that may modify developmentally significant interactions between macromolecules in the immediate vicinity of interacting cell surfaces.

A series of papers that had a marked impact upon the question of the means of induction was published by Niu (see Niu, 1956, for earlier references). Two of the most important conclusions reached by Niu are the following: (1) Induction of nerve by chordamesoderm and other inductor tissues can proceed without immediate physical contact. A medium in which chordamesoderm had been cultured for 7–10 days contained substances (sharing properties in common with nucleoprotein) which induced an ectodermal explant to form nerve and pigment cells. (2) Older cultures (12–16 days) of an inductor tissue (posterior medullary plate) liberated to the medium substances that induced myoblasts to differentiate from presumptive epidermis. The experiments were made with *Triturus*, *Ambystoma*, and axolotl embryos in a medium devised by Niu and Twitty (1953) for culture of salamander tissues *in vitro*. The results were interpreted to indicate the existence of two different kinds of inductor substances in young versus older "conditioned medium," since the concentration of inductor substances was quite similar in spectrophotometric estimations while the maximal ultraviolet absorption of the two differed. Toivonen has suggested that two different inductors diffuse out of the notochord cells at different rates, reaching effective concentrations in the medium at different times. In view of the difficulties inherent in the whole problem of regional specificity of inductors (Section III,A,4 above) one could wish for a more direct proof that two different inductors are involved in neuralization and mesodermalization in Niu's important experiments.

More recent studies by Niu have been concerned with the identification of ribonucleic acids with inductor substances (Niu, 1959). Extracts of adult organs such as calf kidney and liver induce in explants of amphibian gastrula ectoderm the formation of tissues that resemble the inductor source. If these experiments be interpreted as an example of homoiogenetic induction, two further examples come to mind. Benitez *et al.* (1959) have reported that ribonucleic acid and ribonucleoproteins from microsomes of rat and yeast produce nerve-like differentiation of rat fibroblasts *in vitro*. Ebert (1960) reports that adult heart microsomes in conjunction with Rous sarcoma microsomes to facilitate penetration evoke muscle-like elements in the chorioallantoic membrane of chick embryos. The bearing of these three types of "induction" phenomena upon events in the developing embryo is a matter for future investigation.

From the fact that the ribonucleic acids play decisive roles in the synthesis of specific proteins it does not necessarily follow that there is actual transfer of specific RNA molecules from the archenteron roof to the presumptive neural plate during primary induction. The histochemical picture (Brachet, 1960a) shows only that "when late gastrulae or early neurulae are examined with a microscope, under high power, a high RNA content is found at the interval separating the young medullary plate from presumptive chorda."

b. Role of Reacting Tissue. The difficulties in identifying the nature of embryonic inductors and of interpreting the induction process have led some investigators to regard the reacting tissue itself as the seat of specificity and to suggest that rather simple unspecific factors may initiate the process of differentiation within competent ectoderm (Holtfreter, 1951; L. G. Barth in Barth and Barth, 1954; Child, 1941, pp. 501–502). Holtfreter (1938c) contributed an especially thorough study of the qualitative and quantitative changes with time in the reactivity of *Triturus* ectoderm to a variety of inductors. Thus, aside from the question of specific inductors, the differentiation achieved depends also upon the "state of responsiveness" ("competence" according to Waddington) of the ectoderm.

This aspect of differentiation became especially significant when it was discovered that neuralization can occur in the isolated ectoderm of *Ambystoma maculatum* in the absence of any extrinsic inductor (Barth, 1941; Holtfreter, 1944a). Holtfreter correlated the occurrence of neural induction with the amount of cytolysis occurring when *A. maculatum* explants were cultured in a standard salt solution to which *Ambystoma* unlike other urodeles is "susceptible." From this interpretation it would follow that every substance or condition applied to a presumptive epidermis explant killed some cells which thereupon liberated unknown, unidentifiable neuralizing substances. In a reanalysis of the problem (Holtfreter, 1947a) neural differentiation in ectodermal explants was found to occur in the absence of cytolysis if sufficiently mild alterations were made in the ambient medium (Holtfreter's standard solution). Thus neuralization could be prevented in "susceptible" *Ambystoma* explants by "slight acidulation ... by means of orange juice," etc., or the addition of glucose or histone. Conversely, neuralization could be promoted in resistant *Triturus* explants by brief treatment with various agents that increased cellular permeability (Ca-free solutions, hypotonic solutions, alcohol, excessively low or high pH). Holtfreter was led to propose that a "sublethal," reversible cytolysis, by altering the permeability of the explanted cells to water and electrolytes, causes "new combinations of certain cytoplasmic compounds whose specific synthetic activity would shift differentiation from epidermal to neural." This somewhat factitious interpretation avoids the postulation of an unmasking of a specific unknown evocator substance, and substitutes instead the concept that equally unidentified specific synthetic processes are set in motion by nonspecific changes in permeability of the cell membrane. Although Holtfreter states that this process is not likely to occur in normal induction during gastrulation, it seems not beyond the realm of possibility that a change in permeability might occur when cells of the presumptive chordamesoderm have migrated into the interior of the gastrula. Whichever point of view is preferred as a working hypothesis, however, "the conviction is strengthened that the key to an understanding of the induction phenomena is to be sought in the reacting cells rather than in the inductors" (Holtfreter and Hamburger, 1955, p. 273). It is to be hoped that some of our clues will come from continuing studies of the control of specific protein syntheses as envisioned by Brachet (1957, 1958).

The entire matter of neuralization without induction and the notion of sublethal cytolysis are stimuli to a reevaluation of our criteria for a "neutral" medium in which to culture explants and cells *in vitro*. If an explanted bit of presumptive epidermis forms nerve cells in a given culture medium this event is subject to two interpretations: (1) the medium is "physiological" and adequate to permit the explant, free now of normal surrounding host influences, to express another of its potentialities for differentiation; (2) the medium has produced "unphysiological" changes in the explanted cells, as explained above. Our heritage of information as to the "prospective potencies" of the parts of the gastrula comes from the classic isolation experiments of Holtfreter and others of Spemann's school. The medium used contained only inorganic salts and was devised for certain urodeles. The fact that tissues from older embryos (neural plate of the neurula) form neural structures in the same culture medium that fails to support differentiation of gastrular presumptive neural plate is not necessarily conclusive proof of the adequacy of the medium. The physical properties of the cells have changed during development from gastrula to neurula stage, as anyone can confirm who has handled the two stages with glass needle and hairloop. The older tissues are more viscous and resistant to mechanical injury and may also be able to express their potencies in a medium that would inhibit the sensitive young gastrula cells.

It may be recalled that when presumptive epidermis was cultured in the coelomic fluid or in the eyeless eye cavity of older larvae different results were obtained from those observed in the inorganic medium. Presumptive neural plate developed into pure nervous tissue or epidermis, while many isolated regions of the early gastrula of *Triton* were observed to form chordamesoderm (Holtfreter, 1929, 1931; Kusche, 1929). Although one cannot exclude the presence of neuralizing and mesodermalizing inductors in these body fluids (any more than one can categorically deny that the normal embryonic inductors are present even in adult guinea pig liver and kidney), it appears worthy of consideration that possibly large molecules act in an unspecific way to protect the explants and permit them to express some of their latent differentiation potentialities. A "resistant," in Holt-freter's sense, species such as *Rana pipiens* does not neuralize in a simple inorganic medium; it forms neural tissue only when "protected" by a protein such as globulin on proteose-peptone added to the medium (Barth and Barth, 1959). That these proteins are not sources of specific inductors is indicated by the fact that their presence is not required by the cells until after the period of sensitivity to neural inductors has terminated. Transplantation experiments suffer from possible interference from the host tissue surrounding the graft; isolation experiments must be subject to the question of our criteria for a neutral medium.

A number investigators have stressed the apparent "release" character of neuralization; nerve differentiates more readily than any other cell type when ectoderm is treated in a variety of ways. If nerve can be prevented from differentiating, then other potentialities might be exhibited. A beginning in this direction has been made in the experiments mentioned in Section III,A,4, where at a suitable LiCl concentration nerve is entirely suppressed and neural crest derivatives are the sole cell type found. Pigment cells are also "induced" by a medium in which 50% of the NaCl is replaced by KCl (Barth *et al.*, 1960).

Aside from the composition of the medium another factor cannot be ignored when we use explantation as a means to test the differentiation potencies of groups of cells from any region of the embryo. This is the effect of mass of tissue upon types of differentiation observed and will be discussed in Section III,C,1.

What we can hope for in studies of the differentiation of small aggregates of cells cultured *in vitro* is to establish their characteristic differentiation under a given set of conditions and then to learn to change this differentiation not by adding unknown "specific inductors" or "specific inhibitors" but by means of well characterized inorganic or organic compounds. We depend, of course, upon progress in other fields such as biochemistry and microbiology for clues as to how cytodifferentiation may be controlled. Already the correlation between RNA and specific protein synthesis has given direction to the experiments of Niu. Cytodifferentiation has been described by Fraser (1959) as "the evolution of new protein populations." Whatever we can learn about the control of specific protein synthesis will help in our understanding of one aspect of embryonic development. There would still remain the problem of what triggers the release or activation of specific protein syntheses in developing systems; and this may be some very simple factor such as a change in the permeability properties of the cell membrane to ions which have selective effects upon enzyme activities.

Above and beyond cytodifferentiation, embryonic systems exhibit a capacity for "self-organization" which renders them unlike a population of microorganisms and argues for some integrating factor in the control of cellular differentiation in the intact embryo. Two good examples of self-organization are: (1) Upon explantation, a fragment of the prospective somite region from the lateral blastoporal lip differentiates into an axial system with patterning such that a median notochord and spinal cord with anterior brain-like enlargement are flanked by bilaterally arranged myoblasts and mesenchyme (Holtfreter, 1938a). (2) A similar patterning is exhibited even when the cells of *Triton* have been completely disaggregated and allowed to reaggregate (Holtfreter, 1944b). These aspects of differentiation are among those peculiar to developing systems and demand different types of analysis, some of which will be discussed in Sections III,B,2, and III,C,2, below.

c. Inductors of Specific Structures. The present chapter cannot possibly include any reasonably comprehensive review of the large literature on the induction of such structures as lens, nasal placode, ear, etc. These further examples of dependent differentiation have been exhaustively analyzed by the techniques of extirpation, transplantation, and explantation. Only two points will be made here.

(1) The dissociability in *Rana esculenta* of lens determination from morphological stage by means of temperature already has been mentioned in Section III,A,1. In this secondary induction system, therefore, we have reason to believe that although in normal development the optic cup stimulates lens differentiation in the presumptive lens ectoderm, experimental conditions may be imposed whereby the lens potency of the ectoderm manifests itself in the absence of an inductor. It is noteworthy that here again explants cultured in a medium containing only inorganic salts fail to show the self-differentiation of the lens that is exhibited when the presumptive lens epidermis is left in place and the optic cup is removed. Inadequacy of the culture medium rather than of the presumptive lens cells might be invoked here, as it was in the instance of the capacity of gastrular presumptive epidermis to express its differentiation capacities when cultured *in vitro*.

(2) A series of studies by Grobstein (see Grobstein and Parker, 1958, for references) has been made upon the dependence of epithelial tubule formation in nephrogenic mesenchyme upon several embryonic inductors (Wolffian duct, ureteric bud, spinal cord). Since Drew's (1923) explantation experiments tubule formation has been regarded as an instance of dependent differentiation, a conclusion fortified by genetic studies on mutant strains of mice where metanephros formation fails when the ureter does not reach the kidney region (Gluecksohn-Schoenheimer, 1949). Self-

differentiation also had been reported, however. Grobstein's analysis showed that the metanephrogenic mesenchyme would form tubules without exposure to the normal inductor if cultured in the anterior chamber of the eye, in brain, or in subcutaneous tissues. *In vitro* exposure to adult mouse tissues and intraocular fluids gave negative results. Grobstein has compared these findings to "self-neuralization" *in vitro* as observed in amphibian presumptive epidermis cultured without chordamesoderm. Although outside the field of amphibian development, Grobstein's experiments are mentioned here because of their bearing upon the problem of the criteria for "determination" within a given embryonic situation. It begins to look as if the secondary inductions operating in specific organogenesis are not simpler than the primary "organizer" but present some of the same problems.

B. MASS CELL MIGRATIONS IN MORPHOGENETIC MOVEMENTS

1. Significance of Cell Migrations

The most obvious characteristics of any developing system including the amphibian embryo are the changes in form that characterize its early stages. Descriptions of these alterations in the anatomy of embryos have constituted the main body of embryology as this subject has been taught for many decades. To the student of developmental physiology, however, the basic problem is not simply to describe and admire the form-building processes but to understand their significance for differentiation and to probe into the mechanisms whereby cells cooperate in such mass movements as gastrulation and neurulation.

A comprehensive review of the literature in the entire field of cell migrations in various developmental processes has been made by DeHaan (1958). Waddington's (1956) discussion of the formation of pattern and shape is clear and complete as an outline of problems and theories. Holtfreter (1943b, 1944c, 1946) has contributed many ingenious experiments in this area. Having referred the reader to these authoritative sources, we will here outline briefly some of the facts and problems.

The development of exogastrulae has been cited as evidence that the mass cell migrations involved in gastrulation, by bringing various groups of cells into new spatial relations with each other, are developmentally significant. When invagination does not occur and the presumptive neural plate is not underlain by the chordamesoderm, neural differentiation does not take place (Holtfreter, 1933b). With varying degrees of partial exogastrulation more or less neural differentiation is observed (Holtfreter and Hamburger, 1955, p. 237).

Equally significant for cellular differentiation must be the new locations that cell groups assume as a result of the neurulation movements. In neurulation one observes the separation of neural crest material giving rise to various types of migratory cells (chromatophores, ganglionic cells, Schwann cells, etc.) some of whose behavior has been studied intensively by Twitty (1944). In addition, the manner in which the spinal cord differentiates from the neural tube suggests interesting physiological problems. For example, the physiological significance of the migration of cells into the germinal zone to divide and their return journey to a differentiation site in more peripheral regions is unknown.

2. Gastrulation

Amphibian gastrulation involves such a complex of simultaneous cell migrations that it was not correctly visualized until the classic vital staining experiments of Vogt (1929). Previous examination of histological sections had given rise to erroneous interpretations of the process which were perpetuated in textbooks for many years. As a result of the vital staining technique, it became known that several types of movements contributed to the over-all process.

Once gastrulation had been described, various theories were proposed to account for these orderly, cooperative movements of cells. The hypothesis that differential rates of mitosis in the various regions were responsible for the movements of gastrulation and neurulation did not survive actual determination of mitotic rates (Pasteels, 1942; Gillette, 1944). Similarly the hypothesis that the imbibition of water by cells differed among the regions of the embryo and accounted for mass swellings and expansions (Glaser, 1914) had to be discarded as a result of precise measurements of specific gravity by Brown et al. (1941). In more recent years, largely as a result of the elegant experiments of Holtfreter (1944c), attention has shifted to the specific surface properties of different cell types in the search for the motive forces underlying morphogenetic movements.

As early as 1939 Holtfreter had reported that explanted regions or tissues from the embryo assumed characteristic topological relations to each other. Continuing along these lines Holtfreter used "explant systems" to dissect the several partial processes whose sum total are the gastrulation movements. Using an explant from the endoderm as a "base," he studied the behavior of ectoderm and mesoderm when explants of these two germ layers were added to endoderm in various combinations. Simulating the first inturning at the dorsal blastoporal lip, endoderm cells fused into endoderm base by formation of "bottle-necked" cells like those seen in sections through the dorsal lip of the intact early gastrula. Presumptive notochordal cells stretched over the surface of an endoderm substratum. Ectoderm cells demonstrated "epiboly" by spreading over an endodermal explant. It is certain from these observations that the cells comprising

various presumptive regions of the early gastrula already have differentiated in the sense that they now possess inherent affinities and dis-
affinities for mutual associations. That they are not all irreversibly differentiated in the sense of restriction of their potencies is, of course, well known
from the fact that presumptive epidermis transplanted above the dorsal lip
invaginates to form functional chordamesoderm, thus executing movements
and potencies characteristic of its new location. These specific attractions
and repulsions are manifest even when the cells have been dissociated and
thoroughly intermingled before reaggregation is permitted (Holtfreter,
1944b; Townes and Holtfreter, 1955).

   That this specificity resides in surface properties is rendered probable
by experiments of Spiegel (1954) on reaggregation of gastrular cells after
dissociation in alkali. Reaggregation of frog cells was inhibited in the
presence of antisera prepared against frog but not salamander embryos.
DeHaan (1958) has discussed critically the several theories to account for
cellular adhesiveness and has presented evidence that conforms with
Steinberg's (1958) concept of degree of congruity between calcium-binding
sites on cell surfaces. The question of the molecular mechanism for cellular
"recognition" and adhesiveness appears not yet to be settled between ionic
binding sites or complementary protein linkages of the antigen-antibody
type (Tyler, 1955; Weiss, 1947).

   Returning to the problem of the cause of cell migrations, a case has been
made for the role of cellular adhesiveness and repulsion in the various
stretching and inturning movements. According to Waddington (1956):
"Forces arising from the cell membranes may well be the prime cause of the
changes in tissue configuration during the whole process of gastrulation
and neurulation." Cells become different from one another; therefore they
move with respect to each other. It appears that some failure in this
differentiation of surface specificity occurs in certain hybrid embryos that
block at early gastrula stage. Gregg and Klein (1955) observed in the
hybrid cross *Rana pipiens* ♀ × *R. sylvatica* ♂ that explanted presumptive
notochord spread over an endoderm base instead of converging medially as
in normal explant systems of this type. Without an endoderm base, the
hybrid presumptive notochord remained "roughly spherical" instead of
elongating as did control presumptive notochord explants.

   It might also be of interest to ascertain whether dissociated homologous
cells of hybrid and normal gastrulae would aggregate (ectoderm to
ectoderm, for example). In view of the known compatibility of embryonic
regions from groups as widely separated genetically as anurans and
urodeles, it would be surprising if the hybrid cells would not adhere to
their normal counterparts. Yet Spiegel's (1954) observations based upon a
serological method suggest an early appearance of immunological speci-

ficity at cell surfaces. It is possible that there are developmentally irrelevant antibody receptors at the surface of embryonic cells that have nothing to do with their specific adhesive properties.

Gregg and Ornstein (1953) studied the effects of inhibitors upon the morphogenetic movements in explant systems of Holtfreter's (1944c) type. The inhibitors, all of which block gastrulation in the intact egg, suppressed or interfered with different partial processes. Their work indicates that different metabolic reactions are associated with the several morphogenetic movements.

The problem of energy transfer to morphogenetic movements has occupied a number of investigators but has had no clear-cut solution. Measurements of respiration, lactic acid production, and glycogen utilization in whole embryos give an over-all picture of the correlation between energy utilization and stage of development, but do not permit a conclusion as to how much of the energy is consumed by cell movements as compared to the other simultaneous processes involved in differentiation (see Tyler, 1942; Boell, 1955; Brachet, 1950a; Needham, 1942; Barth and Barth, 1954; Løvtrup, 1953a,b). Even comparison of blocked hybrid with normal early gastrulae has failed to elucidate a direct correlation between energy utilization and arrest in morphogenetic movements since some hybrid crosses give blocked gastrulae with entirely normal rates of oxygen consumption (Healey, 1952; Brachet, 1957). It might be suspected that any change in the respiration of the blastoporal region forms too small a fraction of the egg's total respiration to show up in whole embryo measurements but might be picked up by microrespirometry. This possibility is not supported by Sze's (1953a) finding that all parts of the blocked *Rana pipiens* ♀ × *R. sylvatica* ♂ gastrulae are equally depressed in respiratory rate. For an entirely different interpretation of the relation of respiration to morphogenesis see Gregg (1960) whose work is cited is Section II,C,4 above.

It is known that glycogen has been used by the dorsal blastoporal region by the time it forms the center of the archenteron roof (Raven, 1933, 1935; Jaeger, 1945), and also that there is glycogen breakdown during invagination of the ventral lip material. Gregg and Ornstein (1953) showed that this glycogenolysis is not simply associated with partial anaerobiosis since it did not occur in explants in a nitrogen atmosphere. Cohen (1955) presented evidence that the amphibian embryo is normally partially anaerobic. Since other explant studies indicated that the disappearance of glycogen was not correlated with embryonic induction (Jaeger, 1945), it seems reasonable to conclude that glycogen is at least one energy source for the movements of invagination. Rounds and Flickinger (1958) report that yolk breaks down in the chordamesoderm during invagination. Since amphibian embryos are known to possess the biochemical machinery for phosphorylation it has been suggested by several investigators (Boell, 1955; Brachet, 1950b; Barth and Barth, 1954) that the work of development including cellular movements is paid for in a manner similar to muscular contraction; but we lack to date the embryonic counterpart of actomyosin.

Studies and discussions of the movements of isolated cells and the role of substrate, chemical gradients, and the character of cell surfaces in control of cell locomotion are to be found in DeHaan (1958), Abercrombie (1958), Weiss (1947), and Twitty and Niu (1954), all of whose bibliographies contain a wealth of additional references. Holtfreter (1946, 1947b, 1948) in this context also has made many contributions. Even isolated embryonic cells once they have become "determined" exhibit characteristic specific "kinetic tendencies" which Holtfreter attributes to "the elaboration of new tissue-specific compounds, some of which become integrated, localized elements of the cell membrane. . . ." (Holtfreter and Hamburger, 1955, p. 275). He thus considers that the morphogenetic movements are inherent properties of the individual cells, implicit in their specific differentiations. Child (1941, p. 450) pointed out that if the cells were all alike no movements could be initiated. The specific characteristics of cell surfaces have been the subject of a number of recent studies concerning associations and dissociations of cells and tissues cultured *in vitro* (for example, Moscona, 1961a,b; Trinkhaus, 1961). Moscona concludes that "the aggregative behaviour of . . . cells suggests that extracellular materials, in being elaborated by cells in correlation with environmental factors, may have a major role in controlling developmental expressions of cells and tissues." Moscona's work with chick embryonic cells has led him to assume the "production and organization between cells of muco-protein-containing extracellular materials, the formation or effective function of which requires divalent cations and certain large molecules in the cellular environment." New observations by Brachet (1959) on the effects of ribonuclease on amphibian eggs also have demonstrated an important role for RNA and calcium ions in the intercellular "cement," a finding in accord with the earlier work of Curtis (1958). Further work on the composition and interactions of these matrix substances surely is indicated—especially from the point of view of the induction problem (Section III,A,5).

C. POPULATION ASPECTS OF CELLULAR DIFFERENTIATION

1. *Mass or Density Effects*

A phenomenon unlike anything found in a population of microorganisms is the effect of mass of material upon type of differentiation, for which Lopashov's (1935) experiments provide the prototype. Explanting always the same regions from the center of the presumptive head mesoderm region of the early gastrula, Lopashov observed the following differentiations: 2 explants fused formed muscle tissue; 3–4 explants fused gave rise to notochord as well as muscle; with 4–5 fused explants ciliated epithelium covered the notochord and muscle; and when 6–10 explants were combined neural tubes developed in addition to the above tissue types. Thus the cell type was influenced by the number of available cells. Rose (1957) points out that these results are in conformity with the specific inhibition theory he has promulgated. In a large mass, once the presumptive value of the most active region has been realized, self-limiting factors (specific inhibitors) become effective and other differentiation capacities become possible in the remaining cells. One might explain why one region of a mass formed by fusion of originally identical materials becomes "dominant" on the basis of some simple "inside-outside" differential in pH, oxygen supply, etc.

2. Effect of Position within Embryo or Aggregate

Several authorities have made a strong case for the translation of inside-outside relations in a mass of tissue into complex structure (Weiss, 1953; Abercrombie, 1958; Holtfreter and Hamburger, 1955, p. 283). The latter investigators have applied this concept to amphibian development in particular. "In response to the external inorganic medium . . . critical levels of pH, oxygen tension, salts and other diffusible compounds will be established in certain regions; in this way, the necessary conditions are provided for chemical processes that cannot occur in other regions." Once such differentials arise it becomes conceptually easy to visualize a stepwise compounding of complexity throughout egg or tissue mass.

We know that in the unfertilized amphibian egg we have already to begin with unequal distributions of yolk reserves and "active cytoplasm." Upon activation, localized shifts in the position of certain "plasms" take place. There is some evidence for some amphibian eggs that differences in permeability of the surface layer characterize various regions of the egg. It would be improbable that in a group of cells as large as the late blastula (approximately 1.5 mm diameter in *Rana pipiens*) the innermost cells would not exist in a state of semi-deprivation as to oxygen and other environmental factors. Cohen's (1955) data provide actual evidence that the embryo is partially anaerobic, for example. The fact that later development is perfectly normal in eggs kept in an atmosphere of pure nitrogen until early gastrula stage and then returned to air, does not however argue in favor of oxygen as an effective component of such inside-outside gradients.

The causal role of inside-outside gradients may also be correlated with the different behavior of explants depending upon whether or not attachment occurs. When, furthermore, small explants of presumptive epidermis attach to a glass surface the first cells to migrate away from the central mass form epithelial sheets. Those left behind differentiate into neuroblasts and send out a radiating corona of nerve fibers (Barth and Barth, 1959).

That a change in permeability of the cell membrane in response to the ambient medium can redirect the path of differentiation has been proposed by Holtfreter to account for neuralization in presumptive epidermal explants (Section III,A,5). Holtfreter himself has postulated differences in permeability in the intact gastrula on the basis of the strength of the "surface coat" in different areas of the egg. Differences in permeability do not necessarily imply that *all* compounds pass more readily through one surface area than another. There seems no compelling reason to argue that in normal development a local difference in permeability at the marginal zone upon activation may not be a "trigger" for further differentiation.

As in all other theories of development it is not yet possible to specify the character of the new cytoplasmic compounds that could arise under the influence of differential inside-outside gradients and then serve as "cell-determinative agents. That ribonucleic acids may play a role here is becoming increasingly probable as advances are made in apprehending specificity in protein synthesizing reactions (Brachet, 1957). Intercellular relations of the type subsumed under the concept of inside-outside gradients are among the many properties of developing systems that set the latter apart from a population of microorganisms.

3. Cell Populations and Differentiation

Weiss (1958a, p. 850) has cautioned against the error of regarding all cells in a given presumptive area of an embryo as being identical. Grobstein and Parker (1958) expressed a similar idea in speaking of a certain differentiation tendency as being "imminent" in a given cell group "in a probability sense." Such developmental phenomena as regulation, overlapping of fields, and the different differentiations obtained *in situ* as opposed to those in explants demand some such interpretation.

In addition to the effect of mass upon cellular differentiation (Section III,C,1) the degree of patterning of structures is correlated with the number of cells participating. Holtfreter and Hamburger (1955) cite as an example the reduction in complexity of structures induced when an inductor has been inactivated in a graded series of steps.

In tissue culture and in cultures of isolated cells grown *in vitro* the effect of mass or density is well known. When single adult mammalian cells are grown *in vitro* macromolecular serum fractions have been added to the chemically defined small-molecular medium to permit attachment and growth (Puck, 1959). Tissue culture techniques employ a small volume of medium in relation to mass of tissue. The usual interpretation of these facts invokes retention of some essential compounds within the cell or a protective action on the cell membrane. When the differentiation capacities of small cell aggregates from amphibian embryos are being studied it is necessary to ascertain that the standard culture medium permits expression of the cells' potentialities and neither stimulates nor suppresses their differentiation. One test for this would be to observe differentiation in a series of aggregates of increasing size in the same volume of medium. Or, conversely, a comparison could be made of the quality of differentiation in masses of equal size in a series of decreasing volume of medium.

IV. Theories of Differentiation and Development

A. NUCLEOCYTOPLASMIC INTERACTION

It has been convenient to discuss some of the data of developmental physiology under the two broad headings of intracellular and intercellular relationships. That both must be invoked to understand development has been recognized and repeatedly stated in more or less hypothetical terms by many distinguished investigators beginning with Driesch (1894, quoted in Brachet, 1957, p. 358). Weismann's theory, antedating as it did the science of modern genetics, recognized the logical necessity for a continuity of germ plasm between generations coexisting with some means of bringing about the origin of differences within a given generation. He assigned both roles to what we now call genes operating in the manner described in Section II,A,1. It is to Morgan (1934) that we owe the most widely quoted statement of nucleocytoplasmic interaction in development, and his formulation of the process since has been restated many times with slight modifications.

Morgan's hypothesis depends first of all upon a heterogeneous cytoplasm within which originally identical nuclei are distributed. Thereafter a circular interaction is initiated by which gene activity is altered in different cytoplasms while the latter, becoming increasingly varied, further alter nuclear activity (cf. Waddington, 1956, p. 349). More recent reformulations of almost identical ideas are characterized by the attempt to identify the actual nuclear and cytoplasmic compounds taking part in the interactions. Brachet (1957, p. 438) and Markert (1958) have attempted to integrate what is known about DNA and RNA in protein synthesis with the theoretical scheme proposed above. Induction fits into this scheme as a process whereby an environmental influence alters gene activity indirectly through a primary effect upon the cytoplasm in which the gene is replicating (Waddington, 1956, p. 412). The nature of the "environmental influence" could be either specific or nonspecific (see Brachet, 1957, p. 364; Ephrussi, 1953, 1956).

Specificity in protein synthesis and the nature of self-replicating units are among problems currently being widely attacked whose solution may enable eventual specification of the compounds involved in embryonic differentiation (Lederberg, 1952). Model systems from non-amphibian materials have been looked to as guides for specific mechanisms of nucleo-cytoplasmic interactions. Bacterial transformation and transduction as well as enzyme induction in microorganisms have seemed to some workers to provide clues. The actual occurrence in the embryo of similar processes has been confirmed in only a few cases thus far. Feedback controls in biochemical systems similarly have been thought to have usefulness as explanatory factors in differentiation (Gorini and Maas, 1958; Vogel, 1958; Magasanik, 1958). Enzyme repression as a negative feedback phenomenon provides an analogy to the concept of specific inhibition. To what extent such biochemical control systems enter into cellular differentiation in the embryo is a question that must be answered eventually by experiments with embryos, not microorganisms (cf. Moore, 1962).

Ebert (1961) and his group are making sound contributions in the study of enzyme activities during development. Of especial interest are (1) the demonstration of gradients in lactic acid dehydrogenase activity coinciding with those shown by earlier workers for RNA, respiration, etc.; (2) the existence in early frog embryos of two distinct deoxyribonucleases that show striking differences in the patterns of their development. Ebert cautions against premature speculation as to whether such different patterns may reflect differential gene activity.

Ebert's group continues to search in early embryonic development for the operation of such regulatory mechanisms as enzyme induction, enzyme repression, and feedback inhibition of enzyme activity. Applied so successfully to bacterial systems, these mechanisms have been disappointingly difficult to demonstrate in the frog embryo. A pioneer study by Stearns and Kostellow (1958) on tryptophan peroxidase induction in *Rana pipiens* cells provided evidence that implicated enzyme induction as a factor in differentiation. No doubt the extreme fragility of dissociated early embryonic cells has posed a formidable but not insurmountable barrier to progress in this kind of experiment.

B. SOME THEORIES OF INTERCELLULAR REACTIONS DURING DEVELOPMENT

1. Gradient Theories

Theories concerned solely with interactions between cells of the developing embryo usually have invoked gradients—material or dynamic. Even so summary a review of amphibian developmental physiology as the present chapter has repeatedly included phenomena which speak for and fit into the framework of the concept of graded distributions of different compounds and activities. The differences between contemporary gradient theories were foreshadowed by the opposing ideas of Roux and Hertwig more than 60 years ago. The former suggested that most qualities may be derived from quantitative differences, while Hertwig required several qualitatively different forces as a starting point.

Limiting ourselves here to gradient theories which have been applied to amphibian development by embryologists with first-hand experience of the complexities of developmental processes, we come first to Child. Child's well known theory that gradients in metabolic activity (as reflected by rate of respiration and susceptibility to toxic substances) determine the course of development proved a stimulating irritant to other investigators. Although, as observed in Section III,A,3, gradients in oxygen consumption merely reflect gradients in the ratio of yolk:cytoplasm so that the specific character of Child's gradient is not tenable, we are indebted largely to him for the general idea of gradients as causal agents in developmental systems.

Other gradient systems postulated for amphibian development rely upon the distribution of either one or two hypothetical substances. Dalcq and Pasteels (1937) attribute establishment of gradients in "organisine" to the interaction of yolk and cortical gradients in the egg at the time of activation. The yolk (V) factor is considered to decrease sharply from a maximum at the vegetal pole to its low point at the animal pole. The cortical factor (C) has a maximum value on the dorsal side of the egg from which it decreases in graded fashion to the ventral side. The hypothetical product "organisine" of the interaction C × V is maximal at the center of the dorsal marginal zone from which point it decreases gradually in all directions. Dalcq (1949) postulated that groups of cells compete for "organisine" which is present in limited supply and the winners in this "physiological competition" (Spiegelman, 1945) form notochord; the next most active form somites, etc. This theory was based in large measure upon experiments with inverted or centrifuged eggs in which gastrulation was disturbed when yolk was thrown into new contacts with other regions of the egg. The theory has been of satisfactory heuristic value for the

design of experiments on the biological level but the question of the
chemical identity of C, V, and organisine remains unanswered.

Again at the biological level the experiments of Curtis (1960) demonstrate significant differences among the various regions of the cortex of
the newly fertilized amphibian egg. To mention only one aspect of these
intriguing experiments, when Curtis grafted minute pieces of the cell
cortex of the gray crescent region of *Xenopus laevis* into another egg
(both donor and host eggs at or just before first cleavage) he obtained
induction of a secondary embryo. Together with several types of control
grafts this observation provided evidence that the cortical material itself
does possess morphogenetic properties, an idea implicit in the theories of
Dalcq and Pasteels.

Yamada's work with explant systems and with abnormal inductors
(Section III,A,4) led this investigator also to a theory involving two
hypothetical activities, "morphogenetic potentials," distributed in gradient fashion throughout the egg. Interaction of dorsoventral and cephalocaudal activities is proposed to account for the specific differentiation of
a given group of cells depending on the level of the "morphogenetic potentials." As noted earlier, Yamada's work with bone marrow factor
suggests that one of the morphogenetic potentials is related to a specific
chemical substance whose progressive inactivation results in corresponding stepwise changes in the type of inductions obtained. The gradient
theory of Toivonen has been discussed in Section III,A,4, in connection
with the induction problem.

2. Specific Inhibition Theory

Rose (1952, 1957) has challenged all theories of differentiation which
depend upon competition between neighboring cell groups or upon stimulation of one cell group by another (specific induction). According to
Rose a specific inhibitor appears, first in the most active region of a
developing system. The inhibitor serves as a self-limiting agent for its
own production and furthermore diffuses into neighboring regions to
suppress like differentiation there, thus enabling these regions to differentiate in some alternate pathway which in turn is halted when the end-
product reaches a certain concentration. Waddington (1956) has criticized
this theory on the basis of the phenomenon of homeogenetic induction (in
which a tissue once induced itself becomes an inductor, Section III,A,1),
which according to Waddington means that like tissues encourage rather
than inhibit the same type of differentiation. Rose (1952, 1957; Rose and
Rose, 1952) has discussed homeogenetic induction as a phenomenon demonstrated by already differentiated cells. As such it has nothing to do
with the initiation of primary differentiation. The latter process he con-

siders to be a "general" (nonspecific) induction evoking in the reacting cells the ability to behave as part of a field.

The specific inhibition theory is entirely compatible with the concept of gradients. It is indeed necessary to assume gradients such that one region begins to differentiate first, thereby setting in motion the machinery whereby it will sooner or later become self-limiting and permit a new level of the gradient to operate in producing a different cell type. Rose's theory thus depends upon the existence of gradients. Its difference from previous gradient theories lies in his emphasis upon restriction rather than stimulation of developmental potencies. The high point in Rose's gradient issues "restrictive information", rather than dominating neighboring regions by physiological competition or the production of specific inductor substances.

Rose's theory is based upon a wide range of experimental materials both plant and animal. Final judgment as to its validity must await further experimental verification. The active "specific inhibitors" need to be identified and their mode of action clarified. Rose conceives of their acting somewhat in the manner of antibodies.

Tyler (1955) and Weiss (1947) both have elaborated theories of growth and differentiation based upon an immunological type of interaction between cells. Discussion here will be limited to an expression of the opinion that the experimental techniques at hand have not yet permitted a crucial demonstration at the molecular level of the mode of action of surface antigens and antibodies in normal amphibian development.

A quality all the above mentioned theories share is the hypothetical character of the compounds and reactions postulated. Brachet stands almost alone in naming a specific group of chemical compounds, the ribonucleoproteins, as the most likely candidates for the control of specific protein syntheses during differentiation. Brachet (1950a, 1952, 1957, 1958, 1960b) presents a wealth of references to his prolific contributions. He has implicated the ribonucleoproteins in gradients, induction, in the "morphogenetic potentials" of Dalcq and Pasteels, and in regional fields. Brachet has not, however, essayed an all-encompassing theory of development as have other investigators more willing to manipulate hypothetical factors in lieu of concrete compounds. When the relative immaturity of developmental physiology as a discipline is recalled, we may rejoice that both types of investigators are participating in the endeavor. The developmental *physiology* of the amphibian egg as a field of study entered upon its embryonic phase scarcely 30 years ago.

References

The scope of this chapter is too broad to permit a reference list that even approximates a complete bibliography of the literature of developmental physiology. In general the writer has attempted to cite some of the major works in each area mentioned, but even so many important investigations and discussions had to be omitted. Many of the references cited, however, themselves contain excellent bibliographies to which the reader is referred.

In placing the emphasis upon the development of some of the concepts that form the background for contemporary studies, the writer has drawn more heavily upon past than contemporary literature. A comprehensive review of the most recent experimental results in any area of developmental physiology would be impossible in a treatise such as this and in any case is not the objective of this chapter.

Abercrombie, M. (1958). Exchanges between cells. In "The Chemical Basis of Development" (W. D. McElroy and B. Glass, eds.), pp. 318–328. Johns Hopkins Press, Baltimore, Maryland.

Allfrey, V. G., Mirsky, A. E., and Stern, H. (1955). The chemistry of the cell nucleus. Advan. Enzymol. 16, 411–500.

Balinsky, B. I. (1957). South African amphibia as material for biological research. S. African J. Sci. 53, 383–391.

Baltzer, F. (1940). Ueber erbliche letale Entwicklung und Austauschbarkeit artverschiedener Kerne bei Bastarden. Naturwissenschaften 28, 177–187, 196–206.

Baltzer, F. (1950). Chimären und Merogone bei Amphibien. Rev. Suisse Zool. 57 (Supp. 1), 93–114.

Baltzer, F. (1952). The behavior of nuclei and cytoplasm in amphibian interspecific crosses. Symp. Soc. Exptl. Biol. 6, 230–242.

Barth, L. G. (1941). Neutral differentiation without organizer. J. Exptl. Zool. 87, 371–384.

Barth, L. G. (1942). Regional differences in oxygen consumption of the amphibian gastrula. Physiol. Zool. 15, 30–46.

Barth, L. G., and Barth, L. J. (1954). "The Energetics of Development," 117 pp. Columbia Univ. Press, New York.

Barth, L. G., and Barth, L. J. (1959). Differentiation of cells of the Rana pipiens gastrula in unconditioned medium. J. Embryol. Exptl. Morphol. 7, 210–222.

Barth, L. G., and Graff, S. (1938). The chemical nature of the amphibian organizer. Cold Spring Harbor Symp. Quant. Biol. 6, 385–391.

Barth, L. G., and Jaeger, L. (1947). Phosphorylation in the frog's egg. Physiol. Zool. 20, 133–146.

Barth, L. G., Barth, L. J., and Nelson, I. (1960). Induction of pigment cells from the presumptive epidermis of Rana pipiens gastrula. Anat. Record 137: 337–338.

Bautzmann, H., Holtfreter, J., Spemann, H., and Mangold, O. (1932). Versuche zur Analyse der Induktionsmittel in der Embryonalentwicklung. Naturwissenschaften 20, 972–974.

Beatty, R. A. (1954). How many chromosomes in mammalian somatic cells? Intern. Rev. Cytol. 3, 177–197.

Beerman, W. (1956). Nuclear differentiation and functional morphology of chromosomes. Cold Spring Harbor Symp. Quant. Biol. 21, 217–232.

Beetschen, J. (1958). Étude cytologique de germes hétéroploides létaux chez le Triton, Pleurodeles waltlii, Michah. Bull. Soc. Zool. France 83, 242–244.

Beetschen, J. (1959). Modifications des structures nucléaires et cytoplasmiques de l'oeuf fécondé insegmenté soumis à une réfrigération prolongée, chez le Triton Pleurodeles waltlii Michah. Compt. Rend. 249, 173–175.

Bell, E. (1960). Some observations on the surface coat and intercellular matrix material of the amphibian ectoderm. Exptl. Cell Res. 20, 378–383.

Bellamy, A. W. (1919). Differential susceptibility as a basis for modification and control of early development in the frog. *Biol. Bull.* **37**, 312–361.

Benitez, H. H., Murray, M. R., and Chargaff, E. (1959). Heteromorphic change of adult fibroblasts by ribonucleoproteins. *J. Biophys. Biochem. Cytol.* **5**, 25–34.

Bieliavsky, N., and Tencer, R. (1960). Étude de l'incorporation de l'uridine tritiée dans les oeufs d'Amphibiens. *Exptl. Cell Res.* **21**, 279–285.

Blackler, A. W. (1958). Contribution to the study of germ cells in the *Anura*. *J. Embryol. Exptl. Morphol.* **6**, 491–503.

Boell, E. J. (1948). Biochemical differentiation during amphibian development. *Ann. N. Y. Acad. Sci.* **49**, 773–800.

Boell, E. J. (1955). Energy exchange and enzyme development during embryogenesis. *In* "Analysis of Development" (B. Willier, P. Weiss, and V. Hamburger, eds.), pp. 520–555. Saunders, Philadelphia, Pennsylvania.

Boell, E. J., and Weber, R. (1955). Cytochrome oxidase activity in mitochondria during amphibian development. *Exptl. Cell Res.* **9**, 559–567.

Boell, E. J., Needham, J., and Rogers, V. (1939). Morphogenesis and metabolism; studies with the Cartesian diver ultramicrorespirometer. *Proc. Roy. Soc.* **B127**, 322–356.

Bogucki, M. (1923). Nouvelles recherches sur la parthénogenèse experimentale. *Compt. Rend. Soc. Biol.* **89**, 1356–1357.

Brachet, J. (1940). Étude histochimique des protéines au cours du développement embryonnaire des poissons, des amphibiens et des oiseaux. *Arch. Biol. (Liege)* **51**, 167–202.

Brachet, J. (1950a). "Chemical Embryology," 533 pp. Interscience, New York.

Brachet, J. (1950b). Quelques observations sur le mode d'action de l'organisateur chez les Amphibiens. *Experientia* **6**, 56–57.

Brachet, J. (1952). The role of the nucleus and the cytoplasm in synthesis and morphogenesis. *Symp. Soc. Exptl. Biol.* **6**, 173–200.

Brachet, J. (1957). "Biochemical Cytology," 535 pp. Academic Press, New York.

Brachet, J. (1958). Le rôle de l'acide ribonucléique dans la cellule. *Bull. Soc. Chim. Biol.* **40**, 1387–1416.

Brachet, J. (1959). Nouvelles observations sur les effets de la ribonucléase *in vivo* sur les oeufs de Batrachiens. *Acta Embryol. Morphol. Exptl.* **2**, 107–117.

Brachet, J. (1960a). "The Biochemistry of Development," 320 pp. Pergamon, New York.

Brachet, J. (1960b). Ribonucleic acids and the synthesis of cellular proteins. *Nature* **186**, 194–199.

Brachet, J., and Hugon de Scoeux, F. (1949). *Journées cyto-embryol. belgo-néerland,* p. 56. Gand. Cited in Brachet (1957).

Brachet, J., and Ledoux, L. (1955). L'action de la ribonucléase sur la division des oeufs d'amphibiens. 2. Étude cytologique et cytochimique des effets de la ribonucléase chez le Pleurodèle. *Exptl. Cell Res.* **9** (Supp. 3), 27–39.

Brachet, J., Decroly-Briers, M., and Hoyez, J. (1958). Contribution a l'étude des lysosomes au cours du développement embryonnaire. *Bull. Soc. Chim. Biol.* **40**, 2039–2048.

Brahma, S. K. (1957). Induction through the surface coat ectoderm. *Proc. Zool. Soc., Bengal Mookerjee Mem. Vol.* pp. 155–163.

Brahma, S. K. (1958). Experiments on the diffusibility of the amphibian evocator. *J. Embryol. Exptl. Morphol.* **6**, 418–423.

Breuer, M. E., and Pavan, C. (1955). Behavior of polytene chromosomes of *Rhynchosciara angelae* at different stages of larval development. *Chromosoma* **7**, 371–386.

Brice, M. C. (1958). A re-analysis of the consequences of frontal and sagittal constrictions of newt blastulae and gastrulae. *Arch. Biol. (Liege)* **69**, 371–439.

Briggs, R. (1949). The influence of egg volume on the development of haploid and diploid embryos of the frog, *Rana pipiens*. *J. Exptl. Zool.* **111**, 255–294.

Briggs, R., and King, T. J. (1952). Transplantation of living nuclei from blastula cells into enucleated frogs eggs. *Proc. Natl. Acad. Sci. U.S.* **38**, 455–463.

Briggs, R., and King, T. J. (1953). Factors affecting the transplantability of nuclei of frog embryonic cells. *J. Exptl. Zool.* **122**, 485–506.

Briggs, R., and King, T. J. (1955). Specificity of nuclear function in embryonic development. *In* "Biological Specificity and Growth" (E. G. Butler, ed.), pp. 207–228. Princeton Univ. Press, Princeton, New Jersey.

Briggs, R., and King, T. J. (1957). Changes in the nuclei of differentiating endoderm cells as revealed by nuclear transplantation. *J. Morphol.* **100**, 269–312.

Briggs, R., Green, E. U., and King, T. J. (1951). An investigation of the capacity for cleavage and differentiation in *Rana pipiens* eggs lacking "functional" chromosomes. *J. Exptl. Zool.* **116**, 455–500.

Brown, M. G., Hamburger, V., and Schmitt, F. O. (1941). Density studies on amphibian embryos with special reference to the mechanism of organizer action. *J. Exptl. Zool.* **88**, 353–372.

Caspersson, T. O. (1950). "Cell Growth and Cell Function," 185 pp. Norton, New York.

Chen, P. S. (1953). The rate of oxygen consumption in the lethal hybrid between *Triton* ♀ and *Salamandra* ♂. *Exptl. Cell Res.* **5**, 275–287.

Child, C. M. (1941). "Patterns and Problems of Development," 811 pp. Univ. Chicago Press, Chicago, Illinois.

Chuang, H. H. (1940). Weitere Versuche über die Veränderung der Induktionsleistungen von gekochten Organteilen. *Wilhelm Roux' Arch. Entwicklungsmech. Organ.* **140**, 25–38.

Clayton, R. M. (1953). Distribution of antigens in the developing newt. *J. Embryol. Exptl. Morphol.* **1**, 25–42.

Cohen, A. I. (1953). Studies on glycolysis during the early development of the *Rana pipiens* embryo. *Physiol. Zool.* **27**, 128–141.

Cohen, A. I. (1955). Anaerobiosis in the *Rana pipiens* embryo. *J. Embryol. Exptl. Morphol.* **3**, 77–85.

Cooper, R. S. (1948). A study of frog egg antigens with serum-like reactive groups. *J. Exptl. Zool.* **107**, 397–438.

Curtis, A. S. G. (1958). A ribonucleoprotein from amphibian gastrulae. *Nature* **181**, 185.

Curtis, A. S. G. (1960). Cortical grafting in *Xenopus laevis*. *J. Embryol. Exptl. Morphol.* **8**, 163–173.

Dalcq, A. (1949). The concept of physiological competition (Spiegelman) and the interpretation of vertebrate morphogenesis. *Proc. Intern. Congr. Exptl. Cytol. 6th Congr. Stockholm 1947. Exp. Cell Res., Suppl.* **1**: 483–496.

Dalcq, A., and Pasteels, J. (1937). Une conception nouvelle des bases physiologiques de la morphogénèse. *Arch. Biol. (Liege)* **48**, 669–710.

DeHaan, R. L. (1958). Cell migration and morphogenetic movements. *In* "The Chemical Basis of Development" (W. D. McElroy and B. Glass, eds.), pp. 339–373. Johns Hopkins Press, Baltimore, Maryland.

Denis, H. (1956–1957). Influence du facteur temps sur la determination de la plaque nuerale chez les amphibiens. *Ann. Soc. Roy. Zool. Belg.* **87**, 501–536.

Denis, H. (1961). Recherche sur la différenciation protéique au cours du développement des Amphibiens. *J. Embryol. Exptl. Morphol.* **9**, 422–445.

Dollander, A. (1950) Étude des phénomènes de régulation consécutifs à la séparation des deux premières blastomères de l'oeuf de *Triton*. *Arch. Biol.* (*Liege*) **61**, 1–110.

Dollander, A. (1952). Sur la valeur diagnostique du croissant clair et la possibilité de neurulation du fragment ventral de l'oeuf de *Triturus helveticus*. *Compt. Rend. Soc. Biol.* **146**, 1607–1609.

Drew, A. H. (1923). Growth and differentiation in tissue-cultures. *Brit. J. Exptl. Pathol.* **4**, 46–52.

Eakin, R. M., and Lehmann, F. E. (1957). An electronmicroscopic study of developing amphibian ectoderm. *Wilhelm Roux' Arch. Entwicklungsmech. Organ.* **150**, 177–198.

Ebert, J. D. (1960). Aging and development. *In* "Aging," (Nathan W. Shock, Ed.), pp. 101–122. Am. Assoc. Advan. Sci., Washington, D. C.

Ebert, J. D. (1961). Annual report of the director of the department of embryology. *Carnegie Inst. Wash. Year Book* **60**, 395–444.

Ephrussi, B. (1953). "Nucleo-cytoplasmic Relations in Micro-organisms," 127 pp. Oxford Univ. Press, London and New York.

Ephrussi, B. (1956). Enzymes in cellular differentiation. *In* "Enzymes: Units of Biological Structure and Function" (O. H. Gaebler, ed.), pp. 29–40. Academic Press, New York.

Fankhauser, G. (1929). Ueber die Beteiligung kernloser Strahlungen (Cytaster) an der Furchung geschnuerter Triton-Eier. *Rev. Suisse Zool.* **36**, 179–187.

Fankhauser, G. (1930). Die Entwicklungspotenzen diploid-kerniger Haelften des ungefurchten Tritoneies. *Wilhelm Roux' Arch. Entwicklungsmech. Organ.* **122**, 671–735.

Fankhauser, G. (1934). Cytological studies on egg fragments of the Salamander *Triton*. V. Chromosome number and chromosome individuality in the cleavage mitoses of merogonic fragments. *J. Exptl. Zool.* **68**, 1–57.

Fankhauser, G. (1948). The organization of the amphibian egg during fertilization and cleavage. *Ann. N.Y. Acad. Sci.* **49**, 684–708.

Fankhauser, G. (1955). The role of nucleus and cytoplasm. *In* "Analysis of Development" (B. Willier, P. Weiss, and V. Hamburger, eds.), 735 pp. Saunders, Philadelphia, Pennsylvania.

Fankhauser, G., and Moore, C. (1941). Cytological and experimental studies of polyspermy in the newt, *Triturus viridescens*. II. The behavior of the sperm nuclei in androgenetic eggs (in the absence of the egg nucleus). *J. Morphol.* **68**, 387–423.

Ficq, A. (1961). Localization of different types of RNA in amphibian oocytes. *Exptl. Cell Res.* **23**, 427–429.

Fischberg, M., and Blackler, A. W. (1961). How cells specialize. *Sci. Am.* **205**, 124–140.

Fischberg, M., Gurdon, J. B., and Elsdale, T. R. (1958a). Nuclear transplantations in *Xenopus laevis*. *Nature* **181**, 424.

Fischberg, M., Gurdon, J. B., and Elsdale, T. R. (1958b). Nuclear transfer in amphibia and the problem of the potentialities of the nuclei of differentiating tissues. *Exptl. Cell Res. Suppl.* **6**, 161–178.

Flickinger, R. A. (1954). Utilization of $C^{14}O_2$ by developing amphibian embryos, with special reference to regional incorporation into individual embryos. *Exptl. Cell Res.* **6**, 172–180.

Flickinger, R. A. (1957). The relation between yolk utilization and differentiation in the frog embryo. *Am. Naturalist* **91**, 373–380.

Flickinger, R. A. (1958). Regional localization of neural and lens antigens in the frog embryo in relation to induction. *Biol. Bull.* **115,** 201–208.

Flickinger, R. A., and Nace, G. W. (1952). An investigation of proteins during the development of the amphibian embryo. *Exptl. Cell Res.* **3,** 393–405.

Flickinger, R. A., Hatton, E., and Rounds, D. E. (1959). Protein transfer in chimaeric *Taricha-Rana* explants. *Exptl. Cell Res.* **17,** 30–34.

Fraser, R. C. (1959). Cytodifferentiation: Protein synthesis in transition. *Am. Naturalist* **93,** 47–80.

Gall, J. G. (1958). Chromosomal differentiation. *In* "The Chemical Basis of Development" (W. D. McElroy and B. Glass, eds.), pp. 103-135. Johns Hopkins Press, Baltimore, Maryland.

Gallien, L. (1959). Recherches sur quelques aspects de l'hétéroploïdie expérimentale chez le Triton *Pleurodeles waltlii* Michah. *J. Embryol. Exptl. Morphol.* **7,** 380–393.

Gillette, R. (1944). Cell number and cell size in the ectoderm during neurulation (*Ambystoma maculatum*). *J. Exptl. Zool.* **96,** 201–221.

Glaser, O. C. (1914). On the mechanism of morphological differentiation in the nervous system. *Anat. Record* **8,** 527–551.

Gluecksohn-Schoenheimer, S. (1949). Causal analysis of mouse development by the study of mutational effects. *Growth Symp.* **9,** 163–176.

Gluecksohn-Waelsch, S. (1953). Lethal factors in development. *Quart. Rev. Biol.* **28,** 115–135.

Goldschmidt, R. (1927). "Physiologische Theorie der Vererbung," 247 pp. Springer, Berlin.

Gorini, L., and Maas, W. K. (1958). Feed-back control of the formation of biosynthetic enzymes. *In* "The Chemical Basis of Development" (W. D. McElroy and B. Glass, eds.), pp. 469–478. Johns Hopkins Press, Baltimore, Maryland.

Grant, P. (1953). Phosphate metabolism during oögenesis in *Rana temporaria*. *J. Exptl. Zool.* **124,** 513–543.

Gregg, J. R. (1948). Carbohydrate metabolism of normal and hybrid amphibian embryos. *J. Exptl. Zool.* **109,** 119–134.

Gregg, J. R. (1960). Respiratory regulation in amphibian development. *Biol. Bull.* **119,** 428–439.

Gregg, J. R., and Klein, D. (1955). Morphogenetic movements of normal and gastrula-arrested hybrid amphibian tissues. *Biol. Bull.* **109,** 265–270.

Gregg, J. R., and Løvtrup, S. (1950). Biochemical gradients in the axolotl gastrula. *Compt. Rend. Trav. Lab. Carlsberg Ser. Chim.* **27,** 307–324.

Gregg, J. R., and Løvtrup, S. (1955). Synthesis of desoxyribonucleic acid in lethal amphibian hybrids. *Biol. Bull.* **108,** 29–34.

Gregg, J. R., and Ornstein, N. (1953). Explant systems and the reactions of gastrulating amphibians to metabolic poisons. *Biol. Bull.* **105,** 466–476.

Gregg, J. R., and Ray, F. L. (1957). Respiration of homogenized embryos: *Rana pipiens* and *Rana pipiens* ♀ × *Rana sylvatica* ♂. *Biol. Bull.* **113,** 382–387.

Grobstein, C. (1954). Tissue interaction in the morphogenesis of mouse embryonic rudiments *in vitro*. *In* "Aspects of Synthesis and Order in Growth" (D. Rudnick, ed.), pp. 233–256. Princeton Univ. Press, Princeton, New Jersey.

Grobstein, C. (1961). Cell contact in relation to embryonic induction. *Exptl. Cell Res. Suppl.* **8,** 234–245.

Grobstein, C., and Parker, G. (1958). Epithelial tubule formation by mouse metanephrogenic mesenchyme transplanted *in vivo*. *J. Natl. Cancer Inst.* **20,** 107–116.

Gurdon, J. B. (1962). Adult frogs derived from nuclei of single somatic cells. *Develop. Biol.* **4,** 256–273.

Guyer, M. F. (1907). The development of unfertilized frog eggs injected with blood. *Science* **25**, 910–911.

Hadorn, E. (1937). Die entwicklungsphysiologische Auswirkung der disharmonischen Kern-Plasma Kombination beim Bastardmerogon *T. palmatus* ♀ × *T. cristatus* ♂. *Wilhelm Roux' Arch. Entwicklungsmech. Organ.* **136**, 400–489.

Hadorn, E. (1958). Role of genes in developmental processes. *In* "The Chemical Basis of Development" (W. D. McElroy and B. Glass, eds.) pp. 779–790. Johns Hopkins Press, Baltimore, Maryland.

Hamburger, V. (1935). Malformations of hind limbs in species hybrids of *Triton taeniatus* (and *palmatus*) ♀ × *Triton cristatus* ♂. *J. Exptl. Zool.* **70**, 43–84.

Hamburger, V. (1936). The larval development of reciprocal hybrids of *Triton taeniatus*, Leyd. (and *T. palmatus*, Duges) × *Triton cristatus*, Laur. *J. Exptl. Zool.* **73**, 319–373.

Healy, E. (1952). Metabolism of the frog hybrid *Rana pipiens* × *R. clamitans*. Doctoral Thesis, Columbia University Library, New York.

Holtfreter, J. (1929). Ueber die Aufzucht isolierter Teile des Amphibien Keimes. I. Methode einer Gewebezüchtung *in vivo. Wilhelm Roux' Arch. Entwicklungsmech. Organ.* **116**, 421–510.

Holtfreter, J. (1931). Potenzprüfung am Amphibienkeim mit Hilfe der Isolationsmethode. *Verhandl. Deut. Zool. Ges.* **32–34**, 158–166.

Holtfreter, J. (1933a) Nachweis der Induktionsfähigkeit abgetöteter Keimteile. *Wilhelm Roux' Arch. Entwicklungsmech. Organ.* **128**, 584–633.

Holtfreter, J. (1933b). Die totale Exogastrulation, eine Selbstablösung des Ektoderms vom Entomesoderm. *Wilhelm Roux' Arch. Entwicklungsmech. Organ.* **129**, 669–793.

Holtfreter, J. (1938a). Differenzierungspotenzen isolierter Teile der Urodelengastrula. *Wilhelm Roux' Arch. Entwicklungsmech. Organ.* **138**, 522–656.

Holtfreter, J. (1938b). Differenzierungspotenzen isolierter Teile der Anurengastrula. *Wilhelm Roux' Arch. Entwicklungsmech. Organ.* **138**, 657–738.

Holtfreter, J. (1938c). Veränderung der Reaktionsweise im alternden isolierten Gastrulaektoderm. *Wilhelm Roux' Arch. Entwicklunsgmech. Organ.* **138**, 163–196.

Holtfreter, J. (1943a). Properties and functions of the surface coat in amphibian embryos. *J. Exptl. Zool.* **93**, 251–323.

Holtfreter, J. (1943b). A study of the mechanics of gastrulation. I. *J. Exptl. Zool.* **94**, 261–318.

Holtfreter, J. (1944a). Neural differentiation of ectoderm through exposure to saline solution. *J. Exptl. Zool.* **95**, 307–340.

Holtfreter, J. (1944b). Experimental studies on the development of the pronephros. *Rev. Can. Biol.* **3**, 220–249.

Holtfreter, J. (1944c). A study of the mechanics of gastrulation. II. *J. Exptl. Zool.* **95**, 171–212.

Holtfreter, J. (1946). Structure, motility and locomotion in isolated embryonic amphibian cells. *J. Morphol.* **79**, 27–62.

Holtfreter, J. (1947a). Neural induction in explants which have passed througd a sublethal cytolysis. *J. Exptl. Zool.* **106**, 197–222.

Holtfreter, J. (1947b). Changes of structure and the kinetics of differentiating embryonic cells. *J. Morphol.* **80**, 57–92.

Holtfreter, J. (1948). Significance of the cell membrane in embryonic processes. *Ann. N.Y. Acad. Sci.* **49**, 709–760.

Holtfreter, J. (1951). Some aspects of embryonic induction. *Growth* **15** (Suppl), 117–152.

Holtfreter, J., and Hamburger, V. (1955). Amphibians. *In* "Analysis of Development" (B. H. Willier, P. Weiss, and V. Hamburger, eds.), pp. 230–296. Saunders, Philadelphia, Pennsylvania.

Humphrey, R. R. (1948). A lethal fluid imbalance in the Mexican axolotl. *J. Heredity* **39**, 255–261.

Huxley, J. S., and De Beer G. R., (1934). "The Elements of Experimental Embryology," 514 pp. Cambridge Univ. Press, London and New York.

Iyeiri, S., and Kawakami, I. (1962). Inductive effects of various rat tissues upon amphibian gastrula epidermis. *Mem. Fac. Sci. Kyushu Univ. Ser. E*, 117–136.

Jacob, F., and Monod, J. (1961). On the regulation of gene activity. *Cold Spring Harbor Symp. Quant. Biol.* **26**, 193–209.

Jaeger, L. (1945). Glycogen utilization by the amphibian gastrula in relation to invagination and induction. *J. Cellular Comp. Physiol.* **25**, 97–120.

Johnen, A. G. (1956). Experimental studies about the temporal relationships in the induction process. I and II. *Koninkl. Ned. Akad. Wetenschap. Proc. Ser. C* **59**, 554–660.

Kawakami, I., and Yamana, K. (1959). Studies on the inductive capacities of the combined proteins from bone marrow, kidney and liver of guinea pig. *Mem. Fac. Sci. Kyushu Univ. Ser. E.* **2**, 171–182.

Kemp, N. E. (1956). Electron microscopy of growing oöcytes of *Rana pipiens. J. Biophys. Biochem. Cytol.* **2**, 281–292.

King, T. J., and Briggs, R. (1953). The transplantability of nuclei of arrested hybrid blastulae (*R. pipiens* ♀ × *R. catesbeiana* ♂). *J. Exptl. Zool.* **123**, 61–78.

King, T. J., and Briggs, R. (1956). Serial transplantation of embryonic nuclei. *Cold Spring Harbor Symp. Quant. Biol.* **21**, 271–289.

Kusche, W. (1929). Interplantation umschriebener Zellbezirke aus der Blastula und der Gastrula der Amphibien. I. Versuche an Urodelen. *Wilhelm Roux Arch. Entwicklungsmech. Organ.* **116**, 192–271.

Kutsky, P. B. (1950). Phosphate metabolism in the early development of *Rana pipiens. J. Exptl. Zool.* **115**, 429–460.

Kuusi, T. (1953). Sur les effets des acides nucléiques et des protéines dans l'induction hétérogène. *Arch. Biol. (Liege)* **64**, 189–226.

Lederberg, J. (1952). Cell genetics and hereditary symbiosis. *Physiol. Rev.* **32**, 403–430.

Lehman, H. E. (1955). On the development of enucleated *Triton* eggs with injected blastula nucleus. *Biol. Bull.* **108**, 138–150.

Lehmann, F. E. (1945). "Einführung in die physiologische Embryologie." Birkhäuser, Basel.

Lehmann, F. E. (1956). Plasmatische Eiorganisation und Entwicklungsleistung beim Keim vom *Tubifex* (Spiralia). *Naturwiss enschaften* **43**, 289–296.

Liedke, K. B., Engelman, M., and Graff, S. (1954). The selective response of amphibian embryos to benzimidazole and benzotriazole derivatives. *J. Exptl. Zool.* **127**, 201–217.

Lillie, F. R. (1927). The gene and the ontogenetic process. *Science* **66**, 361–368.

Lopashov, G. (1935). Die Entwicklungsleistungen des Gastrulaektoderms in Abhängigkeit von Veränderungen der Masse. *Biol. Zentr.* **55**, 606–615.

Løvtrup, S. (1953a). Energy sources of amphibian embryogenesis. *Compt. Rend. Trav. Lab. Carlsberg Ser. Chim.* **28**, 371–399.

Løvtrup, S. (1953b). Utilization of reserve material during amphibian embryogenesis at different temperatures. *Compt. Rend. Trav. Lab. Carlsberg Ser. Chim.* **28**, 400–425.

Løvtrup, S. (1955). Chemical differentiation during amphibian embryogenesis. *Compt. Rend. Trav. Lab. Carlsberg Ser. Chim.* **29**, 261–314.

Løvtrup, S., and Pigon, A. (1958). Inversion of the dorso-ventral axis in amphibian embryos by unilateral restriction of oxygen supply. *J. Embryol. Exptl. Morphol.* **6**, 486–490.

Magasanik, B. (1958). The metabolic regulation of purine interconversions and of histidine biosynthesis. *In* "The Chemical Basis of Development" (W. D. McElroy and B. Glass, eds.), pp. 485–489. Johns Hopkins Press, Baltimore, Maryland.

Mangold, O., and Seidel, F. (1927). Homoplastische und heteroplastische Verschmelzung ganzer Tritonkeime. *Wilhelm Roux' Arch. Entwicklungsmech. Organ.* **111**, 494–665.

Mangold, O., and Spemann, H. (1927). Ueber Induktion von Medullarplatte durch Medullarplatte im jüngeren Keim, ein Beispiel homöogenetischer oder assimilatorischer Induktion. *Wilhelm Roux' Arch. Entwicklungsmech Organ.* **111**, 341–422.

Markert, C. L. (1958). Chemical concepts of cellular differentiation. *In* "The Chemical Basis of Development" (W. D. McElroy and B. Glass, eds.), pp. 3–16. Johns Hopkins Press, Baltimore, Maryland.

Mazia, D. (1959). Cell division. *Harvey Lectures Ser.* **53**, 130–170.

Mifune, S. (1959). Studies on the inductive effects of mammalian bone marrow in explantation experiments with embryos of *Triturus*. *Mem. Fac. Sci. Kyushu Univ. Ser. E* **3**, 33–41.

Mirsky, A. E., and Allfrey, V. (1958). The role of the cell nucleus in development. *In* "The Chemical Basis of Development" (W. D. McElroy and B. Glass, eds.), 94–98. Johns Hopkins Press, Baltimore, Maryland.

Moore, B. C. (1960). Personal communication.

Moore, J. A. (1939). Temperature tolerances and rates of development in the eggs of amphibia. *Ecology* **20**, 459–478.

Moore, J. A. (1947). Studies on the development of frog hybrids. II. Competence of the gastrula ectoderm of *Rana pipiens* ♀ × *Rana sylvatica* ♂ hybrids. *J. Exptl. Zool.* **105**, 349–370.

Moore, J. A. (1948). Studies in the development of frog hybrids. III. Inductive ability of the dorsal lip region of *Rana pipiens* ♀ × *Rana sylvatica* ♂ hybrids. *J. Exptl. Zool.* **108**, 127–154.

Moore, J. A. (1955). Abnormal combinations of nuclear and cytoplasmic systems in frogs and toads. *Advan. Genet.* **7**, 139–182.

Moore, J. A. (1958a). The transfer of haploid nuclei between *Rana pipiens* and *Rana sylvatica*. *Exptl. Cell Res. Suppl.* **6**, 179–191.

Moore, J. A. (1958b). Transplantation of nuclei between *Rana pipiens* and *Rana sylvatica*. *Exptl. Cell Res.* **14**, 532–540.

Moore, J. A. (1960). Serial backtransfer of nuclei in experiments involving two species of frogs. *Develop. Biol.* **2**, 535–550.

Moore, J. A. (1962). Nuclear transplantation and problems of specificity in developing embryos. *Jour. Cell. Comp. Physiol. Suppl.* **1:** 60–79.

Morgan, T. H. (1934). "Embryology and Genetics," 285 pp. Columbia Univ. Press, New York.

Moscona, A. A. (1961a). Environmental factors in experimental studies on histogenesis. *Colloq. Intern. Centre Nat. Rech. Sci. Paris* **101**, 155–168.

Moscona, A. A. (1961b). Effect of temperature on adhesion to glass and histogenetic cohesion of dissociated cells. *Nature* **190**, 408–409.

Nace, G. W. (1958). Comment during discussion. *In* "The Chemical Basis of Development" (W. D. McElroy and B. Glass, eds.), p. 90. Johns Hopkins Press, Baltimore, Maryland.

Nace, G. W., Suyama, T., and Smith, N. (1961). Early development of special proteins. *Symp. Germ Cells Develop. Inst. Intern. Embryol. Fondazione A. Baselli* pp. 564–603.

Needham, J. (1942). "Biochemistry and Morphogenesis," 785 pp. Cambridge Univ. Press, London and New York.

Nieuwkoop, P. D. (1952). Activation and organization of the central nervous system in amphibians. *J. Exptl. Zool.* **120**, 1–108.

Nieuwkoop, P. D., and Nigtevecht, G. V. (1954). Neural activation and transformation in explants of competent ectoderm under the influence of fragments of anterior notochord in Urodeles. *J. Embryol. Exptl. Morphol.* **2**, 175–193.

Niu, M. C. (1956). New approaches to the problem of embryonic induction. *In* "Cellular Mechanisms in Differentiation and Growth" (D. Rudnick, ed.), pp. 155–171. Princeton Univ. Press, Princeton, New Jersey.

Niu, M. C. (1959). Current evidence concerning chemical inducers. *In* "Evolution of Nervous Control" (Allan D. Bass, ed.), pp. 7–30. Am. Assoc. Advan. Sci, Washington, D. C.

Niu, M. C., and Twitty, V. C. (1953). The differentiation of gastrula ectoderm in medium conditioned by axial mesoderm. *Proc. Natl. Acad. Sci. U. S.* **39**, 985–989.

Ornstein, N., and Gregg, J. R. (1952). Respiratory metabolism of amphibian gastrula explants. *Biol. Bull.* **103**, 407–420.

Panijel, J. (1950). L'organisation du vitellus dans les oeufs d'amphibiens. *Biochim. Biophys. Acta* **5**, 343–357.

Parmenter, C. L. (1933). Haploid, diploid, triploid, and tetraploid chromosome numbers and their origin in parthenogenetically developed larvae and frogs of *Rana pipiens* and *Rana palustris*. *J. Exptl. Zool.* **66**, 409–453.

Pasteels, J. (1942). Sur l'existence éventuelle d'une croissance au cours de las gastrulation des Vertèbres. *Acta Biol. Belg.* **2**, 126–133.

Pasteels, J. (1951). Centre organisateur et potential morphogénétique. *Bull. Soc. Zool. France* **76**, 231–270.

Pasteels, J. J. (1958). Comparative cytochemistry of the fertilized egg. *In* "The Chemical Basis of Development" (W. D. McElroy and B. Glass, eds.), pp. 381–403. Johns Hopkins Press, Baltimore, Maryland.

Paterson, M. C. (1957). Animal-vegetal balance in amphibian development. *J. Exptl. Zool.* **134**, 183–200.

Piepho, H. (1938). Ueber Oxydation-Reduktions-Vorgänge im Amphibienkeim. *Biol. Zentr.* **58**, 90–117.

Porter, K. (1939). Androgenetic development of the egg of *Rana pipiens*. *Biol. Bull.* **77**, 233–257.

Porter, K. R. (1941). Diploid and androgenetic haploid hybridization between two forms of *Rana pipiens* Schreber. *Biol. Bull.* **80**, 238–264.

Porter, K. R. (1942). Developmental variation resulting from various associations of frog cytoplasms and nuclei. *Trans. N.Y. Acad. Sci.* **4**, 213–217.

Puck, T. T. (1959). Quantitative studies on mammalian cells *in vitro*. *Rev. Mod. Phys.* **31**, 433–448.

Raven, C. P. (1933). Experimentelle Untersuchungen ueber den Glykogenstoffwechsel des Organisationszentrums in der Amphibiengastrula. I. *Proc. Koninkl. Akad. Wetenschap. Amsterdam* **36**, 566–569.

Raven, C. P. (1935). Experimentelle Untersuchungen ueber den Glykogenstoffwechsel des Organisationszentrums in der Amphibiengastrula. II. *Proc. Koninkl. Akad. Wetenschap. Amsterdam* **38**, 1107–1109.

Raven, C. P. (1954). "An Outline of Developmental Physiology," 216 pp. Pergamon, New York.

Rose, S. M. (1952). Interaction of tumor agents and normal cellular components in Amphibia. *Ann. N. Y. Acad. Sci.* **54**, 1110–1119.

Rose, S. M. (1957). Cellular interaction during differentiation. *Biol. Rev. Cambridge Phil. Soc.* **32**, 351–382.

Rose, S. M., and Rose, F. C. (1952). Tumor agent transformations in Amphibia. *Cancer Res.* **12**, 1–12.

Rounds, D. E., and Flickinger, R. A. (1958). Distribution of ribonucleoprotein during neural induction in the from embryo. *J. Exptl. Zool.* **137**, 479–500.

Rugh, R. (1934). Induced ovulation and artificial fertilization in the frog. *Biol. Bull.* **66**, 22–29.

Saxén, L. (1961). Transfilter neural induction of amphibian ectoderm. *Develop. Biol.* **3**, 140–152.

Saxén, L., and Toivonen, S. (1961). The two-gradient hypothesis in primary induction. The combined effect of two types of inductors mixed in different ratios. *J. Embryol. Exptl. Morphol.* **9**, 514–533.

Shaver, J. R. (1953). Studies on the initiation of cleavage in the frog egg. *J. Exptl. Zool.* **122**, 169–192.

Sirlin, J. L., Brahma, S. K., and Waddington, C. H. (1956). Studies on embryonic induction using radioactive tracers. *J. Embryol. Exptl. Morphol.* **4**, 248–253.

Spemann, H. (1901). Entwicklungsphysiologische Studien am Triton-Ei. *Wilhelm Roux' Arch. Entwicklungsmech. Organ.* **12**, 224–264.

Spemann, H. (1902). Entwicklungphysiologische Studien am Triton-Ei. II. *Wilhelm Roux' Arch. Entwicklungsmech. Organ.* **15**, 447–534.

Spemann, H. (1903). Entwicklungsphysiologische Studien am Triton-Ei. III. *Wilhelm Roux' Arch. Entwicklungsmech. Organ.* **16**, 551–631.

Spemann, H. (1914). Ueber verzögerte Kernversorgung von Keimteilen. *Verhandl. Deut. Zool. Ges.* **1914**, 16–221.

Spemann, H. (1928). Die Entwicklung seitlicher und dorso-ventraler Keimhaelften bei verzögerter Kernversorgung. *Z. Wiss. Zool.* **132**, 105–134.

Spemann, H. (1938). "Embryonic Development and Induction," 401 pp. Yale Univ. Press, New Haven, Connecticut.

Spiegel, M. (1954). The role of specific surface antigens in cell adhesion. Part II. Studies on embryonic amphibian cells. *Biol. Bull.* **107**, 149–155.

Spiegelman, S. (1945). Physiological competition as a regulatory mechanism in morphogenesis. *Quart. Rev. Biol.* **20**, 121–146.

Spiegelman, S. (1957). Nucleic acids and the synthesis of proteins. *In* "The Chemical Basis of Heredity" (W. D. McElroy and B. Glass, eds.), pp. 232–267. Johns Hopkins Press, Baltimore, Maryland.

Stauffer, E. (1945). Versuche zur experimentellen Herstellung haploider Axolotl-Merogone. *Rev. Suisse Zool.* **52**, 231–327.

Stearns, R. N., and Kostellow, A. B. (1958). *In* "The Chemical Basis of Development" (W. D. McElroy and B. Glass, eds.), p. 448. Johns Hopkins Press, Baltimore, Maryland.

Steinberg, M. S. (1958). On the chemical bonds between animal cells, a mechanism for type-specific association. *Am. Naturalist* **92**, 65–82.

Stern, H., Allfrey, V. G., Mirsky, A. E., and Saetren, H. (1952). Some enzymes of isolated nuclei. *J. Gen. Physiol.* **35**, 559–578.

Sze, L. C. (1953a). Respiration of the parts of the hybrid gastrula *Rana pipiens* ×
  R. sylvatica. Science **117**, 479–480.
Sze, L. C. (1953b). Respiration of the parts of the *Rana pipiens* gastrula. *Physiol.
  Zool.* **26**, 212–223.
Taylor, J. H., Woods, P. S., and Hughes, W. L. (1957). The organization and duplica-
  tion of chromosomes as revealed by autoradiographic studies using tritium-
  labeled thymidine. *Proc. Natl. Acad. Sci. U.S.* **43**, 122–128.
Ten Cate, G. (1956). "The Intrinsic Embryonic Development," 257 pp. North-Hol-
  land Publ., Amsterdam.
Toivonen, S. (1953). Bone-marrow of the guinea-pig as a mesodermal inductor in
  implantation experiments with embryos of *Triturus. J. Embryol. Exptl. Morphol.*
  1, 97–104.
Toivonen, S. (1958). The dependence of the cellular transformation of the competent
  ectoderm on temporal relationships in the induction process. *J. Embryol. Exptl.
  Morphol.* **6**, 479–485.
Toivonen, S. (1961). An experimentally produced change in the sequence of neuralizing and mesodermalizing inductive actions. *Experientia* **17**, 87–90.
Toivonen, S., and Saxén, L. (1955). The simultaneous inducing action of liver and
  bone marrow of the guinea pig in implantation and explantation experiments with
  embryos of *Triturus. Exptl. Cell Res. Suppl.* **3**, 346–357.
Townes, P. L., and Holtfreter, J. (1955). Directed movements and selective adhesion
  of embryonic amphibian cells. *J. Exptl. Zool.* **128**, 53–120.
Trinkhaus, J. P. (1961). Affinity relationships in heterotypic cell aggregates. *Colloq.
  Intern. Centre Nat. Rech. Sci. Paris* **101**, 209–225.
Twitty, V. C. (1936). Correlated genetic and embryological experiments on *Triturus.*
  I and II. *J. Exptl. Zool.* **74**, 239–302.
Twitty, V. C. (1944). Chromatophore migration as a response to mutual influences
  of the developing pigment cells. *J. Exptl. Zool.* **95**, 259–290.
Twitty, V. C. (1959). Migration and speciation in newts. *Science* **130**, 1735–1743.
Twitty, V. C., and Niu, M. C. (1954). The motivation of cell migration, studied by
  isolation of embryonic pigment cells singly and in small groups *in vitro. J. Exptl.
  Zool.* **125**, 541–574.
Tyler, A. (1942). Developmental processes and energetics. *Quart. Rev. Biol.* **17**, 197–
  212, 339–353.
Tyler, A. (1955). Ontogeny of immunological properties. *In* "Analysis of Develop-
  ment" (B. H. Willier, P. Weiss, and V. Hamburger, eds.), pp. 556–573. Saunders,
  Philadelphia, Pennsylvania.
Vogel, H. J. (1958). Feed-back control of the formation of biosynthetic enzymes. *In*
  "The Chemical Basis of Development" (W. D. McElroy and B. Glass, eds.), pp.
  479–484. Johns Hopkins Press, Baltimore, Maryland.
Vogt, W. (1929). Gestaltungsanalyse am Amphibienkeim mit örtlicher Vitalfärbung.
  Wilhelm Roux' Arch. Entwicklungsmech. Organ. **120**, 384–706.
Waddington, C. H. (1932). Experiments on the development of chick and duck em-
  bryos, cultivated *in vitro. Phil. Trans. Roy. Soc. London Ser. B.* **221**, 179–230.
Waddington, C. H. (1956). "Principles of Embryology," 510 pp. Allen & Unwin,
  London.
Waddington, C. H., and Pantelouris, E. M. (1953). Transplantation of nuclei in
  newts' eggs. *Nature* **172**, 1050–1051.
Waddington, C. H., Needham, J., Nowinski, W. W., and Lemberg, R. (1935). Studies
  on the nature of the amphibian organization centre. I. Chemical properties of
  the evocator. *Proc. Roy. Soc.* **117**, 289–317.

Waddington, C. H., Needham, J., and Brachet, J. (1936). The activation of the evocator. *Proc. Roy. Soc.* **B120**, 173–207.

Weber, R. (1954). Strukturveränderungen an isolierten Mitochondrien von *Xenopus*-Leber. *Z. Zellforsch. Mikroskop. Anat.* **39**, 630–640.

Weber, R., and Boell, E. J. (1955). Über die Cytochromoxydase-Aktivität der Mitochondrien von frühen Entwicklungsstadien des Krallenfrosches (*Xenopus laevis* Daud.). *Rev. Suisse Zool.* **62**, 260–268.

Weiss, P. (1947). The problem of specificity in growth and development. *Yale J. Biol. Med.* **19**, 235–278.

Weiss, P. (1953). Some introductory remarks on the cellular basis of differentiation. *J. Embryol. Exptl. Morphol.* **1**, 181–211.

Weiss, P. (1958a). Summation and evaluation. *In* "The Chemical Basis of Development" (W. D. McElroy and B. Glass, eds.), pp. 843–854. Johns Hopkins Press, Baltimore, Maryland.

Weiss, P. (1958b). Cell contact. *Intern. Rev. Cytol.* **7**, 391–423.

Whiteley, A. H., and Baltzer, F. (1958). Development, respiratory rate and content of desoxyribonucleic acid in the hybrid *Paracentrotus* ♀ × *Arbacia* ♂. *Pubbl. Staz. Zool. Napoli* **30**, 402–457.

Wright, S. (1945). Genes as physiological agents. *Am. Naturalist* **79**, 289–303.

Yamada, T. (1958). Embryonic induction. *In* "The Chemical Basis of Development" (W. D. McElroy and B. Glass, eds.), pp. 217–238. Johns Hopkins Press, Baltimore, Maryland.

10

REGENERATION

S. Meryl Rose

I. Introduction

Knowledge of regeneration in the Amphibia began in the eighteenth century when the Abbé Spallanzani (1769) reported complete and functional reproduction of limbs of salamanders. Now after hundreds of investigations it has been established that some salamanders can replace any part whose removal does not kill within a few weeks. The most studied have been the limbs but other parts as well can be replaced. Among them are tails, large parts of eyes including retina, iris, and lens, both peripheral nerves and parts of the central nervous system, and parts of the viscera. References to all but the most recent work may be found in earlier reviews (Luscher, 1952; Morgan, 1901; Korschelt, 1927; Weiss, 1936, 1955; Swett, 1937; J. Needham, 1942; Brunst, 1950b; Polezhayev, 1945, 1946a; Lynn and Wachowski, 1951; A. E. Needham, 1952, 1960; Singer, 1952, 1960; Reyer, 1954b; Nicholas, 1955; Thornton, 1959).

Most of the studies in recent years have centered around four overlapping problems: the stimulus for regeneration, the source of the regenerating tissue, the control of pattern in the regenerate and the special roles of individual tissues and glands. Linked with the major problems and prevading much of recent work is the question why the Anura, which regenerate so well as larvae, fail to regenerate some parts after metamorphosis.

It can be assumed throughout this chapter that, unless stated otherwise, the work being described was done on a urodele. When Anura were used or, when it might be important to know that a larva rather than an adult was being investigated, that will be noted.

II. General Characteristics of Regeneration

There are two essentially different processes that are usually grouped under the general term of regeneration. In most tissues and organs there is constant replacement of cells. The rate varies from tissue to tissue, being high in the blood, lower in the epidermis, and still lower in the liver. If a large part of a tissue or organ is removed the normal rate of replacement is temporarily increased until the normal amount of the tissue is reattained. This more rapid than normal replacement is often called regeneration, but it might be less confusing if it were not and if, instead, an old term for the process, compensatory hypertrophy, were used.

Regeneration as used here means something else. It is the replacement of a part that involves considerable loss of structure in one or more tissues, the accumulation of a mass of relatively undifferentiated cells, called a blastema, and the control of differentiation in the blastema so that its differentiated product closely resembles the part it is replacing. Regeneration as so defined is the subject of this chapter.

A photographic description of the process, as seen in the regeneration of a limb and the regeneration of a lens, is given in Figs. 1, 2, and 3.

III. The Eye

Some urodeles, most notably those of the genera, *Salamandra*, *Triton*, and *Triturus*, can regenerate a functional lens (review by Reyer, 1954b).

Lens regeneration, discovered by Colucci (1891) and by Wolff (1895) and now known as Wolffian regeneration, is accomplished by the transformation of a portion of the iris to lens (Figs. 2 and 3). After extirpation of a lens there is some loss of pigment from the inner surface of the pupillary border of the iris and some swelling of this ring of tissue. Early in the process depigmentation and swelling are observed all around the border but within a few days they are limited to the mid-dorsal region (Mikami, 1941). There depigmentation continues to completion. At the same time the cells lose their flattened appearance and become cuboidal. Cell division occurs and a bud begins to grow out into the fluid of the posterior chamber formerly occupied by the old lens. Eventually as epithelium and lens fibers differentiate the new lens separates from its parent tissue, the iris, and continues growth until it becomes a functional lens normal in size and appearance.

Why does this dorsal spot on the iris close to the position of the old lens transform to lens? First of all, it is not the only part of the iris with lens potency, and other tissues, surface ectoderm and the pigmented tapetum surrounding the retina, can also produce a lens under the proper conditions.

The first tissue to become lens during embryonic development is not iris but the ectodermal tissue at the surface of the embryo just over the eyecup (rev. by Spemann, 1938). Later as eye structure is complicated by development of iris behind the surface ectoderm it is the iris which shows greatest lens potency. This potency for internal tissue to form lens is acquired early. Several investigators have observed that an embryonic eyecup, if transplanted in such a way that its outer surface does not touch surface ectoderm may produce a lens from part of itself. It has been clearly shown by Reyer (1950, 1954a) that after a piece of noncompetent ectoderm is grafted in the presumptive lens position of a young embryo no lens will develop for a long time. Some time later, after an iris has formed, its dorsal portion will transform to lens.

In the larval and in the adult salamander it is a particular spot on the dorsal part of the iris that transforms to lens when a lens is missing. Other parts of the dorsal iris can produce lens but ordinarily do not. If a mid-dorsal strip of iris is replaced by foreign tissue, cornea or ventral iris, and the lens removed, the foreign tissue, although in the proper position, does not transform to lens. Instead, that tissue of the dorsal iris closest to the point where Wolffian regeneration normally occurs now participates. Two lenses regenerate, one just medial to and the other just lateral to the grafted strip (Stone, 1953). These iris areas never transform to lens when the mid-dorsal iris tissue is in place.

Within the iris there is a gradient in potency to transform to lens that drops off from the mid-dorsal spot along the pupillary border where the transformation ordinarily occurs. When bits of iris are implanted in the posterior chamber of lensless eyes parts of some will transform to lens. The frequency of transformation varies from a high of 84% for the mid-dorsal piece to 76%, 75%, and 56% for adjacent areas when isolated and down to 50% and 15% for medial and lateral dorsal areas taken from along the ora serrata and away from the pupillary border (Mikami, 1941). The drop in frequency of transformation to lens is to either side of the mid point and also posteriorly toward the ora serrata (Sato, 1930; Mikami

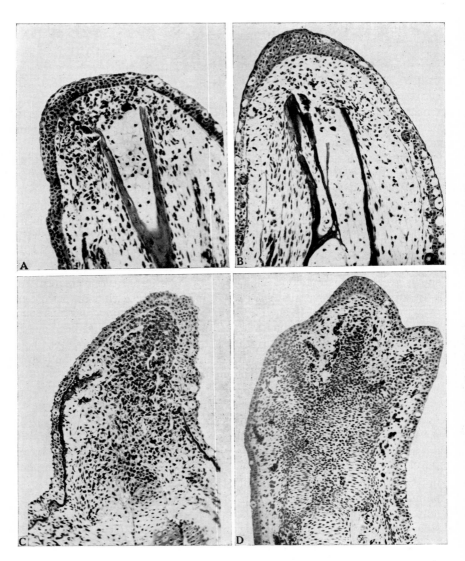

Fig. 1. Regeneration of limbs of 40-mm larval *Ambystoma opacum*. (Photographs kindly furnished by Professor Charles S. Thornton.)

Specimen	Days after amputation	Magnification
A	1	70x
B	4	55x
C	8	65x
D	16	55x

All photomicrographs are of near median longitudinal sections of anterior limbs.
In A, epidermis has already migrated across and covered the wound. The bone ap-

1941; Stone, 1952). There have been a few reports of lens regeneration from ventral iris but the frequency is close to zero.

We learn from the above that in larval and adult eyes, there is a spot in the iris very close to the lens region that can become lens in the absence of lens. Under normal conditions the dorsal iris although capable of forming more, if its parts are isolated, forms only one when it is intact. More lenses do form even without transplantation when parts are partially isolated by bits of celluloid (Okada, 1935) or Pliofilm (Stone, 1954). Some kind of control limiting the regeneration to one lens operates in the iris and requires intact cellular connections. This control is polarized as seen from the fact that it is always from the mid-dorsal free border of the iris or holes in it that a new lens regenerates.

Not only does the dorsal tissue closest to the lens position show the highest frequency of lens regeneration but the only place a normal lens can develop is in or close to that position. Lenses forming at artificial gaps in the iris decrease in size as their distance from the normal lens area increases (Stone, 1954). Identical bits of iris will transform to lens-like structures with too much epithelium if cultured in the anterior chamber or with too much fiber and no epithelium back close to the retina (Mikami, 1941). The normal balance of epithelium and fiber is achieved in the lens position.

The tapetum nigrum lying between the choroid layer and the retina, and sometimes called the pigmented layer of the retina, also possesses great powers of regeneration. It can transform either to neural retina or to lens (Sato, 1951; Stone, 1958a, 1959). Lenses that form in the retinal position far from the normal position for lens are quite abnormal and are spoken of as lentoids. However, if most of the contents of an eye are removed leaving only the tapetum nigrum inside the choroid coat all of the missing parts may regenerate. First, retina and iris are produced from the tapetum and then from the iris a good lens is produced. In this case the lens comes from the tapetum by way of iris (Sato, 1951; Stone, 1958a, 1959).

Just as in the embryonic eye where an eyecup factor operates to favor lens development, so, in the larval and adult eye, the retina, a descendant

---

pears as a long "V" and is surrounded distally by remnants of the old local tissue and a collection of wandering cells.

In B, an apical cap of epidermis has formed. Bone is eroding, especially at its distal end. The soft tissues between bone and epidermis have lost most of their organization. Fibroblasts are widespread, a few clusters of cells representing skin glands are still present, and there is muscle at the lower left.

Four days later, in C, a blastema with a mesenchymal covering traversed by capillaries and covered by epidermis forms a cap projecting beyond the stump.

In D, fingerbuds and developing cartilaginous skeleton foretell a new limb.

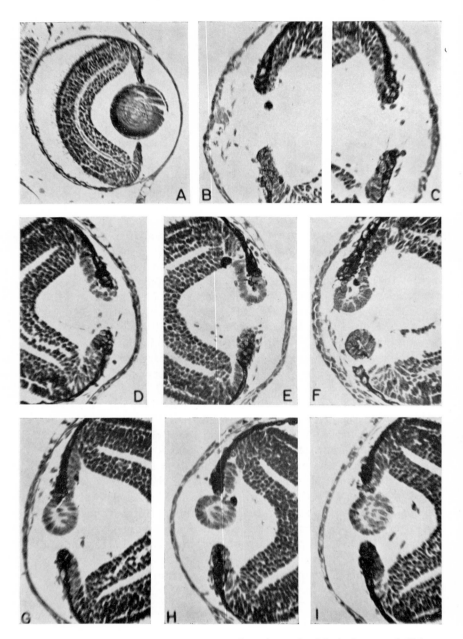

Fig. 2. Stages in the regeneration of a lens from the iris in larvae of *Triturus viridescens* from 4 until 30 days after lens extirpation. At the time of operation, the larvae varied in age from a stage with 3 fingerbuds on the forelimb to one with long hind limb buds. A, Normal unoperated eye (magnification: 90). B, Stage 1, after 4 days. C, Stage 2, after 5 days. D, Stage 3, after 6 days. E, Stage 4, after 7 days. F, Stage 5, after 9 days. G, Stage 6, after 9 days. H, Stage 7, after 11 days. I, Stage 8, after 11 days. (Magnification in B–I, 135.) (Figures 2 and 3 from Reyer, 1954b.)

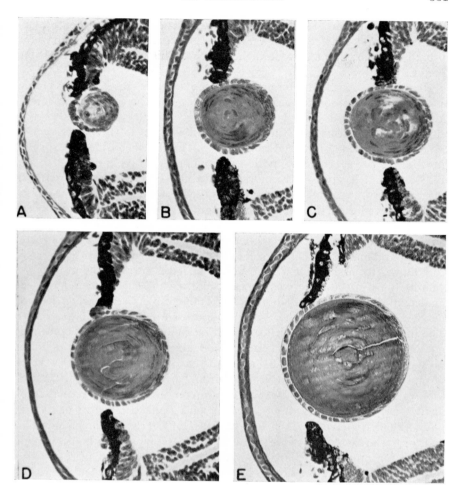

Fig. 3. Stages in lens regeneration (as in Fig. 2, *continued*). A, Stage 9, after 16 days. B, A late stage 10, after 16 days. C, Stage 11, after 18 days. D, Stage 12, after 20 days. E, Stage 13, after 30 days. (Magnification: 135.)

of the eyecup, does the same thing. This has been shown in several ways. A piece of iris in a retina-free eye does not produce lens until a retina has regenerated (Ikeda, 1936; Monroy, 1939; Reyer, 1954b; Stone, 1959). If both retina and iris are lacking and only the pigmented retina remains, neural retina must form before part of the iris can transform to lens. Another way in which it was learned that the transformation, iris to lens, is facilitated by retina was by transplantation of iris to other parts of the body with and without retina. Lens formed from iris only when retina was present (Wachs, 1914; Zalokar, 1944; Stone, 1959). Artificial membranes inserted between retina and iris prevent Wolffian regeneration (Stone, 1958a,b; Stone and Gallagher, 1958). This too indicates a retinal factor.

How absolute is the requirement for an eyecup or retinal factor is now a question. Its absolute necessity was first questioned when Spemann learned that embryos of some species do not require the presence of an eyecup for lens formation from the ectoderm while others do (rev. by Spemann, 1938). Another tissue or tissues could do what had been considered a specific function of the eyecup. The notion of double assurance arose (Spemann, 1938). As time has passed the investigators have become aware of multiple assurance or the very unspecific nature of the induction. Okada and Mikami (1937) showed that, if an eyecup was removed from under the spot where lens should develop, lens differentiation would not be achieved in its absence. A variety of other tissues could be substituted in the eyecup position and make it possible for lens to arise. Only one structure, the eyecup, makes it possible for what could be called a normal lens to develop. Another part of the brain was almost equally good, surface ectoderm was inadequate, and both mesodermal and endodermal tissues when packed into the space voided by the eyecup supported a larger than normal lens. The impression gained is that ectoderm in a particular spot becomes lens not because of specific instructions from any one tissue. This point of view was strengthened by the experiments of Jacobson (1958). Pieces of presumptive lens epidermis isolated from early and late neurulae failed to develop. Only 3% formed lens when in combination with retinal rudiment from neurulae. Presumptive lens plus flank mesoderm or lateral plate mesoderm gave lenses in 10% and 14% of the cases. The endodermal wall of the archenteron, close to the future eye region was the best single partner for presumptive lens epidermis in the production of lens; 31% formed lenses. When in addition lateral plate mesoderm was added to the other two the percentage producing lenses jumped to 42%. We can no longer say that any one tissue contains *the* inductor for a lens. These tissues, which are so good at supporting lens development from presumptive lens cannot induce lens from ventral flank ectoderm. The two tissues, head ectoderm and flank ectoderm, are already different because of their environments. A series of changes in both the reacting tissue and its environment during ontogeny and regeneration lead to the production of a normal lens.

It is quite apparent that there is one position in the eye where the factors favoring lens development reach an optimum. As lens development proceeds in this position, lens regeneration is prevented elsewhere in an intact eye. Not only does a differentiating lens in the dorsal iris site participate in suppression of other potential lens sites, but a fully differentiated lens exercises control over the mid-dorsal site. A lens removed temporarily and grafted back into position or another substituted for it does not allow Wolffian regeneration (rev. by Reyer, 1954b).

Several hypotheses concerning the method by which the lens prevents regeneration of a new lens have been eliminated. That a lens does not act by simply occupying the position was shown by removing a lens and substituting for it various animate and inanimate objects such as potato, waxed lens, and fixed lens (Wachs, 1914; Reyer, 1954b). None of these prevents transformation of iris to lens.

Injury to the iris *per se* or in combination with absence of a lens is not a necessary factor. Lens can be removed without appreciable injury to the iris (Wolff, 1904; Stone, 1952). Yet iris forms lens. Extensive injury to iris does not cause regeneration if a lens is left in position (Wolff, 1904; Wachs, 1920; Zalokar, 1944; Stone, 1952).

Conclusive evidence that injury to the eye is not a necessary forerunner of transformation of iris to lens comes from the already cited experiments of Reyer (1950, 1954a). A larval eye that had remained lensless for weeks because incompetent ectoderm occupied the early lens position formed a lens later from uninjured iris.

Taken together the above experiments demonstrate that the necessary conditions for the development of lens from iris are the presence of retina and the absence of lens. The idea of double control has a long history. For the eye it goes back to Spemann (1905). He realized that the eyecup stimulates lens formation and that lens inhibits lens. The lens was believed to secrete a substance which paralyzes the influence of the eyecup.

Wachs (1914, 1920) furthered the study of positive and negative control and established that lens does inhibit potential lens. He began the study of transformation in grafts of pieces of iris to eye chambers. Wachs (1920) and several subsequent workers (rev. by Stone, 1959) learned that a piece of iris implanted into an eye with a normal lens does not produce another lens. Such an iris piece grafted into a lensless eye can produce lens. Contact between lens and iris is not necessary for the transfer of inhibition. This may be a unique situation with inhibitory substance present and active in the free fluid.

Even in the eye, however, the control is not always by free diffusion. After lensectomy a grafted iris and the host iris will both develop lenses. Only when one potential lens region is in direct contact with another can one suppress the other if they were removed from the iris at the same time. If one piece of iris has had a head start that has enabled it to achieve transformation to a fibrous lens then it can suppress another not in direct contact with it. Even before fiber formation one piece with a head start can decrease the frequency of Wolffian regeneration in the handicapped piece (Sato, 1935; Mikami, 1941).

Quantity seems to be important in this relationship. If a small lens is substituted for a normal larger one it can inhibit transformation to lens in the iris only if the substitute is in the normal lens position and touching the iris. If it lies elsewhere it does not completely suppress Wolffian regeneration (Wachs, 1914).

Position and contact are seen to be important from other experiments. Lenses in different stages of regeneration were transferred to lensless eyes. When they lodged far from the normal lens site their own growth was checked and the host iris proceeded to regenerate a lens unimpeded. In all cases where host iris formed lens there was space between iris and implanted lens (Mikami, 1941). Zalokar (1944) also established that lens in normal position permanently inhibits Wolffian regeneration but if further away only delays it and causes abnormalities in the regenerated lens.

Even though some inhibition spills over into the eye fluid making it possible for inhibition by a well formed lens to work across a fluid barrier there is normally a more direct control of lens over iris. A rod of silver or glass inserted between lens and dorsal iris may break the control (Spirito and Ciaccio, 1931). Small tissue gaps in the iris also prevent the spread of inhibition from the mid-dorsal iris as noted above.

Something is known of the degree of specificity of the inhibitory control by lens. It has been shown that lens can prevent transformation of iris to lens without affecting transformation of iris to retina. Iris in larval urodeles and in some adults can transform to neural retina (Sato, 1935). Sato introduced freshly cut competent iris from larvae of *Triton taeniatus* into eye chambers after extirpation of the host lens. Iris implanted in eyes from which the lens had been removed 1 to 4 days earlier regenerated either retina or lens. As the time between removal of host lens and implantation of iris increased, the incidence of Wolffian regeneration from the implants decreased. When host iris had achieved transformation to a fibrous lens no lenses were formed from implants. Still the incidence of iris to retinal transformation did not change. A regenerating lens under the proper conditions even before it has reached the fiber stage can decrease the frequency of Wolffian regeneration. After fibers have formed and the new lens is exercising complete control over freshly added iris it still has no effect on regeneration of retina.

The specificity is not a narrow species specificity. Lenses of other genera of urodeles and even lenses from Anura can suppress lens regeneration in a urodele eye (Ikeda and Kojima, 1940; Uno, 1943; Stone, 1945).

As far as is known a lens is the only structure that can inhibit lens regeneration across a fluid gap. However, other tissues, liver, heart, brain, and retina when grafted to the dorsal iris can suppress Wolffian regeneration (Mikami, 1941). The effect is spoken of as mechanical, but how the tissues act is not known.

An active lens seems necessary for suppression of lens activity in iris as demonstrated by Politzer (1937). An X-rayed lens may persist for some weeks but eventually its fibers swell and the lens bursts. Regression follows and as the old lens regresses a new one begins to form from iris. Development of such a new lens is abnormal. This is not a direct effect of X-rays on the iris. Similarly irradiated eyes minus lens regenerate normal lens. Abnormality in regeneration seems to result from the presence of a regressing irradiated lens.

The eye might prove an excellent place for the study of chemical controls during differentiation. Both the retinal factor and the lens factor seem to be present in eye fluids. Zalokar (1944) has presented evidence that the retinal factor may be adsorbed by kaolin. Stone and Vultee (1949) and Stone (1953, 1959) have shown that the natural lens inhibitor may be present in aqueous humor. Lensless eyes can be prevented from regenerating lenses for several months, the duration of the experiment, by daily injections of aqueous humor from eyes containing lenses.

IV. Regeneration of Coordinated Activity

A. RETINA AND BRAIN

The most striking example of regeneration is the return of good vision in both Urodela and Anura (Matthey, 1925; Sperry, 1943a, b, 1944) after optic nerves are severed. The portions of the axons leading from the cut to the brain degenerate. Their place is taken by new axons regenerating from the stumps still attached to cell bodies in the retina. These axons regenerate through the connective tissue tunnel of the optic nerve and eventually make connections that insure normal vision. Regenerated vision that does not depend on training is exhibited. As soon as vision returns the newts can move directly toward a food lure outside their glass containers (Stone and Zaur, 1940). The precision of the behavior mediated by regenerated vision indicates something approaching perfect regeneration of synapses enabling particular areas of the retina to initiate impulses resulting in a battery of firing to groups of muscle cells whose response yields the appropriate well coordinated change in motion. Further evidence for regenerated point for point correlation comes from experiments in which optic nerves regenerate from eyes that have been turned upside down. An animal with such a regenerated visual apparatus moves down when a lure is presented in the upper part of its visual field, to the right when the lure is on the left and to the lower left when the lure is at the upper right (Stone and Zaur, 1940; Sperry, 1943b; Stone, 1944). These animals, unlike man, do not adjust to an inverted visual field. There is no evidence either for learning or relearning to see in the Amphibia (Sperry, 1943a, b, 1951).

It is known that impulses must pass through particular localized areas of the optic tectum for vision to occur in local parts of the visual field. Each small lesion in the optic tectum in these salamanders as in other animals results in loss of vision in a part of the visual field (Sperry, 1951). Recordings from different parts of the optic tectum after optic nerve regeneration also demonstrate the return of local activity (Maturana et al., 1959).

How can point for point coordination of function between retina and optic tectum be reestablished? First, there is the problem of how the relationship could have been established during ontogeny.

Either there is built-in correspondence of retinal and brain points or this is acquired during development. Weiss (1936, 1950, 1955) formulated the problems involved in the ontogeny of central and peripheral correspondence and tends to exclude the possibility of the two developing independently yet showing point for point correspondence. If one is not specified by the other during ontogeny, it would seem to mean that two highly detailed differentiated areas that must work together point for point had evolved independently. That such quantity of matched detail could arise independently has not seemed plausible.

Weiss suggested the now generally accepted idea that an organ may impose specific chemical changes on its nerve fibers. Once a nerve fiber had been specified then it could in turn specify other neurons it contacted. Such an explanation seems to be required. Regenerating nerve fibers do not need to follow old pathways. For example, the axons in a regenerated optic nerve are jumbled (Sperry, 1945). Yet point for point vision may be restored. Supposedly the regenerated fibers can grow until they make contact with those dendrites or cell bodies with which they had formerly been in contact and which they had come to know during ontogeny by imprinting (Sperry, 1951).

B. LIMB MOTION

A similar problem is encountered in the study of regeneration of coordinated muscular activity in limbs. Extra limbs may be produced by natural accidents or in a variety of artificial ways (Section VII). If a supernumerary limb develops in a position where it receives only part of the normal innervation of a limb it still acts muscle for muscle and synchronously with the original limb of the field (Weiss, 1924a, 1936,

1950). Even if the supernumerary is turned backward and its motion will impede forward progress, it will respond muscle for muscle and synchronously with the original and normally positioned member of that field. This it may do with all of its nerve fibers derived from only one of the nerves normally supplying a limb. Normally an anterior limb is supplied by the third to the fifth spinal nerves. The fifth contributes the least fibers, but still an extra limb receiving only fibers from the fifth nerve will respond homologously in all its parts.

This poses a real problem. Here is a limb that is completely innervated by nerves that normally supply only a part of the limb, yet it is able to respond muscle for muscle with a normally innervated limb. Although there seems to be something other than circuitry involved here, circuitry does play a role. For the homologous response to occur there must be at least one limb nerve, not just any nerve.

C. RESONANCE AND REGENERATION OF CENTRAL CONNECTIONS

One general explanation of the phenomenon has been offered. Weiss (1924a, 1936) suggested an explanation based on the resonance principle. According to this suggestion, there would be a variety of impulse patterns traveling over all of the limb nerves. Limited and specific response would result when a certain burst of impulses reached a muscle that could respond to this pattern but not to all patterns.

According to the view of Sperry (1951), an amendment to the suggestion by Weiss, this is what might happen if limb nerves made connection with a limb region they had not previously supplied. Their new terminal connections would reimprint them so that they lost their old functional synaptic connections in the central nervous system and regrew centrally until they reached the proper central neurons. This might involve reimprinting a series of neurons but eventually one that would contact the proper muscle fibers would have to be reached.

It seems to be implicit in this view that there is a right point somewhere in the central nervous system for a nerve specified by a point in an end organ. This would seem to require a large number of inherently detailed matching points in the central nervous system and in the peripheral innervated spots.

Other experimental observations seem to require either resonance behavior or respecification of nerves after regeneration or both. Sensory nerves supplying the hind limb of a tadpole were excised. The limb was resupplied by nerves migrating in from the trunk. These were not limb nerves originally. After metamorphosis normal cutaneous reflexes originating in the limb were observed (Miner, 1951). This was not a case of relearning through experience. Such reflexes are perfect from the beginning.

The same relationship was observed when long strips of skin from sides of tadpoles were inverted so that the original ventral end came to lie in the back. Nerves grew into the strip. Supposedly nearby nerves grew in. If so, dorsal nerves were innervating a ventral piece of skin. When the ventral skin, now on the back and supplied with dorsal nerves was stimulated, the frog scratched its underside (Miner, 1951; Sperry, 1951). Either reimprinting of afferent fibers occurred making them "ventral" fibers or the nerves transmitted a ventral pattern of impulses. If the fibers were redifferentiated as ventral fibers, they would then, according to the view of Sperry, ramify centrally until they met and contacted other neurons of the appropriate ventral reflex pathway.

However regeneration of complex function is accomplished, the studies in this area, more than any other area, demonstrate the high degree of matching differentiation of peripheral organs and central nervous system. It would appear that a local differentiated area, possibly a single cell, can induce a change in a neuron so specific that that neuron will establish the appropriate series of central connections leading to the establishment of an appropriate reflex. The regeneration of this function is so well ordered that irritation of the former ventral end of an inverted strip leads to a coordinated sweep of a limb over the place where it used to be.

As the newer theories of nerve correlation and learning develop, it may be necessary to amend the notion that the identical circuitry within the nervous system is reestablished during regeneration. There is now reason to believe that nerves with the same periodicity can be brought into phase as they operate together (Adey et al., 1963). The pulsing together rather than exact positions in a circuit may be the important relationship reestablished during regeneration. The resonance principle still seems to best fit the many observations.

V. Regeneration of Appendages

A. SOURCE OF REGENERATING CELLS

It was relatively easy for the source of regenerating cells to be determined in the eye (Section III). The cells are naturally marked with pigment and their transformations can be followed part way because the pigment persists for a time. The problem in the appendages has been a persistent one but appears at last to have been solved.

The first students of limb regeneration assumed that each old tissue produced more of itself. Doubt arose after it was shown that part of a fibula did not have to be present in a stump for a new fibula to regenerate perfectly (Reed, 1903). Later it became apparent that no skeleton at all need be present in the stump for new to appear from the blastema (Fritsch,

1911; Weiss, 1925b; Bischler, 1926). Likewise dermis was not needed in a stump for it to appear in a regenerate (Weiss, 1927).

After this the consensus of opinion was that there must be a reserve of undifferentiated cells available for the production of a tissue not represented in the stump. This was during the long period dominated by the belief that differentiation results from segregation and that therefore differentiation is irreversible.

Overlapping the time when most investigators favored the reserve cell hypothesis was a period in which structure after structure and tissue after tissue were observed in histological time series to lose organization. There was some death of cells during this process but many cells were seen to survive and were thought to be the source of the mesenchymal cells of the blastema. Connective tissue, skeletal tissues, neurilemma, and muscle were reported to contribute cells. In addition blood cells and epidermis were described as transforming to mesenchyme (rev. by Rose, 1948b; Manner, 1953; Chalkley, 1959).

Chalkley (1954, 1959), in comprehensive and valuable studies, demonstrated that mitoses occur among all tissues of the limb stump during blastema formation. Before Chalkley's work it was generally suspected that the amount of cell division was insufficient to account for the accumulation of a blastema. Now it is clear that there is enough cell division after amputation to provide the cells of the blastema. This is an important advance. It indicates that one need not invoke reserve cells, or any one tissue as *the* source of blastema cells. It in itself, however, does not eliminate the possibility that reserve cells, epidermis, and blood cells contribute to the mesenchymal portion of the blastema.

Rose (1948b) working with the same species, *Triturus viridescens*, had described a loss of cells from the inner portion of the apical epidermal cap of approximately 20,000 cells at the time that a roughly corresponding number of mesenchymal regeneration cells appeared under the epidermal cap. Cells that were still in the epidermal region developed spaces between them, took on the appearance of mesenchymal regeneration cells, developed the cytoplasmic processes of mesenchymal cells, and stained like them (Ide-Rozas, 1936; Rose, 1948b).

Chalkley (1954, 1959) could not confirm the loss of epidermal cells reported by Bassina (1940) and by Rose (1948b). There was a difference in the operations. After amputation of the limb Chalkley cut the protruding bone away. Rose left the bone protruding and thus left a scaffold on which a larger epidermal mound accumulated. This may not be the entire reason for the difference. There are other divergent descriptions of epidermal behavior during regeneration that may be pertinent.

Quite generally, many careful observers do not see evidence of an epidermal contribution to the mesenchymal portion of a blastema. However, others—Godlewski (1928), Rose (1948b), Hay (1952), Peadon (1953), Roguski (1953), Taban (1955), and Scheuing and Singer (1957)—have all noted epidermal cells entering the inner regions of limb stumps and losing integrity as a tissue. Scheuing and Singer (1957) did not observe great migration of cells from the epidermal wound epithelium at the surface into the inner parts of a stump after simple amputation. When amputation was accompanied by injection of beryllium nitrate into the stump, epidermal cells migrated into the interior regions. The description of the behavior of the epidermis when it was migrating internally following internal injections of beryllium nitrate is much like the description of normal epidermal behavior (Rose, 1948b) but more massive and more easily recognized. Singer and Salpeter (1961) have shown that epidermis regularly migrates into the internal parts of a stump. They stress its phagocytic action there. Over the years the number of descriptions of cases of the conversion of an epidermal tissue to free cells in the central portion of a limb stump has been increasing. At the same time there are observers in other laboratories who do not observe this change.

When one studies all of the evidence it appears that the amount of epidermal transformation must vary considerably from case to case and laboratory to laboratory. The most enlightening cases come from those who have seen a real difference in the amount of this transformation. Scheuing and Singer (1957) saw great transformation when beryllium nitrate was injected into a stump. There was much less epidermal transformation, possibly none, when this noxious material was not injected. Rose (1948b) regularly increased the NaCl content of the culture water and always observed some transformation.

Schmidt (1958a,b), working with *Triturus* as had others before him, found that added thyroid did not prevent regeneration. All who had gone before found the opposite (Section VI, C). An epidermal difference may have been the basic difference. The general rule is that the wound epithelium becomes more squamous after thyroid treatment. In many of Schmidt's cases the epithelium became cuboidal and had the appearance now known to be associated with limb regeneration. He mentioned adding Aqua-Aid to the culture water. There is now enough evidence to lead one to suspect that the behavior of the epidermis in regeneration can be varied considerably by a variety of treatments.

So far it has become clear that the character of the epidermis changes considerably during regeneration. There is still the question of whether the epidermal cells that move into the inner regions of a stump can transform to tissues of their new neighborhoods.

The first attempts to learn whether skin or just the epidermis of the skin can transform to other tissues during limb regeneration were made with skin marked in some way. Pigmentation and variations in ploidy were used as markers (Hertwig, 1927; Umanski, 1937; Hay, 1952). All of these early attempts left doubts. Epidermal cells entered the blastema region and the pigmentation of the internal parts of a regenerate might be like that of the skin but there was always the possibility that only pigment cells had moved from the skin to the inner parts of the regenerated limb. It was also quite clear that much of the tissue in these homoplastic transplantations was reacted against by the host and was being eliminated.

Recently the problem of the possible origin of part of the blastema from epidermis has been reinvestigated by the use of radioactive labeling. Tritiated thymidine which is taken up into the nuclei where deoxyribonucleic acid (DNA) is being synthesized will distinguish those cells that were making DNA at the time of injection of the tritiated thymidine. The nuclei containing the relatively long-lived H^3 will continue to emit electrons for a number of years. Radioautographs prepared from histological sections of normal limbs of *Triturus* indicate that the epidermis is the only tissue in the limb that always has many cells producing DNA. Quite often almost every cell in the germinal layer of the epidermis can be labeled. Hay and Fischman (1961) after labeling the epidermis at about the time of amputation found that both the epidermis over the stump and the newly migrated wound epithelium labeled. The labeling in the wound epithelium was quite light. After a blastema had formed there was very little label in the blastema. If, however, labeling was delayed for 5 or more days after amputation both internal cells and epidermis labeled. Such limbs if allowed to develop until a blastema formed showed considerable label in the blastema. The conclusion was that, since very little label appeared in the blastemas when only the epidermis had been labeled and that since most of the cells of the blastema were labeled when both internal cells and epidermis had been labeled, the internal cells which had been labeled were producing the blastema.

A reinvestigation with the same methods but with slight modifications has led to a different conclusion (Rose and Rose, 1964). In the original Hay and Fischman work 1.25 μcuries of the radioactive material was injected per dose into the newts. The resulting label in the wound epithelium was quite weak. A much more intense labeling is achieved by using 3.33-μcurie doses. It appears that a wound epithelium, far removed from blood vessels, can only be labeled well when the dose is increased. When the wound epithelium is well labeled and the internal tissues are not, the label appears in most of the mesenchymal blastema cells and can later be seen in tissues differentiating from the blastema.

Another way to clearly demonstrate that labeled epidermis becomes mesenchymal tissue and then internal tissues is to increase the time of exposure of the photographic emulsion to the action of the emissions from the H³. The exposure time used by Hay and Fischman of 3 weeks is insufficient for distinguishing labeled nuclei at blastema time if the general background contains many silver grains. If the time of exposure of the emulsion is increased by 3 or 4 times nuclei that could not be distinguished from the background are seen to be clearly labeled. It appears that much of the distal mesenchymal portion of a blastema arises from epidermis.

This runs counter to the conclusion of Riddiford (1960). Apical caps were exchanged between tritiated and nontritiated limb stumps 9 to 13 days after amputation. In one combination the apical cap was heavily labeled and the internal tissues were not. The labeled cells of the epidermis were seen later, not in the inner layer of the epidermis, but were underlain by unlabeled epidermis. The labeled epidermal cells moved further out in the cap and were presumably lost. The original works by Rose (1948b) and Hay (1952) indicate that epidermis continues to migrate into the apical cap from the old epidermis of the stump during blastema formation. This migrating epidermis takes its place beneath the original wound epithelium and would be in a position to transform to regeneration cells. The labeled apical caps used by Riddiford were reinforced in their inner layers by unlabeled epidermis. Presumably this unlabeled epidermis in the position to form blastema came from the unlabeled epidermis of the stump (Rose and Rose, 1964). This belief is strengthened by the observation of Riddiford that the unlabeled cap on a labeled stump became indistinguishably labeled from the epidermis of the stump. The Riddiford conclusion was that epidermal cells had been migrating through the internal parts of the stump when it was labeled and that they had subsequently returned to the epidermis. More in keeping with all of the observations is that the cells which came to lie in the lower parts of the cap had migrated to that position from the labeled epidermis of the stump. When all of the experimental data are synthesized, the only conclusion is that the first epidermis to cover the wound of amputation and to form the young apical cap is followed by more epidermis which makes the lower part of the cap, and it is this portion of the cap that transforms to mesenchyme. It is also quite clear that tissues other than epidermis revert to a mesenchymal condition during blastema formation.

B. STATE OF DIFFERENTIATION IN BLASTEMA

The state of differentiation of the cells that constitute the blastema has been a matter of discussion by light microscopists for some years. Regeneration cells all had a mesenchymal appearance and no differences indicating their tissue of origin were apparent (rev. by Schotté, 1940; Polezhayev,

1945). The electron microscope has now been employed in this study. Hay (1958, 1959, 1962) has been able to confirm with electronmicrographs the descriptions of Butler (1933) and David (1934) indicating a conversion of chondrocytes to blastema cells and Thornton's (1938) description of the transformation of multinucleate muscle fibers to mononucleate blastema cells. Muscle fibers fragment leaving portions of the cytoplasm with single nuclei. In a mononucleate fragment of the syncytial fiber, myofibrils dissolve along the A- and I-bands and then disintegrate. Myofibrils have been seen in blastema cells as tell-tale reminders of their tissue of origin (Fig. 4). In time all blastema cells, whatever their source, lose all distinguishing characteristics and all assume the same structure. The nucleus enlarges and becomes round. Nucleoli become more prominent. The endoplasmic reticulum which may have been complex is represented by isolated vesicles. Concurrently the number of free ribosomes increases greatly. The observed features, the same in all cells, indicate a high degree of morphological dedifferentiation (Hay, 1962).

Another feature of blastema formation is that intercellular materials such as collagen and cartilaginous matrix disappear. Other evidence that special intracellular materials disappear comes from serological studies. DeHann (1956) and Laufer (1959) find no evidence of muscle proteins in that period when myofibrils have disappeared.

As tissues begin to form anew from the blastema, cellular organelles assume their special forms and relationships. For example, as cartilaginous matrix develops around some cells their Golgi apparatus changes from a relatively simple structure and becomes a complex of lamellae, vacuoles, and vesicles. At the same time parallel cisternae of the endoplasmic reticulum arise (Hay, 1958).

The above relationships were observed by Hay in larval *Ambystoma* limbs. Salpeter and Singer (1960) in a similar study with the electron microscope but using adult limbs of *Triturus* find the same general loss of structure during blastema formation. Such things as myofibrillae and cartilaginous matrix are lost, but small bits of collagen may remain attached to cells at least for a time.

Salpeter and Singer did not observe extensive fragmentation of the endoplasmic reticulum in the cells of the blastema on adult *Triturus* limbs. Furthermore they report different types of complicated endoplasmic reticulum in the blastema cells. There is a suggestion that the different types of endoplasmic reticulum might indicate incompletely dedifferentiated cell types and that each might revert to its tissue of origin. Against this view of a possible stability of cell types, is the fact that cartilage, bone, and dermis can be missing from a stump, yet blastema cells will produce them (Section V, A).

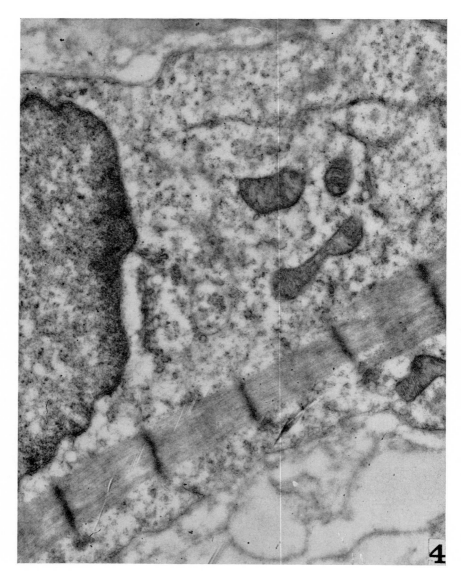

Fig. 4. An electronmicrograph of a portion of a young blastema cell. Extending diagonally across the lower part of the photograph is a still recognizable myofibril indicating the origin of this cell. (The photograph was kindly furnished by Dr. Elizabeth D. Hay.)

The light microscope and electron microscope studies both indicate that cells lose all or most of their tissue-specific characteristics. Associated with this type of evidence for dedifferentiation is the fact that the simplified cells of the blastema do not have to rise from a particular tissue in order to produce that tissue. As noted above various tissues may be lacking in a stump yet form from blastema cells. Whether blastema cells dedifferentiate to the point that they can transform to tissues of another region of the body is another question (Section VII).

C. ADDITION OF NORMAL TISSUES TO X-RAYED LIMBS

A method used to determine what structures and tissues can provide cells for regeneration is based on the discovery that X-irradiation in the range of 1000 r–10,000 r applied locally will prevent limb and tail regeneration (Litschko, 1930; Butler, 1931, 1933, 1935; rev. by Brunst, 1950b). The effect is quite local. A limb irradiated near the elbow will not regenerate if cut through the irradiated portion but will regenerate if cut either above or below the irradiated region (Scheremetjewa and Brunst, 1938; Butler and O'Brien, 1942).

The same dosage that prevents growth of a limb also prevents regeneration (Brunst and Scheremetjewa, 1933; Scheremetjewa and Brunst, 1935). The X-rayed limbs although capable of maintenance for years were incapable of appreciable growth or regeneration (Brunst and Scheremetjewa, 1937; Scheremetjewa and Brunst, 1937). A mitotically active blastema was never observed.

With the above knowledge and the assumption that the mitotic mechanism was irreparably damaged it was possible to design experiments to test what structures and tissues can contribute regeneration cells. Limbs or tails were X-rayed with sufficient dosage to prevent regeneration. Unirradiated tissues were grafted to such appendages. The original work by Umanski (1937) and by Thornton (1942) clearly showed that limbs rendered incapable of regeneration by X-irradiation recovered that ability to a degree after unirradiated structures were grafted to them. The structures that were found capable of supporting regeneration and presumably furnishing the cells for it were skin, bones, and muscles. Muscle and bone enable the limb to form no regenerates or poor or fair ones. Those arising on X-rayed appendages provided with unirradiated skin are consistently better and approach the normal in morphology and size (rev. by Goss, 1957a; Trampusch, 1959; Lazard, 1959).

Limbs X-rayed from the elbow down were amputated through the forearm. At the same time half of the limbs were stripped of their skin back to a region above the elbow where the upper limb had been shielded from the X-rays. An un-X-rayed epidermal wound epithelium migrated down over the X-rayed stump and formed an apical cap. These limbs regenerated all structures (Rose *et al.*, 1955). This indicated that internal tissues of the regenerate had arisen from epidermis. However, there is reason to believe that X-rayed tissues may be reactivated by the migrating normal epidermis.

An attempt to use un-X-rayed skin of a different color than that of a stripped X-rayed stump has indicated that the transplanted skin may cause recovery without contributing cells (Trampusch, 1959). Limbs of white axolotls were rendered incapable of regenerating by X-irradiation. The shoulder and rest of the body were shielded from the X-rays. The X-rayed white limbs were stripped of skin and un-X-rayed black skin transplanted as a covering. The limbs regenerated. In most cases (81) the regenerating limbs were gray during the early stages and then became black as though they had arisen from the black skin. Internal tissues as well as skin were heavily pigmented. This is normal for a black axolotl which does not have its pigment limited to the skin. These 81 cases indicated that skin, possibly both epidermis and dermis or either one, was providing regeneration cells for all tissues.

There were 3 cases in which the black skin transplant moved to the tip of the limb and disappeared. Still the limbs regenerated and they were unpigmented. The suggestion was made that the normal skin as it glided over the X-rayed tissue caused it to recover its regenerative ability. One regenerate was partly black and partly white. According to this interpretation the regenerate would have come partly from the transplant and partly from recovered X-rayed tissue.

It would be very important if irradiated tissues could be made to recover, but there is another explanation in keeping with other studies. X-rayed limbs provided with unirradiated skin or even epidermis alone can regenerate (cited above). In the 3 cases of Trampusch when the black transplant diappeared from the distal tip it was followed by white tissue. It had been shown earlier that the epidermis of a haploid skin transplant put on a knee region of a diploid host just proximal to a surface of amputation glides to the end of the limb. It is followed by diploid host epidermis of the thigh (Hay, 1952). Repeatedly epidermis has been watched as it glides over and away from immobile dermal fibers to cover a limb from the shoulder or thigh to a distal amputation surface. Since only the limb was X-rayed in the Trampusch experiment, the white epidermis which followed the disappearing dark epidermis had an excellent chance of having come from the shielded area. In this case un-X-rayed tissue might have been providing the regeneration cells.

As far as we know at this time X-rayed tissues do not recover regenerative ability, but the possibility must remain open. Recent work by Stinson

(1962a, b) reaffirms the generally held belief that X-rayed tissues do not regain regenerative ability. Unirradiated living tissues when grafted to X-rayed limbs result in regeneration. Unirradiated and boiled or frozen or ethanol-treated or simply X-rayed tissues do not yield regeneration when grafted to X-rayed limbs. The most telling evidence against recovery of X-rayed tissue comes from the result of grafting normal tissues from another individual. A regenerate is produced but it is temporary. Presumably the regenerate has formed from the graft and has been reacted against by the foreign host.

At the same time there have been repeated reports that X-rayed limbs can recover after heavy irradiation either by transplanting quite foreign materials or by injecting homogenates. Sidorova (1951) as quoted by Goss (1957b) observed recovery from radiation induced regenerative failure in axolotl limbs after transplantation of frog muscle or unirradiated lung, liver, or cardiac muscle. Skowron and Roguski (1958) found some recovery after injecting a mixture of cell fragments, isolated cells, and small cell aggregates from nonirradiated limbs or tails. Although the regenerates were poor the injected materials determined their regionality. Polezhayev (1960) did not observe recovery of X-rayed axolotl limbs on shielded bodies after transplantation of pieces of limb muscles but did after injection of limb muscle homogenates from axolotls or rats. In fact the rat muscle homogenate seemed more effective. One wonders how the recovery is effected. X-rayed limbs may maintain themselves for years receiving migrant blood cells and fluids from the unirradiated body fluids but do not recover regenerative ability (Brunst and Scheremetjewa, 1937). What can an injection of a foreign tissue homogenate do that normal blood cannot?

This work has now been extended (Polezhayev, 1960; Polezhayev and Ermakova, 1960) and it is quite clear that heavily irradiated limbs can regenerate in an appreciable percentage of the cases after a variety of foreign materials have been injected. Most of the workers a few years ago were using the hypothesis that the various foreign tissues and homogenates are adding a necessary substance that the X-rayed tissue can no longer produce.

There is an alternative, and one is needed in the light of the recent findings that X-rayed limbs can regain regenerative ability even when nothing is added. A high percentage of X-rayed limbs that were reamputated at 30 days through the X-rayed region regenerated and the outgrowth came from an area that had been X-rayed (Polezhayev and Ermakova, 1960; Polezhayev et al., 1961).

A variety of experiences make it appear that the apparent recovery from X-irradiation may be illusory. First, it is a fact that tissue can come from some distance in back of an X-rayed distal portion of a stump and produce a regenerate there. The greater the length of the X-rayed segment to be traversed, the less chance for regeneration (Wolff and Wey-Schué, 1952). In all of the experiments where recovery was accomplished the X-rayed limbs were attached to bodies that had been shielded. There is the possibility that the injections of foreign materials or the foreign grafts attract cells from the shielded upper arm or body. The fact that rat muscle homogenates were more effective in stimulating axolotl regeneration than were axolotl homogenates (Polezhayev, 1959) suggests that reaction to foreign materials is involved. One thing the epidermis does in regeneration is act as a scavenger tissue invading the inner parts of a stump where it picks up cellular debris. (Singer and Salpeter, 1961) (see Section VI, A). If rat homogenates are injected repeatedly one would expect much epidermis to invade the stump, as happened when Scheuing and Singer injected noxious materials into stumps. This would be expected to cause epidermis to migrate in from a distance, even from the shielded region. An X-rayed limb covered with unirradiated epidermis can regenerate (Rose et al., 1955; Rose and Rose, 1964; S. M. Rose, 1962). Thus we see a distinct possibility that X-rayed tissues do not recover but are added to or replaced. One can observe that heavily irradiated limbs are more likely to regress. After a dosage of only 2000 r to the limb of Triturus viridescens one does not obtain recovery. Higher doses, enough to cause spontaneous loss of fingers, may be followed by apparent recovery of regenerative ability in X-rayed regions (Rose and Rose, 1964). Analysis by histological time series indicated that shortly after amputation of a limb which had received more than 2500 r there was an abnormally great loss of cells. In time, however, the X-rayed segment of the limb was repopulated by cells that divided, grew, and produced regenerates. These behaved differently than did the former occupants of the segment and presumably were migrants from a shielded area.

It became clear that the internal parts of an X-rayed segment, for example of the forearm, were repopulated by large numbers of blood cells and by epidermis. When tritiated thymidine was injected into a newt within 1 day of the time of amputation of the limb, the two tissues which labeled were epidermis and blood. Just as in the case of un-X-rayed limbs, the only tissue that had most of its cells labeled was the germinal layer of the epithelium. Also as in the case of normal limbs the percentage of labeled cells in the internal tissues of the distal part of the regenerate was high, sometimes over 80%. Never did one find anywhere near this percentage of the blood cells labeled. Only the epidermis had a majority of its cells labeled (Rose and Rose, 1964).

This clearly indicates that the X-rayed cells do not recover and make an appreciable part of a regenerate. They may produce some of it, but the high percentage of labeled cells in the regenerate indicates repopulation of the X-rayed segment by former epidermal cells.

It has been clear for some years that X-rayed stumps cannot control the organization of un-X-rayed tissues grafted to them. The basic reason for failure of X-rayed tissues to regenerate may not be a failure of cell division and growth *per se* but a failure to transmit morphogenetic information (Section VII).

VI. Roles of Special Structures

A. THE APICAL CAP

The X-ray studies suggest some special role played by the epidermis in regeneration. Other kinds of studies indicate the same thing.

Tornier (1906) and Schaxel (1921) observed that a salamander limb stump sealed by whole skin does not regenerate. Godlewski (1928) then discovered that an amputation wound on a tail need be free of skin for only a day or so to get regeneration started. He could prevent regeneration by sewing a complete skin over the amputation surface at the time of amputation. However, if the tail was not sealed with whole skin until a day after amputation it might proceed to form a blastema and that blastema could later erode its way through the grafted skin. Jeffimoff (1931, 1933; rev. by Poležajew and Favorina, 1935; Poležajew, 1936) then demonstrated that the necessary condition for regeneration was an epidermal layer in direct contact with the underlying mesodermal tissues without a dermal barrier between them.

An epidermal sheet can migrate over the cut surface of a limb stump within a day and even though whole skin, epidermis plus dermis, is later grafted directly over it the combination of epidermis and underlying tissues may allow regeneration to proceed. What one observes next is loss of internal structure and the building of a blastema. This does not happen unless epidermis and internal tissues are in direct contact. Limbs stripped of skin and unprovided with the epidermal cap do not form a blastema (Poležajew and Favorina, 1935; Morosow, 1938; Goss, 1957a). There is an often expressed belief that because the epidermis is rich in proteolytic activity (Orechowitsch and Bromley, 1934; Adova and Feldt, 1939) it may function as a source of enzymes acting to remove intercellular materials during dedifferentiation. Apparently this idea has not been tested directly.

A study of anuran tadpole limbs indicated that those still capable of regeneration do form the broad epidermal-mesodermal junction. Later, after regenerative ability has disappeared, the skin is looser and contracts over a wound with dermis interposed over most of the wound surface between epidermis and the cut internal tissues (Schotté and Harland, 1943).

There is very little internal dedifferentiation in these nonregenerating limbs. Similarly nonregenerating limbs of postmetamorphic frogs after amputation fail to establish a lasting dermis-free barrier between epidermis and internal tissues (Rose, 1948b).

The change occurring during metamorphosis of the anurans that limits regenerative ability in limbs is not confined to the epidermis. Polezhayev (1939, 1946a), by making the various combinations of epithelium and mesoderm from limbs still capable of regeneration and others past that stage, showed that both ectodermal and mesodermal tissues change so that neither one in the older state can cooperate with a younger partner to produce a limb.

Postmetamorphic frogs were induced to regenerate partial limbs by treating the stumps with strong NaCl solutions (Rose 1942, 1944, 1945). Sometimes treatments were initiated after an epidermal membrane covered the wound. No change was apparent for some time. Eventually a dermis-free epithelium appeared and internal dedifferentiation was observed.

This much seems clear from the early work. Unobstructed contact of epidermis and internal tissues without a dermal barrier is a prerequisite for extensive internal dedifferentiation, blastema formation, and distal outgrowth.

In recent years Thornton has shown the importance of the epidermal cap and its junction region with the underlying mesodermal tissues in several ways. A. E. Needham (1941) had shown that beryllium nitrate is an effective local agent in preventing tail regeneration. If after treatment just the distal half millimeter of the tail is removed, regeneration can occur. What beryllium nitrate does is done very close to or at the amputation surface.

A. E. Needham (1941) and Thornton (1949, 1950) have both demonstrated that the effect of beryllium nitrate is one that occurs very shortly after amputation or at the time of amputation. Needham suggested that it might block the effect of a wound hormone released at the time of amputation. If a limb is dipped in the solution immediately before amputation and then washed before amputation, regeneration occurs. There is no regeneration if limbs are dipped at the time of amputation. Once the wound epithelium has covered the stump, only 6 hours after amputation, the limb is insensitive to the treatment and will regenerate.

Scheuing and Singer (1957) injected beryllium ion into limbs with the Singer microinfusion apparatus (Singer et al., 1955). The tissues of unamputated limbs were quite insensitive to concentrations that caused extensive necrosis of blastema tissue. The effect is not that of an anti-mitotic or some other effect as with colchicine and other compounds that can prevent regeneration (Lehmann and Bretscher, 1962). Instead cells were destroyed and extensive resorption was observed. Injection into a blastema left the wound epithelium mitotically active. Tongues of epidermal cells were seen to invade the blastema and assisted in the elimination of debris.

The internal effects of beryllium treatments of amputation wounds of *Ambystoma* larvae convert them to something resembling a nonregenerating frog stump (Thornton, 1951). An epidermis normal in appearance spreads over the wound, but sometime later there is strong retraction of soft tissues and protrusion of bone. The wound is repaired by epidermis but now a heavy basement membrane develops between epidermis and internal tissues. Some new cartilage and connective tissue develop but in the typical form of the nonregenerating limb.

The apical cap free of dermis has been shown by other methods to be important. If the cap is irradiated daily with ultraviolet light (UV) of 2537Å wavelength, even though no UV is getting through the cap, as tested by application of phosphors to the inner surface, regeneration can be prevented for 30 days, the length of the experiment. If the cap is six cells thick when daily irradiation begins, most of the light is absorbed in the outer layers and regeneration proceeds at half the normal rate. Under these conditions blastema cells gradually accumulate under the cap. Apparently the inner part of the cap even when the outer part is receiving UV can function fairly well (Thornton, 1958).

Thornton saw striking differences between the irradiated epithelium and the normal cap. The irradiated epithelium is thickened and consists of mature cells including the secretory Leydig cells whereas the normal wound epithelium consists of undifferentiated cells that exhibit many mitoses. Thornton points out that the failure of a blastema to form is correlated with the failure of a mitotically proliferating apical cap to develop in the irradiated wound epithelium.

Another experiment by Thornton (1957) points up the necessity for the continued presence of this bit of apical tissue. The wound epithelium was stripped from limbs of larval *Ambystoma* every day. In *Ambystoma tigrinum* this prevented limb regeneration and in *Ambystoma maculatum* regeneration proceeded, but slowly. In *A. maculatum*, which was only slowed down, migration of a new epithelium was more rapid and an apical epidermal layer covered the amputation surface at least half of each day.

A variety of treatments can stimulate the formation of extra limbs (Section VII). Balinsky (1957) and Thornton (1958) emphasize that all of these treatments lead to the formation of epithelium minus basement membrane. An apical cap free of a basement membrane has been observed during normal regeneration by all recent workers. There are a few cases in which apical cap and blastema formation seem normal, and failure results later, as for example with nitrogen mustard treatments (Skowron and Roguski, 1958). In most cases when regeneration fails and for whatever reason, including those already mentioned, and because of abnormal hormone concentrations (Section VI, C) and treatment with P^{32} (Dent, 1949) and neutrons (Horn, 1942) an active apical cap free of a basement membrane is not established. So far, it appears to be an absolute requirement for limb regeneration.

An apical cap or ridge is also necessary during ontogeny of the vertebrate limb (Saunders, 1948; Tschumi, 1956, 1957; Zwilling, 1956). On both embryonic and older limbs during regeneration it is necessary for continued outgrowth. In addition it is required for dedifferentiation, the accumulation of a blastema, and possibly for one further step associated with differentiation (Thornton, 1956) during regeneration.

Two suggestions as to how the cap may function during regeneration are currently serving as hypotheses. Singer and Salpeter (1961) have emphasized the phagocytic and organization-destroying features of the internally migrating cap cells. Roguski (1953) and Taban (1955) have also reported extensive phagocytosis by the epidermal cells.

Thornton (1954) points out that where the cap forms mesenchymal cells will accumulate. This seems to be an important role of the apical cap during regeneration and is being considered as a possible role during embryonic development (Zwilling, personal communication). There is no doubt now that the epidermal cap is involved in loss of old structure internally and the accumulation of a blastema.

Closely allied with the apical cap in the promotion of limb regeneration are the limb nerves.

B. NERVES

Tweedy John Todd (1823) reported that salamander limbs do not regenerate if their nerves are severed. He further stated that division of the nerve causes a regenerate already developing to shrivel and waste. This knowledge lay dormant for many years. The relationship, denervation—no regeneration, was reaffirmed by Wolff (1910) and by Walter (1912). Doubts crept in because sometimes delayed regeneration followed denervation. Schotté (1926) in a definitive work clearly demonstrated that regeneration does not begin until after nerves have regenerated and repopulated the region adjacent to the level of amputation. The fact that regeneration fails in denervated limbs has been clearly established (rev. by Rose, 1948a; Singer, 1952, 1959a).

The next clearly established fact is that intact reflex pathways are not necessary for the action of the nerves in regeneration. Locatelli (1929) demonstrated that a sensory supply alone, and even a part of the sensory supply is sufficient. Motor fibers supplying a hind limb could be severed and all dorsal root ganglia except one extirpated and regeneration would proceed. Furthermore, this one ganglion, the 18th spinal, could be separated from the spinal cord and sometimes regeneration was unaffected. If in addition the 18th ganglion was removed leaving the nerve fibers without their cell bodies, there was no regeneration of limbs. The impression at this time was that the dorsal root ganglion had a regeneration-promoting quality peculiar to itself.

This notion was shown to be incorrect in a series of works by Singer (1946, 1952). It is true that the sensory is the only one of the three components: sensory, motor, and sympathetic, that can support regeneration alone. However, when combinations of sensory and motor nerves were left intact and others in the three spinal nerves supplying the anterior limb in *Triturus* were severed, a new relationship emerged. Limb regeneration in *Triturus viridescens* adults requires one-third to one-half the total number of fibers. This threshold can be met by sensory fibers alone or by a combination of sensory and motor fibers. The sensory component has many more fibers than the others and is the only one to surpass the threshold requirement. However, if dorsal and ventral roots are cut and sensory fibers deflected from a limb, a pure motor supply can be obtained that does support limb regeneration. In conformity with the demonstration that number of fibers is important, is the fact that motor fibers regenerating into a nerveless limb bifurcate and rebifurcate until they produce more than the threshold number of fibers. It is clearly demonstrated by the work of Singer that sensory and motor fibers can support limb regeneration. It has also been shown that transplanted spinal ganglia can restore regenerative ability to denervated limbs (Kamrin and Singer, 1959).

Another fact clearly established is that nerves have some function other than determining the character or form of a regenerate. Locatelli (1925) deviated limb nerves so that they ended at the surface of the body close to the base of a limb. New limbs developed over the ends of the deviated nerves. At the time the results seemed to indicate that the nerve was determining limb development. The works of the Guyénot school (rev. by Guyénot, 1927) clearly showed that the deviated nerve may stimulate regeneration but that the character of the regenerate was always determined by the territory in which it arose. It is true that a sciatic nerve brought to the surface of the body near the hind limb will induce regeneration and the regenerate will be a hind limb, but the same nerve deviated to the vicinity of the dorsal crest will induce an outgrowth that is a piece of crest. An outgrowth induced by deviation of a limb nerve to the side of a tail is tail-like (rev. by Kiortsis, 1953).

Although limb nerves have not been shown to determine the form of the regeneration they stimulate, it cannot be concluded that neural tissue in general does not participate in the control of pattern around it. It certainly does in the case of central nervous tissue and may be the major form-controlling agent in embryonic development and during the regeneration of a tail (Holtzer *et al.*, 1955; Holtzer, 1959). If a portion of spinal cord is grafted to the left or right muscle mass of the tail of a larval salamander a series of induced centra may arise along the motor surface of the cord (S. Holtzer, 1956). Clearly the spinal cord can determine the patterning of the axial structures around it in an embryo (Holtzer and Detwiler, 1953). Furthermore, when the spinal cord of a young larva was inverted and put back in place the vertebrae developed upside down with respect to the rest of the animal but in the proper relationship to the spinal cord (Holtzer, 1959).

There is no doubt that a spinal cord can control the nature of tissue adjacent to it, but limb nerves seem not to. This leaves us to search for another function of nerves.

The time when nerves act during limb regeneration furnishes a clue to their mode of action. Limbs have been denervated at different times after amputation and the effect on regeneration studied (Schotté and Butler, 1941, 1944; Singer and Craven, 1948; Butler and Schotté, 1949). Limb regeneration can proceed without nerves once a blastema resembling an embryonic limb bud has formed. Such a blastema is an epithelial covering densely packed with mesenchymal cells (Fig. 1). Both epithelium and mesenchyme are growing very rapidly. Denervation at this time decreases the rate of cell division after a temporary spurt (Singer and Craven, 1948). The regenerate will be smaller but well patterned with tissues normally arranged. Sometimes fingers and toes are small and abnormal. The distal abnormalities seem to arise when the denervated blastema is too small (Guyénot and Schotté, 1923; Schotté, 1926).

It is of interest that the embryonic limb bud does not require nerves for its conversion to a limb (Harrison, 1904; Hamburger, 1928). Once the regeneration blastema resembles an embryonic limb bud it does not need nerves either. The importance of nerves is to be sought in the period before the blastema is a compact conical outgrowth. The nerves are needed during the period when old structure is being lost, when tissues are becoming cells, and when a mass of cells is accumulating. Butler and Schotté (1949) emphasize that this period during which nerves are needed is the period of induction when the bud is being determined. Not until it has been specified as a limb and could develop into one on a foreign part of the body does the blastema cease to need nerves. This may be the most important clue. The nerves may be involved, directly or indirectly, in the transmission of morphogenetic "messages" to the undifferentiated cells (see discussions by Butler and Schotté, 1949; Thornton in Singer, 1959a).

In summary, one can say that nerves are needed during the period after limb amputation when the distalmost part of the stump is transforming to a bud capable of forming the missing distal structures.

If an adult limb is denervated at the time of amputation there is very little loss of structure (Rose, 1948a). A larval limb (Butler and Schotté, 1941; Schotté and Butler, 1941) or an adult limb with a regenerate (Schotté and Liversage, 1959) does lose structure after denervation and amputation. An adult limb appears to have achieved a level of tissue stability that requires nerves for dedifferentiation. The larval limb and the regenerate on an adult are less stable and can lose structure without nerves. However, some larval limbs do lose the ability to revert from tissues to cells and do not regress if they are denervated 4 days before amputation (Karczmar, 1946). Even though larval limbs can lose structure in the absence of nerves they do not accumulate a mass of cells at the distal tip. Instead the cells seem to migrate away (Schotté and Karczmar, 1944). If a blastema is grafted to such a regressing denervated larval limb regression is stopped (Schotté et al., 1941).

The larval and the adult limb differ in their ability to lose old structure after denervation. Usually they are alike in their complete inability to amass a blastema and transform it to a limb in the absence of nerves. The important function of nerves in both larvae and adults is to be sought in the accumulation and inductive phases (Butler and Schotté, 1949).

The larval and the adult limb are alike in that both fail to accumulate a blastema in the absence of nerves. There are notable exceptions to this general rule in the case of larvae. Polezhayev (1939) with tadpoles and Schneider (1940) with axolotls both found that transplanted limbs could regenerate without nerves. Polezhayev and Ginzburg (1943) observed that old structure was maintained after amputation of limbs of tadpoles too old to regenerate them. Such limbs when transplanted did lose structure and accumulate a blastema. Yntema (1959a) in a careful, well documented study demonstrates that larval limbs that have never had nerves will regenerate without them. Furthermore, when nerves are allowed to enter the nerveless limbs the nerves induce supernumerary parts of limbs and duplicate limbs (Yntema, 1959b). These exceptions to the rule that nerves are necessary may help in the attempt to understand the basic rules of regeneration (Section VII).

It has long been known that there are trophic influences of nerves. How they operate and how they might be involved in limb regeneration has been the concern of Singer and his associates for several years (rev. by Singer, 1959b). An attempt has been made to determine what part if any the acetylcholine mechanism plays. Infusion into limb stumps of atropine, procaine hydrochloride, and tetraethylammonium hydroxide delay and, if used long enough, block regeneration. These are known to block the acetylcholine mechanism, and the substances eserine salicylate, pilocarpine nitrate, methylcholine chloride, and acetylcholine chloride, known to enhance or protect the acetylcholine mechanism, do not interfere with regeneration. Such experiments are consistent with a role, possibly an indirect one, of acetylcholine in limb regeneration. On the other hand there are experiments indicating that regeneration can proceed in the absence of acetylcholine (Singer, 1959b, 1960). It appears that interference with neural activity by upsetting the acetylcholine mechanism may block regeneration but that the positive action of nerves on regeneration may be something other than the secretion of acetylcholine.

There seems to be a basic function carried out by nerves in conjunction with the epidermal wound epithelium. A normal epidermis in a salamander is very poorly innervated but nerve fibers penetrate the epidermal wound epithelium in great numbers (Singer, 1949; Taban, 1949, 1955). The connections between nerve endings and epidermal cells are intimate and as seen in electronmicrographs are of a type found at synapses (Hay, 1960). This intimate contact with epidermal cells, however, is not an absolute requirement for regeneration. When regeneration proceeds with the participation of regenerated efferent nerves alone the fibers do not invade the epidermis (Sidman and Singer, 1960), but end in the subepithelial portion of the stump (Thornton, 1960).

There is some indication that epidermis and nerves function together in the process of limb regeneration. Deviation of nerves long known to stimulate regeneration of extra limbs always causes the epidermal basement membrane at the junction of nerve and epidermis to disappear and an apical cap to appear (Thornton, 1954; Taban, 1955). Under this mitotically active cap mesenchymal cells accumulate (Thornton, 1954, 1956, 1957). It has been suggested that a dermal barrier between epidermis and internal tissues, correlated with failure of regeneration (Rose, 1948), may act by blocking contact of regenerating afferent fibers and epidermis (Singer, 1959a).

Salting apparently stimulated regeneration of frog's limbs by first affecting the epidermis (Rose, 1945). Singer et al. (1957) demonstrated that salting does not induce regeneration if the limbs are denervated. This too indicates the possibility of a functional relationship between epidermis and nerve.

Further evidence of the value of nerves in limb regeneration comes from the fact that naturally nonregenerating limbs of adult frogs can be made to regenerate when the number of nerves is increased. Singer (1954) induced anterior limbs of frogs to regenerate by deviating the sciatic nerves to them. With the normal supply of anterior limb nerves augmented by a posterior limb supply quite good anterior limb regeneration was induced.

A functional relationship between epidermis and nerve is clearly seen in other works as pointed out by Thornton (1953; Singer, 1959a). Both larval and adult salamanders fail to regenerate limbs after denervation. After reinnervation some larval limbs regenerate without further treatment; others fail to regenerate. Those larval limbs that begin to regenerate after reinnervation have a richly innervated apical cap. Those larvae that fail have a dense dermal mat beneath the epidermis and nerves do not make contact with the epidermis. All the adult limbs fail to regenerate after reinnervation and in all a heavy dermis bars contact of nerves and epidermis. When reinnervated adult limbs are reamputated, nerves are able to make contact with epidermis and the limbs regenerate.

Although normally limb regeneration fails if large numbers of afferent fibers fail to contact epidermal cells, limb regeneration can succeed with an augmented efferent supply and with no nerve fibers in the epidermis. In this case some other tissue or tissues must be cooperating with the nerves and doing the work normally done by the epidermis. This work is the control of structural loss and the accumulation of the leftover cells until they are specified as a limb.

C. ENDOCRINE GLANDS

The hormones first attracted students of regeneration because hormone-induced changes occurring during metamorphosis in the Anura when regenerative ability is lost in limbs suggested a possible relationship between hormones and regeneration.

1. *Hypophysis and Thyroid*

a. Urodela. The pioneering was done by Walter (1910), who learned that limb regeneration failed in *Triton* when the thyroid gland was removed, and by Schotté (1926) who demonstrated the need for the pituitary gland during regeneration in *Triton*. These first observations have been confirmed and extended in several directions.

We now know that hypophysectomy does not affect the healing process. Epidermis glides over and seals the wound in normal time. Epidermis begins to pile up distally but dermal fiber begins to differentiate precociously. Normally the under side of the epidermis is free of dermal fiber during blastema formation. In normal regeneration in the period from 10 to 20 days there is extensive loss of structure and formation of a mesenchymal mass. This does not occur in the limbs of hypophysectomized newts. Instead old bone and muscle remain intact almost to their distalmost limits and a new dermal pad forms between the migrated epidermis and the old internal tissues (Hall and Schotté, 1951).

The part of the process that the hypophysis controls occurs early in regeneration. When hypophysectomy was delayed until the compact proliferating blastema stage 20 days after amputation, further regeneration was unimpaired. If the time between amputation and hypophysectomy was shortened to 10 days there was a noticeable effect on some limbs. Some produced normal regenerates and in still others the attempt was abortive. The majority were delayed but normal. When a limb had only a 3- to 10-day headstart before hypophysectomy it might fail to regenerate, produce small abnormal regenerates, or regenerate, but with considerable delay (Schotté and Hall, 1952). The hypophysis is not necessary for normal regeneration from a young regenerate. If a limb bearing a 15- to 30-day regenerate is reamputated through the regenerate, the regeneration from the regenerate does not require the hypophysis. Once a regenerate is a little older, 35–45 days, and new structures are fairly well developed, the hypophysis becomes necessary for limb regeneration again (Schotté and Hilfer, 1957).

A functioning pituitary seems necessary for the considerable loss of limb structure that is involved in the production of a mesenchymal blastema. Without the pituitary the tissue balance is shifted in favor of differentiation. Old tissues fail to dedifferentiate and differentiation of new dermal fiber occurs precociously.

Although hypophysectomy has a profound effect on limb regeneration it does not prevent the transformation of iris to lens (Schotté and Murphy, 1953; Stone and Steinitz, 1953; Stone, 1957). Cellular transformation *per se* seems not to be controlled by the hypophysis.

The thyroid must function within a normal range for limb regeneration to proceed normally. Thyroidectomy (rev. by Lynn and Wachowski, 1951; Schotté and Washburn, 1954), treatment with thiourea (Peadon, 1953), and administration of additional thyroxine (Pawlowsky, 1923; Hay, 1956) all interfere with normal regeneration.

If the thyroid of *Triturus* is removed before blastema formation there is a pronounced lag in dedifferentiation followed by stunting and the production of skeletal abnormalities (Schotté and Washburn, 1954). There seem to be two actions of the thyroid hormone that are partially separable in time. Early removal interferes with dedifferentiation and late removal interferes with growth (Richardson, 1940, 1945; Schotté and Washburn, 1954). Growth retardation in *Triturus* after thyroidectomy was partially compensated for by administration of an anterior pituitary extract

(Richardson, 1945). Added thyroxine has little effect on dedifferentiation but it interferes with growth and differentiation (Hay, 1956).

All of the above experiments with salamanders indicate that interference with the normal control of the thyroid hormone, be this by addition or subtraction, interferes with regeneration. There are two experiments not covered by this generalization and because of this they may be of value in furthering our understanding. Belkin (1934) could find no effect on regeneration of appendages in the axolotl when using concentrations that induce metamorphosis in this normally neotenous form.

Schmidt (1958a,b), in carefully executed and well documented work, shows that thyroidectomy instead of interfering with limb regeneration facilitates it. His predecessors (Richardson, 1940, 1945; Schotté and Washburn, 1954) had found that thyroidectomy delayed dedifferentiation and blastema formation and subsequent growth in *Triturus viridescens*. In contrast Schmidt using the same species observed that dedifferentiation set in precociously and gave his thyroidectomized newts a head start in regeneration that they never lost. Furthermore, the regenerates were normal.

Schmidt noted that the epidermal cap, while building up in both normal and thyroidectomized newts, accumulated faster and became larger after thyroidectomy. Concurrent with rapid enlargement of the blastema the cap thinned out on the limbs of the thyroidectomized animals. Tongues of epidermal cells projected toward the interior of the limb. These tongues are very unusual in a salamander limb but are common in a frog's limb (Rose, 1945). There they project inward as the dermis-free wound epithelium is obliterated and old skin moves in from the periphery. With epidermis of this type one would not expect limb regeneration to proceed normally. Instead regeneration in Schmidt's newts should have been delayed or completely inhibited as it had been in those of Schotté and Washburn. One wonders whether these limbs made to appear histologically like frog's limbs could then have been induced to regenerate by some chemical means as have frogs. The original treatments rendering adult frogs capable of limb regeneration were with concentrated NaCl solutions (Rose, 1942, 1944, 1945). Milder treatments with a variety of chemicals were shown to be equal or better in their effects (Polezhayev, 1946b). Could it be that some additional treatment was making the thyroidectomized newts such good regenerators?

Most of Schmidt's newts were treated with Aqua Aid, a fungicide, used by aquarists. Some others were not treated with it and most of those died. The few untreated survivors would probably not weight the results heavily. It might be important to know whether Aqua Aid, possibly acting in a role other than as a fungicide, can stimulate regeneration by reviving an epidermis made inactive by thyroidectomy. Whether it does or not, true knowledge of the reasons for the exactly opposite results after thyroidectomy might be of great value.

b. Anura. The effects of increasing and decreasing thyroid hormone concentration in Anura are consistently different from those in Urodela. Speidel (1929) and Warren and Bower (1939) found that increasing the hormone concentration during the first few days after amputation inhibited regeneration in tadpoles. A few days later when appreciable growth had started, an increase in hormone was followed by an increased rate of regeneration. These findings are consistent with the hypothesis that limb regeneration in anurans may be blocked as higher concentrations of thyroid hormone are attained during metamorphosis.

Also consistent with the hypothesis are results obtained by the use of antithyroid drugs. If thyroid inhibitors are used prior to amputation, regeneration occurs normally (Ghidoni, 1948). This indicates that a very low level of thyroxine favors the first steps in regeneration in tadpoles. Peadon (1953) using thiourea demonstrated that the step favored is dedifferentiation. Rapid loss of old structure and precocious blastema formation attend the use of this antithyroid drug. In contrast to the effect in salamanders, addition of thyroid hormone is beneficial during growth stages of anuran regenerates. In both groups of animals a decreased amount achieved by use of antithyroid drugs results in decreased growth during late stages.

There is a slight increase in dedifferentiation in limb stumps of older tadpoles treated with thiourea, but if they have passed the stage where regeneration occurs naturally the effect is not great enough to lead to blastema formation (Peadon, 1953). Attempts to revive regenerative ability in adult *Rana pipiens* by a great range of concentrations of thiourea were unsuccessful (Wetstone, private communication). It may be as suggested by Grobstein (1947) that the changes leading to regenerative failure are induced by hormones but once established are no longer dependent upon the hormone.

2. Pituitary, Adrenal Cortex, and Stress

Hypophysectomy in *Triturus viridescens* if performed before or at the time of limb amputation produces the nonregenerating limb with typical histology. As early as 5 days after amputation precocious differentiation of dermal fiber may set in. The unrestricted contact of epidermal cap and inner tissues is blocked and dedifferentiation of muscle and bone is negligible (Hall and Schotté, 1951; Schotté and Hall, 1952).

It is suspected that amputation initiates a stress situation involving greater release of cortical hormones and that this is a part of the complex of factors leading to dedifferentiation in the vicinity of a surface of amputation (Schotté and Lindberg, 1954; Schotté and Chamberlain, 1955; Schotté and Bierman, 1956).

Liversage (1959) demonstrated that there need not be a neural connection between a region of amputation and the adrenal glands for regeneration to occur. All nerves including spinal cord, sympathetic, and lateral line nerves leading to a tail area were cut. The tail stump provided only with local innervation from a portion of isolated spinal cord regenerated. Similarly a transplanted limb with its accompanying isolated segment of spinal cord in a completely denervated tail area could regenerate. In these cases regeneration occurred when there was no possibility of trauma affecting the level of cortical hormones by a wholly neural route. It is still possible that cortical hormones are brought into play after amputation by an effect transmitted to the adrenal cortex at least part way along routes other than a neural one.

That there is a relationship between hormones and regeneration of appendages is now evident. Since the process of dedifferentiation fails when certain hormone situations are produced experimentally, there is reason to suspect that similar changes during development have led to failure of adult Anura to regenerate limbs. Possibly the best evidence is that of Schotté and Wilber (1958) and Mizell (1960) who obtained quite good regeneration in adult frogs by implanting adrenal glands.

VII. Pathways of Control

It has been firmly established that a very small ring of old tissue at the base of a blastema can direct its differentiation (rev. by Guyénot,, 1927; Polezhayev, 1945). A blastema, too young to maintain itself if transplanted to a foreign site, will continue to regenerate if transplanted along with a small disc of old organized tissue at its base (Giorgi, 1924). The disc need be no more than a millimeter thick.

What happens to a young blastema when transplanted without old tissue is still not certain. If a limb or tail stump receives a transplant of a young blastema from another region the regenerate that appears is normal for the host site. Either the host site has taken over control of the foreign blastema or the transplant has been replaced by a blastema from the host site. We shall return to this later.

Now we are concerned only with the fact that a blastema which arises in conjunction with a bit of an appendage will complete the missing distal pattern of that appendage even on another part of the body. Tails have been made to grow on limbs and limbs may grow from the back. A small disc of limb can produce a blastema and control its formation as a limb on the back far from the normal limb position.

Just how the stump controls the form of a regenerating blastema has been the subject of much study. It has become clear that the control is not confined to any one old tissue or structure. The axes of a young blastema can be determined by a ring of whole skin transplanted with it (Milojevic, 1924). If a young blastema is transferred from one anterior limb to another and rotated no evidence of the rotation is apparent after the new limb has developed. Always the regenerate is aligned with the stump, but if a narrow ring of skin is transplanted along with the young blastema the axes are determined by the transplanted skin. For example, when a young blastema with old skin was simply transferred from a left arm to a right arm without rotation, the first finger was lateral rather than medial as would be required by the host site. The skin, dermis and epidermis, can determine the axes.

The skin is certainly not the only structure to exercise control over an attached regenerate. A disc of internal tissue minus the skin can control the quality of the regeneration distal to it (Bischler, 1926). A segment of the tarsal region grafted in place of a femur caused a foot to form distal to it. Had the skin exercised complete control the regenerate would have contained in addition the lower leg between foot and thigh. The rule is that everything distal to but not proximal to stump tissues can form. Here the skinless tarsal graft was controlling the amount and level of regeneration.

Of the internal structures either muscles or bones can control the level and quality of differentiation that occurs distal to them. Tail muscle substituted for limb muscle in limb stumps shared in the control of regeneration. Chimaeras, part tail and part limb, arose (Liosner and Woronzowa, 1937; rev. by Glade, 1957). The tail portions contained vertebrae and tail-like arrangement of skin. This is a case of muscle, actually muscle, blood vessels, and connective tissue, controlling the morphogenesis in other structures composed in part of other tissues.

Bones also can control the form of regeneration distal to them to some extent. Bones have been grafted between anterior and posterior limbs and from different levels of the same or a different limb (rev. by Goss, 1956a). As Goss points out the control by bones is clearly apparent only when a bone from another segment is substituted.

The role of skin has become much clearer in the last few years. Formerly it was believed that skin from other parts of a body if grafted to a limb could either prevent all regeneration or let it proceed as limb regeneration without any effect on morphogenesis. Tornier (1906) had shown that hind limbs stripped of skin and folded up under abdominal skin sometimes formed feet extending out from the surface of the abdomen and these were covered by abdominal skin. Sleeves of ventral or caudal skin grafted to limbs that were subsequently amputated at the graft level regenerated normal limbs (Taube, 1921; Poležajew and Favorina, 1935). Dorsal and cephalic skin sleeves prevented limb regeneration (Umanski, 1937, 1938a;

Poležajew and Favorina, 1935). Even cephalic epidermis alone can prevent limb regeneration when grafted to a limb (Holzmann, 1939). It seemed that although dorsal and cephalic skin could prevent limb regeneration, ventral and caudal skin had no controlling effect on it.

A demonstration that skin was necessary for longer than the dedifferentiation and accumulation periods comes from the work of Poležajew (1936) and Poležajew and Favorina (1935). Head skin transplanted to a limb anytime before morphogenesis was complete caused abnormalities. When transplanted late, after a blastema had formed, only distal abnormalities were observed. This was the first evidence that skin was exercising control of form of the regenerate.

The action of skin was not clear. Foreign skin taken from the back or muscle from the back (Umanski, 1938b) could prevent limb regeneration. Ventral and caudal skin had no effect, yet limb skin had the ability to determine axes. Head skin on a limb interfered with morphogenesis even in late stages of the process.

The picture cleared somewhat when Glade (1957) devised a new method of transplanting tail skin to limbs. There was reason to believe that if a collar of tail skin simply replaced limb skin, epidermis from the limb could still get to the apical cap. It was well known that epidermis can migrate long distances through, over, and under grafts. Weiss (1927) had shown that limbs stripped of their skin and covered by a sleeve of lung regained an epidermis the whole length of the limb and over the surface of amputation. Apparently it had migrated over the lung tissue from the base of the limb or the body. Hay (1952), using grafts of haploid tail skin in the knee region of diploid *Rana pipiens* tadpoles, learned that epidermis can come to an amputation surface in another manner. The haploid epidermal cells were at first lying directly over their dermis at the knee. In a few days after amputation of the limb at the ankle all of the haploid cells had left their dermis behind and had moved down from the knee to the surface of amputation at the ankle. Their place at the knee over the grafted nonmigrating dermal fibers had been taken by diploid epidermal cells that had migrated down from the thigh. These diploid cells from the thigh continued to migrate as a sheet and joined the haploid forerunners to become a part of the epidermal apical cap at the ankle.

With the knowledge that a collar of foreign grafted skin around the surface of amputation might not block migration of limb epidermis to the apical cap, Glade devised a method of skin transplantation that was intended to prevent a contribution of limb epidermis to the cap. Collars of tail skin were inserted part way under limb skin. The cut edge of the limb skin lay free outside the tail skin and not in contact with the rest of the surface of amputation. When the graft was made in this way the distal part of the limb skin degenerated without contributing or contributing very little epidermis to the wound surface.

The regenerates with this type of tail skin graft at their base were unlike regenerates obtained in previous studies in that most showed some signs of tailness. The least tail-like had shelves of tail fin containing the characteristic lophioderm extending out from what were obviously limbs. At the other extreme were outgrowths showing no limb characteristics. These were clearly tail-like. Better tail regenerates were obtained when, in addition to tail skin, pieces of spinal cord from the tail were grafted into limbs. Pieces of spinal cord without tail skin always lost structure and did not affect the course of limb regeneration.

The best tails that regenerated from limb stumps after grafting of tail skin and spinal cord contained vertebrae and muscles arranged segmentally as in tails (Fig. 5). The spinal cord that formed in the regenerates was scattered and bore no obvious spatial relationship to the vertebrae. Although spinal cord from the tail showed no direct control of structure around it even when in combination with tail skin in a limb, tail spinal cord in a tail acts as a center of organization and can be considered the chief form-controlling structure. Under other conditions spinal cord can also control structure outside the tail. Again we see that a variety of structures contain the information to control the development of structure in regenerates (rev. by Holtzer, 1959).

After the Glade type of transplant the distal border of the host limb skin lies free and would not be expected to contribute cells to the cap. Also, because it is not in direct cellular contact with the cap even through the transplant, it would not be expected to transmit any morphogenetic control involving cellular contact.

There is suggestive evidence that the tailness is not a property of the migrated cells. When a tail skin transplant was made at the shoulder of a stripped limb far from the amputation site in the forearm, all regenerates were good limbs and showed no tailness. As in the former cases epidermis from tail skin migrated to the apical cap but there was no organized tail skin close to the amputation surface. Apparently tailness is determined by the ring of organized tail and not just by the epidermal cells from it.

It is quite clear now that both skin and the rest of the limb minus skin can control the nature of a regenerate. Of internal structures, muscles, bones, and spinal cord have been shown to carry the pattern of their region and to impress that pattern on other tissues of a regenerate. In no case has perfect regeneration of a tail on a limb been reported. Combinations of grafted tissues are more effective than single ones but there is always limb tissue at the base and it too exercises some control.

The degree of control of morphogenesis by grafts is enhanced if the

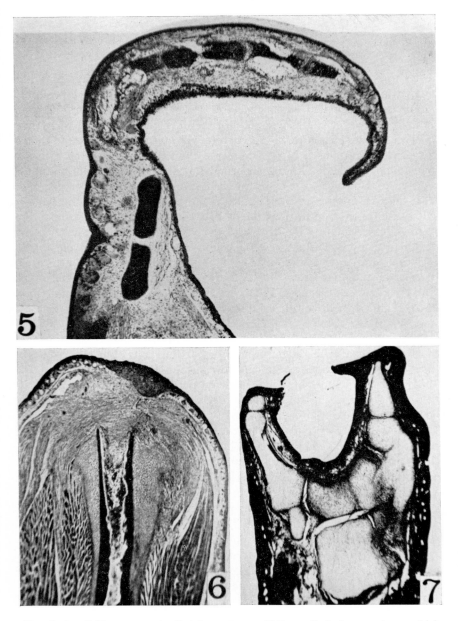

Fig. 5. A tail-like regenerate that formed on a *Triturus* limb from a stump which contained grafts of tail skin and spinal cord from the tail. (Photograph from Glade, 1957.)

Fig. 6. A limb stump from a frog, *Rana clamitans*, 8 days after amputation showing premature development of cartilage and fiber around the distal end of the bone. The old skin, as indicated by the circular skin glands, almost covers the stump. (This photograph is from Rose, 1945).

Fig. 7. A section through a regenerated hand and 2 of the 4 fingers on the stump of a young adult *Rana catesbeiana* provided with a graft of tail skin from a tadpole. (Photograph from Gidge and Rose, 1944.)

host site is X-rayed. For example, Luther (1948) found that limb skin grafted to the surface of amputation of unirradiated tails of larval *Sala-mandra maculosa* had some effect on regeneration. Chimaeras showing some limb characteristics were obtained. When the host tail had received 1500 r a few weeks before, the regenerate was quite a good foot and showed no tailness. Trampusch (1958) doing very much the same thing with axo-lotls found that limb skin on a normal tail did not impart limbness to a regenerate. However, just as in Luther's cases, good feet were regenerated from the combination of irradiated tail and normal limb skin. Luther's re-sults were taken to mean that the other tissues of a limb could be derived from skin, presumably the dermis of the skin. More recent information as it affects this problem is discussed below. The interest here is only in the fact that an X-rayed site may lose its ability to control the pattern of a regenerate and that unirradiated grafted structures show enhanced con-trol. We are not at the moment concerned with the source of the cells. Bones, muscle, and skin have all been shown to control pattern in regenerates from irradiated stumps (rev. Goss, 1956a, 1957a).

Limb stumps after dosages in the range of 500 r–10,000 r are incapable of anything except slight outgrowth of cartilaginous skin-covered spikes after the lowest dosages and no outgrowth after higher dosages (Rose *et al.*, 1955). Although normal bone, muscle, and skin can all participate in restoring regeneration to stumps receiving 1000–10,000 r, only with skin does regeneration approach normal (rev. by Goss, 1957a; Trampusch, 1959; Lazard, 1959). Only limb skin can cause a limb to arise on an ir-radiated stump. The character of the regenerate depends more upon skin than upon other tissues. With epidermis alone quite normal regeneration also occurs on limbs that have received relatively low dosages of irradia-tion (Rose *et al.*, 1955).

Further work demonstrating the role of skin in determining pattern has appeared recently (Droin, 1959). This work is based upon the control of symmetry relationships and will be presented in that section.

There is as yet no clear understanding of why skin should play a leading role in determining pattern in regenerates, but a provisional hypothesis encompassing the available information can be presented.

First of all, the epidermis does not ordinarily control pattern during ontogeny (Harrison, 1904; Zwilling, 1956) but it may in some cases (Fila-tow, 1928; Poležajew, 1936).

One can glean evidence from the literature indicating that the sphere of influence of bone and muscle extends a shorter distance than does that of skin. This was noted in the X-ray experiments. It also appears in recent work by Goss (1957a,b). He has shown clearly that if a limb stump is given an extra bone there will be an extra bone in the regenerate just distal to the extra bone in the stump. The effect of the extra bone extends only a short distance into the regenerate. Arms, each with an extra ulna and amputated through the forearm, produced an extra bone just distal to the transplanted ulna, but the hands were normal with no extra structures. Muscle grafts from tails can also control the form of a regenerate in their immediate vicinity (Glade, 1957).

An analysis of Glade's and Poležajew's and Favorina's regenerates arising from internal limb parts and tail skin discloses that among those that became almost normal limbs all abnormalities were distal. The regenerated parts that are normal limb parts are continuous with the normal internal tissues of the stump. There are no visible abnormalities close to the transplanted tail skin of the stump. The only abnormalities are at the distal tip under the epidermis that had migrated over the wound from the tail skin. One gets the impression that the skin exerts its influence on the form of the mesodermal tissues not from proximal to distal but in the opposite direction from the apical cap toward the base of the regenerate. Sometimes this effect of tail skin is much more extensive and long regenerates arise that are clearly tail-like except at the base where they may be limb-like (Fig. 5). There appears to be an interplay between apical cap and internal tissues of the stump with the two exerting their effects in opposite directions.

The greater effect of skin in controlling the form of regenerates on X-rayed stumps may arise from the fact that the epidermis is the only tissue that has a broad connection with the distalmost internal tissues. If the predominant direction of control is from distal to proximal, as it is in all other regenerating organisms studied, this might well account for the relatively greater morphogenetic effect of epidermis in a larva or an adult as compared to an embryo. When regeneration begins in the adult or larva there is a well differentiated epidermis which would be expected to have a greater effect than the relatively undifferentiated epidermis of an embryo.

Although a stump exerts great control over a regenerate there is a measure of self-determination in a blastema that tends toward wholeness or oneness. Milojevic and Vlatkovic (1926) and Swett (1928) obtained whole regenerates from half blastemas. Weiss produced whole regenerates from half limbs in two ways. Lateral halves were cut away from portions of limbs (Weiss, 1925a). The cut surface was in the form of a long [. There was healing along the upper arm of the [and the long upright representing surfaces facing proximally and laterally. On the lower surface facing distally an appreciable blastema arose. Although these formed distal to just half of a stump some produced not the missing lateral half but a regenerate with whole symmetry.

588 S. MERYL ROSE

In another experiment Weiss (1926) removed hands and split stumps longitudinally. There is a tendency for split limbs to heal. This was counteracted by removing the skin from one-half of the limb and wrapping it around the split limb still partially covered by its own skin. In this way one-half of the limb was denuded and the other half was completely covered, except distally, by the whole skin. The two halves remained separate. Quite regularly the denuded half regressed and the part containing half of the internal structures and the whole skin regenerated a whole limb. The fact that a stump exercises control of the form of a regenerate but not necessarily in some direct point for point relationship led Weiss to formulation of the field hypothesis that has stimulated so much research.

In recent years Goss (1957b) and Lomovskaja (1948) have returned to the half limb experiment with an additional tool, the X-ray. If limbs are simply split and not allowed to fuse, halves consisting of half of the internal tissues and half of the skin may sometimes produce whole regenerates with the full number of toes (Goss, 1957a). This happened in 10% of the cases when hind limbs were operated upon and in 28% of the cases when forelimbs were used. These percentages jumped to 25 and 85 when half of the internal part of the limb was cloaked by a whole skin. Regenerates can produce a whole structure on a half stump but this occurs more frequently when the skin is whole.

Goss (1957b) then went on to X-ray either internal halves or skin halves or both and studied the nature of their regenerates. If just one longitudinal half of a whole limb, both skin and internal tissues, was X-rayed the regenerates were half regenerates. The X-rayed part apparently took no part in regeneration. In fact its presence in the X-rayed condition was worse than its complete removal. As noted above, half limbs can sometimes produce whole regenerates. Also internal half limbs plus whole skin can often produce whole regenerates. However, when an unirradiated half was covered by unirradiated skin but in addition there was irradiated skin covering the region where an internal half had been removed, only half regenerates appeared. In other words both irradiated skin and irradiated internal tissues not only do not participate in regeneration but in addition act to prevent it on their own side. There is one exception to this. When only the posterior half of the skin covering a whole limb was X-rayed the stump still produced a whole regenerate.

The above experiments of Goss with *Triturus* adults gave radically different results from the similar experiments of Lomovskaja (1948). The X-rayed lateral half of an axolotl limb together with the unirradiated half in most cases produced a blastema covering the entire distal surface. Such a blastema covering the entire distal surface produced a whole regenerate. In the Goss experiment the blastema covered only the unirradiated half. The X-rayed part was inert. The dosages used by both investigators were sufficient to prevent all regeneration after simple amputation. In fact the dosage used by Lomovskaja was 7000 r and that by Goss only 2000 r. Why then did Lomovskaja's limbs regulate to wholeness? Goss points out several differences that may have been important. The time between irradiation and amputation was much longer in Lomovskaja's cases and there was extensive injury involved in inserting a lead shield into the limb between tibia and fibula during the irradiation. We do not know, but the injury and subsequent healing involving migration of unirradiated cells may have affected the results. As shown above, regenerative ability can be regained by addition of unirradiated tissue.

In spite of the fact that we do not know for sure why the results differ, it is quite clear from the results of Goss that the control of regeneration is in a longitudinal direction and that the stump of one side can control the regeneration of its own side.

The field nature of the control of regeneration is seen in other ways. Parabiosed limbs can produce a single structure (Weiss, 1924b). Some of the rules for this process have been discovered. Monroy (1946) found that if two limbs are sewed together side by side so that they are parallel each may produce a full blastema, and the regenerate is really two partially fused limbs. As the angle between the two limbs is increased up to 90 degrees, more and more of the central regions fail to develop until no regeneration occurs. This is at first surprising because there is plenty of room for a blastema on the cut open surfaces even when they face each other with an angle of 90 degrees between. Monroy points out that if parallel lines are drawn from the stumps distally and the angle between the stumps is increased from 0 degrees to 90 degrees, more and more of the medial lines cross in the blastema area and eventually even the lateral lines cross. Monroy's suggestion is that the controls operate along lines extending parallel to the main axis of the limb. When these lines cross they interfere and the structures normally produced in the area where now there are crossed lines do not form. Goss (1956b) has combined limbs, ventral surface to ventral surface, and amputated. Sometimes from fused blastemas single regenerates arose. However, here the contiguous areas where lines would first cross were ventral areas. The regenerates that appeared to be single were really two dorsal halves fused together. Goss believes that Monroy's interference lines might account for the findings of all investigators who have studied this phenomenon.

Certainly regeneration is an unsymmetrical and highly polarized process. It has been observed by all that it can occur distally but not proximally, lateromedially, or dorsoventrally. For example a half stump may form a whole regenerate distal to itself, but never will the half complete the whole laterally (Weiss, 1925a; Poleszajew, 1933a).

In this connection Umansky et al. (1951) find that a collar of limb skin on an X-rayed limb will support limb regeneration if its axis parallels the axis of the limb. This collar supports regeneration either when the skin lies in its normal position or is turned through 180 degrees. A turn of 90 degrees prevents regeneration. Correlated with this is the fact that the electrical resistance of limb skin is much less along the distoproximal axis than at 90 degrees to this. This is not true for body skin which appears to show the same resistance along different axes. An electrical polarity may be important for regeneration. All growing, differentiating structures ever studied do show potential differences between distal and proximal regions. Monroy (1941) found potential differences between distal and proximal regions of salamander limbs after amputation. Because, beginning with the studies of Lund (1947), the control of growth and differentiation in plants has been demonstrated to involve polarized transport of charged molecules (Schrank, 1951), this area deserves further consideration in the Amphibia where some aspects of polarization are well understood. Additional work along this line has been done by Becker and is included at the end of this section.

One rule of polarization in the Amphibia is that no matter what the polarity of a regenerating surface, only structures that ordinarily lie distal to that surface can be regenerated (Oberheim and Luther, 1958). This has been observed many times after segments of appendages have been grafted with reversed distoproximal polarity to limb stumps or tails or other parts of the body (Harrison, 1898; Kurz, 1922; rev. Needham, 1942; Butler, 1955).

One of the most effective methods of transplantation is that of Butler (1951, 1955). After removal of a hand, a limb still normally attached can be grafted by its distal end to the body. In time as blood vessels and nerves grow into its distal end from the body it is supplied from both ends. Then if the doubly serviced limb is cut across somewhere between its two attachments two limb stumps remain. One in the old limb site has normal polarity and the other is reversed.

Regeneration of the reversed piece is more likely to occur if nerves have been deviated to the base of the reversed segment (Dent, 1954). The nerves that repopulate the reversed limb and the regenerate show a rather normal pattern in the regenerate (Deck, 1955; Deck and Riley, 1958) as they do when repopulating a limb with normal polarity (Weiss and Walker, 1934), but in general the pattern of nerves in a limb regenerate is not as normal as the muscle pattern (Piatt, 1957). This indicates again that the nerves themselves, although known from other work to participate in patterning, do not impress their own pattern on the limb regenerate.

The other method valuable for study of regeneration from a reversed limb is that of Burchardt (1930) and Efimov (1933) recently used by

Oberheim and Luther (1958). A limb is inserted beneath skin but with the foot extending beyond the skin. After the limb has received a blood supply and a deviated nerve supply to its central region both the distal and proximal parts are cut away. Regeneration may proceed from both cut surfaces of the centrally attached limb.

All of the work on regeneration from exposed surfaces demonstrates that a level can produce only more distal structures. It will produce such structures in inverted limbs even though they are already present closer to the body. For example, the early work of Kurz (1922) demonstrated that if the knee region were inverted and an upper limb surface left exposed, everything distal to that level could be produced including another knee.

The principle that appendages cannot produce more proximal parts extends even to single bones. Ordinarily if a whole bone is removed and a blastema does not extend into the area of loss, the bone is not reconstituted (Schaxel and Böhmel, 1928; rev. by Goss, 1956a). A very slow regeneration of a bone is possible away from a blastema area if just a part of the bone is removed. This process is measured in months rather than in days or weeks as is regeneration from a blastema. If the proximal half of a bone is left in place a distal half forms and the bone is complete. If, however, a distal half is left in place it does not complete the bone by producing a proximal half. Instead it produces another distal half and the two halves may be almost mirror images of each other (Flat-Hauser and Przibram, 1930; Przibram, 1931; Chen, 1933).

Oberheim and Luther (1958) have stressed the fact that proximal parts of a limb regardless of their direction can form only more distal parts. When a part of a limb or a whole limb is inverted this will result in a new part that displays mirror symmetry with the old part. It is not necessary that every point in the old surface specify the adjacent points in the new outgrowth. Agreement of only one point or one line and subsequent spread of pattern from this one line in the blastema is theoretically enough to account for mirror imaging given the observed Oberheim-Luther rule of ability to produce only more distal parts.

The specification of one or a few lines in a blastema but not all seems required to explain other field phenomena such as the ability of a blastema on half a limb to produce a whole distal part and for the blastema to produce structures not represented in the stump. It appears that with one or a few lines in the blastema specified by the stump and subsequent spread of pattern in the blastema, the field phenomena can be understood. The distalmost tissue is the apical cap that has migrated from the cut lateral epidermis. Its position at the distal end and its direct connection with the old skin may account for the fact that grafted skin on X-rayed and on normal limbs shows greater control of regeneration than do internal tissues.

Recent work by Glade (1963) indicates that at least some of the information carried by skin is stored in the dermis.

If the major direction of control is from the old skin to the apical cap and then proximally through the internal tissues, the symmetry of the internal tissues would depend upon the symmetry of the cap and the symmetry of the cap would depend upon the symmetry of the skin. Symmetry in the skin arises during ontogeny from internal mesoderm. (Harrison, 1918). In a sense there would be a circle of control with limb bud mesoderm controlling the ectoderm during ontogeny and the skin, by way of the epidermis, controlling the internal mesoderm during regeneration.

Development of a limb during ontogeny and during regeneration are quite different. Regeneration requires both loss of structure and acquisition of new structure. Relatively undifferentiated tissue must arise in which the new pattern may appear. The blastema is controlled by a highly differentiated and polarized stump whereas the embryonic limb bud is differentiating and becoming polarized along with its environs. The regenerating limb blastema although it consists of relatively undifferentiated cells may never revert to a pre-limb stage of differentiation because it is always under the control of the limb stump.

The question of whether a blastema can transform to tissues of another region is still not answered. The early students of the problem thought their work indicated that a blastema from one region was so dedifferentiated that it could be transferred to another where it would produce structures appropriate for the host region. Difficulty of interpretation always arose because the blastema was being transferred to a region that was itself capable of producing regeneration cells. There was enough delay in regeneration after transplantation so that the host site might have had time to produce its own blastema. Apparently a blastema from the hind limb of a black axolotl on a white forelimb stump could become a white limb with a black hand (Jefimov 1938) but the criteria of a hand were questioned (Polezhayev, 1945).

Single young blastemas were always resorbed or possibly formed back tissue when grafted to a back. These very young blastemas, before they had achieved the late cone stage of differentiation, showed no signs of their limbness in the foreign area. A blastema has been specified a few days later by the time it is in the late cone stage and it can develop as a limb on a back. The fact that the younger blastema did not demonstrate its limbness on the back was taken by some to mean that it had dedifferentiated to a pre-limb stage (see discussions by Guyénot, 1927; Schotté, 1940; J. Needham, 1942; Polezhayev, 1945). An indication that a tail blastema still had tail quality that was not appearing when single blastemas were grafted to foreign territories came from the work of Polejaiev (1936b). He transplanted single young tail blastemas to limb sites and they were resorbed. A mound made of several of these could become a tail-like outgrowth indicating that dedifferentiation had not progressed to a pre-tail stage. There the matter stood for many years.

Recently Farinella-Ferruza (1956, 1957, and earlier) has reported a number of cases where grafted tails have over a long period of time partially regressed and transformed to limbs. Holtfreter (1955) reported some similar cases he had observed some years before. The Farinella-Ferruza work was done xenoplastically. The cells are quite different and nuclear size is sufficiently different so that she can distinguish graft and host tissue. Many of the cells of the limbs were formerly cells of tails. This work demstrates that cells or possibly tissues of one region can transform to those of another region. The transformation is a very slow one, measured in months.

Gill-like structures can also arise when tails are transplanted to limb region (Holtfreter, 1955) or when limb buds are moved into or close to gill region (Wilde, 1952a). This latter type of apparent tranformation may be nothing more than a migration of gill cells from the gill region as suggested by the authors. Apparently a limb can be suppressed by anterior gill structures but not by more posterior tissues (Wilde, 1952b). Here again there is indication of polarized control as in the work of Nicholas (1924).

One of the most enlightening series of studies concerning the control of regeneration comes from the work started by Harrison (1918, 1921) on the origin of polarity in limbs. Very early in the ontogeny of a limb area the anteroposterior axis is set. If such a limb area is removed and reimplanted so that its anteroposterior axis and its dorsoventral axis both oppose those of the host site the limb will develop with the limb pointing forward rather than to the rear. Its anteroposterior axis was determined before the time of transplantation. The dorsoventral axis of the very young limb area is not determined as early and the dorsoventral surfaces of such an inverted area conform to those of the host body. Later the dorsoventral axis is fixed and still later the left-right axis. The above statements are based on the work of Harrison and his students (rev. by Swett, 1937).

These axes are determined by general changes occurring in the environs of the limb. A large ring of tissue surrounding the presumptive limb area when rotated caused the limb to be rotated (Nicholas, 1922). The dorsoventral axis appears to be controlled from a position dorsal to the limb (Nicholas, 1924).

In a sense the entire flank region between the positions of anterior and posterior limbs in an embryo is a limb field. Limbs have been made to arise at many points in this area by the transplantation of various foreign objects under the ectoderm. Ear vesicles, nasal placodes, and even celloidin beads (rev. by Ruben and Frothingham, 1958) have been effective. The most reliable method for producing limbs out of place is that of transplanting heavily X-rayed ectoderm to the flank region of anuran embryos (Perri, 1956). This tissue dies and sets up a center where a limb develops. Induced supernumerary limbs in the posterior part of this field become hind limbs and those in the anterior part are clearly anterior limbs. The size of the induced supernumeraries decreases with distance from the normal limb site. The polarity is not the same in the normal position as it is around this position. In general the supernumeraries are mirror images of the limbs in the normal position. Kiortsis (1953) finds a position close to the limb where the polarity changes. This region, when transplanted, regularly yields doubled limbs.

As limb buds are grafted farther and farther away from a limb site but still in the limb field, the incidence of duplications increases. That this results from incompatibility between limb and limb field is indicated by the fact that duplications are not produced when buds are grafted outside the limb field.

Harrison observed during the course of his studies that often when a limb bud was transplanted two limbs arose. It seemed likely that one arose from the bud and, at least sometimes, one from the host site. This happened most frequently when a limb bud was transplanted into a vacant limb site with its anteroposterior axis reversed or when it was transplanted to the flank with its axis not reversed. However, the polarity sign changes on the flank as indicated above. The general rule then is that duplicate limbs are produced most frequently when the sign of anteroposterior polarity in graft and host site are at a wide angle to each other. The percentage of duplicate limbs may run as high as 90 (Swett, 1937).

Lecamp (1935) doubted that incompatibility of axes was a factor because the frequency did not increase when other axes were made incompatible. The best statement seems to be that incompatibility of anteroposterior axes of two limb fields, one in the bud and the other in the environs, often results in duplications.

The grafting of limb buds at later stages may also cause duplication and triplication. Lecamp grafted older buds and young limbs of the toad *Alytes obstetricans* to a non-limb field and often obtained a supernumerary limb arising from the base of the graft. In addition a third member could arise when the young limb was grafted into a limb field. What do all of these observations teach us about the control of regeneration?

It seems to be controlled along very definite directions, possibly lines. The simple cutting of lines as when a bud is removed but reimplanted without change in orientation does not allow a new limb to arise from a limb field. When buds are implanted with improper alignment a region near the junction of poor alignment is free to produce a new limb. The works of Weisz (1951) and Tartar (1958 and earlier) with *Stentor* where lines of control are actually seen might serve as models for future work with Amphibia.

The polarization in these young limb buds appears to be independent of nerves. Later when nerves enter limbs there may be a repolarization and the polarity of the nerve may determine the polarity of the limb (A. E. Needham, 1952). When a portion of a limb is inverted and still regenerates distal structures it may be because the nerves with proper polarity have already grown into the inverted region (A. E. Needham, 1952; Deck, 1955). Yntema (1959a) finds that limbs that have never had nerves can regenerate without them. Presumably they are using the original polarized controls. Once limbs have had nerves they are dependent upon them and cannot regenerate without them under ordinary conditions. That there may be two different polarized control systems in a formerly nerveless limb which nerves have recently penetrated is suggested by the fact that these limbs produce duplicate parts (Yntema, 1959a,b).

Various local treatments of larval and adult salamander appendages have induced supernumerary appendages or duplicate distal portions of those appendages. X-irradiation (Brunst, 1950a,b; Brunst and Figge, 1951), ultraviolet irradiation (Rieck, 1954; Butler and Blum, 1955), carcinogens inserted locally (Breedis, 1952), insertions of small pieces of the Lucké adenocarcinoma of the kidney of *Rana pipiens* into limbs of *Triturus viridescens* (Ruben and Frothingham, 1958; Ruben, 1960), application of ligatures (Della Valle, 1913; Nassonov, 1930; Kasanzeff, 1930), and deviation of nerves (rev. by Ruben and Frothingham, 1958) have all led to duplications of limbs or parts of limbs.

How do these local treatments break the control? A simple cut along the side of a limb or the removal of a piece of muscle or bone somewhere along the length of a limb never leads to the formation of a supernumerary limb. The damaged areas are simply repaired. Some of the treatments obviously destroy tissue organization locally and might disrupt polarized communication. This is true after implantation of tumor or carcinogen and especially so after heavy irradiation with ultraviolet light when internal structures lose organization and skin sloughs.

Low dosages of X-rays produce their effects more subtly. An X-rayed limb may remain functional for years (Brunst and Scheremetjewa, 1937). It appears normal but it will not grow nor regenerate even years after X-irradiation. Brunst (1950a) and Brunst and Figge (1951) found that if a part of a limb or tail is X-rayed a new distal part may grow out from the unirradiated part just proximal to the zone of irradiation. One can think of the X-rayed portion as being incapable of transmitting effective control as in the Luther (1948) and Trampusch (1958) studies reported above. The region just proximal to the X-rayed region would then be free to produce the apparently missing distal parts.

Brunst (1959) shows that there is a zone of increased mitosis just behind a directly irradiated zone. This is thought of as indirect stimulation or as the result of weak irradiation due to scatter. There is also the possibility that the mitotic stimulation results from blocking of distal morphogenetic control.

Nassonov (1930) and Kasanzeff (1930) applied ligatures close to the elbow of axolotl limbs. These ligatures did not cut through the tissues. Blood continued to flow but at a reduced rate. In time a blastema that yielded distal multiple limb parts appeared proximal to the ligature. The new hands always appeared on the proximal side of the ligature away from the original hand. It appears that the control of distal over proximal was blocked by the ligature.

Della Valle (1913) using ligatures in a different way showed another relationship. In this case limbs were amputated and a ligature applied very close to the level of amputation. The ligature cut through most of the soft tissue exposing in addition to the distal cut surface two new ones made by the ligature where it cut through the soft tissues. One of the new surfaces faced distally and the other proximally. Distal limb parts arose from all three surfaces. That they should arise from the free distal surfaces is not surprising. Whenever distal structures are removed more proximal ones can transform to the missing distal structures. Regeneration from proximal surfaces of more proximal structures does not occur. It did not in this case either, but a proximal surface made very close to the level of amputation did behave as a distal surface. We do not know what relationship the nerves have to such a proximal surface. If they reached the surface they might repolarize it as has been suggested for the repolarization of inverted segments (Needham, 1952). Further study is needed.

The most reliable way to produce a supernumerary limb on an adult is to deviate limb nerves to the surface of the body near the base of a limb. After nerve deviation, surface wounding is important (Poleszajew, 1933b; Bodemer, 1958) and an epidermal apical cap arises at the distal end of the nerve (Thornton, 1954). The connection of epidermis and nerve establishes a new axis along which structures distal to that level may regenerate.

Other methods for inducing extra limbs or duplicate distal parts may be effective because a new lateral or basal connection between nerve and epidermis is established (Ruben and Frothingham, 1958; Bodemer, 1958, 1959). Bodemer (1959) demonstrated that simple deviation of brachial nerves to the chest does not in itself lead to the production of an extra limb. There is some thickening of epidermis and some collection of cells under the epidermis at the end of the nerve but the massive transformation required for limb formation does not occur. It may occur when, in addition to deviation of nerve, foreign tissues are transplanted to the area. The most effective are liver, lung, and bone. An inflammatory reaction is observed and this is followed by all the normal steps in regeneration. The foreign tissue agent is more effective after homogenization and it is thermolabile.

It appears that the new connection between lateral or basal epidermis and nerve may be a short circuit in the control system. Faber (1960) has demonstrated that proximal portions of regenerates even after skeleton has begun to form transform to distal parts when transplanted without their distal parts. Apparently all levels of a blastema tend to become the most distal part not already present. Ordinarily a given level of an intact limb will not lose structure and transform to more distal parts, but when nerves make a sufficient connection with the epidermis at that level the surrounding tissue begins to act as though the distal parts were missing.

A recent paper of Droin (1959) clearly shows that the skin of *Triton* carries and determines pattern during regeneration. The work is based on the finding by Kiortsis (1953) that there is a region in the shoulder where two limbs arise when a nerve is deviated there. Droin found that if the skin from this region was transplanted to a limb and the limb amputated in the region of the transplant 6 of 14 regenerates were double limbs. Exhange of skin between left and right limbs without change of orientation yielded 16 limbs with laterality corresponding to that of the internal tissues, 8 limbs whose laterality was determined by the skin, and 5 in which two limbs regenerated. Glade (1957) also observed secondary regenerates when skin was exchanged between forelimbs. When limbs were cut off by Droin at the base and the shoulder skin turned 180 degrees, the internal tissues determined the orientation of the regenerate in 9 cases, the skin in 12, and in 2 cases double limbs arose. When skin was exchanged between anterior and posterior limbs the anterior skin usually caused limb regenerates with 4 fingers to appear, whereas skin from hind limbs on anterior limbs controlled the pattern less often.

The great unsolved problem of how control is transmitted and what is transmitted in the amphibian limb has recently received a promising new treatment. Becker (1960, 1961a,b) has implicated the nervous system as a part of the information transfer system during regeneration. He starts with the fact that nerves are required for limb regeneration in adult salamanders. The nerves maintain an electrical potential difference along the limb. There is a gradient of negativity with a distal high point. When the nerves are cut the potential difference disappears rapidly (Becker, 1961b).

This potential difference is responsible for the movement of charged particles along the limb. When a magnetic field is applied across an innervated limb the axis of potential difference is deflected indicating a deflected motion of particles (the Hall effect).

An intact salamander limb shows a relatively slight potential gradient with the distal regions negative to more proximal regions. After amputation of a distal portion there is a rapid reversal of the electrical polarity in the stump with the distal part becoming positive. In a few days the end of the stump has become negative again and more strongly so than in the intact limb. The peak of negativity is reached in 1 week and thereafter during the course of regeneration the potential difference slowly returns to normal (Becker, 1961b).

The working hypothesis is that the nervous system is involved in the transmission of morphogenetic data (Becker, 1960, 1961b). It is also possible that the nerves deliver a negative charge to the end of a limb, especially to the wound epithelium where most of the endings are and that this center of negativity results in the flow of information from other non-nervous tissues. An indicated above there seems to be an arc of control from old skin to wound epithelium to internal tissues by way of the apical cap (Rose, 1962). To be looked for are positively charged particles flowing from old skin into wound epithelium.

In the cases where pattern is being impressed upon a regenerate by internal tissues, as for example when regeneration is controlled by motor nerves only, a different tissue arc or arcs of control would be operative. Motor nerves are not found in the epidermis in appreciable numbers. It would be interesting to learn whether regeneration could proceed without epidermis when motor nerves only are charging the limb.

One more observed fact is to be recalled as the new study of intercellular coordinators proceeds. This is the demonstration that the control of the distal part of a limb can be broken by a relatively loose ligature. The breaking of control is followed by regeneration from just proximal to the ligature of distal limb parts (Nassonov, 1930; Kasanzeff, 1930). These ligatures allow sufficient blood to flow through the limb to maintain it but they do block some of the lymph drainage as evidenced by edema distal to the ligature. This makes it necessary to consider the possibility that one part of the arc of control may be from distal to proximal by way of the lymph.

The change in electrical potential is different in the nonregenerating limbs of frogs after amputation. Shortly after amputation, just as in the salamander, there is a reversal of polarity with the distal region becoming positive. The great difference is that the tip of the frog's stump does not become negative. The correlation is that the salamander limb becomes strongly negative and regenerates, whereas the frog limb does not become negative and does not regenerate (Becker, 1961b).

The various facts presented in this section give rise to the suggestion that nerves generate potential differences that furnish the power for the movement of intercellular coordinators. These electrical differences may be quite generally responsible for the transmission of morphogenetic information. There are potential differences in differentiating embryonic systems (Burr, 1941; rev. by Rose, 1957; Lukiewicz, 1962). Nerves may be necessary during postembryonic regeneration for the maintenance of particle-moving potentials.

That there may be stimulating and inhibiting chemical agents of control transmitted in a polarized system in the eye is suggested by the work on the retina-iris-lens system (Section III). The data are sufficient to show a possible relationship to the general problem of control of regeneration being studied in other organisms (Lender, 1960; Rose, 1957, 1963; Tartar, 1958; Tucker, 1959; Wolff, 1962).

A large part of the control of differentiation may be inhibitory. At any time before the fate of a region has been set it is pluripotent. It cannot transform into a more distal structure until more distal structures have been removed or until communication with the more distal region has been blocked.

In recent years the theory of how this inhibitory control is accomplished has been evolving rapidly. Considerable thought has been given to induction-inhibition systems at the enzyme and gene levels (Monod and Jacob, 1961). Most promising is the demonstration that histones can reversibly control the rate of production of RNA by DNA in an *in vitro* system (Huang and Bonner, 1962). This brings to the fore the histone hypothesis of gene control (Stedman and Stedman, 1950; Bloch, 1962a,b). The general idea is that histones in close association with nucleotide segments prevent the production of their messenger RNA (Allfrey *et al.*, 1963).

If histones, passing from cell to cell and thus limiting the activity of like genes downstream, are to be the agents of differentiation they must be as numerous as the genetic areas. The histones do vary from tissue to tissue (Stedman and Stedman, 1950; Busch, 1962). There is a great variety of histones as shown by separation by electrophoresis. Even these groups are extremely heterogeneous as indicated by end group analysis (rev. by Busch, 1962).

The amphibian limb, tail, and eye with their many regional differences and their recognized polar differences promise to yield many answers concerning polarized intercellular control of differentiation. Needed now is knowledge concerning the chemical nature of the intercellular coordinators. This phase of the work is being studied with the more rapidly regenerating lower organisms (Rose, 1963).

VIII. Induced Regeneration

Once students of regeneration in the Amphibia had learned that tadpoles regenerate their hind limbs but lose this ability during early metamorphosis a new problem arose. Did the loss of regenerative ability have to be an irreversible change or might the ability lie latent?

In recent years it has become clear that the loss of the ability to regenerate limbs is not complete in all Anura (Polezhayev, 1945; Thornton and Shields, 1945; Dent, 1962; Goode, 1962). The outgrowths in most cases are no more than abnormal skeletal outgrowths covered by skin but may attain appreciable dimensions and show the beginnings of distal regional differentiation in *Xenopus* (Beetschen, 1952).

It is also clear that the loss of regenerative ability does not extend to all parts of the body. It came as a surprise (Goodchild, 1956) that fully grown *Rana pipiens* could regenerate parts of intestines. This type of regeneration, also observed in adult *Triturus viridescens* (O'Steen, 1958) and in *Rana clamitans* tadpoles (O'Steen, 1959), involves blastema formation and can be very extensive in tadpoles. O'Steen (1959) has observed the complete replacement of the complicated coiled intestine when only small sections of duodenum and rectum were left in place.

Goodchild observed something that seems to be a general relationship. The cut end of an intestine does not undergo dedifferentiation and blastema formation unless it makes contact with a foreign region, usually another region of the intestine. Only when it does make contact does loss of structure followed by production of appropriate new structures occur. Just like a nonregenerating limb a free end of an intestine undergoes very little loss of structure.

Although regenerative ability is not as extensive in the central nervous system of most amphibians as in peripheral nerves it is considerable in the brain of *Xenopus* (e.g., Srebro, 1959; Kwiatkowski, 1959; and a series of papers in *Folia Biologica*, Krakow).

These recent works point up the fact that regenerative ability varies from species to species and from organ to organ. Failure to regenerate is not a bodywide phenomenon. Its causes are to be sought in local areas.

It is interesting that the first person to try to induce limb regeneration in adult Anura tried to change the relationship between skin and internal tissues. T. H. Morgan (1908) realizing a frog's amputation wound is constricted by old skin, tried to induce regeneration by correcting the condition. He thought of the trouble as being too great pressure. To relieve it he amputated a limb and cut back the internal tissues leaving an empty sleeve that he closed so as to make a loose covering. Later through the works of Godlewski and Efimov and many others cited above it was learned that close contact of epidermis and internal tissues was a prerequisite rather than no connection which is what resulted from Morgan's attempt to induce regeneration.

Knowledge that regenerative ability was not irretrievably lost was gained when Liosner (1931) learned that tadpole limbs a little too far advanced to regenerate when left in their normal place did so after transplantation and amputation. In these cases the act of transplantation had apparently started regeneration by causing considerable loss of structure (Poležajew and Ginzburg, 1939). Very little structure was lost when the limbs were simply amputated. A stability had been attained that simple amputation would not eliminate.

The next and very important step was taken by Polejaiev (1936a). He was already aware from his earlier work (Poleszajew, 1933b) that when one induced regeneration out of place by deviating a nerve, trauma was an important factor. This knowledge was used in an attempt to stimulate the recovery of regenerative ability. Polejaiev (1936b) caused late tadpole limbs to recover the ability to regenerate by injuring them excessively with a scalpel. He also demonstrated that regenerative ability could be extended by having a limb regenerating during the period when loss of ability usually occurs. The regenerate could regenerate again after amputation while a normal unregenerated limb on the same tadpole could not (Poležajew and Morosow, 1941). Possibly this is due to a slowing down of dedifferentiation with increase in degree of differentiation (Goodwin, 1946).

Metamorphosed frogs were made to regenerate fairly good limbs by dipping the amputation surface into strong NaCl solutions (Rose, 1942, 1944, 1945: Polezhayev, 1946b; Singer et al., 1957). Limbs amputated half way between elbow and wrist were dipped in a half-saturated NaCl solution for as short a time as 1 min twice daily for 5 days. The treatments caused considerable inflammation. A blastema developed and in some cases there was regeneration of normal forearms, wrist, and part of the hand but the more distal parts were always abnormal. Fused and missing distal cartilages and stumpy fingers were the rule. The salt treatments were employed in an attempt to interfere with healing and to increase the irritation ordinarily resulting from amputation. An analysis of the differences between regenerating and nonregenerating limbs of young and old tadpoles (Schotté and Harland, 1943) and salamanders and frogs (Rose, 1948a) indicated that whereas in the regenerators there is a prolonged period of structural loss and growth of the undifferentiated cells to produce a blastema, this does not occur in the nonregenerators. The frog's limb, like the salamander's, seals itself with a migrating epidermis. A large expanse of epidermis without appreciable basement fiber remains in the salamander until regeneration is well under way. In a frog soon after the wound epithelium has spread across the surface of amputation, it is followed by the complete skin including dermis, and new dermal fiber can be seen to form in a frog long before a salamander has a blastema. Blastema formation may require 15 or 20 days and several more may be needed for new tissue to appear on a salamander's limb. Within a week or two without passing through a blastema stage the frog limb produces a large callus of cartilage and connective tissue around the old bone (Fig. 6). New tissue is produced sooner in a frog, but it is almost entirely callus produced around the old bone.

Histological comparison of salted and nonsalted limbs after amputation showed very little if any difference between the two in the first week. Both began to produce new cartilage, but in time, and it was after treatments had been discontinued, the new cartilaginous matrix eroded away leaving a mesenchymal mass (Rose, 1945).

It seemed that the action of the salt was primarily on the epidermis because the stump could be sealed by the epidermal wound epithelium before treatments began. At the time Singer had not yet shown the close and extensive junction of nerves and epidermis. He has since suggested that the action of NaCl may have been by way of the nerves. Loss of structure and blastema formation fail to occur in salted frogs' limbs if they have been denervated (Singer *et al.*, 1957; Singer, 1959a).

Schotté and Harland (1943) found that as tadpoles are losing the ability to regenerate hind limbs there is an overproduction of cartilage and connective tissue with failure to produce a blastema. They also noted that the loss came at different times in different parts of the limb. The loss proceeded in a proximodistal direction. However, Van Stone (1957) showed that the pelvic level retains regenerative ability longer than the midthigh. This is correlated with a higher density of nerve fibers there (Van Stone, 1955).

Correlated with loss in regenerative ability was the appearance of lymphatic spaces under a loosening skin (Schotté and Harland, 1943). After amputation the whole skin was free to contract over the wound and move into the center behind a shrinking wound epithelium. In this way the epidermal-internal tissue contact was decreased and soon obliterated.

Rapid wound closure by whole skin is only part of the reason for failure. If skin is stripped back from the surface of amputation so that it cannot cover the wound, fibrous tissue still forms prematurely between migrated epidermis and internal tissues (Rose, 1944). Rapidity of healing and premature differentiation of tissues precludes the more leisurely process of dedifferentiation and accumulation of a blastema. A new dermis is present on the frog limb long before an appreciable blastema could be expected on a salamander limb. One gains the impression that loss of the ability to regenerate limbs is the price paid by frogs for their efficient healing mechanism.

Sodium chloride is in no sense a specific agent in inducing limb regeneration. Polezhayev (1946b) has shown that many substances are effective and that some milder treatments, as with glucose, are better. Schotté and Bonneville (1955) while treating one limb of a frog with NaCl found that the opposite stump, not treated in any way, might also regenerate appreciably. By what pathways such an effect is transmitted is still not known. A similar observation has now been made in two other laboratories. Polezhayev (1959) has reported that when he induces X-rayed limbs to regenerate after injecting homogenates the untreated X-rayed control limb may also regenerate. Rose and Rose (1964) find that a left X-rayed limb may be made to regenerate by grafting normal skin to the right X-rayed limb. These three examples of a treatment on one nonregenerating limb being expressed on the contralateral limb await explanation.

There is a general change, in part humoral (Polezhayev, 1945; Schotté, 1961), that leads to loss of regenerative ability in limbs. It is general in the sense that both the mesodermal and the epidermal portions of limbs change as metamorphosis approaches so that neither will cooperate with a younger partner in regenerating a limb (Poležajew, 1939).

After the initial studies of induced regeneration it seemed that the limb skin might be the prime mover in the failure of regeneration. The fact that tadpole tails will still regenerate after limbs have lost the ability offered the opportunity for a test of the hypothesis. Adult limbs stripped of their own skin were provided with a covering of skin from tadpole tails (Gidge and Rose, 1944). The skins are very different in appearance. Limb skin of an adult has a thick fibrous dermis, thicker than the epidermis. The tadpole tail skin is much thinner and has a very fine layer of dermal fiber containing very few cells.

Amputation at the mid-forearm level through the adult limb provided with larval tail skin led to blastema formation and the regenerates were better in distal regions than were those induced by salt treatments. The best arising after larval skin substitution had movable fingers although they were not as long as normal and were excessively webbed (Fig. 7).

At the time this work was done it was already thought that one reason for loss of regenerative ability was that cells had become more resistant to dedifferentiation. The idea behind transplanting larval skin was to provide the adult limb with cells capable of dedifferentiation.

The next important step was limb regeneration induced in adult frogs by increasing the nerve supply (Singer, 1954). A sciatic nerve with central connections intact was removed from a hind limb and deviated to a forelimb. This limb had both its own nerve supply plus that of a hind limb extending to the level of amputation. The regenerates were clearly little limbs but like all that have been induced they were deficient distally.

Schotté and Wilber (1958) and Mizell (1960) obtained some quite good limb regenerates by implanting adrenal glands in adult frogs. These transplants are most effective if made 1 to 2 weeks after amputation. The belief is that they act by preventing the formation of a fibro-cartilage barrier beneath the epidermis and enable a blastema to form instead. The epidermis thickens and cuboidal cells appear. Loss of internal structure and blastema formation follow.

One gains the impression that all of the induced frog regenerates with the exception of a few arising after larval skin transplantation and from gland transplants arose from what would be the proximal part of a blastema, that part which forms within the limbs of the old tissue. There is never great outgrowth of the type associated with apical cap-nerve activity. Direct observation by Thornton (1956) indicates that anuran tadpole limbs while still capable of regeneration receive a rich supply of nerves to the epidermis after amputation. A little later when tadpoles can no longer regenerate limbs there is failure of nerves to populate the epidermis and no apical cap forms. Everything seems to point to the failure of epidermis and nerves to join as the root of regenerative failure. However, it is not simply a case of failure to form a blastema. Fibroblast-like cells can collect under an epidermis and still not form a limb on the stump of an older tadpole. Here again it seems probable that the epidermis-nerve combination is necessary until the blastema is specified as a limb.

In *Xenopus* during the course of metamorphosis there is considerable loss of ability to regenerate limbs, but it is not completely gone even in the adult. During this period of declining ability there is a correlated decline in the ability to produce a thickened active apical cap. Fibroblasts, similar in appearance to, or possibly identical with regeneration cells, come to lie under epidermis, but they are limited to producing cartilaginous outgrowths and fibrous tissues (Dent, 1962). There is also failure of all of the internal structural changes that we have come to recognize as the result of intimate and broad contact between nerves and epidermis.

The ability to regenerate lenses in most Amphibia is quite restricted. Sato (1953) working with *Hynobius* implanted pieces of dorsal iris into eye chambers. In only 2 of 37 cases did a lens regenerate. There was a strong tendency to produce retina and iris stroma. Sato correlates the failure to regenerate a lens with the strong growth tendency of the stroma. Here in the eye as in the limb, rapid fibrous differentiation seems to preclude some kinds of regeneration. Reyer (1956) working with larvae of *Ambystoma maculatum* finds no lens regeneration from iris. This failure is not correlated with excessive stroma production but with a very strong tendency to produce retina.

There is another indication that regenerative failure may depend on the presence of intercellular connective and capsular tissue materials and/or the very great tendency to produce these materials. Sperry (1945) failed as had Stone (1941) to transplant larval anuran eyes to other orbits and have them recover vision. However, Sperry did find regeneration leading to vision after transplantation of eyes from metamorphosing tadpoles of *Rana clamitans*. The rapidly expanding eyes had softened at this time and were difficult to handle but they did recover their function. Here again a loss of regenerative ability in tadpoles, associated with a high degree of fibrous differentiation, was reversed when the fiber and possibly other intercellular materials were reduced. Also as Sperry pointed out these eyes were growing rapidly at the time of the operation.

Tweedell (1958) has observed lens regeneration in eyes of adult *Rana pipiens*. The Lucké renal tumor had been implanted in eyes and had destroyed much of the eye structure. An extreme overgrowth of retina followed and lenses formed in the iris region, but from what tissue is not known. There is a possibility that an increase in retinal factor and/or loss of structure was responsible for lens regeneration.

In recent years new attempts have been made to stimulate regeneration of limbs of adult Anura. Malinin and Deck (1958) had some success after implanting embryonic and tadpole tail tissues into adult frog limbs and Kudokotsev (1960) has shown that tissue extracts have some effect in stimulating limb regeneration. How the cellular and noncellular agents act is still not known. It was suggested that the implanted tissues may provide cells for regeneration. This, like the older work of Gidge and Rose, should be checked with adequately marked transplants.

There is a good possibility that all of the treatments which induce regeneration in naturally nonregenerating limbs or in X-rayed limbs are acting to reinstate a functional epidermal-neural-internal tissue arc of control. The failure of this arc to be established because intercellular materials are not broken down rapidly may be the reason for regenerative failure rather than inherent aging or injury of cells that directly prevent cell division.

IX. Conclusions and Perspectives

Much has been learned about regeneration in Amphibia since the early observations and experiments of Spallanzani. Certain conclusions are now on a firm basis and one can predict what kinds of answers will be forthcoming. It is now clear that in any area, eye, abdominal organ, or appendage, the removal of a part removes controls and enables a variety of tissues to transform to the missing part. It is also a fact that the control information is passed in a polarized system, possibly an arc involving more than one tissue. A variety of structures contain the information to produce new structures when the control is broken. Now that a wealth of information concerning the interrelated roles of substrates, enzymes and other proteins, and nucleic acids is being amassed it seems time to go further and test their roles in differentiation. The new information of molecular biology has been acquired largely through studies of single cells. Needed now is the knowledge of how intercellular and intertissue control of differentiation is mediated.

Locked up in all tissues is the coded information for all types of enzymes, cells, and tissues. The student of development will be concerned with how cells and tissues are limited to the use of only a part of the whole information. The student of regeneration has in addition another problem and that is how tissue cells practicing with only a part of their coded information can become regeneration cells and use certain other or additional parts of the general code.

There is also a practical aspect of the study of regeneration. Although in most groups of organisms, both plant and animal, there are many which can regenerate some or all parts, there are closely related organisms that fail to regenerate certain structures. As one learns how to unlock the controls it is to be expected that a variety of structures that do not now regenerate may be made to do so.

References

Adey, W. R., Kado, R. T., Didio, J. and Schindler, W. J. (1963). Impedance changes in cerebral tissue accompanying a learned discriminative performance in the cat. *Exptl. Neurol.* **7,** 259–281.

Adova, A. N., and Feldt, A. M. (1939). Biochemical peculiarities of axolotl's body connected with form-building under the action of organizers. *Compt. Rend. Acad. Sci. U.R.S.S.* **25,** 43–45.

Allfrey, V. G., Littau, V. C., and Mirsky, A. E. (1963). On the role of histones in regulating ribonucleic acid synthesis in the cell nucleus. *Proc. Natl. Acad. Sci. U.S.* **49,** 414–421.

Balinsky, B. I. (1957). New experiments on the mode of action of the limb inductor. *J. Exptl. Zool.* **134,** 239–273.

Bassina, J. A. (1940). An inquiry into regeneration by the method of calculating mitotic coefficients. *Byul. Eksperim. Biol. i Med.* **10,** 389 (Russian—reviewed by Chalkley, 1959).

Becker, R. O. (1960). The bioelectric field pattern in the salamander and its simulation by an electronic analog. *IRE (Inst. Radio Engrs.) Trans. Med. Electron.* **7,** 202–207.

Becker, R. O. (1961a). Search for evidence of axial current flow in peripheral nerves of salamanders. *Science* **134,** 101–102.

Becker, R. O. (1961b). The bioelectric factors in amphibian limb regeneration. *J. Bone Joint Surg.* **43A**, 643–656.

Beetschen, J. C. (1952). Extension et limites du pouvoir régénérateur des membres après la metamorphose chez *Xenopus laevis* Daudin. *Bull. Bicl.* **86**, 88–100.

Belkin, R. (1934). Régénération des extrémités de l'axolotl pendent la métamorphose. *Compt. Rend. Soc. Biol.* **115**, 1162–1163.

Bischler, V. (1926). L'influence du squelette dans la régénération et les potentialités des divèrs territoires du membre chez *Triton cristatus*. *Rev. Suisse Zool.* **33**, 431–560.

Bloch, D. P. (1962a). DNA-Histone association as a basis for alternative hereditary gene states. *Science* **138**, 985.

Bloch, D. P. (1962b). On the derivation of histone specificity. *Proc. Natl. Acad. Sci. U.S.* **48**, 324–326.

Bodemer, C. W. (1958). The development of nerve-induced supernumerary limbs in the adult newt (*Triturus viridescens*). *J. Morphol.* **102**, 555–581.

Bodemer, C. W. (1959). Observations on the mechanism of induction of supernumerary limbs in adult *Triturus viridescens*. *J. Exptl. Zool.* **140**, 79–99.

Breedis, C. (1952). Induction of accessory limbs and of sarcoma in the newt (*Triturus viridescens*) with carcinogenic substances. *Cancer Res.* **12**, 861–866.

Brunst, V. V. (1950a). Influence of local x-ray treatment on the development of extremities of the young axolotl (*Siredon mexicanum*). *J. Exptl. Zool.* **114**, 1–49.

Brunst, V. V. (1950b). Influence of x-rays on limb regeneration in urodele amphibians. *Quart. Rev. Biol.* **25**, 1–29.

Brunst, V. V. (1959). Roentgen regression and roentgen stimulation in axolotl (*Siredon mexicanum*). *Acta Unio Intern. Contra Cancrum* **15**, 568–575.

Brunst, V. V., and Figge, F. H. J. (1951). The development of secondary tails in young axolotls after local x-ray irradiation. *J. Morphol.* **89**, 111–133.

Brunst, V. V., and Scheremetjewa, E. A. (1933). Untersuchung des Einflusses von Röntgenstrahlen auf die Regeneration der Extremitäten beim Triton. *Wilhelm Roux' Arch. Entwicklungsmech. Organ.* **128**, 181–215.

Brunst, V. V., and Scheremetjewa, E. A. (1937). Ist es möglich, die Regenerationsfähigkeit einer *Triton* Extremität zu vernichten, ohne ihre Lebensfähigkeit zu schädigen? *Byul. Eksperim. Biol. i Med.* **3**, 397–399.

Burchardt, H. (1930). Regeneration und Symmetrie durch den Urodelenkörper gesteckter Gliedmassen. *Wilhelm Roux' Arch. Entwicklungsmech. Organ.* **122**, 230–236.

Burr, H. S. (1941). Field properties of the developing frog's egg. *Proc. Natl. Acad. Sci. U.S.* **27**, 276–281.

Busch, H. (1962). "An Introduction to the Biochemistry of the Cancer Cell." Academic Press, New York.

Butler, E. G. (1931). X-radiation and regeneration in *Amblystoma*. *Science* **74**, 100.

Butler, E. G. (1933). The effects of x-radiation on the regeneration of the fore limb of *Amblystoma* larvae. *J. Exptl. Zool.* **65**, 271–315.

Butler, E. G. (1935). Studies on limb regeneration in x-rayed *Amblystoma* larvae. *Anat. Record* **62**, 295–307.

Butler, E. G. (1951). The mechanics of blastema formation and regeneration in urodele limbs of reversed polarity. *Trans. N.Y. Acad. Sci.* **13**, 164–167.

Butler, E. G. (1955). Regeneration of the urodele limb after reversal of its proximodistal axis. *J. Morphol.* **96**, 265–282.

Butler, E. G., and Blum, H. F. (1955). Regenerative growth in the urodele forelimb following ultraviolet radiation. *J. Natl. Cancer Inst.* **15**, 877–889.

Butler, E. G., and O'Brien, J. P. (1942). Effects of localized x-radiation on regeneration of the urodele limb. *Anat. Record* **84**, 407–413.

Butler, E. G., and Schotté, O. E. (1941). Histological alterations in denervated non-regenerating limbs of urodele larvae. *J. Exptl. Zool.* **88**, 307–341.

Butler, E. G., and Schotté, O. E. (1949). Histological alterations in denervated non-regenerating limbs of urodele larvae. *J. Exptl. Zool.* **88**, 307–341.

Chalkley, D. T. (1954). A quantitative histological analysis of forelimb regeneration in *Triturus viridescens*. *J. Morphol.* **94**, 21.

Chalkley, D. T. (1959). The cellular basis of regeneration. *In* "Regeneration in Vertebrates" (C. S. Thornton, ed.), p. 34–58. Univ. Chicago Press, Chicago, Illinois.

Chen, L. (1933). Regeneration von kleinen Knochenstücken (Dritteln und Sechsteln) im Innern von Molchextremitäten. *Zool. Jahrb. Abt. Allgem. Zool. Physiol. Tiere* **53**, 153–172.

Colucci, V. L. (1891). Sulla rigenerazione parziale dell' occhio nei tritoni. Istogenesi e svilluppo. Studio sperimentale. *Mem. Accad. Sci. Ist. Bologna Sez. Sci. Nat.* [5] **1**, 167–203.

David, L. (1934). La contribution du matériel cartilagineux et osseux au blastème de régénération des membres chez les Amphibiens Urodèles. *Arch. Anat. Microscop.* **30**, 217–234.

Deck, J. D. (1955). The innervation of urodele limbs of reversed proximo-distal polarity. *J. Morphol.* **96**, 301–322.

Deck, J. D., and Riley, H. L., III (1958). Regenerates on hind-limbs with reversed proximo-distal polarity in larval and metamorphosing urodeles. *J. Exptl. Zool.* **138**, 493–504.

DeHaan, R. L. (1956). The serological determination of developing muscle protein in the regenerating limb of *Amblystoma mexicanum*. *J. Exptl. Zool.* **133**, 73–85.

Della Valle, P. (1913). La doppia rigenerazione inversa nelle fratture delle zampe di *Triton*. *Boll. Soc. Nat. Napoli* **25**.

Dent, J. N. (1949). Limb regeneration in *Triturus viridescens* as affected by lethal doses of radioactive phosphorus. *Anat. Record* **105**, 325–336.

Dent, J. N. (1954). A study of regenerates emanating from limb transplants with reversed proximo-distal polarity in the adult newt. *Anat. Record* **118**, 841–856.

Dent, J. N. (1962). Limb regeneration in larvae and metamorphosing individuals of the South African clawed toad. *J. Morphol.* **110**, 61–78.

Droin, A. (1959). Potentialités morphogènes dans le peau du *Triton* en régénération. *Rev. Suisse Zool.* **66**, 641–709.

Efimov, M. (1933). Uber den Mechanismus der Regenerationsprozesse. III. Bleibt die Polarität der Extremität beim Regenerationsprozess erhalten und die Rolle der inneren Teile des Organs in diesem Prozess. *Biol. Zhur.* **2**, 220–231 (German summary).

Faber, J. (1960). An experimental analysis of regional organization in the regenerating fore limb of the axolotl (*Ambystoma mexicanum*). *Arch. Biol. Liege* **71**, 1–72.

Farinella-Ferruza, N. (1956). The transformation of a tail into limb after xenoplastic transplantation. *Experientia* **12**, 304–305.

Farinella-Ferruza, N. (1957). Transformazione di coda in arto nei trapianti xenoplastici di bottone codale di Triton cristatus su Discoglossus pictus. *Acta Embryol. Morphol. Exptl.* **1**, 171–187.

Filatow, D. (1928). Über die Verpflanzung des Epithels und des Mesenchyms einer vorderen Extremitätenknospe bei Embryonen von Axolotl. *Wilhelm Roux' Arch. Entwicklungsmech. Organ.* **113**, 240–244.

Flat-Hauser, E., and Przibram, H. (1930). Regeneration der langen Knochen nach teilweiser Entfernung im Innern der Molchextremitäten (Triton cristatus Laur). Wilhelm Roux' Arch. Entwicklungsmech. Organ. **122**, 237–250.

Fritsch, C. (1911). Experimentelle Studien über Regenerationsvorgänge des Gliedmassenskeletts der Amphibien. Zool. Jahrb. Abt. Allgem. Zool. Physiol. Tiere **30**, 377–472.

Ghidoni, M. B. (1948). Effects of thyroid inhibitors upon tail regeneration in the tadpole. Growth **12**, 181–202.

Gidge, N. M., and Rose, S. M. (1944). The role of larval skin in promoting limb regeneration in adult Anura. J. Exptl. Zool. **97**, 71–93.

Giorgi, P. de (1924). Les potentialités des régénérats chez Salamandra maculosa. Croissance et différenciation. Rev. Suisse Zool. **31**, 1–52.

Glade, R. W. (1957). The effects of tail tissue on limb regeneration in Triturus viridescens. J. Morphol. **101**, 477–522.

Glade, R. W. (1963). Effects of tail skin, epidermis and dermis on limb regeneration in Triturus viridescens and Siredon mexicanum. J. Exptl. Zool. **152**, 169–194.

Godlewski, E. (1928).Untersuchungen über Auslösung und Hemmung der Regeneration beim Axolotl. Wilhelm Roux' Arch. Entwicklungsmech. Organ. **114**, 108–143.

Goodchild, C. G. (1956). Reconstitution of the intestinal tract in the adult leopard frog, Rana pipiens Schreber. J. Exptl. Zool. **131**, 301–327.

Goode, R. P. (1962). Regeneration of limbs in adult Hymenachirus boettgeri. Nature **193**, 1098.

Goodwin, P. A. (1946). A comparison of regeneration rates and metamorphosis in Triturus and Amblystoma. Growth **10**, 75–87.

Goss, R. J. (1956a). The relation of bone to the histogenesis of cartilage in regenerating forelimbs and tails of adult Triturus viridescens. J. Morphol. **98**, 89–123.

Goss, R. J. (1956b). The unification of regenerates from symetrically duplicated forelimbs. J. Exptl. Zool. **133**, 191–209.

Goss, R. J. (1957a). The relation of skin to defect regulation in regenerating half limbs. J. Morphol. **100**, 547–563.

Goss, R. J. (1957b). The effect of partial irradiation on the morphogenesis of limb regenerates. J. Morphol. **101**, 131–145.

Grobstein, C. (1947). The role of androgen in declining regenerative capacity during morphogenesis of the Platypoecilus maculatus gonopodium. J. Exptl. Zool. **106**, 313–344.

Guyénot, E. (1927). Le problème morphogénétique dans la régénération des Urodèles determination et potentialités des régénérats. Rev. Suisse Zool. **34**, 127–154.

Guyénot, E., and Schotté, O. (1923). Relation entre la masse du bourgeon de régénération et la morphologie du régénérat. Compt. Rend. Soc. Biol. **89**, 491–493.

Hall, A. B., and Schotté, O. E. (1951). Effects of hypophysectomies upon the initiation of regenerative processes in the limb of Triturus viridescens. J. Exptl. Zool. **118**, 363–388.

Hamburger, V. (1928). Die Entwicklung experimentell erzeugter nervenloser und schwach innervierter Extremitäten von Anuren. Wilhelm Roux' Arch. Entwicklungsmech. Organ. **114**, 272–363.

Harrison, R. G. (1898). The growth and regeneration of the tail of the frog larva. Wilhelm Roux' Arch. Entwicklungsmech. Organ. **7**, 430–485.

Harrison, R. G. (1904). An experimental study of the relation of the nervous system to the developing musculature in the embryo of the frog. Am. J. Anat. **3**, 197–220.

Harrison, R. G. (1918). Experiments in the development of the forelimb of Amblystoma, a self-differentiating, equipotential system. J. Exptl. Zool. **25**, 413–462.

610 S. MERYL ROSE

Harrison, R. G. (1921). On relations of symmetry in transplanted limbs. *J. Exptl. Zool.* **32**, 1–136.

Hay, E. D. (1952). The role of epithelium in amphibian limb regeneration, studied by haploid and triploid transplants. *Am. J. Anat.* **91**, 447–481.

Hay, E. D. (1956). Effects of thyroxine on limb regeneration in the newt, *Triturus viridescens*. *Bull. Johns Hopkins Hosp.* **99**, 262–285.

Hay, E. D. (1958). The fine structure of blastema cells and differentiating cartilage in regenerating limbs of *Amblystoma* larvae. *J. Biophys. Biochem. Cytol.* **4**, 538–592.

Hay, E. D. (1959). Electron microscopic observations of muscle dedifferentiation in regenerating *Amblystoma* limbs. *Develop. Biol.* **1**, 555–585.

Hay, E. D. (1960). The fine structure of nerves in the epidermis of regenerating salamander limbs. *Exptl. Cell Res.* **19**, 299–317.

Hay, E. D. (1962). Cytological studies of dedifferentiation and differentiation in regenerating amphibian limbs. *In* "Regeneration" (D. Rudnick, ed.), p. 177–210. Ronald Press, New York.

Hay, E. D., and Fischman, D. A. (1961). Origin of blastema in regenerating limbs of the newt *Triturus viridescens*. *Develop. Biol.* **1**, 327–342.

Hertwig, G. (1927). Beiträge zum Determinations- und Regenerationsproblem mittels des Transplantation haploidkerniger Zellen. *Wilhelm Roux' Arch. Entwicklungsmech. Organ.* **111**, 292–316.

Holtfreter, J. (1955). Transformation of a tail into a limb or gill-like structures. *J. Exptl. Zool.* **129**, 623–648.

Holtzer, H. (1959). The development of mesodermal axial structures in regeneration and embryogenesis. *In* "Regeneration in Vertebrates" (C. S. Thornton, ed.), p. 15–33. Univ. Chicago Press, Chicago, Illinois.

Holtzer, H., and Detwiler, S. (1953). Induction of skeletogenous cells. *J. Exptl. Zool.* **123**, 335–360.

Holtzer, H., Holtzer, S., and Avery, G. (1955). An experimental analysis of the development of the spinal column. IV. Morphogenesis of tail vertebrae during regeneration. *J. Morphol.* **96**, 145–172.

Holtzer, S. (1956). The inductive activity of the spinal cord in urodele tail regeneration. *J. Morphol.* **99**, 1–40.

Holzmann, O. G. (1939). Morphogenetic potencies of skin in the regeneration process. I. Participation of foreign skin in the regeneration of the axolotl limb. *Byul. Eksperim. Biol. i Med.* **8**, 128–131.

Horn, E. C. (1942). An analysis of neutron and x-ray effects on regeneration of the fore limb of larval *Amblystoma*. *J. Morphol.* **71**, 185–219.

Huang, R. C., and Bonner, J. (1962). Histone, a suppressor of chromosomal RNA synthesis. *Proc. Natl. Acad. Sci. U.S.* **48**, 1216–1222.

Ide-Rozas, A. (1936). Die cytologischen Verhältnisse bei der Regeneration von Kaulquappenextremitäten. *Wilhelm Roux' Arch. Entwicklungsmech. Organ.* **135**, 552–608.

Ikeda, Y. (1936). Neue Versuche zur Analyse der Wolffschen Linsenregeneration. *Arb. Anat. Inst. Kaiserl. Japan. Univ. Sendai* **81**, 1–16.

Ikeda, Y., and Kojima, T. (1940). Zur Frage der paralysierenden Wirkung der Linse auf die auslösenden Faktoren für die Wolffsche Linsenregeneration. *Japan. J. Med. Sci. I.* **8**, 51–73.

Jacobson, A. G. (1958). The roles of neural and non-neural tissues in lens induction. *J. Exptl. Zool.* **139**, 525–557.

Jefimow, M. I. (1938). Kann die Entwicklung junger Blastemzellen durch Übertragung auf die Amputationswundfläche eines anderen Organs verändert werden? *Byul. Eksperim. Biol. i Med.* **6**, 75–78.

Kamrin, A. A., and Singer, M. (1959). The growth influence of spinal ganglia implanted into the denervated forelimb regenerate of the newt, *Triturus. J. Morphol.* **104**, 415–440.

Karczmar, A. G. (1946). The role of amputation and nerve resection in the regressing limbs of urodele larvae. *J. Exptl. Zool.* **103**, 401–427.

Kasanzeff, W. (1930). Histologische Untersuchungen über die Regenerationsvorgänge beim Anlegen von Ligaturen an die Extremitäten beim Axolotl. *Wilhelm Roux' Arch. Entwicklungsmech. Organ.* **121**, 658–707.

Kiortsis, V. (1953). Potentialités du territoire patte chez le Triton. *Rev. Suisse Zool.* **60**, 301–410.

Korschelt, E. (1927). "Regeneration und Transplantation," Vol. I, 621 pp. G. Borntraeger Berlin.

Kudokotsev, R. P. (1960). Extremity regeneration stimulated in Anura by tissue extract. *Dokl. Akad. Nauk SSSR* **132**, 715 (Russian).

Kurz, O. (1922). Versuche über Polaritätsumkehr am Tritonenbein. *Wilhelm Roux' Arch. Entwicklungsmech. Organ.* **50**, 186–191.

Kwiatkowski, C. (1959). Regeneration of transected nervous connections in the brain of *Xenopus laevis. Folia Biol. (Krakow)* **7**, 309–319.

Laufer, H. (1959). Immunochemical studies of muscle proteins in mature and regenerating limbs of the adult newt, *Triturus viridescens. J. Embryol. Exptl. Morphol.* **7,**, 431–458.

Lazard, L. (1959). Influence des greffes homologues et hétérologues sur la morphologie des régénérats de membres chez *Amblystoma punctatum. Compt. Rend.* **249**, 468–469.

Lecamp, M. (1935). Les formations multiples dans la greffe et la régénération des membres chez le crapaud accoucheur (*Alytes obstetricans* Laur.). *Bull. Biol. France Belg.* Suppl. **19**, 1–149.

Lehmann, F. E., and Bretscher, A. (1952). Wirkungsanalyse regenerationshemmender Stoffe mit Hilfe statistischer Methoden. *Helv. Physiol. Pharmacol. Acta* **10**, 20–41.

Lender, T. (1960). L'inhibition spécifique de la differenciation du cerveau des plainaires d'eau douce en régénération. *J. Embryol. Exptl. Morphol.* **8**, 29–30.

Liosner, L. D. (1931). Über den Mechanismus des Verlusts der Regenerationsfähigkeit während der Entwicklung der Kaulquappen von *Rana temporaria. Wilhelm Roux' Arch. Entwicklungsmech. Organ.* **124**, 571–583.

Liosner, D., and Woronzowa, M. A. (1935). Die Regeneration des Organs mit transplantierten ortsfremden Muskeln. *Zool. Anz.* **110**, 286–290.

Liosner, L. D., and Woronzowa, M. A. (1937). Recherches sur la determination de la processus régénératif chez les amphibiens. I. Régénération du membre avec les muscles de la queue transplantés. *Arch. Anat. Microscop.* **33**, 313–344.

Litschko, E. J. (1930). Observations sur la régénération des extremités des axolotls après l'action des rayons x. *Compt. Rend. Acad. Sci. URSS* **3**, 549–551.

Liversage, R. A. (1959). The relation of the central and autonomic nervous systems to the regeneration of limbs in adult Urodeles. *J. Exptl. Zool.* **141**, 75–117.

Locatelli, P. (1925). Formation de membres surnuméraires. *Compt. Rend. Assoc. Anat.* **20**, 279–282.

Locatelli, P. (1929). Der Einfluss des Nervensystems auf die Regeneration. *Wilhelm Roux' Arch. Entwicklungsmech. Organ.* **114**, 686–770.

Lomovskaja, E. G. (1948). Limb regeneration in the axolotl after x-irradiating half of the limb. *Dokl. Akad. Nauk SSSR* **61**, 157–160. (Russian - reviewed by Goss, 1951).

Lukiewicz, S. (1962). Polar action of electric fields on living organisms; I. General considerations and historical review. *Folia Biol.* (*Krakow*) **10**, 5–35.

Lund, E. J. (1947). "Bioelectric Fields and Growth." Univ. Texas Press, Austin, Texas.

Luscher, M. (1952). Die Ursachen der tierischen Regeneration. *Experentia* **8**, 81–84.

Luther, W. (1948). Zur Frage des Determinationszustandes von Regenerationsblastemen. *Naturwissenschaften* **35**, 30–31.

Lynn, W. G., and Wachowski, H. E. (1951). The thyroid gland and its functions in cold-blooded vertebrates. *Quart. Rev. Biol.* **26**, 123–168.

Malinin, T., and Deck, J. D. (1958). The effects of implantation of embryonic and tadpole tissues into adult frog limbs. I. Regeneration after amputation. *J. Exptl. Zool.* **139**, 307–327.

Manner, H. W. (1953). The origin of the blastema and of new tissues in regenerating forelimbs of adult *Triturus viridescens viridescens*. *J. Exptl. Zool.* **122**, 229–257.

Matthey, R. (1925). Récupération de la vue après résection des nerfs optiques, chez le *Triton*. *Compt. Rend. Soc. Biol.* **93**, 904–906.

Maturana, H. R., Lettvin, J. Y., McCulloch, W. S., and Pitts, W. H. (1959). Evidence that cut optic nerve fibers in a frog regenerate to their proper places in the tectum. *Science* **130**, 1709–1710.

Mikami, Y. (1941). Experimental analysis of the Wolffian lens regeneration in adult newt, *Triturus pyrrhogaster*. *Japan. J. Zool.* **9**, 269–302.

Milojevic, B. D. (1924). Beiträge zur Frage über die Determination der Regenerate. *Wilhelm Roux' Arch. Entwicklungsmech. Organ.* **103**, 80–94.

Milojevic, B. D., and Vlatkovic, B. (1926). Doubles pattes produites chez les Tritons par régénération expérimentale. *Compt. Rend. Soc. Biol.* **94**, 685.

Miner, N. (1951). Cutaneaus localization following 180° rotation of skin grafts. *Anat. Record* **109**, 326–327.

Mizell, M. (1960). Induction of limb regeneration in postmetamorphic frogs by xenoplastic adrenal transplants. *Assoc. Southern Biologists Bull.* **7**, 35.

Monod, J., and Jacob, F. (1961). General conclusions. Teleonomic mechanisms in cellular metabolism, growth and differentiation. *Cold Spring Harbor Symp. Quant. Biol.* **26**, 389–401.

Monroy, A. (1939). Ricerche sulla capacità lentogena dell'iride degli Anfibi. *Wilhelm Roux' Arch. Entwicklungsmech. Organ.* **139**, 536–555.

Monroy, A. (1941). Ricerche sulle correnti elettriche derivabili dalla superficie del corpo di Tritoni adulti normale durante la rigenerazione degli arti e della coda. *Pubbl. Staz. Zool. Napoli* **18**, 265–281.

Monroy, A. (1946). Ricerche sulla rigenerazione degli Anfibi urodeli. Nota III.— Osservazioni su rigenerati formati si su doppie superfici di sezione e considerazioni sui processi determinativi della rigenerazione. *Arch. Zool. Ital.* **31**, 151–172.

Morgan, T. H. (1901). "Regeneration," 316 pp. Macmillan, New York.

Morgan, T. H. (1908). Experiments in grafting. *Am. Naturalist* **42**, 1–11.

Morosow, I. I. (1938). Die Hemmung und Wiederherstellung des Regenerationsprozesses der Extremität beim Axolotl. *Compt. Rend. Acad. Sci. URSS* **20**, 207–210.

Nassonov, N. V. (1930). Die Regeneration der Axolotlextremitäten nach Ligaturanlegung. *Wilhelm Roux' Arch. Entwicklungsmech. Organ.* **121**, 639–657.

Needham, A. E. (1941). Some experimental biological uses of the element beryllium. *Proc. Zool. Soc. (London)* **111B**, 59–85.

Needham, A. E. (1952). "Regeneration and Wound Healing." Methuen, London.

Needham, A. E. (1960). Regeneration and growth. In "Fundamental Aspects of Normal and Malignant Growth" (V. W. Nowinski, ed.), pp. 588–663. Elsevier, Amsterdam.

Needham, J. (1942). "Biochemistry and Morphogenesis," pp. 430–442. Cambridge Univ. Press, London and New York.

Nicholas, J. S. (1922). The effect of the rotation of the area surrounding the limb bud. *Anat. Record* **23**, 30.

Nicholas, J. S. (1924). The response of the developing limb of *Amblystoma punctatum* to variations in orientation of the surrounding tissue. *Anat. Record* **29**, 108.

Nicholas, J. S. (1955). Regeneration in vertebrates. In "Analysis of Development" (B. H. Willier, P. Weiss, and V. Hamburger, eds.), pp. 674–698. Saunders, Philadelphia, Pennsylvania.

Oberheim, K. W., and Luther, W. (1958). Versuche über die Extremitätenregeneration von Salamanderlarven bei umgekehrter Polarität des Amputationsstumpfes. *Wilhelm Roux' Arch. Entwicklungsmech. Organ.* **150**, 373–382.

Okada, Y. K. (1935). The lens potency posterior to the iris. *Proc. Imp. Acad. (Tokyo)* **11**, 115–118.

Okada, Y. K., and Mikami, Y. (1937). Inductive effect of tissues other than retina on the presumptive lens epithelium. *Proc. Imp. Acad. (Tokyo)* **13**, 283–285.

Orechowitsch, W. N., and Bromley, N. W. (1934). Die histolysierenden Eigenschaften des Regenerationsblastems. *Biol. Zentr.* **54**, 524–535.

O'Steen, W. K. (1958). Regeneration of the intestine in adult urodeles. *J. Morphol.* **103**, 435–477.

O'Steen, W. K. (1959). Regeneration and repair of the intestine in *Rana clamitans* larvae. *J. Exptl. Zool.* **141**, 449–475.

Pawlowsky, E. N. (1923). Hyperthyroidismus und Regeneration. *Arch. Mikroskop. Anat. Entwicklungsmech.* **99**, 620–627.

Peadon, A. M. (1953). The effects of thiourea on limb regeneration in the tadpole. *Growth* **17**, 21–44.

Perri, T. (1956). Induzione di arti soprannumerari negli Anfibi (particolarmente negli Anuri) mediante sostanze citolitiche. *Experentia* **12**, 125–135.

Piatt, J. (1957). Studies on the problem of nerve pattern. III. Innervation of the regenerated forelimb in *Amblystoma. J. Exptl. Zool.* **136**, 229–247.

*Polejaiev, L. W. (1936a). Sur la restauration de la capacité régénérative chez les Anoures. *Arch. Anat. Microscop.* **32**, 437–463.

Polejaiev, L. (1936b). La valeur de la structure de l'organe et les capacités du blastème régénératif dans le processus de la détermination du régénérat. *Bull Biol. France Belg.* **70**, 54–85.

Poleszajew, L. (1933a). Über Regeneration auf der lateralen Seite des Unterschenkels eines Tritons. *Biol. Zh.* **2**, 560.

Poleszajew, L. (1933b). Über Resorption und Proliferation sowie über die Verhältnisse der Gewebe zu einander bei der Regeneration der Extremitäten des Axolotls. *Biol. Zh.* **2**, 385 (German summary).

Poležajew, L. W. (1936). Die Rolle des Epithels bei der Regeneration und in der normalen Ontogenese der Extremitäten bei Amphibien. *Zool. Zh.* **15**, 291.

* The names Polejaiev, Poleszajew, Poležajew, Polezhajev, and Polezhayev are different transliterations of the name of one man.

Poležajew, L. W. (1939). Über die Bedeutung des Epithels und Mesoderms beim Verlust der Regenerationsfähigkeit der Extremitäten bei den Anuren. *Compt. Rend. Acad. Sci. URSS* **25**, 538–542.

Poležajew, L. W., and Favorina, W. N. (1935). Über die Rolle des Epithels in den anfänglichen Entwicklungstadien einer Regenerationsanlage der Extremität beim Axolotl. *Wilhelm Roux' Arch. Entwicklungsmech. Organ.* **133**, 701–727.

Poležajew, L. W., and Ginzburg, G. I. (1939). Studies by the method of transplantation on the loss and restoration of the regenerative power in the tailless amphibian limbs. *Compt. Rend. Acad. Sci. URSS* **23**, 733–737.

Poležajew, L. W., and Morosow, I. I. (1941). Neue Methode der Verlängerung der Regenerationsfähigkeit der Extremitäten bei den Anuren. *Compt. Rend. Acad. Sci. USSR* **30**, 675–678.

Polezhajev, L. V. (1945). Limb regeneration in adult frog. *Compt. Rend. Acad. Sci. URSS* **49**, 609–612.

Polezhayev, L. W. (1939). Über die Bedeutung des Nervensystems bei der Regeneration der Extremitäten bei den Anuren. *Compt. Rend. Acad. Sci. URSS* **25**, 543–546.

Polezhayev, L. W. (1945). "Fundamentals of Physiology of Development of the Vertebrates" (Russian), 287 pp. Acad. Sci. USSR, Moscow and Leningrad.

Polezhayev, L. W. (1946). The loss and restoration of regenerative capacity in the limbs of tailless Amphibia. *Biol. Rev. Cambridge Phil. Soc.* **21**, 141–147.

Polezhayev, L. W. (1946b). Morphological data on regenerative capacity in tadpole limbs as restored by chemical agents. *Compt. Rend. Acad. Sci. URSS* **54**, 281–284.

Polezhayev, L. V. (1959). Restoration of regenerative ability of extremities of axolotls after irradiation with Roentgen rays. *Dokl. Akad. Nauk SSSR* **127**, 713–716.

Polezhayev, L. V. (1960). Regeneration of limbs of axolotls with transfer of destructured tissues of axolotls and of mammals. *Dok. Akad. Nauk SSSR* **131**, 1468–1471.

Polezhayev, L. V., and Ermakova, N. I. (1960). Restoration of regenerative capacity of the extremities in axolotls depressed by roentgen radiation. *Dok. Nauk Akad. SSSR* **131**, 209–212.

Polezhayev, L. V., and Ginzburg, G. I. (1943) Investigations of ways of formation of regeneration blastema based on calculation of mitotic coefficient. *Compt. Rend. Acad. Sci. URSS* **43**, 315–317.

Polezhayev, L. V., Teplits, N. A., and Ermakova, N. I. (1961). Restoration of the regenerative property of extremities in axolotls inhibited by x-ray irradiation by menas of proteins, nucleic acids and lyophilized tissues. *Dokl. Akad. Nauk SSSR* **138**, 477–480 (AIBS Transl.).

Politzer, G. (1937). Zur Kausalanalyse der Linsenregeneration. *Wilhelm Roux' Arch. Entwicklungsmech. Organ.* **135**, 349–358.

Przibram, H. (1931). "Connecting Laws in Animal Morphology." Univ. London Press, London.

Reed, M. A. (1903). The regeneration of a whole foot from the cut end of a leg containing only the tibia. *Wilhelm Roux' Arch. Entwicklungsmech. Organ.* **17**, 150–154.

Reyer, R. W. (1950). An experimental study of lens regeneration in *Triturus viridescens viridescens*. II. Lens development from the dorsal iris in the absence of the embryonic lens. *J. Exptl. Zool.* **113**, 317–353.

Reyer, R. W. (1954a). Further studies on lens development from the dorsal iris of *Triturus viridescens viridescens* in the absence of the embryonic lens. *J. Exptl. Zool.* **125**, 1–16.

Reyer, R. W. (1954b). Regeneration of the lens in the amphibian eye. *Quart. Rev Biol.* **29**, 1–46.

Reyer, R. W. (1956). Lens regeneration from homoplastic and heteroplastic implants of dorsal iris into the eye chamber of *Triturus viridescens* and *Amblystoma punctatum*. *J. Exptl. Zool.* **133**, 145–189.

Richardson, D. (1940). Thyroid and pituitary hormones in relation to regeneration. I. The effect of anterior pituitary hormone on regeneration of the hind leg in normal and thyroidectomized newts. *J. Exptl. Zool.* **83**, 407–429.

Richardson, D. (1945). Thyroid and pituitary hormones in relation to regeneration. II. Regeneration of the hind leg of the newt, *Triturus viridescens*, with different combinations of thyroid and pituitary hormones. *J. Exptl. Zool.* **100**, 417–427.

Riddiford, L. M. (1960). Autoradiographic studies of tritiated thymidine infused into the blastema of the early regenerate in the adult newt, *Triturus*. *J. Exptl. Zool.* **144**, 25–32.

Rieck, A. F. (1954). The effects of ultraviolet, and of photorecovery, on the developing forelimb of *Amblystoma*. *J. Morphol.* **94**, 367–408.

Roguski, H. (1953). Dalsze badania nad regeneracja ogona Kijanek *"Xenopus laevis."* *Folia Biol. (Krakow)* **1**, 277–285 (English summary).

Rose, F. C., and Rose, S. M. (1964). Recovery of regenerative ability in x-rayed regions of limbs of Triturus. (in manuscript).

Rose, F. C., Quastler, H., and Rose, S. M. (1955). Regeneration of x-rayed salamander limbs provided with normal epidermis. *Science* **122**, 1018–1019.

Rose, S. M. (1942). A method for inducing limb regeneration in adult Anura. *Proc. Soc. Exptl. Biol. Med.* **49**, 408–410.

Rose, S. M. (1944). Methods of initiating limb regeneration in adult Anura. *J. Exptl. Zool.* **95**, 149–170.

Rose, S. M. (1945). The effect of NaCl in stimulating regeneration of limbs of frogs. *J. Morphol.* **77**, 119–139.

Rose, S. M. (1948a). The role of nerves in amphibian limb regeneration. *Ann. N. Y. Acad. Sci.* **49**, 818–833.

Rose, S. M. (1948b). Epidermal dedifferentiation during blastema formation in regenerating limbs of *Triturus viridescens*. *J. Exptl. Zool.* **108**, 337–361.

Rose, S. M. (1957). Cellular interaction during differentiation. *Biol. Rev. Cambridge Phil. Soc.* **32**, 351–382.

Rose, S. M. (1962). Tissue-arc control of regeneration in the amphibian limb. *In* "Regeneration" (D. Rudnick, ed.), p. 153–176. Ronald Press, New York.

Rose, S. M. (1963). Polarized control of regional structure in Tubularia. *Develop. Biol.* **7**, 488–501.

Ruben, L. N. (1960). An immunobiological model of implant-induced urodele supernumerary limb formation. *Am. Naturalist* **94**, 427–434.

Ruben, L. N., and Frothingham, M. L. (1958). The importance of innervation and superficial wounding in urodele accessory limb formation. *J. Morphol.* **102**, 91–118.

Salpeter, M. M., and Singer, M. (1960). Differentiation of the submicroscopic adepidermal membrane during limb regeneration in adult *Triturus*, including a note on the use of the term basement membrane. *Anat. Record* **136**, 27–40.

Sato, T. (1930). Beiträge zur Analyse der Wolffschen Linsenregeneration. I. *Wilhelm Roux' Arch. Entwicklungsmech. Organ.* **122**, 451–493.

Sato, T. (1935). Beiträge zur Analyse der Wolffschen Linsenregeneration III. *Wilhelm Roux' Arch. Entwicklungsmech. Organ.* **133**, 323–348.

Sato, T. (1951). Über die linsenbildende Fähigkeit des Pigmentepithels bei *Diemyctylus pyrrhogaster*. I. Pigmentepithel aus dorsalem Augenbereich. *Embryologia (Nagoya)* **1**, 21–57.

Sato, T. (1953). Über die Ursachen des Ausbleibens der Linsenregeneration und zugleich über die linsenbildende Fähigkeit des Pigmentepithels bei den Anuren. *Wilhelm Roux' Arch. Entwicklungsmech. Organ.* **146**, 487–514.

Saunders, J. W. (1948). The proximo-distal sequence of origin of the parts of the chick wing and the role of the ectoderm. *J. Exptl. Zool.* **108**, 363–403.

Schaxel, J. (1921). Auffassungen und Erscheinungen der Regeneration. *Arb. a. d. Geb. der. Exp. Biol.* **1**, 1–99.

Schaxel, J., and Böhmel, W. (1928). Regenerations- und Transplantationstudien. II. Ersatzbildung nach Entnahme von Organteilen. *Zool. Anz.* **78**, 157–163.

Scheremetjewa, E. A., and Brunst, V. V. (1935). Untersuchung des Einflusses von Röntgenstrahlen auf die Regeneration der Extremitäten beim Axolotl. I. *Radiobiol. Gen. Venezia* **4**, 57–77.

Scheremetjewa, E. A., and Brunst, V. V. (1937). On the local destruction of the regenerative ability of the limb of axolotls by x-irradiation. *Trav. Inst. Zool. Biol. Acad. Sci. Ukraine* **17**, 137–146.

Scheremetjewa, E. A., and Brunst, V. V. (1938). Preservation of the regeneration capacity in the middle part of the limb of newt and its simultaneous loss in the distal and proximal parts of the same limb. *Byul. Eksperim. Biol. i Med.* **6**, 723–724.

Scheuing, M. R., and Singer, M. (1957). The effects of microquantities of beryllium ion on the regenerating forelimb of the adult newt, *Triturus*. *J. Exptl. Zool.* **136**, 301–327.

Schmidt, A. J. (1958a). Forelimb regeneration of thyroidectomized adult newts. I. Morphology. *J. Exptl. Zool.* **137**, 197–226.

Schmidt, A. J. (1958b). Forelimb regeneration of thyroidectomized adult newts. II. Histology. *J. Exptl. Zool.* **139**, 95–135.

Schneider, G. (1940). Der Einfluss des Nervensystems auf die Regeneration der Gliedmassen der Axolotl. *Bull. Acad. Sci. URSS Ser. Biol.* p. 403 (Russian and German summaries).

Schotté, O. E. (1926). Système nerveux et régénération chez le *Triton*. *Rev. Suisse Zool.* **33**, 1–211.

Schotté, O. (1940). The origin and morphogenetic potencies of regenerates. *Growth* **4**, (Suppl. 1) 59–76.

Schotté, O. E. (1961). Systemic factors in initiation of regenerative processes in limbs of larval and adult amphibians. *In* "Synthesis of Molecular and Cellular Structure" (D. Rudnick, ed.), p. 161–192. Ronald Press, New York.

Schotté, O. E., and Bierman, R. H. (1956). Effects of cortisone and allied adrenal steroids upon limb regeneration in hypophysectomized *Triturus viridescens*. *Rev. Suisse Zool.* **63**, 353–375.

Schotté, O. E., and Bonneville, M. A. (1955). The systemic effects of injury and of repair within dehumerized limbs of hypophysectomized *Triturus viridescens*. *Anat. Record* **121**, 364.

Schotté, O. E., and Butler, E. G. (1941). Morphological effects of denervation and amputation of limbs in urodele larvae. *J. Exptl. Zool.* **87**, 279–322.

Schotté, O. E., and Butler, E. G. (1944). Phases in regeneration of the urodele limb and their dependence upon the nervous system. *J. Exptl. Zool.* **97**, 95–121.

Schotté, O. E., and Chamberlain, J. L. (1955). Effects of ACTH upon limb regeneration in normal and in hypophysectomized *Triturus viridescens*. *Rev. Suisse Zool.* **62** (Guyénot Suppl.), 253–279.

Schotté, O. E., and Hall, A. B. (1952). Effects of hypophysectomy upon phases of regeneration in progress (*Triturus viridescens*). *J. Exptl. Zool.* **121**, 521–560.

Schotté, O. E., and Harland, M. (1943). Amputation level and regeneration in limbs of late *Rana clamitans* tadpoles. *J. Morphol.* **73**, 329–363.

Schotté, O. E., and Hilfer, S. R. (1957). Initiation of regeneration in regenerates after hypophysectomy in adult *Triturus viridescens*. *J. Morphol.* **101**, 25–55.

Schotté, O. E., and Karczmar, A. G. (1944). Limb parameters and regression rates in denervated amputated limbs of urodele larvae. *J. Exptl. Zool.* **97**, 43–73.

Schotté, O. E., and Lindberg, D. A. B. (1954). Effect of xenoplastic adrenal transplants upon limb regeneration in normal and hypophysectomized newts (*Triturus viridescens*). *Proc. Soc. Exptl. Biol. Med.* **87**, 26–29.

Schotté, O. E., and Liversage, O. E. (1959). Effects of denervation and amputation upon the initiation of regeneration in regenerates of *Triturus*. *J. Morphol.* **105**, 495–527.

Schotté, O. E., and Murphy, G. W. (1953). Regeneration of the lens in absence of the pituitary in the adult newt (*Triturus viridescens*). *J. Morphol.* **93**, 447–464.

Schotté, O. E., and Washburn, W. W. (1954). Effects of thyroidectomy on the regeneration of the forelimb in *Triturus viridescens*. *Anat. Record* **120**, 156.

Schotté, O. E., and Wilber, J. F. (1958). Effects of adrenal transplants upon forelimb regeneration in normal and in hypophysectomized frogs. *J. Embryol. Exptl. Morphol.* **6**, 247–261.

Schotté, O. E., Butler, E. G., and Hood, R. T. (1941). Effects of transplanted blastemas on amputated nerveless limbs of urodele larvae. *Proc. Soc. Exptl. Biol. Med.* **48**, 500–503.

Schrank, A. R., (1951). Electrical polarity and auxins. *In* "Plant Growth Substances" (F. Skoog, ed.), p. 123–140. Univ. Wisconsin Press, Madison, Wisconsin.

Sidman, R. L., and Singer, M. (1960). Limb regeneration without innervation of the apical epidermis in the adult newt, *Triturus*. *J. Exptl. Zool.* **144**, 105–109.

Sidorova, V. F. (1951). The regeneration of irradiated extremities of axolotl after the implantation of non-specific tissues. *Dokl. Akad. Nauk SSSR* **81**, 297–299 (Russian-reviewed by Goss, 1957b).

Singer, M. (1946). The nervous system and regeneration of the forelimb of adult *Triturus*. V. The influence of number of nerve fibers, including a quantitative study of limb innervation. *J. Exptl. Zool.* **101**, 299–337.

Singer, M. (1949). The invasion of the epidermis of the regenerating forelimb of the urodele, *Triturus*, by nerve fibers. *J. Exptl. Zool.* **111**, 189–210.

Singer, M. (1952). The influence of the nerve in regeneration of the amphibian extremity. *Quart. Rev. Biol.* **27**, 169–200.

Singer, M. (1954). Induction of regeneration of the forelimb of the postmetamorphic frog by augmentation of the nerve supply. *J. Exptl. Zool.* **126**, 419–471.

Singer, M. (1959a). The influence of nerves on regeneration. *In* "Regeneration in Vertebrates" (C. S. Thornton, ed.), p. 59–80. Univ. Chicago Press, Chicago, Illinois.

Singer, M. (1959b). The acetylcholine content of the normal forelimb regenerate of the adult newt, *Triturus*. *Develop. Biol.* **1**, 603–620.

Singer, M. (1960). Nervous mechanisms in the regeneration of body parts in vertebrates. *In* "Developing Cell Systems and Their Control" (D. Rudnick, ed.), p. 115–133. Ronald Press, New York.

Singer, M., and Craven, L. (1948). The growth and morphogenesis of the regenerating forelimb of adult *Triturus* following denervation at various stages of development. *J. Exptl. Zool.* **108**, 279–308.

Singer, M., Kamrin, R. P., and Ashbaugh, A. (1957). The influence of denervation upon trauma-induced regenerates of the forelimb of the post-metamorphic frog. *J. Exptl. Zool.* **136,** 35–51.

Singer, M., and Salpeter, M. M. (1961). Regeneration in vertebrates: the role of the wound epithelium. *In* "Growth in Living Systems" (M. X. Zarrow, ed.), pp. 277–311. Basic Books, New York.

Singer, M., Weinberg, A., and Sidman, R. L. (1955). A study of limb regeneration in the adult newt, *Triturus* by infusion of solutions of dye and other substances directly into the growth. *J. Exptl. Zool.* **128,** 185–218.

Skowron, S., and Roguski, H. (1958). Regeneration from implanted dissociated cells. I. Regenerative potentialities of limb and tail cells. *Folia Biol. (Krakow)* **6,** 163–173.

Spallanzani, Abbé. (1769). An Essay on Animal Reproductions. (Translated from the Italian, 1768, by M. Maty.) London.

Speidel, C. C. (1929). Studies of hyperthyroidism. VI. Regenerative phenomena in thyroid-treated amphibian larvae. *Am. J. Anat.* **43,** 103–165.

 pemann, H. (1905). Über Linsenbildung nach experimenteller Entfernung der primären Linsenbildungzellen. *Zool. Anz.* **28,** 419–432.

Spemann, H. (1938). "Embryonic Development and Induction," 401 pp. Yale Univ. Press, New Haven, Connecticut.

Sperry, R. W. (1943a). Visuomotor coordination in the newt (*Triturus viridescens*) after regeneration of the optic nerve. *J. Comp. Neurol.* **79,** 33–55.

Sperry, R. W. (1943b). Effect of 180 degree rotation of the retinal field on visuo-motor coordination. *J. Exptl. Zool.* **92,** 263–279.

Sperry, R. W. (1944). Optic nerve regeneration with return of vision in anurans. *J. Neurophysiol.* **7,** 57–70.

Sperry, R. W. (1945). Restoration of vision after crossing of optic nerves and after contralateral transplantation of eye. *J. Neurophysiol.* **8,** 15–28.

Sperry, R. W. (1951). Regulative factors in the orderly growth of neural circuits. *Growth* **15,** Suppl., 63–87.

Spirito, A., and Ciaccio, G. (1931). Ricerche causali sulla rigenerazione del cristallino nei tritoni. *Boll. Zool. Napoli* **2,** 1–7.

Srebro, Z. (1959). Investigations on the regenerative capacity of the between brain and the influence of its removal upon the development of *Xenopus laevis* tadpoles. *Folia Biol. (Krakow)* **7,** 191–202.

Stedman, E., and Stedman, E. (1950). Cell specificity of histones. *Nature* **166,** 780.

Stinson, B. D. (1962a). Failure of devitalized autotransplants to elicit regenerates from x-irradiated limbs of adult *Triturus viridescens. Am. Zoologist* **2,** 562–563.

Stinson, B. D. (1962b). Regression of regenerates formed on x-irradiated limbs of adult *Triturus viridescens* after implantation of homografts of normal limb tissue. *Anat. Record* **142,** 283.

Stone, L. S. (1941). Transplantation of the vertebrate eye and return of vision. *Trans. N.Y. Acad. Sci.* [2]**3,** 208–212.

Stone, L. S. (1944). Functional polarization in retinal development and its re-establishment in regenerating retinae of rotated eyes. *Proc. Soc. Exptl. Biol. Med.* **57,** 13–14.

Stone, L. S. (1945). Heteroplastic lens grafts related to factors inhibiting lens regeneration in *Triturus. Proc. Soc. Exptl. Biol. Med.* **60,** 10.

Stone, L. S. (1952). An experimental study of the inhibition and release of lens regeneration in adult eyes of *Triturus viridescens viridescens. J. Exptl. Zool.* **121,** 181–223.

Stone, L. S. (1953). An experimental analysis of lens regeneration. *Am. J. Ophthalmol.* **36**, 31–39.

Stone, L. S. (1954). Lens regeneration in secondary pupils experimentally produced in eyes of the adult newt, *Triturus v. viridescens*. *J. Exptl. Zool.* **127**, 463–492.

Stone, L. S. (1957). Regeneration of iris and lens in hypophysectomized adult newts. *J. Exptl. Zool.* **136**, 17–33.

Stone, L. S. (1958a). Lens regeneration in adult newt eyes related to retina pigment cells and the neural retina factor. *J. Exptl. Zool.* **139**, 69–83.

Stone, L. S. (1958b). Inhibition of lens regeneration in newt eyes by isolating the dorsal iris from the neural retina. *Anat. Record* **131**, 151–172.

Stone, L. S. (1959). Regeneration of the retina, iris and lens. *In* "Regeneration in Vertebrates" (C. S. Thornton, ed.), pp. 3–14. Univ. Chicago Press, Chicago, Illinois.

Stone, L. S., and Gallagher, S. B. (1958). Lens regeneration restored to iris membranes when grafted to neural retina environment after cultivation *in vitro*. *J. Exptl. Zool.* **139**, 247–261.

Stone, L. S., and Steinitz, H. (1953). Effects of hypophysectomy and thyroidectomy on lens and retina regeneration in the adult newt, *Triturus v. viridescens*. *J. Exptl. Zool.* **124**, 469–504.

Stone, L. S., and Vultee, J. H. (1949). Inhibition and release of lens regeneration in the dorsal iris of *Triturus v. viridescens*. *Anat. Record* **103**, 144–145.

Stone, L. S., and Zaur, I. S. (1940). Reimplantation and transplantation of adult eyes in the salamander (*Triturus viridescens*) with return of vision. *J. Exptl. Zool.* **85**, 243–269.

Swett, F. H. (1928). Experiments in splitting the regenerating limb bud. *Anat. Record* **40**, 297–308.

Swett, F. H. (1937). Determination of limb-axes. *Quart. Rev. Biol.* **12**, 322–339.

Taban, C. (1949). Les fibres nerveuses et l'épithélium dans l'édification des régénérats de pattes (in situ ou induites) chez le triton. *Arch. Sci. (Geneva)* **2**, 553.

Taban, C. (1955). Quelques problèmes de régénération chez les urodèles. *Rev. Suisse Zool.* **62**, 387–468.

Taube, E. (1921). Regeneration mit Beteiligung ortsfremder Haut bei Tritonen. *Wilhelm Roux' Arch. Entwicklungsmech. Organ.* **49**, 269–315.

Tartar, V. (1958). Specific inhibition of the oral primordium by formed oral structures in *Stentor coeruleus*. *J. Exptl. Zool.* **139**, 479–505.

Thornton, C. S. (1938). The histogenesis of muscle in the regenerating forelimb of larval *Amblystoma punctatum*. *J. Morphol.* **62**, 17–47.

Thornton, C. S. (1942). Studies on the origin of the regeneration blastema in *Triturus viridescens*. *J. Exptl. Zool.* **89**, 375–390.

Thornton, C. S. (1949). Beryllium inhibition of regeneration. I. Morphological effects of beryllium on amputated forelimbs of larval *Amblystoma*. *J. Morphol.* **84**, 459–494.

Thornton, C. S. (1950). Beryllium inhibition of regeneration. II. Localization of the beryllium effect in amputated limbs of larval *Amblystoma*. *J. Exptl. Zool.* **114**, 305–333.

Thornton, C. S. (1951). Beryllium inhibition of regeneration. III. Histological effects of beryllium on the amputated forelimbs of *Amblystoma* larvae. *J. Exptl. Zool.* **118**, 467–493.

Thornton, C. S. (1953). Histological modifications in denervated injured forelimbs of *Amblystoma* larvae. *J. Exptl. Zool.* **122**, 119–150.

Thornton, C. S. (1954). The relation of epidermal innervation to limb regeneration in *Amblystoma* larvae. *J. Exptl. Zool.* **127,** 577–601.

Thornton, C. S. (1956). Epidermal modifications in regenerating and non-regenerating limbs of anuran larvae. *J. Exptl. Zool.* **131,** 373–394.

Thornton, C. S. (1957). The effect of apical cap removal on limb regeneration in *Amblystoma* larvae. *J. Exptl. Zool.* **134,** 357–381.

Thornton, C. S. (1958). The inhibition of limb regeneration in urodele larvae by localized irradiation with ultra-violet light. *J. Exptl. Zool.* **137,** 153–180.

Thornton, C. S., ed. (1959). "Regeneration in Vertebrates," 108 pp. Univ. Chicago Press, Chicago, Illinois.

Thornton, C. S. (1960). Regeneration of asensory limbs of *Amblystoma* larvae. *Copeia* pp. 371–373.

Thornton, C. S., and Shields, T. W. (1945). Five cases of atypical regeneration in the adult frog. *Copeia* pp. 40–42.

Todd, T. J. (1823). On the process of reproduction of the members of the aquatic salamander. *Quart. J. Sci. Arts Lit.* **16,** 84–96.

Tornier, G. (1906). Kampf der Gewebe im Regenerat bei Begünstigung der Hautregeneration. *Arch. Entwicklungsmech. Organ.* **22,** 348–369.

Trampusch, H. A. L. (1958). The action of x-rays on the morphogenetic field. II. Heterotopic skin on irradiated tails. *Koninkl. Ned. Akad. Wetenschap. Proc. Ser. C* **61,** 530–545.

Trampusch, H. A. L. (1959). The effect of x-rays on regenerative capacity. *In* "Regeneration in Vertebrates" (C. S. Thornton, ed.), p. 83–99. Univ. Chicago Press, Chicago, Illinois.

Tschumi, P. A. (1956). Die Bedeutung der Epidermisleiste für die Entwicklung der Beine von *Xenopus laevis. Rev. Suisse Zool.* **63,** 707.

Tschumi, P. A. (1957). The growth of the hindlimb bud of *Xenopus laevis* and its dependence upon the epidermis. *J. Anat.* **91,** 149–173.

Tucker, M. (1959). Inhibitory control of regeneration in nemertean worms. *J. Morphol.* **105,** 569–600.

Tweedell, K. S. (1958). Reconstitution of the lens after destruction by intraocular tumor implants. *Growth* **22,** 291–298.

Umanski, E. (1937). Untersuchungen des Regenerationsvorganges bei Amphibien mittels Ausschaltung der einzelnen Gewebe durch Röntgenbestrahlung. *Biol. Zh.* **6,** 757–758 (Russian–German summary).

Umanski, E. (1938a). The regeneration potencies of axolotl skin studied by means of exclusion of the regeneration capacity of tissues through exposure to x-rays. *Byul. Eksperim. Biol. i Med.* **6,** 141–145.

Umanski, E. (1938b). A study of regeneration of the axolotl limb upon substitution of the inner tissues by dorsal musculature. *Byul. Eksperim. Biol. i Med.* **6,** 383–386.

Umansky, E. E., Tkatsch, V. K., and Koudokotsev, V. P. (1951). Anisotropic diélectrique de la peau chez l'Axolotl. *Compt. Rend. Acad. Sci. URSS* **76,** 465–467 (rev. by Kiortsis, 1953).

Uno, M. (1943). Zur Frage des Mechanismus der Wolffschen Linsenregeneration. *Japan. J. Med. Sci. I.* **11,** 75–100.

Van Stone, J. M. (1955). The relationship between innervation and regenerative capacity in hind limb of *Rana* sylvatica. *J. Morphol.* **97,** 345–392.

Van Stone, J. M. (1957). Regeneration of the anuran hind limb following amputation at the pelvic level. *J. Exptl. Zool.* **134,** 327–341.

Wachs, H. (1914). Neue Versuche zur Wolffschen Linsenregeneration. *Wilhelm Roux'*
Arch Entwicklungsmech. Organ. **39**, 384–451.

Wachs, H. (1920). Restitution des Auges nach Exirpation von Retina und Linse bei
Tritonen. *Wilhelm Roux' Arch. Entwicklungsmech. Organ.* **46**, 328–390.

Walter, F. K. (1910). Schilddrüse und Regeneration. *Wilhelm Roux' Arch. Entwick-*
lungsmech. Organ. **31**, 91–130.

Walter, F. K. (1912). Welche Bedeutung hat das Nervensystem für die Regeneration
der Tritonextremitäten? *Wilhelm Roux' Arch. Entwicklungsmech. Organ.* **33**, 274–
296.

Warren, A. E., and Bower, C. M. (1939). The influence of normal and induced metamorphosis on hind limb regeneration in *Rana sylvatica*. *Anat. Record* **73**, (Suppl.
2), 55–56.

Weiss, P. (1924a). Die Funktion transplantierter Amphibienextremitäten. Aufstel-
lung einer Resonanztheorie der motorischen Nerventätigkeit auf Grund abge-
stimmter Endorgane. *Wilhelm Roux' Arch. Entwicklungsmech. Organ.* **102**, 635–
672.

Weiss, P. (1924b). Regeneration aus doppeltem Extremitätenquerschnitt (an *Triton*
cristatus). *Anz. Akad. Wiss. Wien. Math. Naturw. Kl.* **61**, 45–46.

Weiss, P. (1925a). Die seitliche Regeneration der Urodelenextremität. *Arch. Mik-*
roskop. Anat. Entwicklungsmech. **104**, 395–408.

Weiss, P. (1925b). Unabhängigkeit der Extremitätenregeneration vom Skelett. *Arch.*
Mikroskop. Anat. Entwicklungsmech. **104**, 359–394.

Weiss, P. (1926). Ganzregenerate aus halbem Extremitätenquerschnitt. *Wilhelm*
Roux' Arch. Entwicklungsmech. Organ. **107**, 1–53.

Weiss, P. (1927). Die Herkunft der Haut im Extremitätenregenerat. *Wilhelm Roux'*
Arch. Entwicklungsmech. Organ. **109**, 584–610.

Weiss, P. (1936). Selectivity controlling the central peripheral relations in the nervous
system. *Biol. Rev. Cambridge Phil. Soc.* **11**, 494–531.

Weiss, P. (1950). Experimental analysis of coordination by the disarrangement of
central peripheral relations. *Symp. Soc. Exptl. Biol.* **4**, 92–111.

Weiss, P. (1955). Nervous system. *In* "Analysis of Development" (B. H. Willier, P.
Weiss, and V. Hamburger, eds.), pp. 346–401. Saunders, Philadelphia, Pennsylvania.

Weiss, P., and Walker, R. (1934). Nerve pattern in regenerated urodele limbs. *Proc.*
Soc. Exptl. Biol. Med. **31**, 810–812.

Weisz, P. B. (1951). An experimental analysis of morphogenesis in *Stentor coeruleus*.
J. Exptl. Zool. **116**, 231–258.

Wilde, C. E., Jr. (1952a). Studies on the organogenesis of the urodele limb bud. *J.*
Exptl. Zool. **119**, 65–91.

Wilde, C. E., Jr. (1952b). Studies on the organogenesis in vitro of the urodele limb
bud. II. The effect of size of the explant and the interrelation between gill and
limb. *J. Morphol.* **90**, 119–147.

Wolff, E. (1962). Recent researches on the regeneration in Planaria. *In* "Regeneration," (D. Rudnick, ed.), p. 53–84. Ronald Press, New York.

Wolff, E., and Wey-Schué, M. (1952). Démonstration expérimentale de la migration
des cellules de régénération dans la régénération des membres de *Triton cristatus*.
Compt. Rend. Soc. Biol. **146**, 113–117.

Wolff, G. (1895). Entwickelungsphysiologische Studien. I. Die Regeneration der
Urodelenlinse. *Wilhelm Roux' Arch. Entwicklungsmech. Organ.* **1**, 380–390.

Wolff, G. (1904). Entwicklungsphysiologische Studien. III. Zur Analyse der Entwicklungspotenzen des Irisepithels bei *Triton. Arch. Mikroskop. Anat. Entwick-lungsmech.* **63,** 1–9.

Wolff, G. (1910). Regeneration und Nervensystem. *In* "Festschrift F. R. Hertwig" pp. 67–80. Fischer, Jena.

Yntema, C. L. (1959a). Regeneration in sparsely innervated and aneurogenic fore-limbs of *Amblystoma* larvae. *J. Exptl. Zool.* **140,** 101–124.

Yntema, C. L. (1959b). Blastema formation in sparsely innervated and aneurogenic forelimbs of *Amblystoma* larvae. *J. Exptl. Zool.* **142,** 423–439.

Zalokar, M. (1944). Contribution à l'étude de la régénération du cristallin chez le *Triton. Rev. Suisse Zool.* **51,** 443–521.

Zwilling, E. (1956). Reciprocal dependence of ectoderm and mesoderm during chick embryo limb development. *Am. Naturalist* **90,** 257–265.

AUTHOR INDEX

The numbers in italics indicate the pages on which the complete reference is listed.

SPECIES   INDEX

In recent years an increasing number of physiologists have been making earnest attempts to use the correct scientific names of the species used in their experiments. It has not always been easy, however, to keep up with the nomenclatural peregrinations of the taxonomists. The following index lists the species names as they appear in the text where, in turn, they refer to the name used by the author. Thus the list makes no claim to taxonomic correctness. Fortunately the names of the frogs most commonly used in experiments have remained the same in recent years. *Rana temporaria* and *Rana esculenta* of Europe, *Rana pipiens* and *Rana catesbeiana* of North America, and *Xenopus laevis* of Africa are all valid names. The European *Rana fusca* is generally regarded as identical to *Rana temporaria*. The American salamander long known as *Amblystoma punctatum* is now *Ambystoma maculatum*. The situation with respect to the newts brings despair. The common European species, generally referred to as *Triton*, are *Triturus*. The eastern American newts, first *Diemyctylus*, then *Triturus*, then *Diemictylus*, may finally become *Notophthalmus*. The western American *Triturus* is now *Taricha* (with *Triturus torosus* becoming *Taricha torosa*). The eastern Asiatic forms are currently *Triturus*, but there are rumblings of great changes. The axolotl, which has always been served well by this Nahuatl name, has been successively *Amblystoma tigrinum, Ambystoma mexicanum,* and *Siredon mexicanum*. One should always try to use the correct name.

SUBJECT INDEX

A

A bands (defined), 334, 563
Absorption, 81, 106–107, 136–139, 141–142
Acetylation, 43
Acetylcholine, 43
Acetylcholine esterase, 43
Acid phosphatase (see also Phosphatase), 74, 78, 79
Actin, 334, 360–362
ACTH, 36, 291–292, 378, 389, 396, 397, 399, 404–410
Adenohypophysis, 289–292, 372–380, 452
Adrenal hormones (see also specific hormones), 289–292, 398–410
Adrenal hormones and regeneration, 580–581
Adrenalin, 289–290, 394, 398–410
Adrenocorticotropic hormone (see ACTH)
Adrenocorticotropin (see also ACTH), 377
Afterloaded (defined), 331
Aktivierung (Reichel), 234, 235, 238–241
Aldolase, 33
Aldosterone, 290–291, 300, 301, 404, 407, 409
Alkaline phosphatase (See also Phosphatase), 74, 78, 79
Amidases, 47
Amino acids, 44–65
Amino acids in development, 50–55
Amino acid dehydrases, 46–47
Amino acid desulfhydrases, 47
Amino acid oxidases, 46, 74
Ammonia, 56–65
Amylase, 33, 136
Aneuploidy, 485
Antidiuretic hormone, 286, 380–384
Apical cap, 569–572
Arginase, 74
Arginine synthetase, 74
Arginine vasopressin, 381
Arginine vasotocin, 289, 381–384
ASA cleavage enzyme, 75

Ascorbic acid, 19
Asp-α KG transaminase, 75
Asparaginase, 47
ATP, 25–33, 494, 495
ATPase, 72–73, 75
Auerbach's plexus, 116

B

Behavior
  hugging, 301
  sight, 555–556
  water drive, 292, 377
Bidder's ganglion, 217
Bile salt, 133–134, 136
Biological rhythms, 39
Biotin, 21
Bladder (see Urinary bladder)
Blastema (see also Limb regeneration), 546
Blood, 169–202
Blood
  clotting, 184–185
  sugar, 37–38
Body fluids (see also Blood), 253–261
Bohr effect, 53
Bone marrow, 52
Breathing (see also Respiration), 161–164
Breeding, 156, 165
Brunn effect, 381
Brunner's glands, 131
Buccal cavity, 101–107
  glands, 103–104
  mucosa, 103, 104

C

Calcium, 80, 81
Calorimetry, 13–17
Carbamyl phosphate synthetase, 48, 75
Carbohydrates, 23–39
Carbohydates
  in embryos, 4–9, 507
Carbon dioxide transport, 185–191
Carotid gland, 198–199
Catalase, 73

649